TEXTBOOK OF PHYSIOLOGY

TEXTBOOK

OF

PHYSIOLOGY

BY

WILLIAM D. ZOETHOUT, Ph.D.

PROFESSOR OF PHYSIOLOGY IN THE CHICAGO COLLEGE OF DENTAL SURGERY
(LOYOLA UNIVERSITY)

AND

W. W. TUTTLE, Ph.D.

PROFESSOR OF PHYSIOLOGY, COLLEGE OF MEDICINE,
STATE UNIVERSITY OF IOWA

EIGHTH EDITION

With 308 Text Illustrations and 3 Color Plates

ST. LOUIS
THE C. V. MOSBY COMPANY
1943

Press of
The C. V. Mosby Company
St. Louis

PREFACE TO EIGHTH EDITION

In this edition the first chapter, dealing with protoplasm and its environment, has been almost entirely rewritten. In the three chapters on circulation we have striven to indicate more clearly the organization of this involved and lengthy subject by the freer use of headings and subheadings.

The topics of renal hypertension, hemorrhage, traumatic and gravitational shock, blood banks, the hormonal control of the reproductive functions, and many others, have received careful attention.

Much of the advanced chemistry and the more detailed anatomy have been set in smaller type. These passages may be omitted without destroying the continuity of the text.

Several new illustrations have been added and a very large number of the older figures have been redrawn.

W. D. Z.
W. W. T.

FROM THE PREFACE TO SECOND EDITION

This book is intended to fill the gap between the larger texts of which there are many in the field and those offering a briefer course. The student in Dental, Pharmacy, and Normal Schools with but from fifty to one hundred and fifty hours to devote to the subject finds the larger works, admirably adapted for references, altogether too voluminous for class work. The briefer texts are too elementary to be considered seriously.

Also has the author been mindful of the fact that proper association is the golden thread by which the manifold facts and phenomena can be connected to form an integral Science. Constantly, therefore, has he sought to weave the subject under discussion into that already mastered and, in a measure, to anticipate future subjects. Frequent cross references remind the student that no part of Physiology exists unto itself.

Since this work is intended for those having a very limited length of time for the acquisition of a basic knowledge of the subject, references to original papers are very few. However, to monographs dealing with specific topics, especially to those which have within the last few years appeared in physiological reviews, many references have been made. By consulting these, the student is directed to all the original sources.

Finally, the author has tried to keep the golden mean between those who wish "Science for Science's Sake," and those supporting the Baconian view that knowledge should be subservient to action. Somewhere Herbert Spencer says: "Vigorous health and its accompanying high spirits are larger elements of happiness than any other thing whatever, and the teaching how to maintain them is a teaching that yields in moment to no other whatever." Believing this to be true, the author offers no apology for the introduction of a large amount of what may be judged as "practical." This, however, is not a text in "Personal Hygiene," but a relation of those facts upon which all rational personal hygiene must be based. Far more space has, therefore, been devoted to the practical side of nutrition, physical exercise, mental work, fatigue, and kindred topics than usually is found in texts in Physiology.

W. D. Z.

CONTENTS

CHAPTER I

CHAPTER IV

CHAPTER V

CHAPTER VI

CHAPTER VII

CHAPTER VIII

CHAPTER IX

CHAPTER X

CHAPTER XI

CHAPTER XIX

CHAPTER XX

CHAPTER XXI

CHAPTER XXII

CHAPTER XXIII

CHAPTER XXIV

CHAPTER XXX

CHAPTER XXXI

GLOSSARY

COLOR PLATES

Comparison of Metric with English Measures

Length

1 meter = 100 centimeters = 1000 millimeters = 39.37 inches.
1 millimeter = $\frac{1}{25}$ inch (approximately).
1 micromillimeter (1 μ) = $\frac{1}{1000}$ millimeter = $\frac{1}{25000}$ inch.
1 kilometer = 1000 meters = 0.62 mile.
1 inch = 2.5 centimeters (approximately).
1 mile = 1.6 kilometers.

Volume

1 liter = 1000 cubic centimeters = $\left\{ \begin{array}{l} 0.9 \text{ dry quart,} \\ 1.05 \text{ liquid quarts.} \end{array} \right.$
1 dry quart = 1.1 liters.
1 liquid quart = 0.95 liter.
1 fluid ounce = 28.35 cubic centimeters.
1 cubic inch = 16.38 cubic centimeters.

Weight

1 gram = 1000 milligrams = 15.43 grains.
1 kilogram = 1000 grams = 2.2+ pounds.
1 pound = 453.6 grams (approximately).
1 ounce = 28.35 grams.

Energy

1 kilogrammeter (kgm.) = 7.25 foot-pounds.
1 foot-pound = 0.1381 kgm.

Mechanical Equivalent of Heat

1 large Calorie (Kilocalorie) = 426 kilogrammeters = 3,086 foot-pounds.

Temperature

To convert Centigrade degrees into Fahrenheit, multiply by $\frac{9}{5}$ and add 32.
To convert Fahrenheit degrees into Centigrade, subtract 32 and multiply by $\frac{5}{9}$.

TEXTBOOK OF PHYSIOLOGY

CHAPTER I

PROTOPLASM AND LIFE PROCESSES

Organs, Tissues, and Cells.—The human body and all the more highly organized forms of life are composed of various parts, each of which has a definite function to perform. Such parts are called organs; thus we speak of the stomach as an organ of digestion, of the eyes as sense organs of sight, and of the bones as the organs which provide the rigidity for various body segments.

By gross and by microscopic examination, it can be readily demonstrated that these organs are made up of two or more kinds of structures, each of which performs its special duty; these materials are known as tissues. In the stomach we find, for example, muscle tissue and gland tissue; by the former the food is moved about and by the latter the digestive juice is formed. Each tissue, in turn, is composed of a countless number of microscopic structures, cells, which resemble each other closely. The cell constitutes the structural, or morphologic (*morphe,* form; *logos,* science), unit of the body. All cells are composed of protoplasm (*protos,* first; *plasma,* form). According to Huxley, **protoplasm is the physical basis of life.** It is that particular form of matter which exhibits the properties of life; it is living stuff.

Physiology is the science which deals with the bodily functions of living organisms. The human body is so complex and the organs are so interdependent that the study of human physiology is necessarily a somewhat difficult and challenging subject. It may well be prefaced by the study of simpler organisms. In this first chapter we shall discuss the properties of protoplasm and the ways in which it responds to its environment. We shall refer occasionally to the ameba, a one-celled aquatic animal which is about $\frac{1}{100}$ inch in diameter. Seen with the microscope it appears as an irregularly-shaped mass of jellylike matter (Fig. 1). The protoplasm of the ameba is in many respects similar to the protoplasm in various cells of the human body, but it has not become specialized and differentiated.

I. PHYSICAL PROPERTIES OF PROTOPLASM

Our knowledge of the physical structure and chemical composition of protoplasm is in some respects very unsatisfactory. Observed microscopically, protoplasm in most instances appears to be a nearly transparent, colorless, semifluid material. That it is not a solid, in the ordinary meaning of this term, is evident from the mechanical changes it can undergo with such great ease, as we shall notice presently. It is a more or less viscid jellylike substance. On the rupturing of the cell wall the protoplasm flows out and rounds up into globules. It possesses some elasticity and, considering the large amount of water in its make-up, some forms of protoplasm exhibit quite a degree of rigidity.

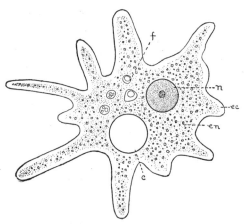

Fig. 1.—Ameba proteus. *n*, nucleus with nucleolus; *c*, contractile vacuole; *f*, food vacuole; *ec.*, ectoplasm; *en*, cytoplasm. (White: General Biology, The C. V. Mosby Co.)

II. PHYSICAL STRUCTURE OF PROTOPLASM: THE CELL

This living material is always found in discrete masses which we have already designated as cells. The cell constitutes the structural unit of all living bodies; it is to the organism what the molecule is to matter. In this small mass of protoplasm it is nearly always possible to distinguish two distinct parts: a more fluid mass, **cytoplasm** (*cyte*, cell), surrounding a spherical and somewhat denser body, the **nucleus.** In general, a cell may be defined as a discrete mass of protoplasm containing a nucleus. It is generally believed that the cytoplasm is contained within a very delicate envelope, the *plasma membrane,* or *protoplast.* The physical structure of the semifluid material of cytoplasm, known as the ground substance, has been variously described as reticular (network), granular, alveolar (honeycomb), fibrillar (threadlike). But as all of these views are based upon observations of protoplasm after it has been treated with fixing agents (which cause coagulation), it is possible that these various structures are artifacts. No definite structure can at present be assigned to cytoplasm.

In the ground substance various solids can be detected; among these we may mention the cell centers, or centrosomes, and centrioles (Fig. 5). Of these and of certain constituents of the nucleus we shall speak in connection with the multiplication of cells.

III. CHEMICAL COMPOSITION OF PROTOPLASM

The chemical investigation of protoplasm as such is impossible because analysis destroys life, and the results are those of a dead body. One thing, however, is certain and fundamental: protoplasm is not a chemical individual substance such as sodium chloride or sugar. It is composed of a large number of chemical compounds, among which we find proteins, fats, carbohydrates, water, and various salts. The elements most frequently present in the various compounds found in protoplasm are: carbon, oxygen, nitrogen, hydrogen, phosphorus, sulfur, sodium, potassium, calcium, magnesium, chlorine, iodine, iron, and copper; none of these are peculiar to protoplasm. A detailed discussion of the above-named compounds belongs more properly in a later chapter (Chap. XX); here we must content ourselves with a few cursory, but necessary, observations.

A. Water

From 50 to 90 per cent of protoplasm is water, sometimes called the water of organization. Deprived of this water nearly all protoplasms die; a few forms (notably plant seeds) pass into a condition of latent (inactive) life from which they can be revived by the addition of water.

In this water we find dissolved some crystalloids but more abundantly colloids (gellike substances, p. 64). It is difficult to picture to ourselves a piece of machinery, such as our muscles, composed of 75 per cent water; it does not suggest the necessary firmness, stability, and rigidity looked for in machines. However, the formation of pseudopods in the ameba is evidence of the semifluidity of its protoplasm. The change in the shape of a contracting muscle proves this also for the contents of these cells. In certain plant cells streaming movements of the protoplasm can be observed. No doubt the viscosity of the protoplasm varies from one cell to another. Soon after death the fluid material of protoplasm becomes firmer in texture; coagulation has taken place.

Certain parts of our body possess a large amount of firmness and solidity, e.g., tendons, ligaments, cartilages, and bones. This, however, does not indicate that the protoplasm does not contain the high percentage of water spoken of above, for these structures are formed of a large amount of solid, dead material found between the living cells of these tissues.

B. Inorganic Salts

Among the most important of the inorganic salts are chlorides, sulfates, phosphates, and carbonates of sodium, potassium, calcium, and magnesium (Chap. XX). The amount of each of these salts present in protoplasm varies with the different kinds of cells; but, like the water, they are indispensable for the life of the cell. No doubt each salt has its particular duty; this is well illustrated in the activity of the heart, which stops beating in the absence of sodium chloride. It appears that iron is present in all cells.

C. Proteins

An example of a protein is the white of egg, or egg albumin. Proteins belong to the most complex substances with which the chemist deals; they are complex because the molecules contain at least five, and frequently more than five, elements, and the size of the molecule is exceedingly large. The elements entering into their composition and approximate percentage by weight are:

Carbon	50%
Oxygen	25%
Nitrogen	15%
Hydrogen	7%
Sulfur—very variable	
Phosphorus—found only in a few proteins.	

There are many kinds of proteins which differ from each other in composition, solubility, and chemical reactions. Among those of our foods we may mention two, albumin and globulin. Peptones are proteins formed in the stomach; nucleoproteins are especially abundant in the nuclei of cells.

Many proteins are soluble in dilute salt solutions, such as milk, blood, and lymph; only a few are soluble in pure water. Nearly all proteins are undialyzable, that is, they do not have the power to pass through vegetable or animal membranes (such as the urinary bladder, lungs, pericardium) and therefore belong to the class of compounds frequently called colloids—the gluelike and jellylike compounds (p. 64).

Proteins in solution are easily precipitated (thrown out of solution) by certain reagents, such as alcohol, tannic acid, and picric acid. A number of the proteins (e.g., egg albumin) are coagulated by heat; by this the previously soluble protein is rendered insoluble.

D. Carbohydrates

Carbohydrates are composed of carbon, hydrogen, and oxygen. They include the simple sugars (e.g., glucose), the double sugars of which cane sugar and milk sugar are well-known examples, and the so-called starches among which we have the ordinary starches and a substance known as glycogen. It is especially in the form of glycogen (sometimes called animal starch) that we find the carbohydrates in the animal cells.

E. Fats

Fats are also composed of carbon, hydrogen, and oxygen. Among the simpler fats are olein, palmitin, and stearin. The food fats, such as butter, are mixtures of two or more of the individual fats. Fats are frequently united with other substances to form more complex compounds, known as compound lipids, among which is one, lecithin, containing nitrogen and phosphorus. The fat in protoplasm is nearly altogether in the form of compound lipids.

In protoplasm we find the above-discussed compounds and many others. However, protoplasm must not be regarded as merely a mixture of these ingredients, for we find practically the same substances in the fluid portion of the blood, to which we surely do not ascribe the properties of life. In all probability, these compounds are properly organized to form an exceedingly complex and labile structure; nothing, however, is definitely known as to the nature of the union holding them together. Each of the ingredients in protoplasm no doubt plays a specific part. The protein material, the most abundant of the solid constituents, may be regarded as the structural basis of the cell; indeed, some speak of it as forming a quasi skeleton which gives protoplasm its rigidity and certain other physical properties.

IV. PHYSIOLOGIC PROPERTIES OF PROTOPLASM

A substance or body is known by its properties. In the inanimate world these are the chemical and physical properties, such as color, elasticity, specific gravity, acidity, etc. In addition to these, protoplasm has also physiologic properties which are, in fact, the expressions of its life; but this does not necessarily imply that the physiologic characteristics are not dependent upon the physical or chemical properties of protoplasm. Among the physiologic properties are contractility, irritability, conductivity, metabolism, and reproduction. These we shall now proceed to discuss briefly.

A. Contractility

One of the most conspicuous characteristics of a living animal is its power to move some parts of its body or to change its own position with respect to its surroundings. This is in sharp contrast with the immobility of nearly all inanimate objects. If we observe an ameba for any length of time, we notice that at a certain point a pimplelike projection arises. The protoplasm seems to stream in this direction so that the projection, or *pseudopod* (*pseudes,* false; *pous,* foot), enlarges; at the same time the protoplasm at some other portion of the body can be seen to withdraw. Several of these pseudopods are shown in Fig. 1. In this manner the ameba moves from place to place. **The power of protoplasm to change its form is called contractility** (*traho,* to draw).

In the human body two structures in particular possess contractility: muscles and leucocytes (*leukos,* white). Leucocytes, or white blood cells, resemble the ameba. They also have the power to form pseudopods, for which reason they are said to have *ameboid movement.* When the protoplasm of a muscle contracts, the muscle decreases in length but increases in diameter; that is, it changes its form or shape but not its size.

B. Irritability

Another matter of general observation is the ease with which slight changes in the environment can induce changes in the activity of a living organism. When an ameba, quiescent for a considerable length of time, is disturbed by placing near it a drop of dilute acid or by heating the water in which it lives, we speedily see a change in its form. The animal by its contractility responded to the disturbance. **The power to respond to an environmental change is known as irritability; the change in the environment is called a stimulus.**

Various kinds of protoplasm differ from each other in the manner in which they respond to stimulation; for example, the protoplasm of a muscle responds by contracting, that of the salivary gland, by manufacturing saliva, and that of the tear glands, by forming tears.

But however they may differ and whatever property or power they may or may not have, they all possess irritability. *Irritability is a fundamental property common to all protoplasm* and, in consequence, we employ it as a diagnostic (*dia,* apart; *gnosis,* knowledge) property by which we tell the living from the dead. A freshly excised muscle of a frog is alive, because when properly stimulated it responds. But if this excised muscle is allowed to remain lying on the desk for some time, sooner or later it dies. How can we know whether this has occurred? By determining whether it does or does not respond to stimulation. When once we have ascertained the form of stimulation to which a particular organ is highly irritable, and the organ loses this irritability and by no treatment can regain it, we say that the organ is dead.

C. Automatism, or Spontaneity

It often happens in studying the ameba that a quiescent ameba begins to form a pseudopod, apparently without any stimulus having been applied. Some claim that this shows the power of protoplasm to initiate its own activity; that is, it has the property of spontaneity. While it may be very difficult, or sometimes impossible, for us to discover any form of stimulation that may have acted upon the ameba, yet for other reasons we cannot grant the existence of this property. One of the fundamental laws of the universe is Newton's law of inertia which states that a body at rest remains at rest until acted upon by some external force. It is more than likely that the ameba is no exception to this law. In the human body also most of the actions are induced by stimulation; but whether all mental activities can be thus explained is still a question.

It is, however, customary to apply the term "spontaneity" to an organ which, after removal from the body, continues its usual activity without any apparent external stimulation. This holds true for the excised heart of a frog, but never for a muscle removed from the leg.

D. Conductivity

It frequently happens that the application of a stimulus to a certain part, *a,* of the body causes activity in a more distant part, *b.* The stimulation of the nose by the odors of fragrant food causes the salivary glands to become more active ("the mouth waters"). Now we shall learn in Chap. V that the nose and the salivary glands are connected by strands of protoplasm, nerves. It must be evident that the stimulation of *a* caused a change in the protoplasm which traveled through the protoplasmic strands to *b* and excited the glands to activity.

As to the nature of this change, which in a nerve is called a **nerve impulse,** we have no certain knowledge (Chap. VII). **The power of the protoplasm to convey this impulse is known as conductivity.** Irritability and conductivity are present in all cells, but find their highest development in nerve tissue. So far as we know, *no nerve impulse ever originates without adequate stimulation.*

E. Metabolism

Protoplasm is characterized by activity, that is, by performing work. As ordinarily understood, to work means: (1) to produce a change; (2) to produce a change it is necessary to overcome resistance, or inertia; (3) to overcome resistance there must be expended a sufficient amount of power, or energy.

1. Energy

Energy we may define as the power to do work or to produce a change. There are many forms of energy: heat, light, sound, and mechanical, electrical, and chemical energy. It is customary to speak of two modes of energy: (a) the energy of motion, or kinetic energy, and (b) that of position, or potential energy.

a. Kinetic Energy.—The energy of motion may be in the form of *mechanical energy* of a moving body; for example, the energy of wind and waves, of flowing blood, and a moving part of the body. *Heat* is the energy of the movements of individual molecules. The movement of electrons gives rise to the *electric energy of a current.* *Radiant energy,* such as light, ultraviolet light, radio waves, is sometimes spoken of as undulations, or waves, of the hypothetical ether.

b. Potential energy may be regarded as stored energy. No change is produced by it, but there is the latent power under the proper conditions of doing work. A suspended weight, a coiled spring, and a stretched rubber band all possess potential energy.

c. Conservation and Transformation of Energy.—The amount of energy in the universe is said to be constant; *no energy can be created, neither can it be destroyed.* This is the law of the conservation of energy.* Energy can be changed, however, from one form into another. Thus, the energy of an electric current can be transformed into heat, light, or sound. We may also transform kinetic into potential energy; for example, a weight is raised from the ground to a certain height and placed on a support. In doing this, the energy of motion obtained from the arm of an individual or from any other

*According to the newer conception of the universe, this statement is not strictly correct, for, "Mass and energy are . . . identical concepts," and matter may be changed gradually into energy, as in the case of radium.

source is transformed into the potential energy of position; it is said to be latent in the weight. It is energy of position by virtue of the attraction existing between the earth and the weight and which was overcome by the force that separated these two bodies. It is energy due to separation. When the support upon which the weight rests is removed, the potential energy of position is transformed into mechanical kinetic energy of motion. When the weight strikes the earth, the energy of the moving body is transformed into sound and heat energy.

d. Chemical Potential Energy.—In the same manner we may speak of the energy of position, or separation, in chemical phenomena. By passing an electric current through water, the water is decomposed into hydrogen and oxygen. The energy of the electric current disappeared, and we find it associated with the hydrogen and oxygen atoms. Because of the "attraction" between the separated atoms, there exists potential energy of position, or separation, known as chemical potential energy. When, under the proper conditions such as the introduction of a spark, the hydrogen and oxygen unite, the chemical potential energy is transformed into kinetic energy of heat, light, sound, mechanical energy, etc. As much energy is liberated in the formation of the water by the union of the gases as was needed to separate the water into the two gases.

OXIDATION OF ORGANIC COMPOUNDS.—The above also applies to the elements carbon and oxygen. In the elemental state they contain chemical potential energy; at the proper temperature, the kindling temperature, they unite and the energy becomes kinetic, in the form of heat and light. The uniting of oxygen with another element or with a compound is called *oxidation;* ordinary burning is an example of this. Any compound containing carbon is known as an *organic compound*, in distinction to the inorganic. Among these compounds are the ordinary illuminating oils and gases, alcohol, coal, and the foods, such as fats, sugars, and proteins. All organic compounds which contain carbon and hydrogen, or carbon, hydrogen, and oxygen, have affinity for more oxygen and therefore are said to contain potential energy.

2. CATABOLISM

As is true for all machines, protoplasm to be active must be supplied with energy. The source of this lies in the chemical potential energy of the organic foods, namely, carbohydrates, fats, and proteins. It will be recalled that these compounds also enter into the composition of protoplasm itself. While it is generally helpful to speak of the food in the protoplasm as fuel and of the protoplasm as the machine, in reality no sharp distinction can be drawn. The chemical potential energy latent in the food (or protoplasm) is of no direct value, for as such it cannot be utilized for the vital processes. The latent energy must be released.

a. Liberation of Energy.—The releasing of potential energy and all it implies is known as catabolism (*kata,* down; *ballein,* to throw). A subsequent chapter is devoted to a more detailed account of the energy transformation in our body, but in order to understand any protoplasmic activity (of, say, a muscle or gland) it will be necessary to anticipate this by a brief preliminary study.

When a large organic molecule is split into two or more smaller molecules, some of the energy latent in the original molecule is set free. For example: during yeast fermentation the large molecule of glucose, $C_6H_{12}O_6$, is broken up into two molecules of carbon dioxide, CO_2, and two molecules of ethyl alcohol, C_2H_5OH. This cleavage of glucose is accompanied by the formation of heat; the products formed contain less potential energy than the original glucose. In our body the glucose molecule is split into the smaller molecules of lactic acid, $C_3H_6O_3$, and some of the chemical potential energy is liberated. But by far the larger amount of potential energy is set free by the process of oxidation spoken of in a previous paragraph.

b. Utilization of the Released Energy.—The energy liberated during catabolism can be utilized by the protoplasm for its particular functions. In the muscle protoplasm it is transformed into mechanical energy; in a gland it is used for manufacturing chemical compounds. In the mammalian body most of the liberated energy (about 80 per cent) takes the form of heat; this is of great value in maintaining the proper body temperature. In a few of the lower animals a considerable amount of the energy appears as light or as electric energy.

c. Site of Catabolism.—Catabolism takes place in every cell without exception, but the amount of catabolism varies from one type of cell to another, and in any one given cell it varies according to the demand for energy by the cell. Muscles and certain glands are the most active structures; in connective tissues, such as bones, catabolism is far less intense.

d. Excretion.—The oxidation of the food has a twofold result: (1) the transformation of potential into kinetic energy and (2) the material change of food into simpler compounds, called waste products. Among these products we may mention water, carbon dioxide, urea, and uric acid. Some of these waste products are more or less injurious and the accumulation of those not poisonous would, for reasons to be considered later, "clog" the machinery. They must therefore be removed by a process known as excretion, or elimination. In the human body there are special organs for this purpose. By means of the kidneys we excrete water, urea, and uric acid. Carbon dioxide and water are eliminated by means of the lungs. A very small amount of waste material derived from the cells of the body is eliminated along with the indigestible and undigested food by means of the alimentary canal.

e. **Respiration.**—As the greater part of the energy is liberated by the process of oxidation, a continual supply of oxygen is needed. The oxidations result in the formation, as we have seen, of carbon dioxide, a gas, which must be removed. This necessitates, therefore, an exchange of these gases between the organism and its environ-

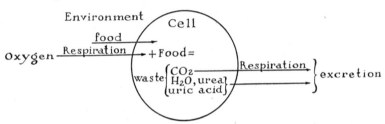

Fig. 2.—Diagram to illustrate respiration.

ment, a process called respiration (Fig. 2). In man this takes place in the lungs, which have two functions: (1) the transfer of oxygen from the air into the blood and (2) the elimination of carbon dioxide (and, to a lesser extent, of water) from the blood into the air.

f. **Source of Energy for Animal Life.**—The potential energy in the food utilized by the animal is in all cases derived, directly or indirectly, from the plant world. The plants are able to synthesize, or build up, the simple inorganic compounds, such as water, carbon dioxide, nitrates, sulfates, and phosphates, into highly complex organic substances, such as sugars, starches, fats, and proteins. These last-named substances contain much potential energy, while the materials from which they are derived are practically devoid of energy. To bring about this change, energy must have been expended and stored. This takes place in the chlorophyll (green coloring matter) of the plant where the radiant energy (light) from the sun is transformed into the chemical potential energy found in the carbohydrates, fats, and proteins. This synthesis is impossible for the animal to perform; in consequence the animal is dependent for these materials and their potential energy upon the plants.

3. Anabolism

In the preceding section we learned that protoplasmic activity is associated with the consumption of the food in the cell. If a distinction can be made between the food and the protoplasm, we may be allowed to say that, as in all mechanisms, the machinery undergoes some wear and tear. For the continued existence of the protoplasm this wear must be repaired and the food must be replenished. This constitutes the process of anabolism (*ana*, up).

a. Ingestion.—The first and preliminary step in anabolism is supplying the cell with the necessary materials for recouping its losses. The ameba ingests its food (small plants or animals) by letting a pseudopod flow around it; the food is engulfed. The process by which the protoplasm of a cell, devoid of a cell wall, flows around a small body is termed *phagocytosis*, and the cell is called a phagocyte (*phagein*, to eat; *osis*, process). The white corpuscles in our blood have the power to engulf solids, for example, bacteria, and are spoken of as phagocytes.

b. Digestion.—The carbohydrate, fat, and protein molecules of the ingested food are too large to be used in the reconstruction of the protoplasm. In addition to this, most of our foods are insoluble; starch (which constitutes at least one-half of our diet), fats (butter, etc.) and proteins (such as we find in a cut of meat) do not dissolve in water. They are, therefore, also undialyzable (see p. 65). In this state they cannot enter the cells of the body, for these cells, in their great differentiation and specialization, have lost the power to engulf solid materials. Hence, it is necessary to prepare the food for the cells.

On watching an ameba with an ingested food particle, we notice that the food undergoes changes; it seems gradually to be corroded or dissolved. This process is brought about by chemical agents, known as enzymes or ferments (Chap. II), which split the large food molecules into smaller molecules. The large starch molecule, for example, is split into 25 or more molecules of glucose. As such processes continue, the materials become more and more soluble and dialyzable, and are rendered utilizable by protoplasm. This constitutes digestion.

c. Absorption.—In the human body the digestion of food is carried on in the alimentary canal, which is a coiled tube extending the full length of the body. To supply the cells of our body, the soluble products of digestion pass through the walls of the alimentary canal and of the blood vessels found in the walls of this canal and thus into the blood stream. **The transfer of a substance from a free surface** (such as the lumen of the alimentary canal) **into the blood is called absorption.**

d. Anabolism Proper.—The food having entered the cell is used for various purposes; of these only two need concern us at this time: (1) It is used immediately by the protoplasm for the production of kinetic energy, or (2) it is built up into protoplasm (assimilation).

It is in this latter function that one meets with a radical difference between protoplasm as an animated machine and all inanimate machines. In performing work both types of machine undergo wear and tear; the animate machine restores its own losses, something utterly beyond the power of a dead mechanism. This wonderful power of **self-restoration** becomes still more marvelous when we consider that this synthesis is exceedingly specific.

There are literally thousands of different types of protoplasm. This sweeping statement is substantiated by the following easily ascertained facts. The particular function of a machine, whether animate or inanimate, is determined by the physical and chemical construction of that machine. As the function of the protoplasm of a muscle is to contract, that of a nerve to conduct impulses, and that of a gland to manufacture chemical compounds, these three protoplasms must differ quite radically from each other. Although such diverse structures as the salivary glands, the thyroid, the stomach glands, and many others are all supplied with food from a common source, the blood, yet each gland constructs from this material its own particular secretions. And the saliva made by the gland-protoplasm of a dog is not the same as that made by human glands. The fig tree and the thistle growing side by side are nourished by the same soil and air, but "men do not gather figs from thistles."

Generally speaking, all plants and animals are developed from a seed or an egg, respectively. The physical and chemical nature of the protoplasm in a particular seed or egg determines the species of plant or animal to be evolved from it. When the ingredients of the food are built up into protoplasm the newly formed protoplasm is of the type characteristic of this particular cell—a truly astounding performance.

4. Quantitative Relationship Between Anabolism and Catabolism

a. Physiologic Equilibrium.—The twofold process of anabolism and catabolism is frequently referred to as *metabolism;* consequently this term includes all the material and energy changes that occur in the body, and in its broadest meaning is coextensive with the term life (Fig. 3). We may say, therefore, that life consists in a continual building up and a tearing down of protoplasm. In the normal adult body these two processes balance each other; there is then neither gain nor loss of body weight inasmuch as the amount of material taken up by the body equals that lost in the excretions. This condition is known as *physiologic*, or *complete nutritive, equilibrium*. We have shown this diagrammatically in Fig. 4, *a*.

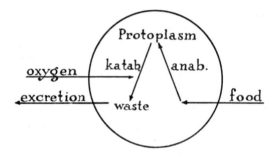

Fig. 3.—Diagram to illustrate metabolism.

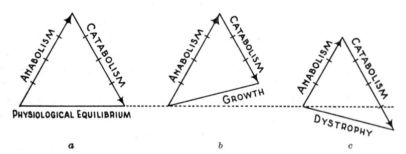

Fig. 4.—To illustrate quantitative relationship between anabolism and catabolism.

b. Growth.—During the period of growth anabolism exceeds catabolism; Fig. 4, *b*. Growth of a tissue or organ may arise either from an increase in the number of cells, or from an increase in the amount of protoplasm within the cells without any multiplication of the number of cells. A nerve cell in the body of a child may increase a hundred times in length, but after the age of one year, it is very doubtful whether any new nerve cells are ever formed. On the other hand, the red blood cells and the epithelial cells of the skin are constantly renewed.

Under certain circumstances the protoplasm of a tissue or organ may increase after the period of true ''growth'' (youth and adolescence) has ceased. This is seen, for example, during convalescence following a debilitating illness. In speaking of the effects of repetitive stimulation (p. 95) we shall note another form of increased anabolism.

c. Dystrophy and Atrophy.—Most of us have seen instances in which catabolism outstrips anabolism. Almost any severe illness results in a loss not only of the dead fat present in the body, but of the very protoplasm; the patient literally burns up his own flesh (consumption, or tuberculosis). In some tissues the extent of anabolism is in proportion to the amount of the activity. This is especially true for muscles. An unused muscle suffers in its anabolism and gradually dwindles away, a condition known as dystrophy or atrophy (*dys,* bad; *a,* not or without; *trophe,* nourishment). The shrunken limb seen in infantile paralysis is, unfortunately, a not uncommon example.

5. Influence of Stimulation Upon Catabolism

a. Dynamic Equilibrium.—An inanimate system may be in equilibrium in two distinct ways. Consider a uniformly colored top with its point firmly pressed into a support; it maintains a constant position with respect to surrounding objects; it is at rest. A similarly colored top spinning at great velocity around its vertical axis also shows this steady state; indeed, casual observation reveals no difference between it and the first mentioned top. The constancy of the first top may be called static equilibrium. The constancy and apparent resting state of the second top are due to a balance between two opposing forces, namely, gravitational force and the centrifugal force of the swiftly revolving top; this is dynamic equilibrum.

Again, the constancy and uniformity of a candle flame, to which life has been frequently compared, are the result of the continual burning of the fat in the flame and the continual feeding of fat to the flame—dynamic equilibrium. A bit of protoplasm or a whole organ may appear to be at perfect rest and may retain its constancy for a long time. This also is the result of two opposing forces: anabolism and catabolism. To make this possible, a continual exchange of material and energy exists between the protoplasm and its environment.

b. Basal Metabolism.—The dynamic equilibrium of a cell may take place at various levels of energy and material exchange. In the normal, so-called "resting" organism, the amount of energy expended is the least amount consistent with the maintenance of life. This is known as the basal metabolic rate.

It is pertinent to inquire why, if the cell is "resting" or, at least, shows no evidence of work accomplished, should there be any expenditure of energy? Here we meet with another pronounced difference between the animate and the inanimate machine. An automobile does not cease to exist when its fuel or oxygen supply is cut off. But in the living organism the very existence of the machine, protoplasm, is conditioned upon a continual expenditure of energy. **The essence of life is activity;** a "resting cell" is a misnomer.

c. Stimulation.—When "resting" protoplasm with its minimal (basal) energy expenditure is properly stimulated, there is a momentary upsetting of the balance between anabolism and catabolism in that the destructive processes are increased. This results in a greater liberation of energy which is used by the protoplasm to adjust itself to the environmental change. A stimulus, or excitation as it is frequently called, may be regarded as a small amount of external energy applied to the protoplasm by which the catabolism and the activity of the protoplasm are increased. Personal observation clearly demonstrates that the amount of energy released in the stimulated organism is generally greater, often infinitely greater, than that possessed by the stimulus. Why is so small a cause followed by such a large result? The answer to this question lies in the instability of protoplasm.

d. Stability and Instability.—Physical stability and instability may be illustrated by means of a cone. Placed on its base, the cone is a physical stable body; it opposes outside disturbances and in consequence considerable energy must be expended upon it to cause a change in its position. Balanced on its apex, it is exceedingly unstable, because its center of gravity lies relatively high over a narrow base of support; in this condition a small amount of external force causes it to fall. Dynamite and other explosives are chemically unstable; here also the application of a small amount of kinetic energy (a burning fuse) leads to the transformation of the unstable explosive into stable products. We may say that an unstable object always has a "tendency" to change, and the application of a small amount of kinetic energy is the "opportunity" given it to alter its state. With a physically or chemically unstable body there is always associated a certain amount of potential energy which becomes kinetic when the unstable becomes stable.

Protoplasm, as we have seen, must be regarded as a highly complex mixture of many distinct ingredients which are in some unknown manner bound to each other. The resulting physical and chemical structure is an unstable system which has a constant tendency to break down. This instability we heretofore called irritability.

e. **The amount of energy released** upon the application of a stimulus depends: (1) upon the characteristics of the stimulus, and (2) upon the condition of the protoplasm. Among the many kinds of stimuli of daily occurrence are mechanical (e.g., pressure), thermal (heat and cold), chemical, photic (light), and acoustic (sound). In the laboratory electrical stimulation is used very largely. A stimulus of any kind may vary in strength (intensity), duration, frequency, and abruptness. That these characteristics influence the nature and the extent of the protoplasmic reaction is a matter of daily observation. Within certain limits, the response will be the greater, the greater the intensity of the stimulus. The least intensity of the stimulus to which a certain organ or tissue responds is known as the *threshold, liminal,* or *minimal stimulus.* By determining the liminal stimulus we are able to compare the relative irritability of two protoplasmic structures, such as two nerves or muscles, for the less the intensity of the liminal stimulus the greater the irritability.

f. **The condition of the stimulated protoplasm** modifies the degree of the response. A fresh muscle responds by a vigorous contraction, but a muscle fatigued by previous work, or under the influence of an anesthetic, responds feebly to the same strength of stimulus. In man we see this pronouncedly demonstrated during sleep. These conditions—fatigue, anesthesia, sleep—are all characterized by a state of lessened irritability.

The particular type of the protoplasm is also a factor in the extent of its response to any given stimulus. While light is a very efficient stimulus for the eye, it has no effect whatever on the sense organs of the tongue or ear.

EXTERNAL AND INTERNAL STIMULI.—In addition to the above-mentioned stimuli, which are changes in our external world, and therefore are sometimes called external stimuli, changes take place in the environment of the individual cells of our body. As we shall learn, these cells are bathed by a fluid known as tissue fluid; changes in its chemical composition may cause stimulation of the cells. Such stimuli may be regarded as internal stimuli, but it must be borne in mind that they are always external to the stimulated cell. A cell may also be influenced by certain changes befalling a nerve in direct contact with the cell.

g. **Inhibitors.**—Everyday experience shows us that certain environmental changes instead of increasing may lessen or even totally suppress the activity we happen to be engaged in. The sudden stopping of a man crossing a street upon hearing a blast of an automobile horn supplies a well-known example. The decrease in func-

tion in response to an environmental change is called an inhibition.*
A moment's reflection shows the tremendous importance of inhibition in our physical, mental, and social life.

6. Influence of Stimulation on Anabolism

In consequence of its instability there is always a tendency in
protoplasm to break up. In fact, as we have seen, this is not only
a tendency but a reality; the basal metabolism of an apparently
quiescent animal is the expression of this tendency. It is for this
reason that "resting" protoplasm is impossible. This tendency to
break up must be offset by an opposing tendency. And so it is. We
may figuratively speak of a constant "striving" on the part of
protoplasm to maintain a balance between the running down of its
unstable body and its rewinding. When, therefore, by the application of a stimulus the catabolism is increased, the protoplasm "en-
deavors" to maintain or to regain its status quo by also increasing
its anabolism. By the greater intake of food and the accelerated
assimilation of this food, the balance between anabolism and catabolism is restored, but at a higher level than that existing previous
to the stimulation.

The above situation is generally found under the ordinary conditions of life. But as the power of maintaining its former state of
metabolic balance has its limits, an excessively strong environmental
change or a milder form continued for a longer time may exceed
the ability of protoplasm to rebuild fast enough to compensate for
the greatly increased catabolism. This, of necessity, leads to a
diminution in the amount of protoplasm (atrophy) and finally to
the cessation of life.

Hypertrophy.—Repetitive stimulation of the proper intensity, frequency, and duration may be associated with an increase in anabolism which exceeds the accelerated catabolism. As a net result there
is a gain in the amount of protoplasm in the tissue or organ—hypertrophy (*hyper,* above, excess). The hypertrophy of the properly
exercised and trained muscles of arms and legs will suggest itself
to the reader. Extra work thrown upon the heart may cause this
organ to undergo similar hypertrophy.

V. LIFE AS A STIMULUS-RESPONSE PHENOMENON

A. Adjustment

By this time, no doubt, the question has arisen in the reader's
mind, "What is life?" To this age-old question a satisfactory an-

---

*Some writers use the word "stimulus" to include both the environmental
change which induces an increase and that which causes a decrease in function.
Other authors try to limit it to an increase in function.

swer has as yet not been found, chiefly because we have nothing with which to compare life. All definitions hitherto proposed have taken cognizance of one or two features of this extremely complex phenomenon, to the exclusion of the other components.

As the weight of the body immediately after death is the same as that before death, life is not matter. Neither can life be regarded as a ''living principle'' which tenants the body and on death departs.

What are the characteristics which most sharply differentiate the living from the dead? To the casual observer it is the power of the living body to respond to relatively slight environmetal changes. Upon this Herbert Spencer based his classical definition: **''Life is the continuous adjustment of internal relations to external relations.''** But this concept of life lacks inclusiveness; it views life, so to speak, from the two ends, namely, the stimulus at the beginning, and the response at the end of, a series of events; what happens between these two events is ignored. However, the concept embodied in Spencer's definition is of utmost value; we may epitomize it: **Life is a stimulus-response phenomenon.** Physiology concerns itself with the study of the stimulations and the internal changes which result from these stimuli and which finally culminate in the adjustment of the organism to the environmental changes.

B. Adaptation

Concerning the responses by the organism to the various stimuli we may note that:

1. They are nearly always, if not always, advantageous to the organism; in other words, they are adaptive.

2. This adaptiveness serves, broadly speaking, three purposes:

a. Defense and escape reactions, thereby protecting the organism against injury.

b. Procuring materials for the growth and maintenance of the protoplasm and for supplying energy.

c. Perpetuation of the species.

We may summarize: **all protoplasmic activities serve for self-preservation and perpetuation of the race.**

C. The Sense Organs

At this time we may call attention to the exceedingly great importance of the sense organs. These structures, e.g., eyes and ears, are endowed with a surprisingly high degree of irritability towards certain types of stimuli. It is through his sense organs that the animal becomes "aware" of the environmental changes to which he must adjust himself. All our knowledge of the outside world is gained, directly or indirectly, through sense organs. Very appropriately we may term **the sense organ the alpha of all life, physical and mental.**

D. Maladjustment

To some environmental changes the body is wholly unable to adjust itself, or the adjustment is incomplete or imperfect. The first results in death; in the second, there is maladjustment or maladaptation. Physical and mental diseases and social infractions are instances of maladjustment. These maladjustments may be due: (1) to the severity of the environmental change; (2) to the absence in a given species of animal of the proper adjustors (e.g., a mammal dying below water and a fish perishing out of the water); or (3) to some defect in the physical or chemical constitution of the individual. This is frequently a matter of inheritance, as in color blindness. It may reveal itself in the lack of proper defensive powers against certain external conditions, as in hay fever. And, no doubt, the "irrational" and eventually destructive behavior of the insane can be accounted for on the basis of a physical or chemical defect in the make-up of the nervous system.

E. Acquiring Adjusting Mechanisms

In some instances the organism has the power to acquire an adjusting mechanism with which it was not equipped previously. For example, the average person may succumb to the toxic effects of smallpox of sufficient intensity. But the inoculation with vaccine confers upon his body the power to adjust itself adaptively to a previously lethal dose of the infection.

VI. DIFFERENTIATION, ORGANIZATION, INTEGRATION

A. Differentiation

We have seen abundant evidence of the great diversity of activities in the animal body. And the most cursory examination teaches us that these many and divers functions are severally performed by highly differentiated structures. There is a great division of labor in the animal economy. Even in a unicellular animal, such as the ameba, this holds true to a limited extent. When this cell is cut into two parts so that the one consists only of cytoplasm and the other of some cytoplasm and the nucleus, the part devoid of a nucleus exhibits certain signs of life, such as the formation of pseudopods, the ingestion of food, and the power of responding to stimuli; but the power to digest the food and to utilize it in building up protoplasm seems to be lost. The part containing both nucleus and cytoplasm shows the usual cell activities and grows until it has attained its original size. From this we may conclude that the cytoplasm is able to perform the catabolic processes coupled with the expenditure of energy, but that the anabolic functions of the cell are associated with **the nucleus as the trophic center.** In a later chapter we shall have occasion to speak of the highly specialized function of the plasma membrane.

B. Organization

It is self-evident that all the various activities in a highly differentiated animal do not take place at random, that is, without any regard to their sequence and frequency. In an animal fleeing for its life, the contraction and relaxation of the many muscles of its legs and trunk, the increased activity of the heart by which more food is brought to the highly active muscles, the acceleration of the respiratory pump, the bursting into action of the sweat glands, the outpouring of more food by the liver, all these and many more activities must be in very close cooperation with each other. In other terms, there must exist a high degree of organization. By organization we mean an intimate functional relationship between all parts of the body which results in the proper sequence of the multitude of physical and chemical processes with respect to each other, and the control of each process as to its frequency, intensity, and duration. To accomplish successfully the final objective for which these activities take place, organization is indispensable.

In the organism we note, therefore: (1) specialization or individuality in the activity of each distinct organ; (2) a great diversity of actions throughout the whole body; (3) a unity of purpose whereby the entire organism acts as one piece of machinery; this latter phase we designate as integration (*integer,* whole).

C. Integration

What constitutes the control for this integration? In the more highly developed animals this unification is mediated to a large extent by the close intercommunication between practically all parts of the body. This intercommunication is accomplished by: (1) the nervous system and (2) chemical messengers, or internal secretions (pp. 82 and 481). By one or the other of these (and in some in-

stances by both) the increase or decrease in the activity of one part
of the body influences the activity of many other parts.

D. Advantages of Differentiation

What advantages does an animal derive from this extreme structural and functional differentiation of its tissues and organs? A
comparative study of a very simple form of life, say, the ameba, and
of a highly developed animal reveals the greater ability of the latter
to adjust either itself to the environment or the environment to
itself. Indeed, man is the most adaptable of all living creatures,
for which reason he is generally said to occupy the highest position
in the scale of life. This superiority flows mainly from the following:

1. The highly differentiated protoplasms of the sense organs are
receptive to many types of environmental changes.

2. The high degree of sensitivity of the sense organs to minute
environmental changes.

3. The large number of structures by which adjustments to the
environmental changes can be made.

4. The greater power to store up impressions of stimuli and of the
responses to these stimuli (memory) ; by these impressions future
activities can be influenced for better adjustment.

5. Surpassing all, the greater degree of organization existing between the large number of organs which receive the stimulation and
those by which final adjustment is made.

In consequence of the foregoing, instead of responding in the
simple and stereotype manner seen in most animals ("instincts?"),
man is able to vary his adjustment to a given environmental change;
his behavior is determined not only by the stimulus under consideration but also by other stimulations befalling him at that same time
and by the impressions retained from previous stimulations and responses. These last two factors find their anatomical basis largely in
the extensive and intricate structure of the brain.

VII. CELL DIVISION

Into the complicated process of cell multiplication by cell division
we cannot enter except in very general terms. It will be recalled
that in the cytoplasm lies the cell center (attraction sphere, or
centrosome) with two centrioles (Fig. 5). In the nucleus is found,
in the form of a network or twisted filaments (Figs. 5 and 6), a
chromatin (*chroma,* color) material which stains readily with certain dyes.

In a dividing cell, the centrioles separate and travel to opposite poles of the cell. In Fig. 6 only the nucleus is shown, the centrioles may be imagined as situated at m and n and connected by a spindle-

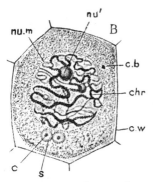

Fig. 5.—Plant cell. *c.w*, cell wall; *s*, two centrospheres; *chr*, chromatin network; *nu.m*, nuclear membrane; *c*, centrosome; *nu'*, nucleolus. (After Guignard.)

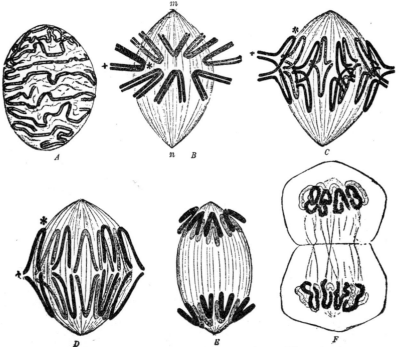

Fig. 6.—Diagrams illustrating cell division. (Flemming.)

shaped series of lines, forming the asters. The chromatin network now divides into a number of short V-shaped pieces, known as *chromosomes*, Fig. 6, *B*, and the nuclear membrane disappears. The number of chromosomes is constant for any given animal, but varies from one species to another. All the chromosomes in a cell are not always of the same size or shape, but whenever they differ, there are always two of each kind. These structures are generally said to be the bearers of hereditary characteristics (see p. 677).

In the next stage of cell division, the chromosomes arrange themselves in pairs midway between the two centrosomes and each chromosome now divides lengthwise. One of the chromosomes formed from each original chromosome travels to one of the centrioles, *m;* the other moves in the opposite direction to *n.* There new nuclei are formed, each containing the same amount and the same kind of chromatin material as the original nucleus. The chromosomes at each of the poles now unite to form a network, a nuclear membrane is formed, and the cytoplasm divides, by constriction or by the formation of a cell wall, thereby forming two daughter cells. This manner of cell division is known as *karyokinesis* (*karyon,* nucleus; *kineo,* to move), or *mitosis* (*mitos,* thread).

CHAPTER II

ENZYMES OR FERMENTS

I. Importance of Ferments

Few subjects are of greater importance in physiology than that of ferments. So general and essential is the part played by these agencies that someone has referred to the living body as a collection of ferments. We have already spoken of these compounds in the previous chapter, when we stated that nearly all the changes that constitute digestion are examples of ferment activity. And as researches progress, more and more of the chemical actions taking place in the cells themselves (anabolism and catabolism) are shown to be brought about by ferments.

But it is not only in the animal body that ferments play such a prominent part, for many of the common phenomena occurring around us are also processes of fermentation. We may call attention to a few of these: the production of alcohol from sugar, the production of vinegar, the souring of cabbage in the formation of sauerkraut, the formation of silage, the ripening of certain fruits after they are picked, the discoloration of peeled apples, the decay of vegetable matter, the putrefaction of animal matter, the souring of milk, and the becoming rancid of butter. Nearly all the fermentations here enumerated are produced by living ferments, most of which belong to a class of microorganisms, the bacteria.

Because of their widespread occurrence and great significance in the functions of the animal body, it is necessary to study the activity of ferments somewhat in detail. For this we may take yeast as an example. Ordinary baker's yeast is a collection of microscopic plants. Each plant is composed of a single cell, about 0.01 mm. in diameter. When we add a small quantity of yeast to a dilute solution of sugar, we soon notice the formation of gas bubbles. By passing these bubbles through limewater (calcium hydroxide), a precipitate is formed; this proves that the gas is carbon dioxide. If we take a large quantity of sugar solution and let the process go on for a few days, we can distill some of the liquid and prove that alcohol has also been produced. These two products originate from the sugar under the influence of the yeast. The sugar which is generally used in this experiment is glucose which has the formula

$C_6H_{12}O_6$. By the action of the yeast one molecule of glucose gives rise to two molecules of carbon dioxide and two of ethyl alcohol:

$$C_6H_{12}O_6 = 2CO_2 + 2C_2H_5OH.$$

II. Characteristics of Fermentation

The process of fermentation has several characteristics that are of great interest from a physiologic and an economic point of view.

1. **The Necessity of Water.**—If dry sugar and dry yeast are mixed, no action takes place. No fermentation ever proceeds without water; a dry substance never decays. Upon this principle depends the preserving of desiccated fruits, vegetables, and animal products. One of the great functions of water in our body is to make fermentation possible.

2. **Dependence Upon Temperature.**—Most of us are familiar with the fact that when sugar solution and yeast are cooled, the fermentation is retarded; when the temperature is reduced to near the freezing point, the action of the yeast stops altogether; this is true for practically all ferments. Because of this, we can preserve perishable foods by refrigeration. If a fermenting fluid (sugar solution plus active yeast) which has been frozen is allowed to warm up, the fermentation soon becomes as vigorous as before; hence. the ferment is not destroyed by freezing.

On the other hand, if the fermenting fluid is heated to about 70° C. the fermentation comes to a standstill and cannot be revived by lowering the temperature. Heat, especially in the presence of water, destroys all ferments. Upon this depends the preserving of food by boiling or pasteurization; but to keep the food indefinitely, the material must be sealed hermetically while in the heated condition; that is, the entrance of other ferments from the air, etc., must be prevented, as in canning.

Ferments, therefore, can work only within a limited range of temperature. For each ferment there is an *optimum temperature* at which its action proceeds with the greatest economy; for the ferments in the human body this temperature is about that of the body (37° C.).

3. **Hydrogen Ion Concentration.**—The activity of an enzyme depends upon the reaction of the medium, i.e., upon the degree of acidity or alkalinity of the fluid in which the action takes place. There is an optimum degree of acidity or alkalinity for each enzyme. Deviation from this optimum slows the fermentation and, if deviation is large, the enzyme is destroyed.

4. Catalysis.—A ferment is peculiar in its action in that it is not used up. At the end of the operation there is as much ferment as at the start, hence, it takes no part in the end products; that is, the end products are derived solely from the material upon which the ferment acts. Neither does the ferment furnish any of the energy which may be liberated during fermentation. In these respects ferments are like certain agencies in chemistry, the catalysts. We may recall the part played by the manganese dioxide in the production of oxygen from potassium chlorate. A catalyst, such as the manganese dioxide in our illustration, is a substance that increases the speed of a chemical action without itself undergoing any permanent change. Some have defined ferments *as catalysts of organic* (plant or animal) *origin.*

If it is true that a ferment is not consumed by its own activity, it must follow that, granting a sufficient length of time, a small amount of ferment can do as much work as a large amount. The difference between the two is in the velocity of the reaction. Any small amount of ferment can ferment an unlimited amount of material. Sherman found that one part of a certain ferment was able to digest four million parts of starch and that the activity of this ferment was detectable when the ferment was diluted with one hundred million parts of water.

5. Hydrolytic Cleavage, or Hydrolysis.—In many instances of fermentation, the decomposition of the fermentable material takes place by the addition of one or more molecules of water to the fermenting substance. To give a well-known example of this: Milk contains a sugar, lactose, or milk sugar, which is split up by the action of bacteria (ferments) into four molecules of lactic acid (the souring of milk). This reaction we may state chemically thus:

$$\underset{\text{lactose}}{C_{12}H_{22}O_{11}} + H_2O = \underset{\text{lactic acid}}{4C_3H_6O_3}$$

A process whereby water becomes incorporated into the end products when a large molecule is split up is called hydrolytic cleavage, or hydrolysis (*hydor*, water; *luein*, to loose). All the digestive ferments in the alimentary canal by which fats, proteins, and carbohydrates are split up into simpler compounds belong to this class of enzymes. In addition to this class, we have oxidases which produce the oxidations in the body.

6. Energy Set Free.—Glucose contains a certain amount of potential energy. The carbon dioxide formed from the grape sugar has no energy, and the energy found in the alcohol derived from a definite amount of glucose is less than that of the sugar. Hence, the combined end products possess less energy than the mother substance; this can be accounted for only by the liberation of heat during the fermentation.

7. Specific Action.—One of the most striking features of the organic catalysts is the specificity of their action. By this we mean that a certain ferment will act upon a certain substance or chemically closely related substances and, generally, upon no other. To give an illustration of this: There are three sugars, disaccharides (see Chap. XIV), which are very closely related chemically; in fact, they are so closely related and so similar to each other that the same chemical formula applies to them all—$C_{12}H_{22}O_{11}$. These three sugars are lactose, maltose, and cane sugar. Now, the molecule of a disaccharide can readily be split into two molecules of a monosaccharide—$C_6H_{12}O_6$—according to the equation:

$$C_{12}H_{22}O_{11} + H_2O = C_6H_{12}O_6 + C_6H_{12}O_6.$$

This cleavage can be brought about by fermentation, but for each one of the three disaccharides there is a particular ferment that has the power to split up that particular disaccharide and is unable to influence the other two.

The question suggests itself why three distinct ferments are necessary to split up three sugars so closely allied as to have the same chemical composition. This can hardly be answered at present, because we do not definitely know the relation between the ferment and the fermentable substance. But this we may say with some degree of certainty: an intimate contact, or union, must exist between these two substances in order that the one shall be able to act upon the other. To explain this specific action, Emil Fischer proposed the *"lock-and-key"* theory. From organic chemistry we know that a molecule of a certain substance has not only a definite composition so far as the kind and number of atoms entering into its composition are concerned, but that it has also a definite shape or configuration. That is, the various atoms in the molecule are arranged in a definite position with respect to each other.

We may illustrate the meaning of *molecular configuration* by a simple example from organic chemistry. C_2H_6O is the formula for ethyl alcohol and also for an ether, known as methyl ether. Although these substances have the same composition in that they contain the same kind and the same number of the respective atoms, they are radically different substances, as shown by their properties and reactions; this difference depends, as we indicated above, upon the configuration of the molecules, which may be expressed by the following structural formulas:

ethyl alcohol   methyl ether

Lactose, maltose, and cane sugar, the three disaccharides, differ from each other in this manner, although all three have the common formula, $C_{12}H_{22}O_{11}$. According to Fischer's theory the molecule of the ferment also has a certain configuration. When the configuration of the fermentable material is such that it allows of intimate contact with the molecule of the ferment, the ferment has the power to decompose the material; if the configurations do not fit into each other, the ferment has no action. Fischer likened this to the action of a lock and a key. Both the key and the lock have a certain shape or form (configuration); only when the two are adapted to each other can the key throw the bolt of the lock.

8. **Reversible Action: Point of Equilibrium.**—In many cases it has been found that, if the products formed by the fermentation are allowed to accumulate in the fermenting fluid, the activity of the ferment gradually decreases until finally it ceases altogether. The fermentation, therefore, comes to a standstill before all the fermentable material (or substrate, as it is called) has been split up. On the other hand, if the products are removed as fast as they are formed, fermentation proceeds until no substrate remains.

Thus far we have been speaking of fermentation as an analytic process, a splitting of a large molecule of the substrate into smaller molecules. But certain instances have been found in which, when the smaller molecules were brought into contact with the enzyme (or ferment), a combining of these molecules into a larger molecule (synthesis) took place. Let us consider the digestion of fat. A molecule of a fat is formed by the union of glycerol and fatty acid. The digestive enzyme, lipase, hydrolytically splits the fat into glycerol and fatty acid:

$$\text{Fat} + H_2O \rightleftharpoons \text{glycerol} + \text{fatty acid}$$

If, on the other hand, lipase is added to a mixture of glycerol and fatty acid, we note that fat is being formed and that the concentration of the fatty acid and glycerol grows less. If the product, fat, is not removed, the synthetic process gradually slows down and finally ceases. The activity of the enzyme is, therefore, reversible; this is indicated by the two arrows in the above equation.

When the ferment (lipase, in our illustration) is placed in a substrate (fat) and by the analytic action forms some cleavage products (fatty acid and glycerol), the synthetic action of the ferment begins. At first this is very slow, but as the concentration of the cleavage products increases, the speed of the synthesis also increases. At the same time, because of the decrease in the concentration of the substrate, the speed of the analytic action decreases. After some time a condition is reached where the two antagonistic processes balance each other. Apparently then no change takes place; in reality the two processes are going on side by side to an equal extent; *the system is in equilibrium.* An enzyme is merely an accelerator; and whether it accelerates the analytic or the synthetic reaction depends upon the condition of the substrate with respect to its point of equilibrium.

9. **Nature of Ferments.**—Most fermentations occurring around us in vegetable and animal matter take place in the presence of microorganisms, such as yeast and, to a much larger extent, bacteria. Nearly all the processes that we alluded to at the beginning of this chapter are of this nature, and the bacteria and other living organisms are looked upon as *organized, or formed, ferments.*

But in addition to these ''living ferments,'' as we may designate them, there are dead substances whose activities, in the main, bear the same characteristics as those we have been discussing with respect to the yeast. From the saliva, for example, there can be obtained a dead material which, acting as a catalytic agent, has the power to change starch into maltose. In fact, all the ferments which we referred to as taking a part in digestion and metabolism are of this nature. Such ferments are called *enzymes* (*en,* in; *zyme,* yeast).

Formerly great stress was laid upon the difference between the organized and the unorganized ferments. Many physiologists and chemists, among whom Pasteur was very prominent, held that, while certain fermentations were caused by dead ferments (enzymes), there were other fermentations in which the chemical action was directly produced by the living protoplasm of the organism, such as the yeast and bacteria. Others, among whom we may mention Liebig, held that in every instance the fermentation was brought about by a dead material, that is, by enzymes, and that the protoplasm of the yeast, bacteria, and such organisms was necessary for the fermentation only so far as the production of the enzyme is concerned. That is, the protoplasm of the yeast or bacterium bears the same relation to fermentation that the protoplasm of the salivary cell bears to digestion. The protoplasm of the salivary gland produces the enzyme and throws it into the mouth, where it acts independently of the cell. Buchner proved this to be the correct view in regard to the alcoholic fermentation produced by yeast. After grinding the yeast thoroughly with sand, Buchner subjected the thick mass thus obtained to a pressure of 300 atmospheres (4,500 pounds per square inch). By this method he obtained a juice which, after careful filtration to remove any yeast cells or fragments of cells, had the power to transform sugar into alcohol and carbon dioxide. The active principle of this extract, zymase, shows all the characteristics of a ferment, but is, of course, a dead material; it is the alcoholic enzyme.

Other enzymes have been extracted by this or other methods from various microorganisms, and it is possible that with improved methods all the so-called organized ferments will yield enzymes which are the real agencies in bringing about the activities generally attributed to the microorganisms. Similarly, it has been found possible in many instances to extract from the tissues or organs of the highly developed animals enzymes which have the same actions, at least in part, as those exhibited by the living tissue or organ.

10. Proferments, or Zymogens.—In many instances it has been shown that the cells which produce digestive enzymes do not store or throw out the enzymes as such. From materials furnished by the blood they elaborate a substance known as a proferment, or zymogen. This is frequently stored in the protoplasm in the form of granules and differs from the enzyme, of which it is the antecedent, in not being active. As the enzyme is needed, the zymogen granules are transformed into the active enzyme; this change is in some cases brought about outside of the cell by agents known as kinases which are specific in that each kinase activates only one particular proferment. In other instances, the enzyme is not active unless it is accompanied by, or intimately associated with, a second agent which is called a coferment or coenzyme.

11. Antiferments.—Sometimes it becomes necessary to restrain the activity of a ferment. In several instances it has been demonstrated that the living body has the power to do this by producing substances, *antiferments,* which neutralize or antagonize the action of the enzyme (p. 365).

12. Composition of Enzymes.—Some enzymes have been isolated in what is regarded as a pure form; among these are pepsin (the important digestive ferment in the stomach) and urease, which decomposes urea. From the analysis of these enzymes it has been concluded that in all probability enzymes are protein in character.

Most enzymes are soluble in water and glycerin, are precipitated by alcohol, do not dialyze, and are destroyed by a relatively low temperature, 65° to 75° C. While the organized ferments (bacteria, etc.) are very easily destroyed by small quantities of certain chemical compounds, antiseptics, most enzymes are not readily affected in this manner, except some that are quite sensitive to formaldehyde.

13. Cell Enzymes.—Many, if not all, of the chemical actions constituting what we have called anabolism and catabolism, are processes of fermentation. To produce the large number of distinct chemical changes occurring within a cell a variety of catalysts are required; in fact, the cell is a swarm of catalysts. In this swarm each catalyst produces its particular action, but all act in a coordinate manner; they constitute a train of catalysts, "each a link in a serial suite of chemical action"—a train which someone has compared to a "bucket brigade." Death upsets this harmonious activity; the cell itself is then destroyed by its own enzymes.

14. Retarding Fermentation.—We have already indicated various ways in which the actions of ferments can be retarded or inhibited altogether. Among these we may mention: (*a*) freezing; (*b*) heating to a sufficiently high temperature; (*c*) by disinfectants which stop the activity of the organized ferments; a few of the disinfectants also influence the enzymes; (*d*) drying; (*e*) the removal of water, which may also be effected by the addition of a sufficient quantity of salt, sugar, etc.; (*f*) change in the degree of acidity or alkalinity of the fluid in which they are found.

CHAPTER III

THE TISSUES

In an earlier chapter we have learned that, as an animal becomes more highly evolved, there arises a division of labor among the various parts of the body which acquire specialized structure; this enables the organism to react better and to more of the various changes in the environment. In the higher animals, therefore, we find many parts or organs, each having its own structure and performing that particular function for which, by reason of its structure, it is best adapted. Thus, the eye is set apart for light stimulation; the stomach, for the digestion of food; the heart, for pumping blood to the various parts of the body.

But even in a single organ, such as the eye, there are several parts which can readily be distinguished and which also have distinct functions in that organ; such parts are called tissues. Each tissue has its characteristic structure, being composed of cells which for any given tissue are of the same kind and have fairly definite general characteristics and constant arrangements. A tissue may, therefore, be defined as a group of more or less similar cells and a certain amount of intercellular material formed by the cells. The tissues are usually classed into four groups:

1. Epithelial tissue.
2. Connective tissue.
3. Muscle tissue.
4. Nerve tissue.

A. Epithelial Tissue

The epithelial tissue is the covering tissue. In the human body we have many structures or organs that may be called tubular, or hollow, organs. Some of these organs communicate by means of smaller tubes, called ducts, with the exterior; others may be regarded as mere depressions of the external surface of the body. Among the tubular organs which have exterior openings are (1) the whole of the alimentary canal with its glands (salivary and gastric glands, pancreas, liver, and the small glands of the intestine); (2) the respiratory tract (nose, pharynx, larynx, trachea, bronchi, alveoli); (3) the urogenital tract (kidneys, ureters, bladder, urethra, and the reproductive organs); and (4) the glands of the skin.

There are also tubular organs and cavities which do not open to the exterior, such as the vascular system (heart, blood vessels and lymph vessels), and the pleural, pericardial, and peritoneal cavities. The free surfaces of all these tubes and cavities, as also that of the

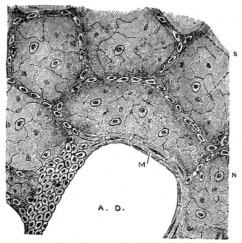

Fig. 7.—Squamous epithelial cells of the air sacs of the lung. (Klein and Noble Smith.)

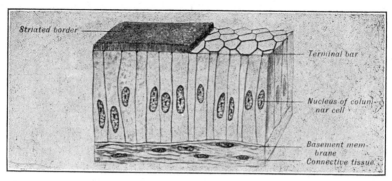

Fig. 8.—Diagram of columnar epithelium of the intestine. The striated border has been removed in the right half. (Maximow and Bloom: Histology, W. B. Saunders Co.)

body itself, are covered with epithelial tissues. In addition to serving as a covering and protective tissue, all the glands and many essential parts of the sense organs are constructed of epithelial cells.

Epithelial tissue is composed of cells arranged in a compact manner; it contains but little intercellular substance (cement substance) and very small or no intercellular spaces. The outlines of the cells are fairly regular and the nucleus is distinct. The shape of the epithelial cells may be flat, or scalelike (pavement, or squamous, epithelium), Fig. 7; they may assume a greater thickness and form what is known as cuboidal epithelium; or they may be very much deeper than they are broad and form the columnar epithelium, Figs. 8 and 168. These cells may or may not be provided with *cilia*. Cilia may be regarded as hairlike projections of the protoplasm, protruding beyond the free border of the cells, Fig. 9. Such cells are found in the respiratory tract and parts of the reproductive organs of both the male and the female.

The various-shaped epithelial cells may line the free surface of the organs as a single layer or many layers of these cells may be present. In the first case we speak of simple epithelium; the other is known as stratified epithelium.

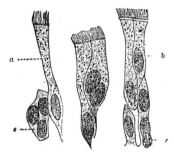

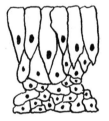

Fig. 9.—Ciliated epithelium, *a*, from the trachea; *c*, developing cells. (Cadiat.)

Fig. 10. — Stratified squamous epithelium.

Fig. 11.—Diagram of stratified columnar epithelium.

Simple pavement (squamous) epithelium is found lining the very end pockets (alveoli) of the air tubes of the lungs (Fig. 7), and the ends (Bowman's capsule) of the tubules of the kidneys, Fig. 222. The smallest blood vessels, capillaries, consist of merely one layer of flat epithelial cells which are sometimes called endothelial cells.

The serous membranes which line the internal cavities of the body (thoracic, abdominal) and which cover the organs found in these cavities (lungs, heart, stomach, intestines) are also lined with simple pavement epithelium. In these locations the cells secrete a serous or watery fluid, which lubricates the moving surfaces that come in contact with each other. These fluids (sometimes called transudates and generally classed under *lymph*) are found in very small quantities in the pericardial sac (around the heart), between the two layers of the pleura, in the peritoneal cavity, and in the cavities of the joints. In the last-named location the fluid is called *synovia,* or synovial fluid. When a joint is injured, as by spraining, there may be a great increase in the formation of this fluid which causes the joint to be much swollen.

Simple columnar epithelium (Fig. 8) lines the stomach and small intestine. In the ciliated form (Fig. 9) it is found in the smaller bronchi of the lungs and in the uterus and oviduct.

Stratified pavement (squamous) epithelium is the most common of all epithelial tissue. It is found in the epidermis of the skin, in the mouth, esophagus, and pharynx, on the anterior surface of the cornea of the eye, and other regions. In this tissue, Fig. 10, the lower or deeper situated cells are prismatic, those above this are polyhedral, and, as the cells approach the surface, they become more and more flattened. Epithelial tissue is not supplied with blood vessels, and consequently the outermost layers are not well nourished. The cells of the lower layer multiply and crowd upward; the upper cells become much modified in chemical composition (see subject of skin) and are gradually worn away.

Stratified columnar epithelium is composed of several layers, Fig. 11. The outer layer consists of true columnar cells; the cells of the lower layers are irregular in shape; some are triangular, others polyhedral. This form of epithelial tissue is found in the nose, larynx, trachea, and larger bronchi of the respiratory tract and in certain parts of the male reproductive organs; in these situations they are supplied with cilia.

Glandular Epithelium.—In many places in the alimentary canal the columnar epithelium dips down into the underlying tissue, forming little narrow depressions. These depressions constitute the various glands of the stomach and intestine, Fig. 170. The mouth of the gland is formed by the columnar cells like those that form the surface layer, but lower down the cells may assume a more cuboidal shape. These cuboidal cells frequently contain granules which are destined to form the ingredients of the secretions made by these glands, some of the granules being the zymogen granules spoken of in the previous chapter. Certain parts of the gland-tubules forming the kidneys are composed of simple columnar (glandular) epithelium. The materials manufactured by the gland cells are either poured upon a free surface or into the blood.

In general, the functions of the epithelial tissue are: protection, secretion, excretion, and absorption.

B. Connective Tissue

The most widely distributed of all the tissues is a tissue that performs almost entirely a passive part in our body, namely, the connective and supporting tissue.

Connective tissue includes many diverse structures, the more important forms being: white fibrous, yellow elastic, areolar, and adipose tissue; bone, dentine, and cartilage. Some authors speak of blood as a special tissue; others include it with the connective tissues. In all these forms the number of cells is small, while the intercellular substance is very abundant; in other words, the cells constituting the connective tissue are widely separated from each other by an intervening material.

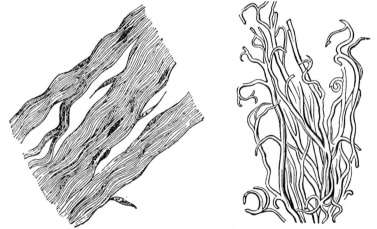

Fig. 12.—White fibrous connective tissue of a tendon. (Stricker.)　　Fig. 13.—Elastic connective tissue fibers. (Sharpy.)

a. White Fibrous Tissue.—The intercellular material is composed of a soft, structureless ground substance in which are embedded fibers and the connective tissue cells. The white fibers are exceedingly minute (average about $\frac{1}{30,000}$ inch thick), do not branch, and are grouped together in wavy bundles, Fig. 12. These fibers have great strength and pliability but are inelastic and form, therefore, the proper constituents of tendons (cords uniting the muscles to the bones) and ligaments (the bands by which articulated bones are held together). This form of connective tissue is also found in the pericardium of the heart, in the cornea of the eye, in the dura mater (a membrane protecting the brain), and in the sheaths (fasciae) which surround the muscles. In all these situations inelasticity, great strength, and pliability are needed; in fact, the tendon which links the muscle to the bone is stronger, for its size, than the bone or muscle, and hence less liable to fracture than either of these. The white fibers are largely made up of collagen, a protein, which on boiling with dilute acid is transformed into gelatin (see subject of foods).

b. Yellow Elastic Tissue.—The fibers of this tissue are thick and branched, Fig. 13. They contain a protein, known as elastin, which is not affected by boiling. As the name indicates, the tissue possesses a great deal of elasticity and is, therefore, found in such membranes as the pleura (covering of the lungs) and the peritoneum, in the walls of the air tubes, of arteries, and, to a lesser extent, of veins; it is also found in the vocal cords.

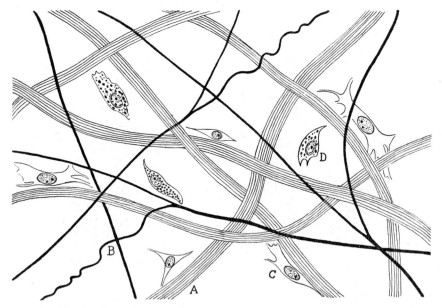

Fig. 14.—Areolar connective tissue. *A*, collagen fiber; *B*, elastic fiber; *C*, connective tissue cell; *D*, phagocytic cell with ingested granules. (Francis, Knowlton and Tuttle: Textbook of Anatomy and Physiology, The C. V. Mosby Co.)

c. Areolar Tissue.—This tissue is composed of a loose network of white and yellow fibers and a ground substance containing cellular elements, Fig. 14. It is the most abundant of all the various kinds of connective tissue. It penetrates the muscles, nerves, and glands and forms sheaths around them. It also occurs beneath the skin and in the walls of the alimentary, respiratory, and urogenital tracts.

d. Adipose Tissue.—In this modified form of areolar tissue the cells become charged with fat droplets, Fig. 15. This is described under the subject of Fat Metabolism.

e. **Cartilage.**—In cartilage the widely dispersed cells and groups of cells lie in small cavities (lacunae) which are found in a dense, resilient matrix, Fig. 16. It is found at the anterior end of the ribs, at the articular surfaces of joints, in the distal portion of the nose, and in the external ear.

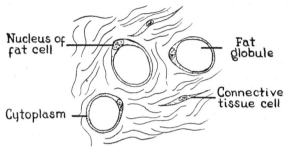

Nucleus of fat cell   Fat globule   Cytoplasm   Connective tissue cell

Fig. 15.—Adipose tissue.   (Francis: Fundamentals of Anatomy, The C. V. Mosby Co.)

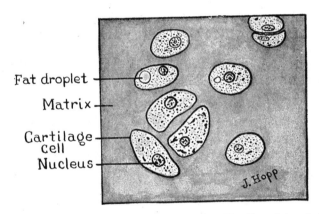

Fat droplet   Matrix   Cartilage cell   Nucleus

Fig. 16.—Cartilage cells in the matrix.   (Francis: Fundamentals of Anatomy, The C. V. Mosby Co.)

f. Bone is the most rigid of all connective tissues, due to the large amount of mineral matter deposited in the organic matrix. The formation of bone tissue will be dealt with in Chapters XX and XXII.

FUNCTIONS OF CONNECTIVE TISSUES

The chief functions of the connective tissues are:

1. To give support to the body as a whole; this is especially performed by bones and cartilages.

2. To connect two distinct organs, as when tendons bind muscles to bones.

3. To bind together the various parts of an organ; this forms one of the functions of areolar tissue.

4. To envelop certain organs, as, for example, the capsule surrounding the kidney.

5. To protect delicate organs mechanically, as is seen in the adipose tissue incasing the eyeball.

6. To serve as a storehouse for fat.

All these functions are passive, but from a mechanical point of view indispensable.

Other tissues will be discussed in subsequent chapters: muscle in Chap. VI, nerve in Chap. VII, and blood in Chap. VIII.

CHAPTER IV

THE TRANSLOCATION OF MATERIALS

The Movement of Materials.—In a foregoing chapter we stated that the protoplasm of the ameba may be regarded as a solution of crystalloids and colloids. As the ameba lives in water containing various salts, it is pertinent to inquire why the environmental water does not pass into the ameba and dissolve the cell, thereby causing its death, or why the soluble constituents of the protoplasm do not ooze out of the ameba. And this applies with equal force to the cells of our body, for all the cells are constantly bathed by a fluid known as lymph, or tissue fluid. Under the circumstances, how can the cells, being water solutions, maintain their physical integrity and life?

We have also learned that certain substances, foods for example, must pass from the environment into the protoplasm; and other materials, waste products, must pass out of the cell into the external world. This migration of matter in one or the other direction with respect to the cell we encounter everywhere in our study of physiology: the passage of oxygen into, and carbon dioxide out of, the cell during respiration; the excretion of waste products from the blood through the kidney cells; the secretion of juices and fluid onto a free surface by the gland cells; the absorption of foods from the alimentary canal into the blood and their passage from the blood stream through the capillary wall into the tissue fluid and from the tissue fluid into the cell. In all these cases *the movement of the material takes place across, or through, a membrane composed of protoplasm.* In this chapter we shall discuss some of the many physical and chemical factors concerned in the transportation of materials in the animal body.

Diffusion

Diffusion of Gases.—Respiration, the exchange of gases between the organism and the environment, depends upon the diffusion of gases. That gases rapidly spread from one point to another is a commonplace observation. Illuminating gas escaping from an open jet soon makes itself known in all parts of the room. Even gases much heavier than air, like bromine gas, diffuse upward against the force of gravity. According to the *kinetic theory of gases,* the molecules of a gas are constantly in motion and in consequence spread apart as far as the confines of the receptacle allow. The heavier the gas (greater molecular weight) the slower the diffusion; a rise in temperature increases the velocity of the molecules and therefore of diffusion.

Diffusion in Liquids.—Similar to the gas molecules, the molecules of a liquid and of the materials dissolved in a liquid are in constant motion. This motion, however, is restrained by the attraction exerted by the molecules upon each other. The velocity of the molecules in solution varies inversely as the molecular weight and directly as the temperature.

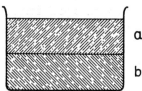

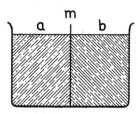

Fig. 17.—To illustrate diffusion. *a,* pure water; *b,* salt solution.   Fig. 18.—To illustrate dialysis. *a,* sugar solution; *b,* water, and *m,* parchment membrane.

Let us suppose that a strong salt solution, *b* in Fig. 17, is carefully overlaid with pure water, *a.* Immediately some of the salt molecules in *b* will penetrate the pure water *a.* As soon as some salt molecules have penetrated *a,* some of them re-enter *b,* but the number doing so is less than that of those going from *b* to *a.* After a sufficient length of time, so many molecules have entered *a* that the molecular concentration of *a* is equal to that of *b;* from that time on as many molecules pass from *a* to *b* as in the reverse direction. The system is now in equilibrium, but it must be borne in mind that the motion of the dissolved molecules continues. From this we may conclude that *when the molecular concentration is greater in one part of a liquid than in another, diffusion sets in,* thereby establishing a uniform distribution of the molecules.

Solutions

Molecular and Colloidal Solutions.—When water and sand are shaken together, it is evident that the particles of the sand are large enough to be seen with the naked eye, and that they are quickly deposited when the mixture is allowed to stand. Let us suppose that some sand is ground exceedingly fine. On being mixed with water, some of the finer particles will stay in suspension for a considerable length of time. Let us continue this pulverizing still further until the particles, being brought into suspension in water, are no longer visible under the microscope; in this state no settling will take place. The mixture is now called a *colloidal solution.* Theoretically we could continue this process until the particles are no more than single molecules; this would constitute a *true, or molecular, solution.* From this point of view these systems may be grouped into three classes:

(1) TRUE SOLUTIONS are those in which the particles are molecules and have a diameter of less than 0.00,000,1 mm. A true solution is stable in that there is no "settling" out of the particles from the medium in which they are found. To this class belong the solutions of the common salts, acids, bases, and sugars.

(2) SUSPENSIONS AND EMULSIONS.—In these the particles are more than 0.00,01 mm. in diameter. Both suspensions and emulsions are quite unstable. The fat in milk is in an emulsified state in which the fat globules measure from 0.00,24 to 0.00,46 mm. in diameter. On standing, the particles of an emulsion generally separate from the fluid.

(3) COLLOIDAL SOLUTIONS are those in which the diameter of the particles ranges from 0.00,01 to 0.00,00,1 mm. Colloidal solutions are fairly stable; the smaller the particles, the greater the stability. To this class belong boiled starch, gums, soap, agar, and most proteins.

It can readily be understood that no sharp lines of demarcation can be drawn between these three classes; and whether a substance is in suspension, in colloidal solution, or in molecular solution is determined by its behavior as well as by the size of its particles. We may now discuss how the materials in suspension or in colloidal solution may be separated from those in true solution.

Hydrostatic Pressure and Filtration.—Let us take a mixture of sand in a water solution of sodium chloride—NaCl. When this is placed upon a sheet of filter paper, the hydrostatic pressure forces the water and any substances dissolved in it (NaCl, e.g.) through the pores of the filter; but the suspended matter, sand, is retained by the filter. The greater the hydrostatic pressure and the larger the surface of the filter to which the material is exposed, the more fluid is squeezed through in a unit of time. *By filtration we mean the passage of a substance in solution through a membrane by a mechanical force* (e.g., gravity, blood pressure). By means of it suspended materials (e.g., blood corpuscles) can be separated from the fluid in which they are suspended.

Filters differ in the size of their pores. In filter paper the holes are fairly large and allow suspended particles of minute size, such as bacteria, to pass through. Filters constructed of unglazed porcelain or similar material, such as the Pasteur and the Berkefeld filters, through which the material is forced by a considerable amount of pressure, retain all bacteria excepting the very smallest. The pores of these filters are sufficiently large to allow the particles of a colloidal solution to pass through. Filters with exceedingly small pores and able to restrain these last-named particles can be made by treating a piece of filter paper with gelatin and then hardening it with formaldehyde. Such filters, of which cellophane is also an example, are known as *ultrafilters*. In our study of lymph formation we shall learn that the capillary walls may be regarded as ultrafilters.

Characteristics of Colloids.—Although crystalloids and colloids gradually merge into each other with respect to the size of the particles in solution and other properties, yet, all in all, we find certain characteristics in which they may differ greatly. As protoplasm is generally looked upon as a solution of crystalloids and colloids (such as proteins, carbohydrates, and fatlike substances) and as many of the activities of protoplasm are explicable only in terms of colloids, we may briefly examine some of these properties.

1. DIFFUSIBILITY.—We have seen that a crystalloid, like NaCl or cane sugar, diffuses rapidly in water. In contrast, it is a familiar fact that a piece of soap left in a basin of water dissolves very slowly and that an exceedingly long time is needed for the complete mixing of all the soap with the entire body of water. The same holds true for egg albumin. Sodium chloride diffuses about twenty times faster than albumin; this is due to the larger size of the albumin molecule (about 34,000) as compared with that of sodium chloride (58.5).

2. DIALYSIS.—If a sugar solution, *a* in Fig. 18, and pure water, *b,* are separated by a membrane, *m,* such as vegetable parchment paper, the sugar molecules diffuse through the membrane from *a* to *b,* and the water molecules will pass in both directions. This process, called dialysis, will continue until the concentration of the sugar is the same on both sides of the membrane. If instead of a sugar solution we use a solution of egg albumin, to which the membrane, *m,* is impermeable, that is, through which egg albumin cannot pass, none of the albumin will be found in *b;* we therefore say that egg albumin is not dialyzable. Graham called such substances *colloids* (*kolla,* glue), to distinguish them from crystalloids, which are dialyzable.

By dialysis we are able to separate the more diffusible substances in solution (crystalloids) from the less diffusible, provided a proper membrane is chosen. For this purpose we may use a parchment paper tube (Fig. 19) in which is placed a mixture of NaCl and a protein in solution. This is suspended in a large amount of distilled water which is frequently renewed. By the passage of the NaCl through the paper, the protein in the solution, free of salt, is finally left in the dialyzer. It must not be overlooked, however, that the power of a substance to dialyze is determined not solely by the nature of the substance itself (size of molecule, etc.), but also by the nature of the membrane. For any substance some membrane may be found which is permeable to this substance; hence the classification of colloids and crystalloids and the terms dialyzable and nondialyzable are not fixed. Again, certain compounds, e.g., hemoglobin of the red blood corpuscles, behave as colloids, and yet can be obtained in crystalline form.

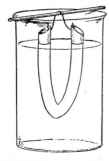

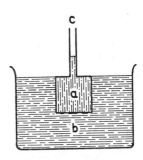

Fig. 19.—Dialyzer made of parchment paper tube. (Pearce and Macleod: Fundamentals of Human Physiology, The C. V. Mosby Co.)

Fig. 20.—To illustrate osmotic pressure.

3. GELATION.—Certain colloids are known as *emulsoids;* of these we may use the well-known gelatin as an example in our study. When solid gelatin is stirred up in hot water, a colloidal solution is formed; this is known as a *hydrosol.* On cooling, the sol sets, or ''gels,'' to a more or less firm mass; it is now called a *hydrogel,* or gel. In it there is a more solid phase which forms a meshwork in the interstices of which a more fluid part is held. The gel has a very great affinity for this fluid, for it requires boiling at a temperature of 120° C. (boiling point of water = 100°) for a considerable length of time or a great mechanical pressure to drive the water from the gel. Gelation is a reversible process.

4. IMBIBITION.—When a small sheet of gelatin or some other substance (agar, cellulose) which is immiscible in water is placed in cold water, it is soon seen to swell; this taking up of water without going into solution is known as imbibition (*bibo,* to drink). Gelatin may thus take up and hold very tenaciously as much as 1,000 times its volume of water; during this process an exceedingly large amount of pressure is generated. In this we are reminded of the regaining of turgor by a wilted plant on being placed in water. This may ex-

plain how it is possible for the protoplasmic framework of a jellyfish to hold in an organized manner the 96 per cent water of which it is composed. As to the cause of imbibition there is much doubt; perhaps it is closely related to the forces operative in osmotic pressure (see below). Imbibition is largely influenced by the nature of the salt present in the water; some salts (e.g., the sulfates, citrates, tartrates) increase and others (chlorides, nitrates, bromides) decrease the amount of water taken up.

5. OSMOSIS AND OSMOTIC PRESSURE.—As indicated above, certain membranes may be permeable to one substance and not to another. Let us suppose that in Fig. 20 the walls of the inner vessel, a, are permeable to water but not to sodium chloride. Such walls, or *semipermeable membranes*, as they are called, can be formed in the laboratory; we may describe one method. An unglazed clay or porcelain flask is filled with a dilute solution of copper sulfate and is then set in a solution of potassium ferrocyanide. The two salts penetrate the pores of the jar and, on meeting, a precipitate of copper ferrocyanide is formed; this insoluble salt forms a membrane in the pores of the walls. Frequently vegetable parchment paper, a pig's bladder, the skin of a frog, or the peritoneum is used for this purpose. These membranes are semipermeable in that they allow water but not the common salts and sugar to pass through.

Such a jar, or osmometer, is filled with a dilute sugar solution, hermetically sealed, and a glass tube, c, inserted in the cover; the jar is then placed in a large amount of distilled water, b. After a while, we notice that the solution in a enters the glass tube, c, and keeps on rising; that is, the volume in a has increased. This increase is due to the distilled water, b, passing into a, thereby exerting pressure and forcing the fluid up into the tube c against the force of gravity. The passage of water through a semipermeable membrane is known as *osmotic flow*. If we let this apparatus stand for a sufficient length of time, the solution in the tube will attain its maximum height. By measuring the height of the column in millimeters we find the amount of pressure the liquid in a is now exerting upon the walls of the container; this is the amount of pressure developed by osmosis. Osmotic pressure may be defined as the force under which a solvent moves from a solution of lower solute concentration to a solution having a higher solute concentration when these solutions are separated by a semipermeable membrane. It is equivalent to the hydrostatic pressure which a solution exerts when it is separated by a semipermeable membrane from the pure solvent or from a less concentrated solution.

As to the cause of this migration of molecules and the resultant osmotic pressure, there is still much question. Two views may be presented:

(1) *The Hydrostatic Theory.*—The molecules of the solute in *a*, Fig. 20, exert an attraction upon the water molecules in *b* and draw them from the solvent into the solution, *a*. This causes an accumulation of liquid in *a* which thereby exerts pressure.

(2) *The Kinetic Theory.*—The water molecules, in both *a* and *b*, Fig. 20, are in constant motion, and the membrane separating *a* and *b* offers equal resistance to their passage in either direction. But the concentration (number of molecules per unit volume) of the water is greater in the pure solvent, Fig. 20, *b*, than in the solution, *a*. In consequence more water molecules hit the membrane per unit of time and per unit of surface in the direction from *b* to *a* than in the opposite direction; the result, again, is an increase of volume in *a*. A moment's reflection will show that the amount of osmotic pressure is equal to the hydrostatic pressure (in the osmometer) necessary to prevent the further entrance of water.

Molar Solutions.—The molecular weight of hydrogen is 2 (twice the atomic weight). Let us suppose that two grams of hydrogen are placed in a receptacle of 22.4 liters' capacity. Due to the impact of the always moving molecules, a certain amount of pressure is exerted upon the walls of the container. At 0° C. this is found to be equal to one atmosphere, or 760 millimeters of mercury (mm. Hg) pressure. An amount of oxygen or any other gas equivalent in grams to the molecular weight of the gas exerts under the above conditions one atmosphere pressure. For oxygen this amount is $2 \times 16 = 32$; for carbon dioxide, CO_2, it is $12 + (16 \times 2) = 44$ grams. If the 22.4 liters of the gas be reduced by an outside force so as to occupy one liter of space, the pressure of the gas will be found to be 22.4 atm.; that is, the gram-molecular weight (or mole) of a gas confined in a liter of space at 0° C. exerts 22.4 atmospheres pressure.

The mole of glucose—$C_6H_{12}O_6$—is 180. If this amount of glucose in grams could be transformed into a gas and at 0° C. be confined to one liter of space, it also would exert 22.4 atm. pressure. Instead of this, let us dissolve 180 grams of glucose in a quantity of water sufficient to make one liter of solution. This is known as the *gram-molecular solution,* or molar solution. Placed in an osmometer, this solution gives rise to an osmotic pressure of 22.4 atm.[*] As in gas pressure, the osmotic pressure is independent of the nature of the sub-

---

*Because of the tremendous pressure, this experiment can be performed only with more dilute solutions.

stance and is determined by the number of particles per unit volume
of solution, and therefore a half molar solution of glucose exerts 11.2
atm. pressure.

From the method of making molar solutions it must be evident that
molar solutions of all substances have the same molecular concentration; they are said to be equimolecular, i.e., in unit volumes they contain the same number of molecules. As the osmotic pressure of a
glucose solution is due to the number of molecules in solution, we
might infer that a molar solution of NaCl would exert the same
osmotic pressure as a molar solution of glucose. However, in experimentation it was found that the NaCl solution exerts about twice
as much pressure as the glucose solution. The reason for this lies in
the electrolytic dissociation of the NaCl molecules, a matter we must
now stop to explain.

Electrical Constitution of Matter

The atom may be defined as the unit structure of matter. According to the nuclear theory, an atom is composed of a central
nucleus and electrons. The hydrogen atom is formed by one proton
and one electron; in all other atoms the nucleus consists of two or
more protons and a smaller number of electrons. A **proton** is the unit
of positive and an **electron,** the unit of negative electricity. The
nucleus of an atom is, therefore, always electrically positive. In
addition to the nuclear electrons, the atom contains other, the so-called
planetary, electrons; the number of these is equal to the difference
between the number of the protons and that of the nuclear electrons.
The positive and negative charges in the atom are, therefore, equal
in number, and the atom is electrically neutral. The planetary electrons are said to revolve around the nucleus in one or more orbits.

The number of the nuclear protons and electrons and the number
of the planetary electrons and their arrangement in the varying
number of orbits around the nucleus determine all the physical and
chemical characteristics of the atoms of which the 90-odd elements
are severally composed. All matter is in essence electrical, and all
chemical action is the interplay of the electrical charges which constitute the atoms.

Ionization or Electrolytic Dissociation

When a molecule of NaCl dissolves, the Na atom loses one of its
electrons; this electron is taken up by the Cl atom. By this the Na
atom is rendered more positive and the Cl atom more negative. An
atom which has lost one or more electrons is known as a *positive ion,*

or cation, and an atom holding extra electrons is the *negative ion,* or anion. Dibasic acid radicals and bivalent elements give rise to ions which carry two electrical charges; e.g., Ca^{++} and SO_4^{--}.

While strong mineral acids, bases, and their salts ionize freely, most organic compounds (e.g., sugars, alcohols) dissociate very feebly, or not at all. Water, as we shall learn in Chap. VIII, gives rise to an extremely limited number of hydrogen and hydroxyl ions. This difference explains the behavior of these compounds towards the electric current. The passage of an electric current through a fluid is due to the moving ions; hence water and water solutions of most organic compounds (e.g., sugar, alcohol) are poor conductors. Such substances are spoken of as nonelectrolytes. In contrast, the freely ionizing compounds in solution are good conductors and are known as electrolytes.

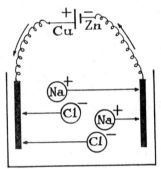

Fig. 21.—Diagram to illustrate electrolysis.

Like the molecules of a gas, the ions in solution are in constant motion (ion, from the Greek, "to go"). When a current of electricity passes through a NaCl solution (see Fig. 21), it *directs* the movement of the ions in such a manner that the positively charged Na ions move toward the negative pole (connected with the zinc plate of a dry cell) and the Cl ions, toward the positive pole (copper, or carbon, plate).

Osmotic Pressure of Electrolytes.—The observed fact that a molar solution of NaCl exerts twice as much osmotic pressure as a molar solution of glucose finds a ready explanation if we hold that not only molecules but also ions give rise to osmotic pressure. As the NaCl molecules break up into two ions, a molar solution will contain twice as many particles as a molar solution of glucose, and its pressure is therefore $2 \times 22.4 = 44.8$ atm. A 0.58 per cent NaCl solution and a 1.8 per cent glucose solution are both m/10 solutions, but the osmotic pressure of the former is equal to that of a 3.6 per cent glucose solution.

We may summarize: The osmotic pressure of a molar solution of a substance not undergoing dissociation is equal to 22.4 atmospheres; that of a substance undergoing dissociation is equal to 22.4 multiplied by the number of particles (ions) derived from the molecule. Thus, the osmotic pressure of a $10/m$ Na_2SO_4 solution is 3×22.4 divided by 10, or 6.72 atm.

Isosmotic Solutions.—When two solutions having the same osmotic pressure are separated by a semipermeable membrane, the concentration of the water, the volumes, and therefore the pressures, of the solutions remain the same; such solutions are said to be *isosmotic* (*iso*, equal). If two solutions have different particle concentrations and are separated by a semipermeable membrane, the water passes from the one with the lower to the one with the higher osmotic pressure. The solution having the lower osmotic pressure is said to be *hyposmotic* with respect to the second solution, while the second is *hyperosmotic* to the first.

Colloidal Osmotic Pressure.—Because of the extremely large size of their molecules, and therefore the low molecular concentration of their solutions, the colloids (starch, proteins, etc.) exert very little osmotic pressure. For example: 36,000 grams of gelatin (a protein) would have to be dissolved in 1,000 c.c. of water in order to obtain an osmotic pressure of 22.4 atmospheres. As, however, the most concentrated solution of gelatin contains but 30 grams per liter (i.e., a 3 per cent solution and equivalent to a 0.001 molar solution) the greatest pressure gelatin can exert is about 0.02 atmosphere or 15 mm. Hg.

Surface Tension.—A large array of well-known phenomena are based upon surface tension. Among these we may allude to the spherical or nearly spherical form of a falling drop of water, of a soap bubble floating in the air, and of a globule of mercury resting on a flat surface.

Let us consider a beaker of water. The molecules of the water attract each other; this is shown by the energy (heat) necessary to break them apart, as in evaporation. Now the molecules in the center of the water are attracted equally by their neighbors from all sides and are therefore free to move in any direction. But the molecules forming the topmost layer are attracted downward only, since there are no water molecules above them to pull them upward. This causes the surface of the water to pull itself together, as if the mass of water were surrounded by a stretched elastic skin. That a certain amount of force is operative at the surface can be gathered from the behavior of a drop of mercury on a flat surface. Notwithstanding the gravitational force, *g*, Fig. 22, which is pulling upon every part of the mercury so as to bring it as close as possible to the surface upon which it is resting, the attractive force, *a*, of the molecules for each other causes the mercury to assume a mass in which the area of the surface exposed to the air is the least possible, that is, a spherical surface. The force with which the surface molecules are pulled toward the interior is known as surface tension. As heat lessens the attraction of the molecules, it lowers the surface tension.

Surface tension is beautifully demonstrated by the following experiment. A film of soap solution is caught in a wire ring, Fig. 23, *A*. Attached to this ring is a loop of thread which may assume any irregular form as it drifts in the soap film. But when the film inclosed in the loop is broken by touching it with filter paper, the loop immediately takes on a perfectly circular form, *B*, due to the surface tension of the soap film outside of the loop.

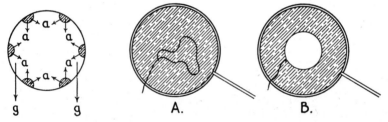

Fig. 22.—Diagram to illustrate surface tension.

Fig. 23.—Diagram to illustrate surface tension. (Macleod; Physiology, The C. V. Mosby Co.)

When water is allowed to flow out of a narrow tube held vertically, a small amount of water collects at the end of the tube; this grows in volume until the weight of the water just exceeds the force of the surface tension; it then breaks away and falls. By noting the size of the drop (or the number of falling drops to the cubic centimeter), we can approximately estimate the relative amount of surface tension. Thus, a drop of ether is considerably smaller than a drop of water; this indicates that the surface tension of water is greater than that of ether.

Surface tension always exists at the surface of separation between a liquid and a gas, between two immiscible liquids (e.g., water and oil), and between a liquid and a solid. Foreign substances dissolved in the water alter its surface tension; it is increased by the common salts and decreased by nearly all organic substances, such as ether, alcohol, fat, and soap. Oil lowers the surface tension of water; this enables it to quiet waves in a storm.

Certain phenomena in physiology can perhaps be best understood in the light of surface tension. The flow of sap in plants and the formation of pseudopods by the ameba are among the biologic activities which have been explained in this manner. We shall meet with other instances as we proceed with our study.

Adsorption.—Because of the surface tension exerted by a liquid, there is a concentration, or condensation, of the liquid at its surface. Certain solid substances which present a large amount of surface are able to cause the condensation upon these surfaces of gases and substances in solution. As an example of this we may mention the use of charcoal in gas masks because of the enormous quantity of gases this material can gather and hold to itself. When a colored solution of Congo red or methylene blue is allowed to pass slowly through bone-black, glass wool, or absorbent cotton, the fluid loses its color to a greater or lesser extent; the pigment clings to the surface of these substances; this is known as adsorption. In the *absorption* of a gas by a liquid, the gas is uniformly distributed throughout the liquid; in *adsorption* there is a local condensation of the adsorbed material upon the surface of the adsorber.

CHEMICAL ACTION.—In addition to the separation of dissolved substances from their solvents, other changes may be effected by adsorption. Chemical actions (such as the union of hydrogen and oxygen passed through spongy platinum) which ordinarily do not take place at room temperature, or only at an infinitely slow rate, are made possible or are accelerated. Enzymes are colloidal. As the particles in a colloidal solution have a diameter ranging from 0.00,01 to 0.00,000,1 mm., the amount of surface they present is enormous.* Upon this surface the fermentable materials are condensed and, similar to the hydrogen and oxygen in the previous illustration, chemical action between these materials is tremendously accelerated. As alcohol and other substances are readily adsorbed by the enzyme particles, these agencies must inhibit the catalytic action. Heat causes a clumping of the enzymic colloidal particles (similar to the coagulation of egg albumin by heat) and thereby very greatly reduces the amount of surface and in consequence renders fermentation impossible.

Plasma Membrane

To account for the qualitative and quantitative regulation of the exchange of materials between the protoplasm and its environment, spoken of in the opening paragraph of this chapter, some investigators have sought aid in the plasma membrane. The outermost layer of the protoplasm differs, it is held, from the interior mass in a very im-

---

*A sphere of iron having a diameter of 1 mm. has a surface area of 0.0314 square centimeter. If this bit of iron is pulverized until the particles have a diameter of 0.00,01 mm., the total surface area amounts to 314 sq. cm,

portant respect, namely, semipermeability, or perhaps better stated, SELECTIVE PERMEABILITY. This selective permeability, operative in both directions, determines, according to this theory, the kind and amount of the substances passing into and out of a cell. The plasma membrane, or protoplast, constitutes the limiting membrane standing as a guardian at the very limit between the cell and the environment. While this must be regarded as a theory, it is at present perhaps the most acceptable explanation offered for an extensive array of facts; we may briefly consider a few of these.

a. **Plasmolysis.**—Most plant cells have a rigid, dead cell wall inclosing the protoplasm of which the outer layer constitutes the plasma membrane. If a plant cell is placed in a strong solution of cane sugar to which the plasma membrane is impermeable, the greater osmotic pressure of the sugar causes water to leave the cell. In consequence, the protoplasm decreases in volume and shrinks away from the rigid cell wall, Fig. 24, *B;* the more concentrated the sugar solution, the greater the withdrawal of water from the cell, Fig. 24, *C.* This process is known as plasmolysis. On placing the plasmolyzed cell in water or a hypotonic solution of sugar, water re-enters the cell.

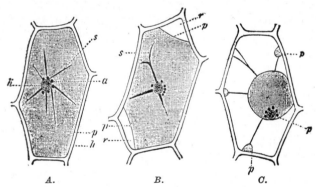

A.   B.   C.

Fig. 24.—Plasmolysis in cells from Tradescantia discolor. *A,* normal cell; *B,* plasmolysis in 0.22 M. cane sugar; *C,* pronounced plasmolysis in 1.0 M. KNO₃; *h,* the cell wall; *p,* the protoplasm. (After DeVries.)

b. **Hemolysis.**—When a cell, not surrounded by a rigid cell wall, e.g., the red blood cell, is placed in water or a highly diluted sugar solution, the volume of the cell increases, even to the point of rupturing; and, although the hydrostatic pressure is considerably greater than that in the surrounding fluid, the materials in the corpuscle do not diffuse out (p. 153). The protoplast of the corpuscle acts as the semipermeable membrane of *a* in Fig. 20; the cells follow the laws of osmotic pressure as long as they are alive; death destroys the selective permeability of the plasma membrane.

c. Distribution of Salts.—The difference in the concentration of the inorganic salts in the cells and in the fluid surrounding the cells is most striking. The red blood cells are practically devoid of sodium but contain about 0.5 per cent of potassium (in the form of salts) ; the fluid, plasma, in which these cells float contains 0.44 per cent sodium and but 0.026 per cent potassium. Again, a muscle contains 20 times as much potassium and only $\frac{1}{10}$ as much sodium as the fluid which surrounds and nourishes the muscle cells. Although other explanations have been proposed, the theory of the impermeability of the plasma membrane to these salts is very attractive. The coloring matter, hemoglobin, found in the blood cells is very soluble in water, yet under normal conditions it never passes out of the corpuscles into the surrounding plasma.

d. Electrical Resistance.—Another fact in accord with the plasma membrane theory is based on the reduced electrical conductivity of a salt solution containing cells. It will be recalled from our previous discussion that the electric current is carried through a solution by ions. Let us image, in Fig. 21, a large number of red blood cells suspended in a solution of NaCl; these cells, if permeable to the ions, should not interfere with the migration of the ions. But Stewart found that the conductivity of the solution is decreased by the presence of the cells, a fact readily understandable if the plasma membrane of the cells is impermeable to the ions. Destroying the life of the cells increases the electrical conductivity.

e. Osmotic Resistance.—The immiscibility of the protoplasm of a cell, like the ameba, with the fluid surrounding it, although the interior of the cell is composed of a water solution of various substances, is a strong argument in favor of regarding the outer layer of the cell as a special protecting skin. By means of this membrane the cell maintains its individuality as a cell.

f. Physical Resistance.—That cells have shape and resist any force tending to deform them also speaks for the existence of a membrane of greater rigidity than the interior of the cell. By microdissection the plasma membrane of an ameba or a paramecium can be torn and some of the fluid protoplasm can be seen to escape through the rent; sometimes the break in the membrane heals over and thus saves the life of the animal.

Variability of the Semipermeability

The semipermeability of the protoplast is not the same for all cells, nor is it constant for any one cell.

1. The limiting membrane varies according to the function of the cell. The red blood cell is impermeable to Na or K salts, but these salts readily pass through the capillary wall.

2. Even when the functions appear to be identical, the membranes may differ; e.g., the permeability of the red blood cells of a dog is not the same as that of the cells of a cat.

3. On the theory that the semipermeability of the protoplast is the deciding factor in the exchange of materials between the protoplasm and the environment, it is necessary that the degree of permeability vary with the needs for this exchange as determined by the activity of the protoplasm. It is conceivable that protoplasmic activity by the production of chemical compounds causes such changes in the protoplast. This view is supported by many facts, among which we may mention the observation that the electrical conductivity of a muscle is greater during activity. Under the subject of the nerve impulse we shall discuss the current belief that the effect of the stimulus is an increase in the permeability of the protoplast.

4. The differentiation existing between the outer layer of the protoplasm and the interior is no doubt due to the interaction between this external layer and the environment (see infra); consequently, changes in the environment also may cause changes in the permeability. It has been found that many environmental changes increase the permeability; among them we may mention: increase in temperature, radiations (light, ultraviolet light, x-ray), electric currents, and certain chemical compounds. The latter is well illustrated by placing a cell in a NaCl solution. In this solution the cell gradually dies and the permeability of the protoplast steadily increases; now all materials find a ready ingress into the cells. If a little calcium chloride be added to the sodium chloride solution, the normal permeability is retained for a greater length of time and the life of the cell is prolonged.

NATURE OF THE PROTOPLAST

How the layer of protoplasm exposed to the exterior is altered so as to acquire the property of selective permeability is still a moot point. The protoplast is frequently described as a condensation layer of fatlike substances (lecithin and cholesterol) and proteins. Fats and fatlike substances lower the surface tension and always tend to accumulate at the surface of the solution in which they are found and thereby increase the density of this outer layer. Inasmuch as these two fatlike substances are always present in protoplasm, some physiologists maintain that they enter largely into the composition of the protoplast.

Perhaps it is correct to regard the protoplast as formed by gelation (p. 65) of fat-protein particles. When an ameba is slightly torn, the protoplasm tends to flow out. If the solution surrounding the organism is a "balanced" solution (one containing the proper concentration of Ca, K, and Na), a surface membrane is immediately formed and the outflow stops. This has been called a surface precipitation reaction. The limiting membrane thus formed is a jelled membrane having a greater density, viscosity, and elasticity than the interior substance. If this experiment be made with a solution deficient in Ca or having an excess of Na or K, no gelation occurs and the protoplasm flows out freely to mix with the solution. Calcium has a "clumping" effect upon the contents of a cell; Na or K causes a dispersion, or diffusion, of the fat-protein particles.

The manner in which the various materials find entrance into cells is a perplexing question. Some authors advocate a sievelike, and others, a solvent-like, plasma membrane. According to the sieve theory the semipermeability is looked upon as a matter of the size of the pores of the membrane. This readily explains why most crystalloids pass without any difficulty through the capillary wall, while colloids do so to but a slight extent, if at all (ultra-filtration); it may also explain why glucose with a smaller molecule can enter the red blood cell while the larger molecule of cane sugar is barred. But how can this be reconciled to the fact that this same membrane is impermeable to NaCl and KCl (p. 153) which have smaller molecules than glucose? It is also difficult to explain why NaCl is barred by the membrane of a blood cell but finds ready passage through the capillary wall.

According to the solvent-like membrane theory, any substance seeking entrance into a cell must be dissolved in the membrane. Space does not allow us to enter into a discussion of the evidence for or against this view.

Although many facts of absorption, secretion, excretion, and lymph formation fit in quite well with the idea of a semipermeable protoplast, it must, however, be admitted that at present physics and chemistry can offer no adequate explanation for all the exchanges of materials between the cell and its environment. These processes are brought about and regulated by the cell itself in ways still unknown to us; we therefore frequently speak of the highly "selective action" of the cell, which disappears on the death of the cell.

OSMOTIC PRESSURE OF PROTOPLASM

The protoplasm, as a solution of crystalloids and colloids, exerts a certain amount of osmotic pressure. The amount of this pressure can be ascertained by methods suggested in our study of plasmolysis. A frog muscle retains its weight in m/8 NaCl solution; in a solution a little more concentrated it loses weight; and in a more dilute solution it gains in weight. Granted that the protoplast is impermeable to NaCl, the osmotic pressure of the muscle must be equal to that of m/8 NaCl. An eighth molar NaCl solution (58.5 gram-molecular weight ÷ 8, in 1,000 c.c.) is approximately a 0.7 per cent solution. For this reason a 0.7 per cent NaCl solution is used as a physiologic salt solution for cold blooded animals. In man, the red blood cells and, therefore, the blood as a whole have an osmotic pressure equal to that of a 0.9 per cent NaCl; such a solution exerts an osmotic pressure of 7.3 atmospheres, or about 100 pounds per square inch.

CHAPTER V

CONTROL OF TISSUE ACTIVITY

I. INTRODUCTION

Receptors and Effectors.—The animal body is a machine capable of adjusting itself to the changes in its environment. In the more highly organized forms of life, this machinery is exceedingly complex and exhibits a high degree of differentiation and specialization. To enable the organism to adjust itself more efficiently to environmental changes, certain organs are especially constructed to receive the stimulations from the outside world or from changes in the body itself. Such organs are called receptors; in some cases, among which we may mention eyes, ears, and the taste buds of the tongue, they are also known as sense organs. We also find highly specialized structures by means of which the animal responds to the stimulation befalling the receptors; these organs, known as the effectors, comprise the muscles and glands.

As the receptors and the effectors are frequently located in widely separated parts of the body (e.g., the eyes and the muscles of the legs which are to respond to the stimulation of the eyes), a line of communication must exist between these two structures. In addition to this, we learned that the activities of the effectors must be carefully controlled and regulated in order that coordinated responses of an adaptive nature may result. These two functions, the one of furnishing communication and the other of control, are mediated by two distinct mechanisms: the nervous or neural, and the chemical or humoral. By the neural mechanism is meant the protoplasmic communicating lines, collectively known as the nervous system. The humoral control is brought about by chemical compounds, hormones, manufactured in certain parts of the body and influencing the activities of other parts.

II. NEURAL CONTROL

The nervous system may be divided into the central and the peripheral systems. The former includes the brain and spinal cord (Fig. 266) and by the latter we mean all the various nerves which spring from the central nervous system and pass throughout the whole body. This entire system is made up of anatomical units known as nerve cells, or neurons.

The Neuron.—A nerve cell, or neuron, is composed of a cell body and one or more processes. In what we may call a typical neuron the cell body (Fig. 25) gives rise to one or more much branched processes, known as dendrites, or *dendrons,* and an *axon,* which in most cells is generally longer and less branched, Fig. 287. It is by means of these processes that the receptors and effectors are brought into communication with each other as is illustrated in Fig. 26. The process of the neuron which we have called the axon is more generally known as a nerve fiber (see, however, page 121).

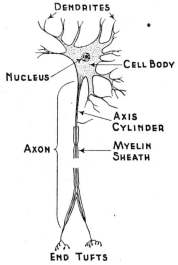

Fig. 25.—A typical neuron.

Gray and White Matter.—In the central nervous system the thousands of neurons are arranged in such a manner that the cell bodies are grouped together in masses which are grayish in appearance. In the spinal cord this gray mass forms a column throughout the length of the cord; in cross section it has somewhat the shape of a capital letter H (the stippled area in Fig. 26). The nerve fibers are arranged in bundles around the *central gray matter* and constitute the white matter of the cord.

In Fig. 26 are depicted two neurons. One of them has its cell body in the central gray matter and sends its nerve fiber out of the cord to make connection with a skeletal muscle. The other neuron has its cell body located outside of the cord; one of its processes enters the cord and the other extends to the sense organ. These two neurons make close contact with each other in the central gray matter of the cord. The fibers of the cell bodies located in the central gray matter on leaving the cord are grouped to form what are called the *ventral roots*. The processes of the cell bodies located outside, but very close to, the cord are grouped to constitute the *dorsal roots*. Fig. 266 shows the 32 pairs of these roots springing from each side of the spinal cord.

A collection of nerve cell bodies outside of the nervous system is known as a **ganglion**. Those on the dorsal roots, as shown in Fig. 26, constitute the dorsal root ganglia, or the spinal ganglia. The fibers of the dorsal and ventral roots unite to form one bundle of nerve fibers; it is now called a spinal nerve.

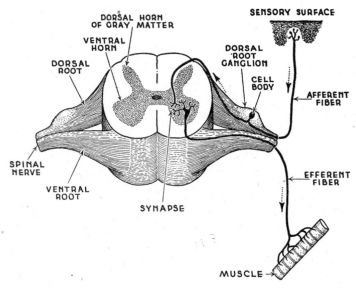

Fig. 26.—Cross-section of the spinal cord showing the gray matter in the form of a letter *H* surrounded by white matter. (After Morat.)

Afferent and Efferent Nerve Fibers.—The stimulation of a sense organ generates an impulse which is transmitted to a nerve fiber and is conducted by this fiber to the spinal cord (or brain). Since this fiber carries the impulse to the central nervous system, it is known as an afferent nerve fiber (*ad*, towards; *fero*, to carry). The afferent fiber enters the cord by the dorsal root; and the impulse it carries is transferred in the central gray matter to the neuron which conducts it out of the cord to the skeletal muscle. This last named fiber is, therefore, an efferent fiber (*ex*, out). The afferent fibers are sometimes called sensory nerve fibers; the efferent fibers are also known as motor or secretory fibers.

Reflex Action.—When a sense organ is stimulated (Fig. 26) and the impulse generated thereby finally reaches and stimulates the responding organ, the activity thus induced is called a reflex action; this action concerns the function of either a muscle or a gland. Nearly all the actions of our body are of this sort; to give only one illustration: a foreign body falls into the eye and, as a reflex, the tear gland secretes more abundantly.

Reflex Arc.—The nerve chain between the sensory surface, Fig. 26, and the responding organ is known as the reflex arc. This arc is composed of three parts: (1) the afferent nerve fiber, (2) the efferent nerve fiber, and (3) the connection these two fibers form in the gray matter of the central nervous system. This connection we shall call the *reflex center*. In a reflex center, as shown in Fig. 26, there are many points of contact between one neuron and the processes of an-

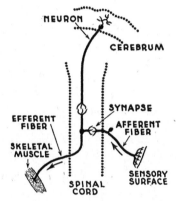

Fig. 27.—Diagram illustrating somatic nerves which directly connect the skeletal muscles and the sensory surfaces with the central nervous system.

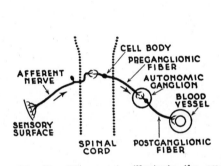

Fig. 28.—Diagram to illustrate the autonomic nerves by which smooth muscles (as in blood vessels) and glands are connected with the central nervous system.

other neuron; such a point of contact is known as a synapse (*syn*, together; *aptein*, to clasp). The reflex centers are always located in the central gray matter of the spinal cord or the brain. If one of the members of the reflex arc is broken, the reflex action ceases.

Voluntary Actions.—Besides reflex action, we speak of voluntary action. Observation teaches us that the reflexes may take place whether we are conscious of them or not, and that over many of them we do not exercise any volitional control, that is, we cannot by our will start or stop them. But, in the ordinary sense of the term, we can volitionally begin or stop the action of a skeletal muscle. In this instance the impulse causing a muscle to act issues from the uppermost part of the brain, known as the cerebrum or cerebral hemispheres (see Figs. 266 and 277). In Fig. 27 a nerve cell body located in the cerebrum sends out a process which makes synaptic connection with a spinal neuron. The latter neuron sends a process out of the cord to the skeletal muscle. When an individual is said to contract a muscle voluntarily, a cell in the cerebrum is activated and discharges an impulse over the route described to the skeletal muscle. Parenthetically stated, in all probability the motor nerve cells in the cerebrum never spontaneously generate impulses; the impulses issuing from them are derived from some other part of the cerebrum.

Somatic and Autonomic Nerves.—As depicted in Fig. 27, skeletal muscles and sensory surfaces are innervated by a nerve issuing directly from the spinal cord or brain. Such a nerve is known as a *somatic nerve* (*soma*, body).

The smooth muscles (found in the walls of blood vessels, alimentary canal, etc.), the heart, and the glands receive their innervation from the central nervous system in an indirect, or relayed, manner. By consulting Figs. 28 and 295 it will be seen that the cell body lying in the cord sends its fiber (known as the preganglionic fiber) out by the ventral root to end in a ganglion. Here it makes synaptic connection with another neuron which sends its fiber (the postganglionic fiber) to the plain muscle of, say, a blood vessel or to a gland. The work of the muscles of the heart, blood vessels, and alimentary canal and that of many of the glands is regulated by such relayed nerves which collectively constitute the *autonomic nervous system;* see Chap. **XXX**. In distinction from the skeletal muscles, the impulses sent to the above-named organs are not of the so-called volitional type; we exercise no voluntary control over them.

The various organs in our body are, therefore, by this great system of nerves brought into communication with each other so that what befalls one organ may influence another organ in perhaps a remote part of the body. This "nervous" communication is remarkable for its speed, for the nerve impulse travels from one to 100 meters per second.

III. HUMORAL CONTROL; HORMONES

In addition to the neural control, the organs are able to influence each other chemically. Certain organs (e.g., the thyroid, adrenals, pancreas, and sex glands) manufacture specific compounds which are thrown into the blood stream and thus carried to every part of the body where they may stimulate or inhibit the activity of other organs. A substance of this nature is called an *internal secretion,* or *hormone.* Some organs respond only, or better, to nervous control; other organs are more susceptible to hormonic regulation. Compared with the nervous regulation, that by hormones is very slow, but great speed of action is never required of the organs controlled by them. The details of this subject will be studied in Chap. **XXX**.

CHAPTER VI

CONTRACTILITY: MUSCLE PHYSIOLOGY

In adjusting the human body to environmental changes, muscles, as responding organs, play a most important part. Because of their contractile power we are able to move the whole body from one point in space to another as the need may arise; or by the movement of a certain part of our body we can produce such changes in our environment as may be conducive to our well-being.

Two other structures show the physiologic property of contractility, namely, leucocytes (and closely allied structures) and cilia. The former will be discussed under the subject of blood, and at the conclusion of this chapter we shall briefly study the latter.

I. ANATOMY

Classes of Muscles.—There are *three classes of muscles* which differ histologically, anatomically, and physiologically:

1. Striated (striped), skeletal, or voluntary muscles.
2. Plain (smooth or unstriated), visceral, or involuntary.
3. Cardiac muscle (imperfectly striated).

Muscle Fibers.—The anatomical, or structural, unit of a muscle is the muscle fiber, which is an elongated cell containing one or more nuclei. A large number of fibers are bound together by areolar connective tissue into bundles, or fasciculi, which, in turn, are surrounded by connective tissue sheaths and grouped together into still larger bundles; finally, the whole muscle is enveloped by a connective tissue sheath, known as the epimysium (*epi*, on; *mus*, muscle). The muscles are abundantly supplied with blood vessels which enter the muscle along the areolar tissue.

The fibers of a *striated muscle* are about $\frac{1}{500}$ inch in diameter and may be one inch or more in length; they very seldom branch. The protoplasm of a muscle fiber is composed of a large number of very delicate fibrils, termed *myofibrils* (*mus*, muscle) or *sarcostyles*, embedded in a semifluid substance, the *sarcoplasm* (*sarx*, flesh); and surrounding the protoplasm (Fig. 29) is an exceedingly thin and structureless sheath, the sarcolemma (*lemma*, husk). The surface of the fibril is characterized by alternate light and dark bands, as shown in Figs. 30 and 54. For this reason skeletal muscles are called striated muscles.

Tendons.—Nearly all striated muscles are attached, by means of tendons, to the bones, for which reason they are commonly spoken of as the skeletal muscles, Fig. 31. A tendon is composed of very dense white fibrous (inelastic) connective tissue. These fibers, extending in the direction of the length of the tendon, are grouped into small bundles, or fasciculi, in which the fibers are held together by an interfibrillar cement substance. The fasciculi are grouped into larger bundles surrounded by areolar connective tissue, and between these bundles are found the tendon cells. A number of such larger

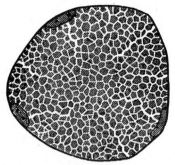

Fig. 29.—Cross section of a striated muscle fiber showing a large number of myofibrils embedded in the clear sarcoplasm, and three nuclei. Surrounding the fiber is the sarcolemma. (Schafer: Essentials of Histology, Longmans, Green and Co.)

Fig. 30.—Section of a striated muscle fiber. In the upper half of the figure the myofibrils appear separated. (Maximow and Bloom: Histology, W. B. Saunders Co.)

bundles are held together by a layer of areolar tissue, the peritendineum, to form the tendon. The blood vessels, lymph vessels, and nerves pass into the tendon along the areolar tissue. Where the muscle and the tendon meet, the fibers of the tendon are affixed to the sarcolemma of the muscle fibers. Further to strengthen this union between the muscle and its tendons, the areolar tissue surrounding the tendon bundles forms a continuation of that enveloping the muscle bundles. Because of its great strength, a tendon is less liable to rupture or break than a muscle or bone.

Levers.—By the contraction of a muscle its two ends approach each other and, as these ends are attached to two articulated bones, the result is a movement of one or both of the bones. As shown in Fig. 31, the biceps muscle (*bi,* twice; *caput,* head) of the arm has its two upper tendons affixed to the scapula (shoulder blade) and its lower tendon to the radius of the forearm. The radius makes a hinged joint with the humerus at the elbow. By the contraction of the biceps muscle, the forearm is moved through an arc of a circle. The bones of the limbs, the ribs, and certain other bones act as levers. In most cases the muscles are attached to the levers so as to *enhance the extent of the movement* produced by a certain amount of contraction, *at the expense of the force.* Depending upon the position of the tendons upon the two bones and the manner of the articulation of the bones, various modes of motion, such as flexion, extension, circumduction, rotation, gliding, are possible. The attachment of the muscle to the immovable or less movable bone is called its *origin;* its attachment to the more readily movable bone is known as the *insertion.*

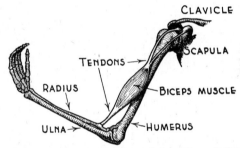

Fig. 31.—Diagram illustrating the origin and insertion of the biceps muscle.

Extensibility and Elasticity.—Muscle tissue has two physical properties we wish to call attention to; namely, extensibility and elasticity. When a muscle is excised from the body and one end is fixed in a clamp and weights are attached to the free end, the muscle elongates, and, within limits, the greater the weight, the more the muscle stretches. When the weights are removed, the muscle shortens almost to its original length. These two properties are of value to us; first, they tend to keep the muscle in continuous readiness for contraction, secondly, they prevent or lessen danger of rupturing when excessive strain is placed upon a muscle, and, in the third place, they make the work of the various parts of our body smooth. A contracted muscle has more extensibility than a resting muscle, for which reason an overloaded muscle may elongate rather than shorten when stimulated.

II. MUSCLE STIMULATION

Skeletal Muscles Not Automatic.—When a skeletal muscle is removed from the body, it remains quiescent until it is stimulated by an outside disturbance; that is, it possesses no automaticity. This condition also exists in the living body. What furnishes the stimulus to initiate muscle activity? All skeletal muscles are supplied with nerves which, as we have already learned, have the power to carry impulses. The fibers composing these nerves make intimate contact with the muscle fibers, and when the nerve fibers are stimulated (in a manner to be discussed in the next chapter) the impulse created is conveyed to and stimulates the muscle fibers.

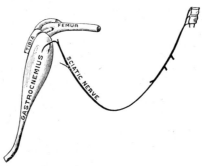

Fig. 32.—The muscle-nerve preparation. (W. S. Hall.) The free end of the muscle ends in the tendon of Achilles; to the free end of the nerve is attached a small part of the spinal column.

Muscle-Nerve Preparation.—Much of our knowledge of the activity of muscles has been gained by the study of the frog's muscles. Very frequently the muscle-nerve preparation used for this purpose is the gastrocnemius muscle and its motor nerve, the sciatic nerve, Fig. 32. On being stimulated either directly or indirectly (by stimulating the sciatic nerve), the muscle is seen to contract. Many forms of stimuli (thermal, mechanical, chemical, etc.) can be applied, especially to the nerve; but, because it is easily applied, readily controlled as to strength, and does minimal damage to the stimulated structure, the electric current is by far the most commonly used form of stimulation. For this purpose we may use either the galvanic current (voltaic, or direct battery current) or the faradic, also called the induced, current.

Faradic or Induced Current.—The primary coil, Fig. 33, *a,* of the inductorium is composed of a few turns of heavy wire, and is connected by means of the binding posts *c* and *d* or *c* and *e* with the battery. This constitutes the primary circuit and carries the galvanic current. The secondary coil, *b,* composed of many turns of very fine wire, is connected with the terminals f and f'; to these are attached the electrodes carrying the induced current to the tissue; this forms the secondary circuit. At the instant of closing the key in the primary circuit, the passage of the galvanic current through the primary coil, a, induces a momentary electric current in the secondary coil, b, which is of higher voltage than that of the galvanic current passing through the primary coil. When the key in the primary circuit is opened, another induced current is formed in the secondary coil (break shock).

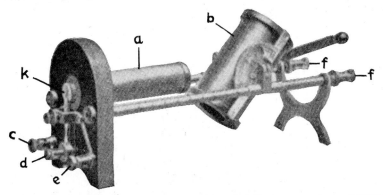

Fig. 33.—The inductorium. For explanation of lettering see text. (Harvard Apparatus Co.)

The apparatus is so arranged that stimuli may be delivered manually or mechanically. By placing a battery and key in series with the primary coil of the inductorium through binding posts c and d, Fig. 33, stimuli can be delivered at any desired rate, within the limits of one's ability to tap the key (make-and-break stimuli). If one wishes to deliver stimuli at a rapid rate, the primary coil of the inductorium is connected in the circuit through the binding posts c and e, Fig. 33. By holding the key closed, the primary circuit is mechanically interrupted by a vibrating mechanism, k. Stimuli delivered by this method are known as tetanizing stimuli.

The strength of the faradic current can be varied in three ways: 1, by varying the distance between the primary and the secondary coils; 2, by tilting the secondary coil out of its horizontal position; 3, by increasing or decreasing the strength of the galvanic current.

The induced current is of very short duration (about $\frac{1}{10,000}$ sec.) and, therefore, reaches its maximum intensity very quickly. This renders the induced current very efficient as a stimulus for nerves and striated muscles. Since the rise of the primary current to full strength takes longer than the fall to zero, the break shock of the induced current is stronger than the make.

The Kymograph.—Many changes occur in a muscle when it is thrown into action; among these we may enumerate mechanical, thermal, chemical, acoustic, histologic, electric, and photic changes. In the mechanical change the muscle becomes shorter and correspondingly thicker. To study this more carefully, it is necessary to record the contraction on a moving surface.* The apparatus most commonly used for this purpose is called the kymograph (*kyma,* wave). A common form of kymograph is shown in Fig. 34. It consists of a

Fig. 34.—The spring kymograph and its aluminum drum. About ⅙ the actual size. (Harvard Apparatus Co.)

drum which is caused to revolve by a spring in the base; its speed is easily controlled. The contraction of the muscle is recorded on smoked paper placed around the drum. The data thus secured are made permanent by passing the smoked paper through a "fixing" bath,† after which it is allowed to dry.

---

*The apparatus and technique for recording the muscle contraction are described in detail in: Laboratory Experiments in Physiology, W. D. Zoethout, The C. V. Mosby Co., 1943.

†Directions for making a suitable "fixing" bath are given in: An Introduction to Experimental Physiology, W. W. Tuttle and G. Clinton Knowlton, The C. V. Mosby Company, 1939.

III. MECHANICAL CHANGES

Galvanic Stimulation.—A muscle having been properly arranged (see Fig. 35) to write the mechanical changes occurring during its contraction on the drum, and a signal magnet, *S*, having been placed in the circuit, let us stimulate the muscle by means of a galvanic current of sufficient strength. The moment the key, *K*, is closed, the current is sent into the muscle (at *M* in Fig. 36), and a single contraction is recorded at *1*. A single contraction is known as a *twitch*

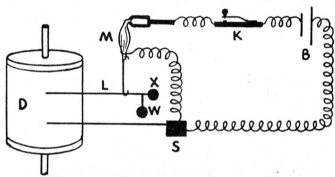

Fig. 35.—Apparatus set up for galvanic stimulation. *B*, battery; *D*, kymograph; *K*, key; *L*, muscle lever; *M*, muscle; *S*, signal magnet; *W*, weight; *X*, axis of lever.

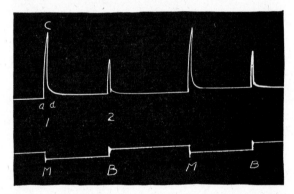

Fig. 36.—Muscle curve showing the make and the break contractions obtained by stimulation with the galvanic current. The lower tracing, written by the signal magnet, shows at the breaks in the horizontal line the time at which the current is passed into (at *M*) and out of (at *B*) the muscle. In the muscle curve *1* represents the make contraction and *2*, the break contraction. The current is flowing steadily through the muscle from the closing, *M*, to the opening, *B*, of the key.

and the one here obtained is spoken of as the *make twitch*. At the break of the current, *B*, another contraction, the *break twitch, 2,* is recorded. From Fig. 36 it will be seen that the make twitch obtained by galvanic stimulation is greater than the break twitch. As can be seen from the tracing, during the steady flow of the galvanic current (from *M* to *B*) there is no visible change in the muscle;* this will be discussed more fully on page 129.

The galvanic current is not used generally for stimulating purposes since it alters the irritability and conductivity of the tissue in the region of the point of application; these changes are known as electrotonus.

Faradic Stimulation.—When we wish to stimulate the muscle with a faradic, or induced, current, the apparatus is set up as shown in Fig. 37. A signal magnet, *L,* is introduced into the primary circuit. On closing the key in the primary circuit, a make contraction, *M*

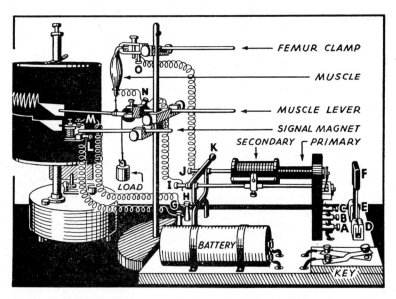

Fig. 37.—Setup for recording the contraction of an excised frog muscle stimulated by faradic current. When switch *F* is in contact with *D,* the stimulating unit delivers make-and-break stimuli as the key is closed and opened. When switch *F* is in contact with *E,* tetanizing stimuli are delivered when the key is kept closed. If an automatic interrupter, such as a swinging pendulum, is required in the primary circuit, it is connected to binding posts *G* and *H.* For the details of the arrangement of the apparatus, see *An Introduction to Experimental Human Physiology* by W. W. Tuttle and G. Clinton Knowlton, 1939, The C. V. Mosby Company.

in Fig. 38, is obtained; the opening of the key causes the break contraction at *B.* It will be noticed that with the induced current the break contraction is greater than that obtained with the make shock. The reason for this was given on pages 87 and 88.

The Form Curve.—In order to study some of the characteristics of a muscle twitch, the form curve is employed. This curve is secured by recording a single muscle twitch, obtained by faradic stimu-

---

*A very intense galvanic current may evoke two or three contractions, because adaptation (spoken of on pp. 95 and 129) is not instantaneous.

lation, on a rapidly moving drum. It is necessary to know the time relationship between the various events which take place during muscular contraction. For this purpose a signal magnet is placed in the primary circuit. Next we place on the drum, and directly beneath the stylus of the muscle lever, the stylus of a tuning fork or of an electrically driven bar having 100 double vibrations per second. In order to have the time relationship correct, the writing points of all recording apparatus must be aligned vertically.

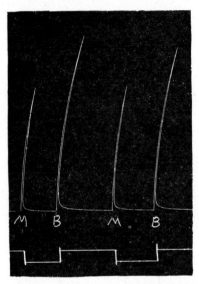

Fig. 38.—Stimulation of the muscle by faradic current. *M* is the make, and *B*, the break contraction.

The closing of the primary circuit depresses the stylus of the signal magnet at *A*, Fig. 39, and sets up a faradic current which causes a make contraction to begin at *B*. It will be noticed that there is a short lapse of time between the application of the stimulus, *A*, and the beginning of the response, *B;* this is known as the *latent period*. The length of this time interval is determined by counting the number of tuning fork vibrations between the two parallel lines erected at the points *A* and *B*, respectively. In Fig. 39 this is about ¾ double vibration, or 0.0075 second. The length of the contraction period (*B* to *C*) varies with the nature and condition of the muscle; generally it is found to be about 0.04 second. The relaxation, *CD,* occupies about 0.05 second; the whole twitch therefore consumes about 0.1 second in a frog's muscle at 21° C.

The relaxation of the muscle is a passive phenomenon brought about by the load which the muscle is lifting or by its own weight.

This can readily be shown by placing a muscle on the surface of mercury and noticing that after the muscle has ceased to contract, no elongation takes place.

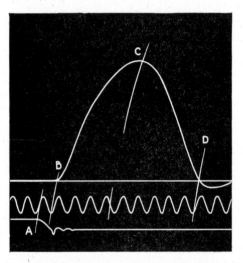

Fig. 39.—The form curve of a muscle twitch. *A*, stimulus applied; *B*, beginning of contraction; *C* to *D*, relaxation; time in 1/100 second.

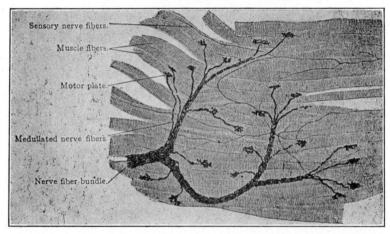

Fig. 40.—Motor nerve-endings in skeletal muscle. (Lewis and Stöhr: Textbook of Histology, P. Blakiston's Son and Co.)

Independent Muscle Irritability.—On entering a muscle, the fibers of which the nerve is composed separate to distribute themselves among the thousands of muscle fibers, Fig. 40. Prior to making connection with the muscle fibers, the nerve fiber branches repeatedly so that a single nerve fiber innervates from 5 to as many as 200 muscle fibers. The small terminal branch, just before penetrating the sarcolemma, loses its coverings or coats and ends in what is regarded as a special structure known as the motor end-plate or *myoneural junction*. The individual nerve fiber with all the muscle fibers it innervates is the functional neuromuscular unit, or the *motor unit*.

When a muscle-nerve preparation is placed in a dilute solution of a drug known as curare for a sufficient length of time, stimulation of the muscle directly causes a contraction, but stimulation of the nerve does not. This is not due to the action of curare upon the nerve fibers, for, when the motor nerve is placed in the solution (the muscle not being in the solution), the stimulation of the nerve is capable of causing the muscle to contract. Hence, it must be the myoneural junctions that are paralyzed by the curare.

The resultant contraction when a normal muscle is stimulated directly may be due to the stimulation of either the muscle fibers or of the nerve fibers in the muscle. But when a curarized muscle-nerve preparation is used, the contraction produced by stimulating the muscle itself must be due to the fact that the muscle has irritability, independently of the nerve.

IV. FACTORS DETERMINING THE EXTENT OF THE CONTRACTION

As in all stimulus-response phenomena, the response by a muscle to a stimulus is determined: (1) by the characteristics of the stimulus and (2) by the condition of the protoplasmic structure. We shall proceed to study these in some detail.

A. Strength of the Stimulus

By varying the distance between the secondary and the primary coil or by rotating the secondary coil from its parallelism with the primary coil, the inductorium furnishes us a ready means of grading the strength of the stimulus applied to a muscle or nerve. Let us send into a muscle a very feeble induction shock; in all probability the muscle does not respond. In Fig. 41, each successive stimulus from *A* to *B* was of greater intensity than its predecessor, but all are ineffective; these are known as subminimal, or subliminal, stimuli. On still further increasing the strength of the current, we finally obtain a stimulus just sufficiently strong to evoke a feeble contraction, *B;* this strength of stimulus is called the minimal, liminal (*limen,* threshold), or threshold stimulus. The liminal stimulus is a measure of the irritability of the tissue; it enables us to compare the irritability of two muscles or that of the same muscle under various conditions. As the strength of the stimulus is increased (from B to C, Fig. 41) the height of the contraction also increases, until a point is reached (at C) beyond which no further increase in contraction occurs because all the motor units have been thrown into action; this is called the *maximal stimulus*. It will be seen, therefore, that the extent of the contraction of a skeletal muscle varies, within limits, with the strength of the stimulus. A stimulus of a strength between that of the liminal and the maximal is known as the *submaximal stimulus*.

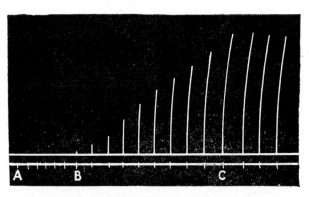

Fig. 41.—Curve illustrating the influence of the strength of the stimulus (single faradic, or induction, shocks) on the height of muscle contraction (registered on a stationary drum). The stimuli between A and B are subliminal; B is the liminal stimulus; C, the maximal stimulus.

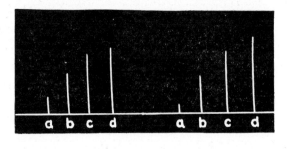

A.   *B.*

Fig. 42.—A, contractions obtained with gradually increasing strength of current, from a to d, but of constant duration. In B the intensity was kept constant but the duration increased from 0.20 millisecond in a to 0.40 millisecond in d.

B. Duration of the Stimulus

We have seen that a very weak stimulus is without any effect, no matter for how long a time it may be applied—the subminimal stimulus. A slightly stronger stimulus (the minimal) must be applied for a considerable length of time before it becomes effective. The stronger the stimulus, the shorter this duration. But if this length of time is shortened sufficiently, no effect is produced, no matter how strong the stimulus may be. As all the fibers in a muscle do not have the same threshold of irritability, it must follow that the length of time a stimulus is applied to a muscle must influence the results. This is illustrated in Fig. 42. In the first tracing, *A*, the duration of the stimulus was held constant but the strength was gradually increased from *a* to *d*. In part *B* the strength was kept constant but the duration was increased from 0.20 millisecond in *a* to 0.40 in *d*.

C. Abruptness of the Stimulus

The efficiency of a stimulus is also determined by the rapidity with which the strength of the stimulus develops from zero to its maximum (DuBois-Reymond's law). At *M*, Fig. 43, the full charge of a dry cell is sent into a muscle by the mere closing of the key and the mus-

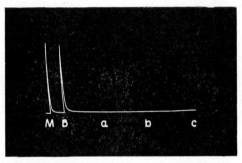

Fig. 43.—Tracing showing the effect of suddenly introducing, at *M*, and withdrawing, at *B*, a constant current; and of very gradually applying the current at *a*, *b*, *c*.

cle responds vigorously; the sudden withdrawal of the current from the muscle also produces a contraction, *B*. At *a* the current is very gradually introduced into the muscle by means of a rheocord and reaches its full intensity at point *b* without having any effect upon the contractile activity of the muscle. From point *b* to *c* the current is equally gradually withdrawn. What we have said about electric stimulation applies equally well to all other types of stimuli.

D. Repetitive Stimulation; Summation of Subliminal Stimuli

When a muscle is stimulated by a single subliminal or inadequate stimulus, apparently nothing happens. But if two or more of these inadequate stimuli are used in rapid succession, a muscle contraction is evoked. In Fig. 44 the muscle was stimulated a number of times with subliminal stimuli before a contraction was obtained. It is evident that although the first inadequate stimulus was unable to produce to its full extent the local excitatory process necessary for muscle activity, *it nevertheless increased the irritability of the tissue,* so that a subsequent stimulus of the same strength was able to complete the process. We shall learn that this most important property of proto-plasm is also exhibited by isolated nerves and by the central nervous system.

Summation of Twitches.—When two stimuli, each capable of caus-ing the muscle to contract, follow each other rapidly so that the sec-ond stimulation occurs before the first twitch is completed, the second contraction is somewhat greater than the first twitch, as shown in Fig. 45. The phenomenon is known as the summation of twitches

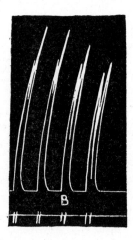

Fig. 44.—To illustrate summation of inadequate stimuli. (Francis, Knowlton and Tuttle: Textbook of Anatomy and Physiology, The C. V. Mosby Co.)

Fig. 45.—Showing summation of twitches.

and is the more striking, the more closely the second stimulus fol-lows the first (except as noted in a subsequent section). Even when the first twitch is maximal, that is, when no increase in the strength of the first stimulus can call forth a higher contraction, the second stimulus is nevertheless followed by a higher contraction. As the first maximal stimulus throws all the muscle units into action, the greater contraction following the second stimulus can be explained only by supposing that the tension produced by the muscle fiber is greater with the second stimulus. This apparently runs counter to the law of all-or-none, but it is highly likely that the activities which are responsible for the first twitch leave the muscle fiber in a better con-dition for the liberation of energy when, within a sufficiently short length of time, a second stimulus is applied.

Tetanus.—When a large number of stimuli are applied to a muscle in rapid succession, so that little time is given for the relaxation between the contractions, the curve described is as shown in *A* to *D* of Fig. 46. This is known as *incomplete tetanus.* Finally, by increasing the rapidity of stimuli still more (about 30 per second for the gastrocnemius muscle of the frog), the curve written by the muscle is a perfectly smooth line, *E,* and the muscle appears to be in a steady state of contraction. This is called *complete tetanus,* which may be defined as a sustained contraction of a muscle due to the fusion of many twitches following each other in rapid succession; the external cause lies in the large number of stimuli sent into the muscle in a unit of time. The extent of the tetanic contraction depends upon the

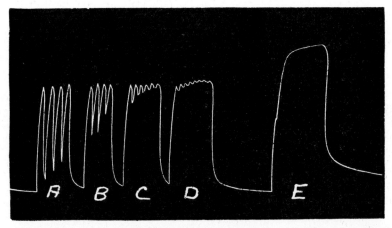

Fig. 46.—Muscle curves showing the genesis of tetanus. *A, B, C, D,* incomplete tetani; *E,* complete tetanus.

effectiveness of the stimulus, but because of summation the height is generally considerably greater than that of the twitch produced by a single stimulus of the same intensity. Compare *E* in Fig. 46 with *A.* The number of stimuli required to give any degree of tetanus depends upon the physiologic condition of the muscle (see infra).

It has been established by proper experiments to which we shall refer under the subject of nerves, that the voluntary contractions of our muscles, even when of extremely short duration, as the winking of an eye, are never simple muscle twitches but are more or less prolonged contractions due to the fusion of many twitches; that is, they are tetanic in nature. These twitches are the result of a large number of distinct impulses (according to Adrian from 45 to 50 per second) sent by the brain cells over the motor nerves. A complete tetanic contraction is not necessarily a maximal contraction in which all the muscle fibers participate. In tetanus only a small number of the motor units may be active, but if these units act asynchronously, i.e., "out of step," the final result is a smooth, sustained contraction.

E. Effect of Temperature

An increase in temperature decreases, and a decrease in temperature increases all phases of muscle contraction; this is shown in Fig. 47. The results of cooling a muscle by applying ice to it are given in Table I.

TABLE I

	PER CENT INCREASE ABOVE NORMAL		
	LATENT PERIOD	CONTRACTION	RELAXATION
Cooling for 5 min.	12.5	21	62
Cooling for 15 min.	25.0	46	115
Cooling for 20 min.	37.5	82	172

From Table I it will be observed that the relaxation period is prolonged most by cooling. This sluggishness in relaxation may be responsible for the poor performance in short bouts of exercises when there is an improper "warm-up."

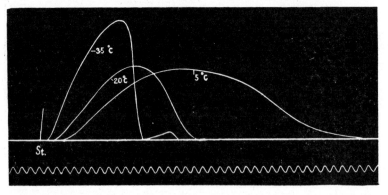

Fig. 47.—The influence of temperature on muscle contraction. *St.*, the point of stimulation is the same for each of the three twitches. (Bainbridge and Menzies: Essentials of Physiology, Longmans, Green and Co.)

F. All-or-None

It was formerly held that the increase in the extent of the contraction as the effectiveness of the stimulus increases was caused by a greater contraction of the individual muscle fibers. This explanation, however, has been abandoned in favor of the view that the contraction of the muscle fibers is always maximal; i.e., a feeble stimulus causes the individual muscle fiber to contract to just as great an extent as a stronger stimulus. This phenomenon, known as "all-or-none," is very easily demonstrated in the heart muscle, as we shall learn in Chapter X. The greater contraction of a skeletal muscle following a stronger stimulation may be attributed to a larger number of fibers participating in the contraction. It is possible that some fibers are less irritable and require a higher threshold stimulus, and the maximal stimulus is just sufficiently strong to cause all the fibers to contract. While the individual skeletal muscle fibers follow the law of all-or-none, the muscle as a whole does not, and, therefore, *it is possible for the muscle to execute contractions of graded extent or force;* a moment's reflection shows us the tremendous importance of this in everyday life. It must be emphatically stated that with varying conditions of nutrition, exercise, and fatigue, the extent of the contraction of the muscle fiber will vary; but the law of all-or-none holds good for any given condition of the fiber, or the motor unit.

G. Refractory Period

We have seen that if two successive stimuli, say $\frac{1}{30}$ to $\frac{1}{50}$ second apart, are thrown into a muscle, both elicit a twitch. But Adrian and others discovered that if the second stimulation occurs within 0.003 second after the first stimulation, the muscle fails to respond to the second stimulus. This failure to respond indicates a lack of irritability. It seems that *the activity of all protoplasm is associated with a loss of irritability during a certain phase of the activity.* This is known as the refractory period. While in the frog muscle the refractory period is very short (about 0.005 sec.) and has passed before the muscle begins to contract, in the heart it is relatively long; we shall, therefore, study this phenomenon more closely in dealing with that organ.

V. WORK PERFORMED

The amount of mechanical work done by a muscle is determined by multiplying the grams (or kilograms) of the load lifted by the height to which the load is lifted as measured in millimeters (or meters); the result expresses the work in gram-millimeters (or kilogram-meters). Table II gives the result obtained with a frog muscle:

TABLE II

Weight in grams	0	50	100	150	200	250
Height in millimeters	14	9	7	5	2	0
Work in gram-millimeters	0	450	700	750	400	0

When a muscle contracts without any weight being lifted or when the weight is so heavy that the muscle cannot lift it, no mechanical work is done. During its contraction a muscle develops tension. The amount of tension is equal to the weight that must be used to stretch the contracted muscle back to its original, resting length. If a muscle is loaded considerably beyond its power to lift the load, the active muscle stretches; a contracting muscle is evidently more extensible than a resting muscle. When a muscle is loaded so that on being stimulated effectively it neither shortens nor lengthens, the tension developed is the maximum the muscle is capable of generating and expresses the maximum strength of the muscle. As the length of the muscle is constant, the contraction is called an isometric contraction. If the developed tension is greater than the load, the muscle shortens; this is called an isotonic contraction. It will also be seen from Table II that, up to a certain point, an increase in the load is followed by an increase in the amount of work done. The load at which the most work is done per contraction is known as the *optimum load;* in the above experiment this was 150 grams. We may make the general statement that, with the same strength of stimulus, a fairly well-loaded muscle does more work than one underloaded or overloaded.

Maximum Strength.—Aside from factors which influence the nutrition and the general state of the muscle, the maximum strength is determined by the number of muscle fibers. Because of the oblique arrangement of its fibers, the gastrocnemius muscle is composed of a very large number of short fibers, and in consequence the extent of its contraction is small but the maximum strength is great. The nature of its protoplasm also influences the maximum strength; thus, per square centimeter of cross-section, human muscle is from two to five times as strong as the muscle of a frog.

Effect of Stretching.—The above-discussed increase in work done by a muscle lifting a medium-sized load over that of a lesser loaded muscle is generally attributed to the stretching of the muscle. It has been found that the oxygen consumption and the heat production (see infra) by a stretched resting muscle are greater than those of an unstretched muscle. This also holds true for a muscle that is stretched at the very beginning of its contraction. We may therefore hold that the liberation of energy is the greater, the greater the length of the muscle fiber. As the muscles in the body are generally in a more or less stretched condition, the value of this is apparent.

The effect of stretching is well shown in Fig. 48. In curve B the resting muscle was not after-loaded and therefore was stretched more and more as successively larger weights were used (from 0 to 80 grams). In curve A the same weights were used but the muscle was after-loaded, i.e., the weight was supported so that the muscle retained its original length. This muscle, it will be noticed, was unable to lift the 80 gram weight and therefore no mechanical work was accomplished. In contrast, in curve B, the 80 gram weight was lifted to about the same height as the 10 gram weight and much work was done.

Muscle Tonus.—The so-called resting muscles in the animal body are not in a perfectly relaxed condition. Although showing no outward sign of activity, yet they are in a mild and constant state of contraction which causes the muscle to resist stretching; this is known as muscle tonus. Such tonus is well exemplified by the masseter and temporal muscles which raise the lower jaw. Although we may be unconscious of the position of the jaw and are not volitionally sending impulses to the muscles, yet they are, as long as we are awake, constantly holding the jaw up, in opposition to the force of gravity. The cause of muscle tonus lies in the continuous stream of impulses descending from the central nervous system; therefore, if the motor nerve to a skeletal muscle be cut, the tonus of the muscle is abolished. The further discussion of this subject must be postponed until later.

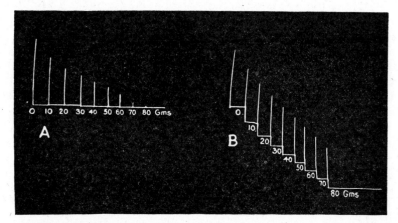

Fig. 48.—To illustrate the effect of stretching on muscle activity. In *A* the muscle is after-loaded and therefore not stretched. In *B* the muscle is stretched by the addition of each weight. Same strength of stimulus throughout in both *A* and *B*. The abscissae indicate grams. (Bainbridge and Menzies: Essentials of Physiology, Longman's, Green and Co.)

The importance of tonus lies in the fact that **in a skeletal muscle nutrition and function are inseparable.** A muscle which is never active feels soft and flabby and gradually wastes away or undergoes atrophy, as is well illustrated in a bedridden patient. This atrophy is known as *atrophy of disuse.*

VI. CHEMICAL CHANGES

The energy utilized by a muscle in the performance of mechanical work can be supplied only by the chemical potential energy of the organic foodstuffs (see p. 315), namely, the proteins, fats, and carbohydrates. Although any one of these three substances can perform this function, in Chap. XXI we shall furnish evidence that under the usual conditions of life, the carbohydrates must be regarded as the main muscle fuel.

In the animal body there are two chief methods by which the potential energy of a complex organic compound can be liberated: (a) The large molecules of the compound are broken up (generally under the influence of an enzyme) into simpler molecules. For example, the carbohydrate known as glycogen is split into lactic acid, according to the equation:

$$n \; C_6H_{10}O_5 + nH_2O = 2n \; C_3H_6O_3.$$

As the potential energy of the resultant lactic acid is less than that of the glycogen, there must have been a liberation of energy (an exothermic process). Since these chemical changes can take place in the absence of oxygen, they are said to be *anaerobic* (*an,* without; *aer,* air). (b) The second method for the release of the potential energy is by oxidation, an *aerobic* process. In both of these methods, the steps by which they take place are many and complex.

In one of the earliest attempts to explain the origin of the muscle energy, it was held that some material in the muscle underwent oxidation. The fact that during physical work the glycogen, always present in a resting muscle, disappears, and that the consumption of oxygen and the production of CO_2 are increased favored this view. But when it was shown by placing an excised muscle in an atmosphere of nitrogen or hydrogen, that muscle work can be performed in the absence of oxygen, another source of the energy had to be looked for. In this anaerobic muscle activity, the amount of glycogen in the muscle decreases and that of the lactic acid (normally present to the extent of about 0.015 per cent) is greatly increased (0.3 per cent in an exhausted muscle). It was also learned that when a thoroughly fatigued muscle is placed in oxygen, the lactic acid gradually disappears, the amount of glycogen is augmented, and the production of heat and of carbon dioxide and the consumption of oxygen are increased. As the lactic acid disappears, the irritability of the muscle is restored. These chemical changes do not occur if the fatigued muscle is placed in an atmosphere devoid of oxygen; the muscle does not regain its irritability and gradually dies. These and other related facts were until recently held to demonstrate that the transformation of glycogen into lactic acid was the source of muscle energy. But in 1930 Lundsgaard showed that, by poisoning a muscle with iodoacetic acid, it is possible to prevent this decomposition of glycogen, although the muscle is still able to give a fairly large number of contractions upon stimulation.

In the muscle there is always present (to the extent of about 0.5 per cent) a nitrogenous substance known as creatin. Creatin readily unites with phosphoric acid and forms a still larger and more complex molecule known as phosphocreatin. The stimulation of a muscle causes hydrolytic cleavage of the large molecule of phosphocreatin into phosphoric acid and creatin. The energy thereby liberated may supply the muscle with power to do mechanical work. To understand the rôle played by the phosphocreatin, glycogen, lactic acid, and oxygen and the interrelation of the various processes taking place during muscle activity, we must consider the following facts :

(*a*) A muscle treated with iodoacetic acid is able to do work but speedily fatigues. In this the phosphocreatin disappears and phosphoric acid and creatin are produced; no glycogen and oxygen are consumed, neither are lactic acid and carbon dioxide formed.

(*b*) A normal muscle in the absence of oxygen can do more work before fatigue sets in than occurs in (*a*). Now both phosphocreatin and glycogen disappear, and much lactic acid but no carbon dioxide is produced.

(*c*) A normal muscle in oxygen can do still more work. Here oxygen is consumed, carbon dioxide is given off, and there is less lactic acid than in (*b*).

In (*a*) we prove that, without glycogen or oxygen consumption, a muscle obtains its energy from the cleavage of phosphocreatin into its two constituents. Since the store of phosphocreatin is very limited, the muscle fatigues readily. The greater capacity for work in (*b*) is due to the resynthesis of the phosphoric acid and creatin into phosphocreatin. This is an endothermic process, and the energy required for it is supplied by the breaking down of glycogen into lactic acid. But if the glycogen is to furnish energy for this purpose for any length of time, it also must be remade from its products, i.e., from the lactic acid. To supply energy for this synthesis, some of the lactic acid is oxidized into water and carbon dioxide; this takes place in (*c*). According to Hill, about one out of every four or five molecules of lactic acid is oxidized and the energy thereby liberated is used in recombining the remainder of the acid into glycogen. The cleavage of glycogen into lactic acid is a highly involved process in which, it seems, the glycogen first unites with phosphoric acid to form a hexosephosphate. This new compound by many successive changes, some of them not fully understood, is finally broken down into lactic acid.

Oxygen Debt.—If oxygen is not delivered fast enough to oxidize the lactic acid into CO_2 and H_2O or to reconstruct it into glycogen, the acid accumulates in the body for subsequent oxidation. This constitutes what Hill termed the "oxygen debt," a matter which will be elaborated in our discussion of the influence of muscle work on respiration (Chap. XIII). From the above it is clear that oxidations are not directly responsible for the energy supply of the muscle, but that the oxygen is used for the recovery of the muscle. If the oxygen is supplied in a sufficient quantity to all parts of an excised muscle (for example, the thin sartorius muscle, suspended in an oxygenated Ringer's solution), the muscle can give, according to Hill, as many as 10,000 twitches. In this experiment the lactic acid was oxidized as rapidly as it was formed, and the restoration of the glycogen and the phosphocreatin was immediate. It is also apparent that the carbohydrates of the food (sugars, starch, glycogen) must be regarded as the ultimate or "primary fuel" for the muscle. A small amount of the lactic acid formed during severe muscle work is thrown into the blood; a part of this is excreted by the kidneys but the largest part is transported to the liver where it is transformed into glycogen (see Fig. 190).

VII. THERMAL CHANGES

As related above, the transformation of the potential energy of the food into muscle energy is accompanied by the liberation of heat. Our muscle machinery is somewhat like the locomotive in which only a small percentage of all the energy set free from the fuel is utilized for mechanical work, the larger part escaping in the form of heat. The proportion of the liberated energy that can be used by our muscles for mechanical work varies with the nature and the condition of the muscle and with the amount of load the muscle lifts. This last is illustrated in Table III.

TABLE III

WEIGHT LIFTED	WORK DONE	HEAT SET FREE	% OF ENERGY TRANSFORMED INTO MECHANICAL WORK
grams	gram-mm.	micro-cal.	
0	0	14.6	0
20	465	18.0	6
40	802	19.7	10
200	2,905	25.6	30

When no load is being lifted, all the energy is changed to heat. Table III shows that, within certain limits, increasing the load increases not only the mechanical work done, but also the percentage of energy utilized for the work; in other words, a fairly well-loaded muscle works more economically than one more lightly loaded.

A part of the heat is set free during the contraction of the muscle and occurs in either the absence or presence of oxygen. Another part is evolved for some time after the cessation of the contraction and relaxation period and fails to appear in the absence of oxygen. From this it has been concluded that the first-mentioned outburst of heat is associated with those anaerobic chemical changes which are the immediate source of energy for the contraction; that released subsequent to the contraction and largely dependent upon a supply of oxygen is set free by the processes concerned with the recovery phase of the muscle.

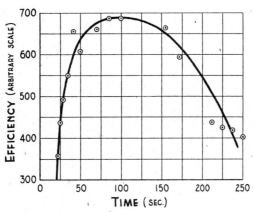

Fig. 48-A.—Efficiency of stair-climbing at different speeds. (From Lupton.)

Mechanical Efficiency of Muscles.—By muscle efficiency we mean the ratio between the amount of mechanical work done and the amount of energy expended. As stated above, a large amount of the energy is lost or wasted in the form of heat. Benedict found that in working a bicycle ergometer (*ergon*, work) in the respiratory calorimeter (p. 439) the efficiency percentage varies from 18.1 to 21.6. This compares favorably with the steam engine, in which from 9 to 19 per cent of the energy is utilized. The modern Diesel engine is said to have an efficiency of from 29 to 35 per cent.

The efficiency of the human machine varies slightly from one individual to another, and also with many conditions, among which we may mention:

1. THE RAPIDITY WITH WHICH WORK IS DONE.—For example, in climbing stairs (Fig. 48-*A*) the greatest efficiency occurred when the work was done in 100 seconds. Doing this same amount of work

in 25 or in 250 seconds very markedly reduced the efficiency. In this experiment the efficiency was highest when each step occupied 1.3 seconds.

2. FATIGUE.—As fatigue sets in, efficiency decreases; therefore, suitable rest periods are highly desirable to maintain efficiency.

3. RHYTHM.—Most people work with a certain rhythm; e.g., some people walk with longer and slower steps, others with shorter and faster steps. It is a familiar fact that adopting a new rhythm brings on fatigue more speedily.

4. BODY WEIGHT.—Efficiency is greatest in persons having a correct body weight, being less in the underweight and still less in the overweight individuals.

5. TRAINING.—It is generally held that a person trained to a certain kind of work performs this work with a smaller consumption of energy and therefore greater efficiency by as much as 5 per cent. This is due largely, if not altogether, to the better coordination by which unnecessary and antagonistic muscle contractions are avoided. In the trained subject there is a better utilization of oxygen as shown by the greater removal of oxygen from the inspired air and the smaller oxygen debt. It has also been demonstrated that preliminary "warming-up" improves performance in athletic contests.

The muscles in our body work at a great *mechanical disadvantage*. For example, the biceps muscle which flexes (raises) the forearm has its two origins on the scapula and its insertion on the radius a short distance below the bend of the elbow, Fig. 31. The forearm is a lever of the third order; the fulcrum is placed at the elbow (joint of radius and humerus), the arm and hand constitute the weight, and the power is applied, as stated above, a short distance from the fulcrum. This causes the power arm to be very short, an arrangement which does not lend itself to the development of great power. However, because of the long weight arm this anatomical structure does admit of great speed of movement of the hand.

The electrical changes occurring in a muscle will be discussed in our study of Nerves (p. 123).

VIII. FATIGUE

The "Staircase" Phenomenon.—That the performance of work has an influence upon the muscles themselves is common knowledge. These effects, some beneficial and others injurious, we shall now study in greater detail.

When an excised frog muscle is stimulated with a single induction shock and the contraction registered, a tracing of a certain height is obtained. If another stimulus of the same strength is applied, say, one second after the first, the second contraction is a little higher than the first. By thus stimulating the muscle once per second with stim-

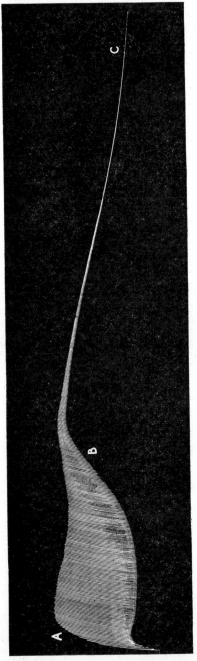

Fig. 49.—Fatigue curve showing, *A*, staircase; *B*, contracture; *C*, complete fatigue. (From Francis, Knowlton and Tuttle; Textbook of Anatomy and Physiology, The C. V. Mosby Co.)

uli of a constant strength, a series of contractions in which each contraction is greater than the preceding can be obtained, *A*, Fig. 49. This phenomenon is known as the "treppe," or staircase. Since it is also found in other structures, e.g., the heart (p. 208), it may be regarded as evidence that previous activity increases the irritability and thereby places the protoplasm in a more favorable condition for further work, a "warming-up" process. It is possible to regard it as a residual effect of the products formed during activity.

Fatigue.—After the contractions of an excised muscle have reached their maximum, this height may be maintained for a short time, but soon the continued stimulation causes a gradual decrease in the height of the contractions (Fig. 49). As shown in Fig. 50, the rapidity of the contraction proper is only slightly affected; the relaxation becomes more and more prolonged. Finally the muscle fails to respond even to the strongest stimulation that can be applied; in other words, the muscle gradually loses its irritability, to which condition the term fatigue has been applied.

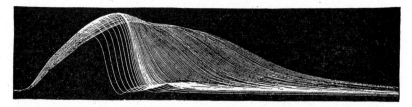

Fig. 50.—Showing effect of fatigue on the muscle curve. (Waller.)

Contracture.—Under certain conditions repeated stimulation of a muscle gives rise to the peculiar effect in which there is a period of incomplete relaxation; this is known as contracture and is not to be confused with tetanus. The accumulation of lactic acid in a muscle may produce a similar condition. For this reason contracture does not take place so readily when the circulation is intact.

Cause of Fatigue.—If a fatigued muscle is perfused* with physiologic salt solution, the fatigue gradually disappears. This is due to a certain extent to the washing away of the waste products, CO_2, lactic acid, and acid phosphate, formed during the activity of the muscle. These products are sometimes spoken of as *fatigue substances*. If to the physiologic salt solution with which the muscle is being perfused there is added a little glucose, the fatigue is removed more quickly. Moreover, if an active muscle is supplied with such a solution its power is increased, that is, the amount of work

---

*An excised organ, such as a skeletal muscle, is perfused with a certain solution, by inserting a tube into the artery of the organ and, under pressure, forcing the solution through the arteries, capillaries, and veins of the organ. As the fluid issues from the vein, it may be caught and used over and over, if so desired.

it can do is greater and fatigue sets in later than when it is supplied with pure physiologic salt solution. These experiments indicate that the cause of fatigue may be: (a) deficiency in the energy-furnishing material; it is conceivable that the resynthesis of the phosphocreatin or of the glycogen is not keeping pace with the destruction; (b) the accumulation of the waste products (fatigue substances) lessens the irritability of the tissue; the cause of this may lie in the failure either to remove the CO_2 and lactic acid, or to supply oxygen necessary for the oxidation of the lactic acid. This failure is due to incapacity of the circulatory or the respiratory system to meet the increased demands.

Disposal of Waste Products.—In our body the cause of fatigue generally lies in autointoxication of the muscle or other structures by the fatigue substances, for very seldom is the available energy-producing material exhausted. Of these waste products, the CO_2 readily enters the blood stream and is promptly eliminated by respiration. As to the lactic acid, we have learned four things may happen:

1. It is oxidized in the muscle.

2. It is synthesized in the muscle into glycogen.

3. After absorption into the blood stream it is carried to the liver, there to be reconstructed into glycogen.

4. A very small amount is excreted, as lactates, by the kidneys.

Although lactic acid, when present in sufficient concentration, aids in the production of fatigue, in view of the first three of the above statements, lactic acid must not be looked upon primarily as a waste product.

Seat of Fatigue.—On stimulating the nerve of a muscle-nerve preparation for a sufficiently long time, the muscle refuses to contract, that is, fatigue has set in. If now the muscle is stimulated directly, contractions are obtained; hence, the fatigue shown when the nerve was stimulated cannot be referred to the muscle, and must, therefore, be attributed to either the nerve fibers or the myoneural junction. It will be shown in the following chapter that a nerve fiber is practically incapable of experiencing fatigue as it is generally understood; we must conclude, therefore, that the fatigued structure is the myoneural junction. Like curare, the fatigue substances have no effect upon the nerve fibers but do influence the activity of the endings. That the muscle itself can also experience fatigue is readily shown by stimulating the muscle directly. Of the three structures, the myoneural junction is the most susceptible to fatigue. Some one has well compared them and the synapses in the central nervous system to the fuses in an electric circuit which are more vulnerable but also more readily restorable than the other parts of the circuit.

Removal of Fatigue.—As fatigue is generally caused by the harmful effects of accumulated waste products, it is evident that the circulation of blood through the muscle, by which food and oxygen are brought to, and waste products removed from, the muscle, is a most important factor in restoring muscle irritability. During prolonged tetanic contraction in the body, the blood supply to the muscle is interfered with because of the increased tension in the muscle tissue; as a consequence the muscle in this form of work fatigues very speedily.

The taking of food, especially carbohydrates, hastens the recovery from fatigue. Hellesen found that, 30 or 40 minutes after its ingestion, sugar improves the capacity for work. The removal of sugar from the body by means of the drug phloridzin causes a large decrease in the power of the muscle. This also may be one of the many reasons why a diabetic person fatigues so readily (p. 415).

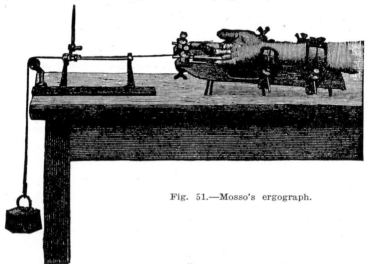

Fig. 51.—Mosso's ergograph.

Conditions Influencing Fatigue in the Human Body.—The production of fatigue under various conditions and its removal in human beings have been subjects of frequent investigations. By means of the ergograph (Fig. 51), the amount of work done by a muscle can be calculated and recorded. The muscle generally experimented upon is the flexor or, in another form of apparatus, the abductor of the index finger. Without going into the details, we may briefly state a few of the most important results gained by this and other methods of studying the effect of work on the muscles themselves and on the body in general and show how the various conditions of body and mind affect the muscular work.

1. RAPIDITY OF THE WORK.—The amount of work a muscle can do and the rapidity with which fatigue sets in depend very largely on the number of contractions executed in a unit of time, as is shown in Table IV.

TABLE IV

	FATIGUED BY	WORK DONE
One contraction every second	14 contractions	0.912 Kgm.
One contraction every 2 seconds	18 contractions	1.080 Kgm.
One contraction every 4 seconds	31 contractions	1.842 Kgm.
One contraction every 10 seconds	No fatigue	Almost indefinite

For every load there is a certain rate at which the most work in a given length of time can be accomplished. Too rapid a rate of work fatigues the muscle quickly and, therefore, cuts down the total amount of work that the muscles can do; too slow a rate, while preventing all fatigue, also decreases the output. It is, therefore, wiser to spread the contractions over a sufficient length of time, as is illustrated in Table V.

TABLE V

NUMBER OF CONTRACTIONS	WORK DONE
15 every 30 minutes for 14 hours	26.9 Kgm.
60 every 2 hours for 14 hours	14.7 Kgm.

It will be noticed that in both cases the muscle executed the same number of contractions (420) in the fourteen hours, but when the contractions were performed in larger groups, the amount of work done was much less.

2. TIME FOR RECOVERY.—The length of time necessary for recovery from fatigue varies from one muscle to another and also with the degree of fatigue experienced. Manzer found 80 per cent recovery in 10 minutes and 95 per cent in 20 minutes from fatigue brought on by ergographic work. But after severe and prolonged athletic contests an hour or even a day may be needed for complete restoration. It has been shown that if volitional impulses are sent to the muscle after it is fatigued, that is, if the person strains himself to continue the work even though no visible contractions result, the time necessary to recover from the fatigue is increased.

3. REMOVAL OF WASTE PRODUCTS.—Interference with the removal of waste products or with the supply of food and any condition that may lower the general vitality of the body, such as want of sleep, sleeping or working in badly ventilated rooms, and dissipations of all sorts, lessen the power of the muscle and hasten fatigue.

4. VOLUNTARY FATIGUE, as in the above experiment, is of central origin. If the motor nerve of the so-called fatigued muscle is electrically stimulated through the skin, strong contractions are obtained. The fatigue is therefore neither in the muscle nor in the myoneural junctions but must be in the brain or in the spinal cord from which the motor nerve springs. This will be discussed in our study of the central nervous system.

5. SPREADING OF FATIGUE.—The fatigue of a certain set of muscles causes more or less of a general fatigue which, to a greater or lesser extent, affects the other muscles of the body.

6. INFLUENCE OF DRUGS.—As to the effect of alcohol, Rivers found that if the taste of alcohol is disguised (in order to abolish the psychologic effects), a small amount (5 to 20 c.c. absolute alcohol) had no effect on the work as shown by the ergograph, and that in larger doses it generally decreases the amount of work. Rivers also found that although smoking caused pleasure and there was a strong sensory stimulation (for which reasons we would expect a decided increase in the amount of work done) yet smoking caused a decrease in the capacity for work.

According to Schumburg, coffee and tea have no recuperative power over muscles of a fatigued body except when taken with other foods. More recent experiments by Rivers showed that caffeine increases the capacity for muscular and mental work without any reaction, if the drug is taken in moderate doses; in large doses it may hasten fatigue.

7. The influence of physical exercise and training will be considered on pages 117 to 119.

IX. PALE AND RED MUSCLES

A muscle fiber is composed, as we have seen, of a number of delicate fibrils surrounded by the more fluid sarcoplasm. The sarcostyles are generally regarded as the contractile elements of the muscle fibers. In some muscles the amount of the sarcoplasm is greater, and the fibers contain granules and a pigment known as myohemoglobin. These muscles are red or dark in appearance. The pale, or white, muscles so conspicuous in the pectoral muscles of a chicken are poor in sarcoplasm and contain no pigment. In man and some animals, e.g., frog, a muscle frequently contains both pale and red fibers.

The red pigment of muscle, myohemoglobin, is closely related to, if not identical with, the pigmented protein, hemoglobin, of the red blood cells. It is generally held to be more abundantly present in the slower acting muscle where the contractions are maintained for a considerable length of time, e.g., in the breast muscles of flying birds, the leg muscles of running birds, and in the heart. In more rapidly acting muscle, there is a smaller amount of myohemoglobin. It has been suggested that myohemoglobin serves as a storehouse for oxygen.

X. VISCERAL OR SMOOTH MUSCLES

Location.—The visceral, plain, or smooth, muscles are composed of spindle-shaped fibers, each with a single, elongated nucleus, Fig. 52. These muscles are found chiefly in the walls of the four great tracts of hollow organs: the circulatory, the respiratory, the alimentary, and the urogenital. They are also found in the interior of the eye (the ciliary muscles and the muscle in the iris), in the skin (the arrector pili, the contraction of which erects the hairs and produces "goose skin"), and in the ducts of glands.

Functions.—From their wide distribution in the various organs of the body, it can readily be understood that the smooth muscles perform many and diverse functions. Not a few of these have to do with the dilation or constriction of an opening or a tube. For example, in the iris they regulate the amount of light entering the eye; in the arteries they govern the amount of blood passing through the vessels and thus its distribution. The muscles in the alimentary canal

Fig. 52.—Smooth muscle fibers. (Francis, Knowlton, and Tuttle: Textbook of Anatomy and Physiology, The C. V. Mosby Co.)

and in the urinary and reproductive systems are actively concerned with the propulsion of materials. In the skin and the blood vessels of the skin they aid in regulating the body temperature. By moving the body or parts of the body *the skeletal muscles adjust the organism to its environment; the visceral muscles are concerned with those processes necessary for the maintenance of the receptors, the skeletal muscles, and the nervous system—homeostasis.* Collectively these activities are sometimes spoken of as the vegetative functions.

Innervation.—These muscles differ from the striated muscles in their innervation in that the latter receive their impulses directly, without any relaying, from the spinal cord or brain, while the nerves for the plain muscles run in the autonomic nervous system (p. 82). That is, a spinal or cranial nerve fiber carrying an impulse for a smooth muscle ends in an autonomic ganglion (a collection of nerve cell bodies) lying outside of the central nervous system; another nerve fiber takes the impulse from the ganglion to the muscle (Fig. 28). Many smooth muscles have a double nerve supply, one for excitation and one for inhibition.

Action of Smooth Muscles.—The contraction of the smooth muscle may be studied by cutting a narrow ring from the pyloric end of a frog's stomach, and suspending it in a proper holder so that its contraction can be recorded on the drum; in this manner the tracing in Fig. 53 was produced. By comparing this curve with the one of the striated muscle, it will be seen that, whereas the contraction of the striated muscle lasts only one- or two-tenths of a second, that of the plain muscle lasts several seconds. This experiment also teaches that the action of the smooth muscle is frequently spontaneous and rhythmical. In fact, the contractions recorded in the accompanying tracing were produced without any external stimulation and are, as can be seen, rhythmical. Whether this automaticity is due primarily to the muscle or to the nerve tissue found in the wall of the stomach will be discussed on page 382. Excitations of a slower and more prolonged nature, such as contact, pressure and, more particularly, *stretching,* form very efficient stimulations for many smooth

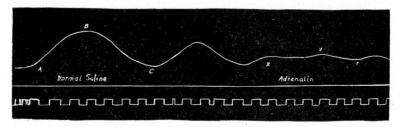

Fig. 53.—Tracing of the contraction of a frog's stomach.

muscles; from the location of these muscles in the walls of hollow organs (intestines, bladder, etc.), the importance of this is apparent. Chemical stimuli are also very effective. The visceral muscles develop considerably less power than the skeletal muscles. Similar to these last-named muscles, the extent of the response of the visceral muscles varies with the strength and duration of the stimulus. Some smooth muscles, in all likelihood, follow the law of all-or-none; concerning others there is much doubt.

Tonus.—Smooth muscles, as illustrated by those found in the walls of the stomach and urinary bladder, are generally in a state of mild constant contraction (a condition known as *tonus*) by which the organ or structure resists more or less the effort to stretch. Thus, when the stomach is empty, its cavity is virtually obliterated by the tonus of the gastric muscles. As food is put into the stomach, the muscles relax and the wall thereby stretches without any change in the degree of its tension. For this reason, the intragastric pressure rises but little, or not at all, as the stomach is filled. *The walls of* *the hollow organs accommodate themselves by their tonus to the volume of the contents without any marked alteration in the internal pressure or in the tension of the wall.* In contrast with the tonus of skeletal muscle (p. 598), the tonus of many smooth muscles is influenced by, but not dependent entirely upon, the central nervous system.

XI. HISTOLOGIC CHANGES

The surface of the fibril is marked by alternate light and dark bands, as shown in Figs. 30 and 54. Through each of the white bands extends an exceedingly delicate membrane by which the fibril is divided into a large number of segments, or sarcomeres (*meros*, a part). A sarcomere is therefore composed of one central, less transparent transverse band and one white, more transparent band at each end.

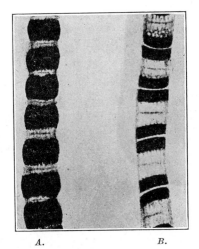

A.   B.

Fig. 54.—*A*, a muscle fiber in the contracted state; *B*, in the relaxed state. (Schafer: Essentials of Histology, Longmans, Green & Co.)

When a relaxed fiber (*B*, Fig. 54) and a contracted fiber, *A*, are compared, it will be readily observed that during contraction the dark bands have greatly expanded at the expense of the lighter bands. The significance of these striations is not fully understood. In examining various contractile structures we note that totally undifferentiated protoplasm exhibiting a feeble amount of contractility, such as in a leucocyte, presents no striations. In the more highly evolved contractile cells of the visceral muscles longitudinal striations appear, and these striations, which are the outward manifestation of the internal structures (fibrils), become the more pronounced the greater the efficiency of the muscle. In the most highly specialized contractile organs—the skeletal muscles—where high speed of action and great strength are required, we note not only the longitudinal but also the well-marked cross striations. We may therefore conclude that in muscles great rapidity or strength is associated with, and dependent upon, an internal machinery of which the striations are the outward evidence. For the details of this the reader is referred to larger treatises.

XII. COMPOSITION OF MUSCLE TISSUE

The average composition of lean muscle may be put in table form:

TABLE VI

Water	75%
Protein	20%
Other nitrogenous material and carbohydrates	2%
Fats	2%
Salts	1%

The chief solid component of muscle is a soluble protein, myosin. The muscle proteins, together with the water and other soluble constituents, can be squeezed, in a liquid form, out of the cooled minced muscle. This liquid, called muscle plasma, on being warmed to the room temperature, undergoes coagulation similar to that of the blood, in that myosin undergoes a change by which it is rendered insoluble and forms myosin fibrin.

The red pigment of the muscle, *myochrome,* resembles the blood pigment (hemoglobin). The principal salt is potassium phosphate; only traces of Na, Ca, and Mg are present. The salts are chemically united with the organic constituents of the muscle. The muscle also contains various enzymes by which the many chemical changes occurring in the muscle are brought about. We have already noted the presence of the carbohydrate, glycogen (from 0.5 to 1 per cent). Among the nitrogenous constituents, exclusive of the proteins, are uric acid, urea, creatin, hypoxanthin, and related bodies (see pp. 398 to 403). In the making of *meat extracts* these compounds, together with the salts, are extracted from the meat. While formerly this extract was regarded as the quintessence of the beef, we now know its food value is practically nil. We have already spoken of the phosphocreatin as the direct source of muscle energy.

Rigor Mortis.—Most of us are familiar with the fact that soon after death the body passes into rigor mortis, the stiffening of death. An excised frog muscle appears translucent and is flaccid and extensible. In dying the muscle gradually loses its irritability and becomes opaque, rigid, and inextensible; these changes are generally attributed to the coagulation of the muscle proteins. Normally as the muscle passes into rigor mortis, there is a disappearance of the glycogen and, pari passu, the formation of lactic acid. The cause of rigor is not well understood. Rigor mortis generally sets in from ten minutes to four or five hours after death and disappears in from one to six days. It begins in the muscle of the jaw and passes successively down the neck, arms, trunk, and legs. When the glycogen is completely removed from a muscle, rigor mortis sets in almost immediately after death; this may account for the sudden rigor in case of prolonged and wasting diseases or of great fatigue just previous to death.

XIII. EFFECTS OF MUSCULAR WORK AND TRAINING

No other factor affects the various functions of the body more profoundly and more frequently than muscle work does.   Indeed, its influence on the heart, respiration, perspiration, appetite, etc., is a matter of common observation.   As even a brief discussion of these effects necessitates some knowledge of the bodily functions concerned, we shall postpone this until we have completed our study of these functions.   At this time we shall focus our attention upon the changes brought about in the skeletal muscles themselves.   The effects of exercise depend, in general, on its intensity and duration.   It must be remembered that exercise causes both an immediate (acute) and a lasting (chronic) effect.   The best recognized chronic effects of exercise on skeletal muscle and muscular work are an increase in size, strength, efficiency, and endurance.

a. Size.—It is a well-known fact that a muscle which is not used undergoes atrophy; it is also equally well known that, under the proper conditions of work, muscles may show a considerable increase in size, as shown by the arm muscles of the blacksmith or the general musculature of an athlete.   The greater size of the trained muscle is *caused by a true hypertrophy of the individual fibers,* and is not due to the appearance of new fibers.   The increased size of the fiber is attributed wholly to an increase in the amount of sarcoplasm present.   An increase in the toughness of the connective tissue which binds the fibers together makes the muscle better able to withstand any additional mechanical demands placed upon it.

b. Strength.—The increase in strength is due chiefly to an increase in the size of the muscle.   But the strength gained by exercise is frequently greater than can be accounted for by this increase in the size of the muscle.   More than one explanation has been offered for this increase in strength; we may picture it as follows:

It will be recalled that the feeble stimulation of a motor nerve generates impulses in but a few of the nerve fibers and as a result only a few of the motor units of the muscle contract; with a stronger stimulus more units are thrown into action and a stronger contraction results.   Sometimes we wish to lift a light object, at other times, a heavier object; it is well known that, because of previous experiences, we gauge the amount of contraction necessary in each case quite accurately, using just sufficient force to lift the object with ease.   The neural impulses for these contractions are the result of the activation of cells in the cerebral cortex of the brain (see Cerebral Hemispheres).   It is possible that when a light object is to be lifted only a few of the cortical cells are activated, and, in consequence, only a limited number of the motor units receive impulses for contraction; on the other hand, when a more powerful contraction is necessary, more motor nerve cells are activated and impulses are sent to more units. Some maintain that under the ordinary conditions of life we can voluntarily, even with our best endeavor, innervate only a part of the motor units of any skeletal muscle. We have heard of the marvelous strength of people under great mental excitement, such as intense fear, religious mania, etc., as also during delirious conditions. It is conceivable that in these unusual states of mind more nerve pathways are activated and hence more motor units are thrown into action.

c. Efficiency.—By increased efficiency we mean that by a trained individual a given amount of work is accomplished with a smaller expenditure of energy than is possible in an untrained individual. For example, Zuntz found that with the bicycle ergometer a person trained for this work had a muscle efficiency of 25 per cent, in contrast with 20 per cent for the untrained. Benedict found in the trained an efficiency as high as 33 per cent; this was never true for the untrained. As common experience teaches us, unaccustomed work is done very inefficiently. The causes of this greater efficiency in the trained lie in:

(1) Finding the proper rate at which the work should be done (p. 111).

(2) This greater economy on the part of the trained man has by some been explained as due to a better coordination of the muscles of the body. In performing a piece of work which is entirely new to us, we are likely to contract too many muscles that are not concerned in the work. By practice we gradually eliminate these useless and extravagant contractions; it is then said that we do the work with greater ease, or that the work is done more smoothly.

(3) By training, the body may rid itself of undesirable fat which impedes the movements of muscles or parts of the body or, as in walking and climbing, adds an unnecessary load and thus causes a greater expenditure of energy.

(4) Efficiency always decreases as fatigue sets in (see next section).

(5) In the trained individual there is an increased efficiency due to more effective circulatory and respiratory adjustments.

d. Endurance.—We are familiar with the fact that the length of time a person can continue a certain piece of work is increased markedly by training. As fatigue increases, endurance is reduced. From our study of muscle physiology it is readily perceived that endurance is governed by the rapidity with which the proper amount of food and oxygen can be brought to, and the waste products removed from, the muscles.

THE AIM OF PHYSICAL TRAINING is (1) the proper and harmonious development of the body during the period of growth. In training, opposing muscle groups should be properly balanced as to length and strength. Inequality in this respect leads to faulty position of various parts of the body with respect to each other, and to inefficiency in action. The training should be of such a nature as to be generally useful to the individual, more especially in rendering him proficient in standing, walking, and running. (2) The object of physical exercise is to maintain the healthy condition of the vital organs. We have pointed out that physical work causes both a histologic change in the organs and an alteration of their functions. However, whether these changes are an asset or a detriment to the individual, and whether physical training aids in building resistance to infection or adds to one's longevity are much debated questions. Nevertheless, it is believed that participation in a regular schedule of exercise promotes a feeling of well-being and increases zest for the more sedentary work which many are compelled to do.

POSTURE.—Lack of training frequently leads to an improper body posture.* A slumped posture displaces the center of gravity of the body and thereby throws more work upon the muscles; this leads to greater fatigue than is experienced in maintaining a correct position in standing and walking. It places extra and unnecessary strain upon the ligaments and may lead eventually, especially in an immature individual, to skeletal deformities. Incorrect posture crowds the walls of the thoracic cavity upon the lungs and thereby interferes with proper breathing. It may also lead to disturbances in the circulation of the blood in the organs of the alimentary canal and in the functioning of these organs.

XIV. CILIA

Location.—Cilia are protoplasmic filaments projecting beyond the free surface of epithelial cells (Fig. 9), which are generally columnar in form; each cell gives rise to from ten to thirty cilia. Ciliated epithelium occurs in many locations, among which we mention the respiratory tract, the eustachian tube (which connects the middle ear with the pharynx), the tear duct and sac, the cavities of brain and cord, and certain parts of the reproductive organs.

---

*The subject of postural tonus is discussed on p. 655.

Action.—By their contractility the cilia sway backwards and forwards. During the forward motion the cilia are rigid, but they are limp during the backward stroke. Their action may be conveniently studied in a pithed frog whose lower jaw has been removed. When a small particle of cork is placed on the roof of the mouth, the swift forward motion of the cilia causes the cork to move downward toward the esophagus. In our body, the dust and mucus are in this manner moved upward in the respiratory tract; in the reproductive organs the ova or the spermatozoa, and the accompanying secretions, are moved along the ducts; in general, the function of the cilia is to move the fluid and suspended matter bathing the epithelium.

CHAPTER VII

CONDUCTIVITY: NERVE PHYSIOLOGY

I. ANATOMY

In the preceding chapter we have seen that the nervous system is constructed of morphologic units, the neurons. The cell bodies of most of the neurons lie either in the gray matter of the brain and spinal cord or in the dorsal ganglia in close proximity to the cord. From many of the neurons a process (either a dendrite or an axon) extends out of the brain or cord by one of the roots (see Fig. 26) and proceeds towards a receptor or effector. Immediately upon issuing from the cord, the nerve fibers are bound together by connective tissue and form a nerve trunk.

The Nerve.—What we ordinarily call a nerve, such as the optic or the sciatic nerve, is a collection of a large number of nerve fibers (Fig. 55). Each fiber is composed of a central core, the axon or axis cylinder (Fig. 56, C), which forms the active part of the fiber; this is surrounded by a rather thick white covering known as the myelin (*myelon*, marrow) sheath, S; enveloping all is a very thin connective tissue membrane, the neurilemma, P. These are known as myelinated, or medullated, nerve fibers. While the neurilemma is an independent living structure formed by nucleated cells distinct from the neuron itself, the dead myelin sheath, on the other hand, is to be regarded as a secretion produced by the axis cylinder. The postganglionic fibers of the autonomic nerves, spoken of in Chap. V, are devoid of the myelin sheath, for which reason they are sometimes called nonmedullated nerves.

II. THE BIO-ELECTRIC PHENOMENA AND THE NERVE IMPULSE

The function of a nerve is the generation of a nerve impulse at the point of stimulation and the propagation of this impulse along the nerve. A nerve has therefore the properties of irritability and conductivity. As far as we have knowledge of the matter, no nerve impulse ever starts spontaneously; the origin of impulses in this manner would be highly destructive to the organism. The impulse is always conducted to another protoplasmic structure which is either a muscle, a gland, or another neuron.

Similar to that in a muscle, the activity of a nerve is always associated with a number of changes. Of these the electric changes were the first to be discovered and are, no doubt, among the most interesting. As the excitation of any piece of protoplasm is accompanied by these disturbances in its electric condition, their basic

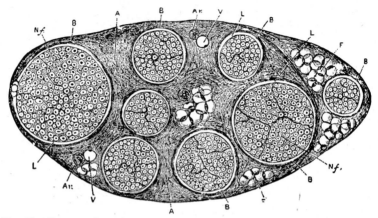

Fig. 55.—Cross section of a nerve trunk. *A*, the connective tissue (epineurium) which separates the nerve bundles from each other; *B*, the perineurium surrounding each bundle; *Nf*, the nerve fibers which are separated by connective tissue known as the endoneurium; *Ar*, artery; *V*, vein; *L*, lymph spaces; *F*, fat. (Harris.)

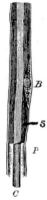

Fig. 56.—A portion of a medullated nerve consisting of *C*, axis cylinder; *P*, neurilemma and its nucleus, *B*; *S*, myelin sheath.

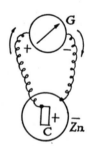

Fig. 57.—Diagram to illustrate the flow of current from the carbon, *C*, of the cell, through the galvanometer, *G*, and to the zinc, *Zn*.

importance in all living matter is obvious. Except in animals, like the electric torpedo and eel, which are equipped with special electric organs, the electrical changes are so feeble that delicate apparatus is necessary in order to detect them.

Difference of Electrical Potential.—According to the electron theory, in a body in its neutral state the electrons (which are the units of negative electricity) of the atom are balanced by the positive charges of the protons. When a body is electrified, it either loses some of its electrons, or it gains electrons from some other source. Between these two bodies, the one with a deficiency and the other with an excess of electrons, there exists a difference of potential. It is conventional to say that the former body is positively charged and has a higher potential than the latter which is said to be negatively charged and to have a lower potential. Because of chemical action, the carbon plate in a dry cell becomes positively charged (loss of electrons) and the zinc plate, negatively charged (gain of electrons). When these two plates are connected by a metallic conductor, the electrons flow from the zinc through the metallic conductor to the carbon. But, it is conventional to say that the current of electricity flows in the outside conductor from the carbon to the zinc (as shown in Fig. 57), and inside the cell, from the zinc to the carbon. An electric current is always, and only, established when two points of unequal electric potential are connected by a complete circuit. The terminal of the carbon plate is called the positive pole, or anode; that of the zinc is the negative pole, or cathode. If the positive and negative poles are connected with a galvanometer (Fig. 57), the current will cause the needle (or whatever other indicator may be used) to move in a certain direction; reversing the direction of the current through the galvanometer causes the needle to swing in the opposite direction. The galvanometer therefore reveals: (1) the presence of an electric current; (2) the direction of the flow; and (3) if properly graduated, the strength of the current. If the electrodes of the galvanometer are both placed on the carbon plate of a cell, there is no deflection of the galvanometer because all points of this plate have the same potential (isopotential); the same is true when the two poles of a run-down (''dead'') cell are tested.

Electric Changes in Tissues.—By the use of appropriate apparatus the following facts regarding the electric potential of tissues have been demonstrated:

1. ISOPOTENTIAL.—When lead-off electrodes of the device for detecting electric potentials (say, a galvanometer) are placed upon the uninjured surface (*b* and *c* in Fig. 58, 1) of a resting nerve, no current is revealed. We therefore conclude that *all the points of an uninjured and resting organ or tissue are isopotential.*

2. CURRENT OF INJURY.—If, however, the electrodes are placed upon a severed nerve in such a manner that one electrode is on the injured and the other on the uninjured surface, the galvanometer shows the presence of a current; this is known as the current of in-

jury. From this we conclude that the injured and the uninjured surfaces are not isopotential; the potential existing between them is called the injury potential. From the indicator we learn that the injured surface is electrically negative towards the uninjured. We may therefore compare the injured tissue to a dry cell; the injured and uninjured are comparable to the zinc and the carbon poles, respectively, in that an electric potential exists between them. When these two points are connected by an outside conductor, an electric current is established. But it must be borne in mind that in the injured tissue there are no electric currents, no more than in a disconnected dry cell. The current of injury is the result of the injury potential when the points of unequal potential are properly connected.

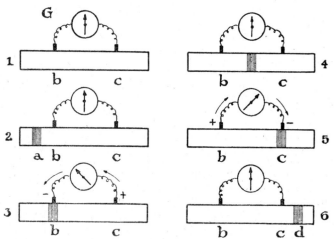

Fig. 58.—Diagram illustrating the action potential and action current.

3. ACTION CURRENT.—To understand readily the electrical changes occurring during the stimulation of a nerve, the reader should follow in order the six diagrams shown in Fig. 58. Let us place the electrodes b and c of the galvanometer, G, upon a stretch of nerve. As this is an uninjured tissue the points b and c are isopotential and the galvanometer shows no change. The nerve is now stimulated at a, resulting in the formation of a nerve impulse (the shaded area). When the impulse reaches b (as shown in Fig. 58, 3) the galvanometer indicates the passage of an electric current; this is known as the action current. From the direction of the movement of the indicator we learn that the active part b is electrically negative toward the inactive part c. The impulse moves onward and reaches a point midway between b and c; the galvanometer assumes its neutral position, showing that b and c are again isopotential. When the impulse ar-

rives at *c*, this part of the nerve is negative toward *b*. The action current is the outward manifestation of the action potential existing between the active and the inactive part of a nerve. We may therefore state: *The active part of a protoplasmic structure is electrically negative toward the inactive part. The action potential and the nerve impulse are inseparable;* where we find the one, there the other is also; and whatever increases or decreases the strength of the impulse, or the velocity with which it travels, causes corresponding changes in the action potential. The electrical nature of the stimulation is not responsible for the generation of the electrical changes in the nerve, for they have also been demonstrated in a nerve mechanically or chemically stimulated.

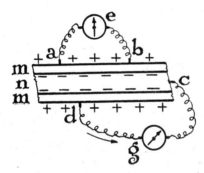

Fig. 59.—Illustrating the injury potential.

Origin of the Injury Potential.—The origin of the above-discussed potential differences is sought in a polarized state of a resting nerve; that is, there is a separation of the positive and negative ions. This segregation is of such a nature that the positive ions collect nearer to the periphery and the negative ions at the center of the nerve (Fig. 59). When the electrodes of a galvanometer are placed on the uninjured surface, *a* and *b*, these two points are found to be isopotential. But if one electrode is placed upon *d*, the uninjured, and the other at *c*, the injured surface, the former point acts as the positive pole and the latter, as the negative pole of the dry cell, and a difference of potential is revealed by the galvanometer, *g*. The injury has nothing to do with the generation of the current or the polarized state of the nerve; it merely allows us to get on the inside of the nerve.

Nature of the Nerve Impulse.—As to the cause of this polarized state of the nerve, the *plasma membrane theory* has many supporters. It will be recalled that semipermeability characterizes this membrane (p. 73). Due to this semipermeability, the positive ions are able to penetrate into and perhaps pass through this hypothetical membrane, *m*, in Fig. 60; the ions of the opposite charge remain on the other side, *n*, of the membrane; this results in a polarized state, or a difference of potential between the two sides of the membrane (Helmholtz's double layer). If in this condition the nerve is stimulated, there is, according to this theory, an *increase in the permeability of the protoplast, mm;* as this allows the previously segregated ions to commingle, *depolarization at the point of stimulation* takes place. The membrane depolarization at *a*, Fig. 60, causes a difference of potential between *a* and point *b*, which is not yet in the active state; this is known as the action potential. If the two points, *a* and *b*, are led off to a galvanometer, *e*, a current (the action current) is found to pass from *b* through the galvanometer to *a*. The depolarization at the point of stimulation is associated with the liberation of energy which is capable of acting as a stimulus for the adjacent portion of the nerve fiber, and this part, in turn, becomes depolarized. Thus in the form of a wave the action potential progresses along the nerve fiber and constitutes the nerve impulse.

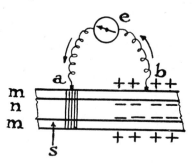

Fig. 60.—Illustrating the action potential.

Soon after depolarization has taken place at *a*, Fig. 60, constructive forces are set to work by which the membranes are restored to their original state of polarization and irritability. The separation of the positive from the negative ions (which always exert an attraction for each other) can be brought about only by an expenditure of energy. As we shall learn in a subsequent paragraph, neural activity is always associated with chemical and thermal changes.

Summary of the preceding discussion:

1. A resting nerve is in a polarized (charged) state, in which all external points are isopotential.

2. The injured part of a nerve is electrically negative toward the uninjured.

3. The active part is electrically negative toward the inactive.
4. According to the above outlined theory:

    a. The first effect of a stimulus is an increase in the permeability of the protoplast.

    b. This leads to a depolarization of the nerve at the point of stimulation and the establishment of the action potential.

    c. This depolarization acts as a stimulus for the adjacent portion of the nerve.

    d. The traveling action potential is the nerve impulse.

    e. The increase in permeability is very soon followed by a recovery period during which the permeability and polarization are brought back to the resting state.

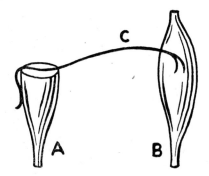

Fig. 61.—To illustrate generation of injury potential.

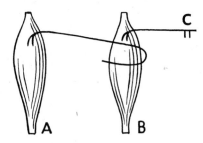

Fig. 62.—To illustrate generation of action potential.

The stimulation of a muscle also results in an action potential. As the action potential precedes, in time, the actual contraction of the muscle, it is associated with the excitatory process which always precedes and induces the mechanical change. When a muscle is repeatedly stimulated so as to cause tetanus, the action potentials correspond in number and rhythm with the frequency of the stimuli, thereby giving evidence of the discontinuity of the excitatory processes taking place in the muscle, notwithstanding that the outward appearance, as registered on the kymograph, gives the impression of a continuous activity. The contraction of the heart is also associated with an action potential; this will be discussed in Chap. X.

Galvani's Experiment.—These potentials can also be demonstrated, without the use of a galvanometer, by means of a nerve-muscle preparation. In Fig. 61, one end of muscle *A* has been cut off. If the nerve, *C*, of another muscle, *B*, is placed so that it comes in contact with both the injured and the uninjured surface of *A*, it establishes a connection between the positive and the negative portions of *A*. As a result of the potential difference between the injured and the uninjured surface of *A*, a sufficient current flows through nerve *C* to stimulate it and thereby cause muscle *B* to contract.

The action potential may be demonstrated by placing, as shown in Fig. 62, the nerve of *A* on muscle *B*. If now nerve *C* is stimulated, muscle *B* by its contraction generates an action potential difference of sufficient intensity to stimulate the nerve of muscle *A*.

By the same method it can also be demonstrated that the heart during its activity creates an action potential. On the exposed heart of a frog, or, better, of a warm-blooded animal, the nerve of a muscle-nerve preparation is properly placed; with each contraction of the heart the muscle gives a single twitch.

III. RELATION BETWEEN THE STIMULUS AND THE NERVE IMPULSE

Frequency of Stimulation; the Refractory Period.—Many of the relations between stimuli and muscle contractions also hold good for nerve tissue. It will be recalled from p. 99 that the onset of the activity of a muscle is associated with a great reduction in irritability. This has also been found to be true for nerve tissue, for if a second stimulus is sent into a nerve within 0.0025 second after the application of the first stimulus, the second stimulus is ineffective. The stimulated nerve loses all its irritability, from *a* to *b* in Fig. 63, for about 0.003 second, and a second stimulus, no matter how intense, is unable to generate an impulse unless the two stimuli are separated by this length of time, which is known as the absolute refractory period. The nerve gradually regains its irritability (relative refractory period, from *b* to *c* in Fig. 63); now a stimulus of greater intensity than the threshold stimulus is needed to evoke an impulse. This period, in a frog's nerve, lasts about 0.02 second. The refractory period follows the moving action potential, and as a result the nerve cannot convey more than 300 impulses per second.

The existence of the refractory period naturally follows from the above-outlined theory of nerve conduction, according to which the irritability of the nerve fiber is its polarized condition and the generation of the impulse, its depolarization. If a stimulus is thrown in during the time that the fiber is still in the depolarized state and before repolarization has taken place, the fiber cannot, of course, be depolarized, and therefore no impulse can be created.

Summation of Subliminal Stimuli.—Although the application of a subliminal stimulus does not generate a nerve impulse, the condition of the nerve is altered, for, if within 0.001 second another subliminal stimulus be applied, a nerve impulse may be formed. This change in the nerve, known as the *local excitatory state,* is not propagated along the nerve, is not followed by a refractory period, nor does it obey the law of all or none, and it rapidly fades away.

Fig. 63.—Curve of irritability of a stimulated nerve. *a,* time of stimulation; *ab,* absolute refractory period; *bc,* relative refractory period.

Adaptation.—Let us suppose that the nerve of a muscle-nerve preparation is stimulated by a galvanic current of uniform and medium intensity for one or more minutes; a single contraction is made at the moment of closing the key, Fig. 36. During the flow of the current no impulse is formed. That this lack of response is not due to fatigue is shown by the fact that the nerve can respond for hours to faradic shocks of the same or even lesser intensity than that of the galvanic current used in this experiment. It is generally said that *the nerve adapts itself to the presence of the constantly flowing current.* The cause of this adaptation is not clear. Not infrequently nerves in the human body are constantly pressed upon, e.g., by tumors, without giving rise to pain or any other response; finally the pressure may become great enough to cause a blocking. Adaptation is especially evident in those instances where the stimulus increases very gradually from zero to a fairly high intensity, Fig. 43.

Influence of Duration and Development of the Stimulus.—The effectiveness of an electric stimulus is also determined by the length of time it acts upon the irritable tissue. As the strength of the current is decreased, the length of time it must act in order to stimulate is increased. This is graphically shown in Fig. 64, in which the ordinates

indicate the strength of the stimulus and the abscissae the length of
time the stimulus must act in order to be effective. The time required
for the strong stimulus, *a*, is very short; for the progressively weaker
stimuli, *b*, *c*, and *d*, the duration gradually increases. A stimulus
of *e* strength, i.e., of threshold value (*1* in Fig. 64) evokes an impulse
only if its duration is relatively long; and a stimulus feebler than the
rheobase strength has no effect, no matter what its duration. This
matter may therefore be stated: *the product of the strength of a
stimulus and the minimal duration are constant;* it expresses the total amount of energy used during the stimulation to produce a result.

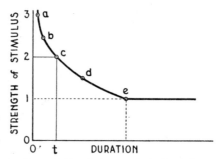

Fig. 64.—To illustrate the relation between the strength and the duration of
stimuli.

The important part played by the duration of a stimulus is well
illustrated by the fact that high frequency alternating current of
less than 0.00,001 second duration has been found to be ineffective
as a stimulus for nerves; in fact, if the shocks are of sufficient rapidity (and of sufficient shortness of duration), their passage through
the body causes no muscle contractions, even though the current is
strong enough to fuse an iron wire. Clearly, a certain length of time
is required to set up in a nerve that change which we call the nerve
impulse, no matter how powerful the stimulus may be. This is, in
general, the characteristic of all stimulations: *the environmental
change must occur with a certain rapidity* (p. 95) *and must operate
for a certain length of time in order to influence the irritable structure.*

Chronaxie.*—The minimal strength of current spoken of in the preceding
paragraph we have already learned to call the threshold stimulus, or rheobase
(*rheo,* flow or current). Arbitrarily choosing a strength twice as great as the
rheobase, Lapicque determined the length of time this current must operate upon
a tissue in order to stimulate it; this duration he called the chronaxie (*chronos,*
time). To illustrate: by experimentation we find the threshold stimulus or rheo-

*Chron′-ak-se.

base, for the sciatic nerve of a frog to be given by a current of about 0.3 volt; to be effective, a current of 0.6 volt (*2 c*, Fig. 64) must act for 0.00,04 second, *ot;* this length of time is its chronaxie.

The chronaxie varies from one tissue to another and the slower acting tissue has the longer chronaxie. Thus, the faster conducting nerve of a mammal has a chronaxie of 0.2 millisecond (0.00,02 second) as compared with 0.4 millisecond of the more slowly acting sciatic nerve and gastrocnemius muscle of a frog. The chronaxie of the very sluggish muscles of a frog's stomach varies from 30 to 100 milliseconds, that of the frog's heart is placed at about 3.5 milliseconds. The chronaxie of the faster acting pale muscles is shorter than that of the slower and darker muscles.

IV. CONDUCTION OF THE IMPULSE

Double Conduction.—A nerve impulse generated in the middle of the course of a nerve spreads in both directions as can be shown by the action potential. Let us suppose a motor nerve is stimulated at *a*, Fig. 65; the impulse formed at *a* spreads to *b*, for not only does

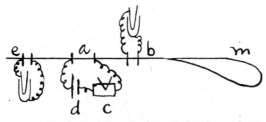

Fig. 65.—Apparatus for determining the law of double conduction: *m*, muscle; *e* and *b*, the electrodes of galvanometer resting on the motor nerve; *a*, electrodes of the galvanic current produced by *d*, the battery; *c*, electric key.

the muscle, *m*, contract, but the galvanometer at *b* shows the passage of an action potential. By means of a galvanometer placed at *c*, it can be shown that the action potential and, therefore, the impulse travels in the opposite direction as well. While any nerve can thus convey the impulse in both directions when stimulated in the middle of its course, it must be borne in mind that in our body nerves are very seldom thus stimulated, being normally stimulated at one end. In the brain or spinal cord the impulses travel, for any great distance, only in one direction; how this is brought about we shall discuss in a later chapter.

Isolated Conduction.—A nerve trunk is composed of thousands of nerve fibers, distributed, it may be, to many organs. When an impulse is generated in a certain fiber which makes connections with a given effector, the impulse in passing down this fiber does not spread to the adjacent fibers in the nerve trunk and thereby innervate other effectors. Without isolated conduction, the coordination of structures depending upon nerve impulses would be an impossibility; for example, the graded contraction of skeletal muscles and the tactile discrimination in the sense organs of the skin (p. 585). It is comparable to an electric cable composed of many wires, in which some insulating material separates them and prevents an electric current which is passing through any one of the wires from escaping to the others. What restrains the impulse from spreading to the other fibers in the nerve trunk is not known.

STIMULUS   TO GALVANOMETER

Fig. 66.—For explanation, see text.

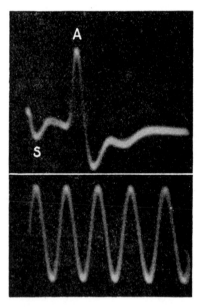

Fig. 67.—Action potential from the sciatic nerve of a frog. *S*, stimulus artifact; *A*, action potential of the fibers which conduct the fastest. Time: 1/1000 second. (Francis, Knowlton and Tuttle: Textbook of Anatomy and Physiology, The C. V. Mosby Co.)

Velocity of the Nerve Impulse.—The velocity of the nerve impulse can be determined by finding the velocity of the passage of the action current along a stretch of nerve. In Fig. 66, the stimulus is applied at the point *A;* the leads of the galvanometer are placed at *B.* On a traveling surface (e.g., a photographic film) both the application of the stimulus and the response by the galvanometer are recorded; below this time is recorded in, say, 1/1000 second. Fig. 67

is a reproduction of such a record; in this S is the record of the stimulation and A, that of the action potential. Noting the time elapsing between the application of the stimulus and the change in the galvanometer and knowing the distance between A and B in Fig. 66, the rate of travel of the impulse can be calculated. The rate varies with the diameter of the nerve fiber; a coarse fiber may conduct at the rate of 100 meters per second, while in the fine, unmedullated fiber the rate is about 0.5 meter per second. The velocity does not vary with the strength of the stimulus.

The coarse fibers in the sciatic nerve of a frog conduct at the velocity from 30 to 43 meters per second; in the thinnest fibers the velocity is about 16 meters. These values for the large medullated nerve fibers and for the fine nonmedullated fibers in mammals are 90 and 1, respectively. Another method for determining the velocity of the nerve impulse is to measure the velocity of the action current which always accompanies this impulse.

Blocking of a Nerve Impulse.—There are many ways in which a nerve impulse may be blocked, that is, prevented from proceeding any farther along the nerve. We have already shown how curare blocks the impulse at the myoneural junction between the nerve and muscle fiber. In the nerve fiber itself this blocking may be caused by cooling a stretch of the nerve to a little below 0° C.; on warming the nerve the conductivity is restored.

The same results can be obtained by applying narcotics, such as chloroform, ether, alcohol, cocaine, etc.; the conductivity returns on removal of the drugs. In the chemical nerve blocking the sensory nerve fibers, especially those conveying the impressions of pain, are affected before the motor fibers. Pressure applied to a nerve may also reduce its conductivity, as is seen in the going "asleep" of a limb when its nerve is pressed upon for any length of time. The removal of the pressure may stimulate the nerve, producing, in the case of a "sleeping" limb, the prickling sensation. Stretching a nerve to a moderate extent may have the same effect as pressure; severe stretching may cause permanent injury.

The "All-or-None" Phenomenon.—The reader will recall that the individual muscle fiber responds to any effective stimulus, irrespective of its intensity, with a maximal contraction. The work of Adrian, Lucas, and other investigators demonstrates that the nerve fiber also follows the law of all-or-none.

Yet it is a common laboratory observation that the stimulation of the sciatic nerve by a shock of low intensity causes a feeble contraction of the muscle and that an increase in the intensity of the stimulus is associated with a more forcible contraction. This finds its explanation in the fact that a feeble stimulus creates an impulse in only a few of the fibers in a nerve. Two reasons can be assigned for this: (*a*) The fibers more centrally placed in the nerve may be out of the physical range of a mild external stimulus and (*b*) all the fibers do not have the same threshold of irritability. A maximum stimulus affects all the fibers in a nerve.

Conduction Without Decrement.—When it is stated that a nerve fiber follows the law of all or none, it must not be inferred that the impulse traversing a particular fiber is always of the same strength. Let us inclose a stretch of nerve, *a* to *b* in Fig. 68, in a glass tube and place upon the nerve the leads of four galvanometers, *1*, *2*, *3*, and *4*. On stimulating the nerve at *s*, all four galvanometers will show the same intensity of potential difference; i.e., the action potential, which we may regard as identical with the nerve impulse, in traveling down the nerve suffered no decrement (waning). If now the nerve inside

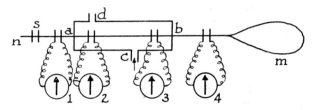

Fig. 68.—For explanation, see text.

the tube be subjected to the fumes of alcohol, the conductivity gradually decreases. Before this is totally lost, let us again stimulate at *s;* the action potential at *1* is of the usual strength, but that shown at *2* and *3* is greatly reduced. However, the intensity of the potential at *3* is the same as that at *2*, showing that the action potential, or impulse, although greatly reduced, is conducted without decrement. When the weakened impulse arrives at *b*, it regains, as shown by *4*, its original intensity. And what was said concerning the strength of the impulse is also true for its velocity. Now Adrian found that the lowest intensity of stimulus applied at *s* able to excite a maximal contraction of the muscle *m*, before the nerve was narcotized, is also the strength necessary when the conduction between *a* and *b* has been reduced to almost the vanishing point. This offers additional proof of the all-or-none phenomenon.

Fatigue.—Whatever chemical changes may take place in an active nerve fiber, these changes are either exceedingly small or there is very speedy and almost complete recovery, for under the usual conditions of stimulation a nerve fiber cannot be fatigued. The indefatigability of a nerve may be demonstrated in the following manner. The sciatic nerve is stimulated at a certain point, and a stretch of nerve between this point and the muscle is cooled in order to block the impulses. The stimulation, at the rate of 10 to 20 per second, is maintained for an hour or more. At the expiration of this time, without any interruption in the stimulation, the nerve is allowed to warm up; and when the proper temperature has been reached, the muscle goes into contraction. This has also been shown by using curare to block the impulse at the myoneural junctions and, after a sufficiently long time of stimulation, removing the block by injecting salicylate of physostigmine.

Energy Requirement.—From the above, it is evident that the amount of energy consumed by the impulse in its passage through the nerve must be exceedingly slight. Evidence for this will be presented on page 137. That this energy is not derived from the stimulus follows from the observation that the impulse, which has been greatly weakened by passing through a partially narcotized stretch of nerve (Fig. 68), is immediately restored to its original strength on reaching the normal nerve. And as it will also be recalled that the impulse is always conducted without decrement, we must conclude that as the impulse travels along the nerve fiber it gathers energy from the nerve fiber itself. This enables the impulse to traverse any length of nerve fiber and to pass into any number of arborizations (as in the skeletal muscle) without losing in strength.

Rhythmicity of Impulse; Impulse Frequency.—From our study of the refractory period it must follow that nerve conduction cannot be a continuous process. When a nerve ending is continuously stimulated, as by pressure applied to the skin or light to the eye, the impulse generated is not a steady uninterrupted event, like a stream of water, but, as shown by the galvanometer, is discontinuous or rhythmical like the bullets from a machine-gun. It was determined by Adrian that *the frequency of the impulse increases with the strength of the stimulus*. The number of impulses passing over the various nerves differs greatly. It is obvious that the maximum number per second is determined by the length of the refractory period. In motor nerves they are found to vary from 10 to 100 per second; in the cutaneous nerves of touch as many as 200 have been registered.

When a sense organ is stimulated by two stimuli, the one of greater, and the other of lesser, intensity, the sensation experienced from the former stimulus is greater, or more intense, than that from the latter stimulus. Yet the sense organ follows the law of all-or-none, and, therefore, the only explanation of why the stronger stimulus gives rise to a more intense sensation must lie in the greater rhythmicity of the impulse.

Nerve Impulse and the Electric Current.—Although the evidence that the nerve impulse is a bio-electrical phenomenon is very strong, it must not be supposed that an impulse is similar to an electric current passing through a wire. From our study, four notable differences between the conduction of an impulse by a nerve and that of an electric current by a wire reveal themselves:

1. The wire is a passive conductor; the nerve fiber is an active agent.

2. The energy of the electric current is derived directly from the battery or some other source of electricity outside the conducting wire. The energy of the nerve impulse is not obtained from the stimulus but from the nerve itself.

3. As the electric current passes along a stretch of wire, its potential gradually declines, due to resistance encountered. The strength of the nerve impulse is maintained at a constant level from an internal source.

4. While the electric impulse travels at the rate of 186,000 miles per second, the velocity of a nerve impulse in man is 100 meters or less.

A Fitting Analogy.—We may, not inaptly, compare the action potential, or nerve impulse, to the spark in a train of gunpowder:

1. Both travel at the expense of energy.

2. This energy is derived from within and not from without, i.e., not from the stimulus.

3. Both are conducted without decrement.

4. The passage of the impulse through a narcotized stretch of nerve is similar to that of a spark through dampened gunpowder.

5. The refractory state of a nerve is comparable to the burned products of the fuse; both the nerve and the fuse must be restored to their former state before an action can again occur.

6. They both follow the law of all or none.

V. INTERCELLULAR CONDUCTION

According to the "membrane theory" discussed in the foregoing pages the nerve impulse is a wave of negativity, or action potential, passing from one part to the neighboring part of the fiber. When this electrical disturbance reaches the end of the neuron, how is the next structure (muscle, gland, or another neuron) influenced by it?

Electrical Transmission.—According to the older concept the transmission across the microscopic gap separating two adjacent protoplasmic structures is by means of electric charges.

Neurohumoral Theory.—According to a more recent view the nerve impulse as an electric phenomenon ceases when the end of the nerve fiber is reached; on arriving at the synapse or myoneural junction it causes the formation of a chemical compound which excites the next structure to activity. The nerve endings have been referred to as microglands, and the compounds have been compared to the hormones secreted by the ductless glands. As most of our knowledge of these humoral mediators is derived from the activity of the autonomic nervous sytem, especially in relation to the heart, we shall postpone our discussion until we deal with these subjects.

VI. CHEMISTRY OF NERVE ACTIVITY

Nutrition of the Nerves.—Entering into the composition of the nerves are especially the *lecithoproteins,* or *lecithans,* which are compound proteins formed by the union of a simple protein with lecithin. Lecithin may be regarded as a phosphorized nitrogenous fat (p. 420).

The nerve fiber, being an offshoot from the cell body, depends for its nutrition upon that cell body. Hence when a nerve trunk is cut, the central ends of the fibers remain normal, but the peripheral ends (the parts no longer attached to the cell body) undergo degeneration. In this process the fat of the lecithins and lecithans of the myelin sheath is set free in the form of droplets which are finally removed by the lymphatics. This process, known as Wallerian degeneration, begins in about three or four days after the nerve has been cut. After some time regeneration sets in. Regeneration begins with increased activity and growth of the neurilemmal cells; this is followed by the outgrowth of the living axons in the central stump which follow the already laid down neurilemmal cells and thus reach, whenever possible, the proper end organ. The myelin sheath is the last to be reformed. As the axons in the brain and spinal cord lack neurilemmal sheaths, no regeneration takes place there.

Chemical and Thermal Changes.—During the activity of a nerve there is a consumption of oxygen, a production of CO_2, and the generation of heat. Oxygen is necessary to maintain the conductivity of the nerve fiber, for in an atmosphere of nitrogen this property gradually disappears, to be restored on the admission of oxygen. Most likely glucose or simple derivatives of glucose are the fuel used by the nerve fiber.

The generation of heat during nerve activity was demonstrated by means of delicate thermopiles from which the electric current was led to a sensitive galvanometer. From the results obtained it has been calculated that a single impulse causes an initial rise of temperature of 0.00,000,01° C.; this is followed by a prolonged recovery phase in which about nine times as much heat is liberated. We may, therefore, conclude that the depolarization of the nerve fiber, i.e., the generation and propagation of the impulse, is associated with but a very limited energy transformation; it is during the restoration of the polarized state that most of the energy is required.

CHAPTER VIII

BLOOD: THE MIDDLEMAN

I. THE INTERNAL MEDIUM

The adjustment of the body to the external environment is largely brought about by the skeletal muscles and their nerve supply—the neuromuscular system. This system secures for the body as a whole the necessary food and by it are mediated almost all of the defense and escape reaction discussed in Chap. I.

The high degree of specialization and coordination admirably fits the neuromuscular system for these functions. But specialization is always accompanied by a loss of other, and frequently vital, functions. Because of this we here meet with a paradoxical situation: The neuromuscular system provides the whole body with food and protects it from deleterious environmental changes, yet the individual cells constituting this system are unable to take up food from the environment or to defend themselves against untoward changes. They have lost the power of digesting the crude food obtained from the outer world. On being removed from the body and exposed directly to the outer environment, they perish in a brief space of time; they are utterly helpless.

In addition to this, these cells are grouped together in masses of considerable size; by this they are withdrawn from the environment and all exchanges of food, oxygen, and waste products between them and the environment are rendered impossible. Moreover, the body is surrounded by a membrane, the skin, which is impervious to practically all materials needed by the cells and to those substances which must be eliminated.

To supply the cells of the internal organs with food and oxygen, to remove their waste products, and to protect them from injurious external conditions, a number of special organs have been evolved which are collectively known as the *vegetative organs.* Thus, food is prepared by the digestive system; oxygen is made available to the body by the respiratory organs; waste products are removed by the organs of excretion. To connect the skeletal muscles and their nerve supply with the vegetative organs in order to be served by them, a carrier has been provided, namely, the blood stream. The blood, however, does not come in contact with the cells; this fluid is always retained within the blood vessels. Each cell of the body is provided with its own diminutive environment, in the form of a layer of fluid—tissue fluid—bathing the entire cell. The products of digestion and the oxygen acquired by the respiratory system are taken up by the blood (absorption) and brought by the circulating blood to all parts of the body. Here these materials pass out of the blood stream into the tissue fluid and thence into the cells. In reverse order, the waste products are carried by the blood from the cells to the lungs and kidneys.

The Internal Environment.—The tissue fluid constitutes the environment for the cells; it is to the individual cell what the external environment is to the whole body. The blood is the middleman between the external and the internal environment, Fig. 69. Together the blood and tissue fluid are known as the internal medium.

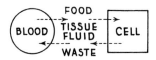

Fig. 69.—Showing relation between blood, tissue fluid, and cells.

Homeostasis.—To serve the cells efficiently and to protect them from injurious internal environmental changes against which they cannot defend themselves, it is necessary to maintain as nearly constant as possible the physical and chemical constitution of the internal medium. Every activity of the body produces many changes in the tissue fluid; the continued functioning of the cells and their very existence demand that these changes be promptly corrected. We may list the most important changes which may befall the internal medium: (1) changes in the concentration of various foods upon which the activity of the cells depends; (2) in the concentration of oxygen; (3) in its chemical reaction, i.e., the concentration of the H and OH ions; (4) in its temperature; (5) in its osmotic pressure; (6) in the concentration of waste products; (7) in its volume; (8) in its colloidal content.

The act of maintaining as closely as possible the constancy of the internal medium has been called by Cannon homeostasis (*homoios,* like; *stasis,* standing); as was remarked above, this is the function of the vegetative organs. The neuromuscular system concerns itself with the external adjustment of the whole body to the environment; the vegetative organs adjust the internal environment to the needs of the external adjustors. In this chapter we shall discuss the composition and some of the properties of the blood and the functions of its cellular components.

II. FUNCTIONS, COMPOSITION, AND PROPERTIES OF THE BLOOD

A. Functions of Blood

The functions of the blood may be stated under three headings:

1. The transporting functions:
   a. Food is carried from the alimentary canal to the cells.
   b. Oxygen is carried from the lungs to the cells.
   c. Waste products are carried from the cells to the organs of excretion.
   d. The heat formed in the more active tissues is distributed to all parts of the body, thereby aiding in regulating the body temperature (p. 245).
   e. The hormones made by the ductless glands (e.g., thyroid, adrenals) are carried to all parts of the body.
2. Aid in maintaining the proper acid-base balance.
3. Immunologic reaction.

B. Composition of Blood

From the above enumerated functions it can be gathered that the blood is a complex fluid containing the food absorbed from the alimentary canal, the oxygen taken up in the lungs, the waste products produced by cellular activity, the hormones, the antibodies, etc. From this it must also be apparent that the composition of the blood varies from place to place and from time to time.

By microscopic investigation it can be seen that what appears to the naked eye as a perfectly homogeneous fluid is in reality a fluid in which float a countless number of small bodies, or corpuscles. By means of the centrifuge we can separate these solids from the liquid, for the corpuscles are considerably heavier than the liquid. The composition of the blood may be stated as follows:

1. Plasma, a light yellow liquid; 50 to 60 per cent by volume.
   a. Water; 90 per cent of the plasma.
   b. Dissolved solids:
      (1) Proteins, forming from 6 to 8 per cent of the plasma: serum albumin, serum globulin, fibrinogen. The last named plays an indispensable part in the coagulation of the blood; it is definitely known to be made in the liver. This last statement may also be true for the two other proteins. The proteins give a certain amount of viscosity and osmotic pressure (colloidal) to the blood.
      (2) Carbohydrates: glucose; amount quite constant at about 0.07 per cent.
      (3) Fats and fatlike substances.
      (4) Salts. Cations in the following descending order: sodium, potassium, calcium, magnesium. Anions: chlorides, bicarbonates, phosphates.

(5) Nitrogenous waste products (urea, uric acid, etc.) and amino acids.

(6) Enzymes.

(7) Hormones, or internal secretions.

(8) Antibodies (p. 163).

   c. Gases: oxygen, carbon dioxide, nitrogen.

2. Solids. From 40 to 50 per cent.

   a. Red blood corpuscles (erythrocytes).

   b. White blood corpuscles (leucocytes and lymphocytes).

   c. Platelets (thrombocytes).

C. Properties of Blood

The amount of blood in the body is generally stated to be about one-twelfth of the body weight. About one-fourth of the blood is in the heart, lungs, and large blood vessels of the thorax, one-fourth in the liver, one-fourth in the skeletal muscles, and the other fourth in the remaining structures of the body. The amount of blood is very constant and is not increased or decreased for any length of time by drinking, injections, or hemorrhage.

The specific gravity of the blood varies from 1.050 to 1.065; average 1.060. By specific gravity we mean the ratio of the weight of a certain volume of a substance to the weight of an equal volume of water. As the specific gravity of the blood depends largely on the amount of hemoglobin, it is much decreased in anemia. The method by which we determine the specific gravity of a small quantity of blood is as follows: A mixture of chloroform and benzol, having a specific gravity of about 1.060, is placed in a cylinder. A drop of blood is added; if the drop sinks, it is heavier than the mixture and a little chloroform is added so as to make the specific gravity of the mixture the same as that of the blood. If the blood floats, it is lighter than the mixture and some benzol must be added. When finally the blood and the mixture have the same specific gravity (determined by the fact that the blood will be stationary) a hydrometer is placed in the mixture, which will indicate by the distance to which it sinks into the fluid the specific gravity.

The osmotic pressure of human blood is equal to that of a 0.9 per cent NaCl solution or about 7 atmospheres (about 100 pounds per square inch). It is due chiefly to the various salts, waste products, sugar, and other crystalloids dissolved in the plasma. The colloids (proteins, for example) found in the plasma also exert a small amount of osmotic pressure which is of great value, as we shall learn later in our discussion of absorption, excretion, and the formation of lymph. As the composition of the blood undergoes continual, though small, changes, because of the passage of water, dissolved foods and waste products into and out of the blood, the osmotic pressure also varies. Such variations, however, are very limited for the body speedily corrects any rise or fall in the concentration of the various constituents of the blood.

Viscosity.—The molecules or particles of a fluid cohere to each other and thereby give rise to the property of viscosity. The viscosity of the blood is about six times as great as that of water. Whatever increases or decreases the number of blood corpuscles or the amount of protein affects the viscosity in the same sense. The degree of viscosity is of importance because the greater the viscosity, the more slowly a fluid flows through a tube and the greater the force necessary for its propulsion.

III. REACTION OF THE BLOOD: HYDROGEN ION CONCENTRATION

Acids and Bases.—From our discussion of ionization it will be recalled that when an acid, e.g., hydrochloric acid—HCl—dissolves in water, the molecules of the acid give rise to positive hydrogen ions, H^+, and negative chlorine ions, Cl^-. When a base such as sodium hydroxide—NaOH—dissolves, the ions formed are a positive Na^+ and a negative OH^- (hydroxyl) ion. All acids are characterized by the formation of H^+ and all bases, by the formation of OH^- ions.

Neutralization.—Let us make a molar solution of HCl by adding 36.5 grams of the acid to one liter of water; if all the acid molecules ionized, a liter of this solution would contain one gram of H^+ ions. Similarly, a liter of a molar solution of NaOH ($23 + 16 + 1 = 40$) has 17 grams of OH^- ions. Now, as we have taken the gram-molecular equivalent of H^+ (one) and of OH^- (17), the number of H^+ in a liter of a molar HCl solution must be the same as the number of the OH^- in an equal quantity of a molar NaOH solution. If these two solutions are mixed, the H^+ and the OH^- ions unite to form H_2O; this constitutes neutralization, for all H^+ and OH^- ions have disappeared (see infra).

Normal Solutions.—The above molar solutions of HCl and of NaOH are known in chemistry as normal solutions. A normal solution of an acid contains in one liter of the solution as many grams of the acid as its molecular weight divided by the number of replaceable hydrogen atoms in the molecules. As this number is one in the case of HCl, the molar and the normal solutions are the same. For a normal sulfuric acid—H_2SO_4—we take $2 + 32 + 64 \div 2$, or 49 grams of the acid; for phosphoric acid—H_3PO_4—the amount will be $3 + 31 + 64 \div 3 = 32.66$ grams. A liter of a normal solution of any acid contains therefore one gram of replaceable hydrogen; a liter of a normal solution of any base contains 17 grams of replaceable hydroxyl—OH^-—ions.

Actual Acidity.—The normal solution of any acid will neutralize an equal quantity of normal solution of any base. But all normal acids are not equally strong. For example, a fourth normal (n/4) HCl has an extremely sour taste and is very destructive to living tissue; n/4 lactic or acetic acid is much milder in its action. This difference depends upon the degree of ionization the acid undergoes. In a given concentration of a strong acid, such as hydrochloric, nitric, or sulfuric, the ionization takes place to a greater extent (i.e., more ions are set free per unit of volume) than in weak acids, such as lactic or carbonic, of the same concentration. For example, if in a certain concentration of HCl the degree of ionization is expressed as 100, the ionization of acetic acid of the same concentration is 0.4.

The same course of reasoning holds for the bases. While normal solutions of all bases have the same power to neutralize acids, the strength of the base depends upon the degree of ionization; this causes sodium hydroxide—NaOH—and potassium hydroxide—KOH —to be much more powerful than calcium hydroxide (limewater)— $Ca(OH)_2$.

The number of H^+ or OH^- ions present gives the actual degree of acidity or alkalinity, respectively; the number of replaceable H or OH (whether in the ionic form or lodged in the undissociated molecule) gives the neutralizing power which is sometimes called titrational acidity or alkalinity.

The Degree of Acidity or Alkalinity.—According to the theory of electrolytic dissociation, some of the molecules of pure water ionize to form an equal number of positive hydrogen and negative hydroxyl ions. The number of molecules thus dissociating is such that a liter (1,000 grams) of water contains 1/10,000,000 gram of hydrogen ions, H^+, and 17/10,000,000 gram of hydroxyl ions, OH^-. This value for the H^+ may be expressed as 10^{-7}.* From this it follows that in 10,000,000 liters of water there is present one gram of hydrogen ions and water is therefore a 0.00,000,01 normal acid; but, as it contains at the same time an equal number of OH^- ions, water is also a 0.00,000,01 normal alkaline solution and hence is a neutral substance. The concentration of hydrogen ions in a neutral solution is designated by cH^{-7} and as the concentration of the hydroxyl ions is equal to that of the hydrogen ions, their concentration is cOH^{-7} and the product of the two is equal to –14. It is customary, for the ease of expression, to transform the concentration of the hydrogen ions into the power of the hydrogen ion by using the symbol pH and

---

*0.00,000,01 $= 1/10,000,000 = 1/10^7 = 10^{-7}$. Pure water has only 1/10,000,000 gram of H^+ ions per liter, yet there are 60,000,000,000,000,000 (6x10^{16}) H^+ ions in 1/10,000,000 gram of water.

placing the exponent without its negative sign behind the symbol: thus cH⁻⁷ equals pH7. As the concentration of the hydroxyl ions under these conditions is also 7, it is evident that pH7 stands for a neutral reaction.

Let us suppose that to a liter of water there be added a quantity of an acid until the concentration of the H^+ is equal to 0.00,000,1 gram, or the cH value is 10^{-6}. But the OH^- in the water will be correspondingly decreased, and, as the sum of the pH^+ and the pOH is always constant at 14, the concentration of the hydroxyl ions will be 10^{-8}. In this solution the power of the hydrogen ions is pH6; this represents a 0.00,000,1 normal acid which is ten times stronger than the pH7. It will be noticed that as the degree of acidity increases, the pH value decreases. The cH value of a 0.01 normal acid solution is cH⁻² or pH2. As pH7 stands for neutrality, a pH value greater than 7 designates an alkaline solution: thus, pH8 is an alkalinity of 0.00,000,1 normal, and pH9 equals 0.00,001 normal alkalinity. We may represent these facts by the scheme shown in Fig. 70.

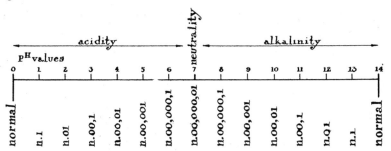

Fig. 70.—Diagram illustrating the hydrogen ion concentrations in normal acid and alkali solutions.

Actual Alkalinity of the Blood.—When sodium bicarbonate, $NaHCO_3$, is dissolved in water, testing with proper indicators (such as litmus) shows the solution to be alkaline. This is due to the interaction of the $NaHCO_3$ and H_2O by which $NaOH$ and H_2CO_3 are formed. The $NaOH$ ionizes freely, giving rise to many hydoxyl ions; the H_2CO_3 dissociates but slightly and few hydrogen ions are formed. The preponderant hydroxyl ions cause an alkaline reaction. This always occurs when a salt of a strong base, such as sodium, and of a weak acid, such as carbonic acid, dissociates in water. Disodium phosphate—Na_2HPO_4—also belongs to this class. It must, however, be borne in mind that only a small amount of the $NaHCO_3$ dissociates, the remainder being present as dissolved, but undissociated, molecules.

These two salts are found in the blood and render it very slightly alkaline. Its reaction is generally stated at pH7.4 which is equivalent to an NaOH solution somewhere between 1/1,000,000 and 1/10,000,000 normal.

Buffers.—If we take 100 c.c. of a 1/1,000,000 normal NaOH and add to it 100 c.c. 1/1,000,000 normal HCl, complete neutralization takes place. But if we take 100 c.c. of blood (which contain the same number of OH^- ions as the 100 c.c. NaOH) and add the above quantity of HCl, the reaction will be found to be practically unchanged. In fact, to neutralize the blood a very large amount of acid must be added. The reason for this is as follows: When a small amount of acid is added to blood or to an $NaHCO_3$ solution, the H^+ ions of the acid unite with the free OH^- ions of the blood; but, as fast as these free OH^- ions are removed from the solution, the $NaHCO_3$ molecules dissociate to form more hydroxyl ions.

The presence of the sodium bicarbonate and basic disodium phosphate therefore makes it possible to add a considerable quantity of acid to the blood without any change in its actual pH value. Because of this power these substances are called *buffer substances,* which someone has likened to "a sponge having the capacity of soaking up either hydrogen or hydroxyl ions." A buffer system may be defined as a solution which contains a weak acid and a salt of this weak acid with a stronger base; three examples of this are solutions containing carbonic acid and sodium bicarbonate, acetic acid and sodium acetate, or phosphoric acid and sodium phosphate. From the above it will be seen that a large amount of acid must be added to a buffer system before all the undissociated alkali (e.g., $NaHCO_3$) is used up and the neutral point reached; the amount of acid needed to bring this about gives the titrational, or total, alkalinity of the blood or sodium bicarbonate solution.

What we have said of the $NaHCO_3$ also holds true for the Na_2HPO_4, but as the latter salt is present in the plasma only to the extent of 0.001 mol, it plays but a small part as compared to the bicarbonate which has a concentration of about 0.03 molar solution. As we shall learn subsequently (p. 326), proteins have the power to unite with either acids or bases and, therefore, are to be classed with the above-mentioned salts; but, because of their low molecular concentration, they are of minor importance. The amount of these substances in the blood is known as the *alkali reserve,* and is equivalent to about a 0.5 per cent sodium carbonate solution.

Acid-Base Balance.—The proper ratio of hydrogen and hydroxyl ions in the blood and body is spoken of as the *acid-base balance.*

Now, because of the ingestion of acid or alkaline foods and because of the production of acids and alkalies in the body itself, there is a constant tendency for the reaction of the body to vary. Such an untoward result is prevented (*a*) by the buffers of the blood, (*b*) by the loss of carbon dioxide from the lungs and (*c*) by the excretion of the excess of acid or alkaline salts by the kidneys. Due to these safeguards the acid-base balance of the blood is a very stable one.

Acidosis; Alkalosis.—The tremendous importance of the proper acid-base balance can be appreciated when we learn that the tissues are highly susceptible to the influence of hydrogen and hydroxyl ions; an exceedingly slight decrease in the pH value of the blood is followed by marked results, such as increased respiration, alteration in the permeability of the plasma membrane and in the character of the protoplasm itself.

A marked reduction in the alkali reserve of the blood is known as acidosis; it is always present in the last stages of diabetes. In severe acidosis coma and finally death may result with a pH 6.95; this, it will be noticed, is but a little on the acid side of the neutral point. On the other hand, a decrease in the hydrogen ion concentration (and therefore an increase in the hydroxyl ions) beyond a pH value of 7.8 causes convulsions and is incompatible with life; this constitutes alkalosis.

IV. RED BLOOD CORPUSCLES OR ERYTHROCYTES

A. Size

The red blood cells in man and nearly all other mammals are biconcave circular disks, Plate I, *B*. There is no nucleus present. The size varies with different conditions but is generally stated to be about 7.7 micromillimeters ($\frac{1}{3200}$ inch).* Because of the similarity in shape and size we cannot distinguish between the corpuscles of man and those of some of the common animals, such as the dog, rat, rabbit, mouse, or ox.

B. Number

The number of the corpuscles is about 5,000,000 per cubic millimeter (0.00,006,1 cubic inch) in the male; in women the number is about 4,500,000; in the newborn infant the count may be considerably higher. Individual variations are by no means small. In 137 healthy men between the ages of nineteen and thirty, the number varied from 4.7 to 6.5 million; in 100 women the variations extended from 4.3 to 5.3 million.

---

*One millimeter = 1/25 inch. A micromillimeter = 1μ = 1/1000 millimeter.

The number is increased when the blood is concentrated by a great loss of fluid from the body through the skin (as after muscular exercise), by the intestines (in diarrhea), or by the kidneys; on the other hand, dilution of the blood by a great influx of liquid (as after a considerable hemorrhage) is associated with a decrease in the number. Whenever there is an interference with the oxygenation of the blood, as in high altitude, the erythrocytes are more numerous. The total number in the body is about 25 trillion, with an area estimated at 3,500 square meters (0.9 acre) which is about 1,600 times the area of the entire body. This enormous amount of surface is of extreme importance in the function of the erythrocytes.

The counting of the corpuscles is done by means of the hemocytometer; for the description of this apparatus and directions for its use the reader is referred to a laboratory manual.

C. Hemoglobin

1. Composition

The characteristic and most important constituent of the red blood cells is a protein, hemoglobin. This is a chromoprotein (*chroma,* color) formed by the union of a protein, globin, and a coloring matter known as *heme.* Heme is widely distributed throughout the plant and animal world. In combination with another compound it forms cytochrome which plays an important part in cell respiration.

2. Function

The hemoglobin of the red blood cells is exceedingly important in the transportation of oxygen and carbon dioxide. When a solution of hemoglobin or blood is shaken with air, the oxygen unites with the hemoglobin, forming **oxyhemoglobin.** This process occurs in the lungs and the oxyhemoglobin gives the *arterial blood* flowing from the lungs its bright red color. If now the oxyhemoglobin is placed under the bell jar of an air pump and the air (and therefore the oxygen) removed from over the solution, oxyhemoglobin decomposes into oxygen and hemoglobin, the oxygen escaping into the air. This is what occurs in the tissues. The tissues, always in need of oxygen and constantly consuming it, take some oxygen from oxyhemoglobin; the *venous blood* leaving the tissues contains, therefore, less oxyhemoglobin and more hemoglobin which renders the color of the venous blood darker. In the tissues the blood also acquires more carbon dioxide which, being taken up to a certain extent by the hemoglobin, is carried to the lungs for excretion. Hence we may consider the carrying of oxygen from the lungs to the tissues and the

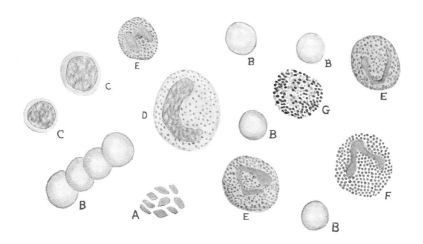

Plate I.—Blood cells. *A*, platelets; *B*, erythrocytes; *C*, lymphocytes; *D*, monocyte; *E*, neutrophiles; *F*, eosinophile; *G*, basophile. (Francis, Knowlton, Tuttle: Textbook of Anatomy and Physiology, The C. V. Mosby Co.)

carrying of carbon dioxide from the tissues to the lungs as the two great functions of the hemoglobin and of the red blood cells. For these reasons hemoglobin is sometimes spoken of as the *respiratory protein;* see Chap. XIII.

3. Amount of Hemoglobin

As the hemoglobin supplies the tissues with oxygen, it is very important that a sufficient quantity of this protein be present in the blood. The relative amount is determined by an apparatus called the hemoglobinometer, or hemometer, of which several kinds have been devised. In all of them the color of a small sample of blood, or of blood diluted with a certain volume of a liquid, is compared with a standard color scale; the depth of the color indicates the amount of hemoglobin. If the color of a sample of the blood or of the diluted blood is such as we find in blood containing the normal amount of hemoglobin, the hemoglobin content of that sample is said to be 100 per cent. It will be noticed that by this method we obtain not the actual but only the relative amount of hemoglobin; the actual amount is stated at 16 grams per 100 c.c. of blood in men and about 14 in women. At birth the hemoglobin content may be very high (23 grams); this speedily drops to a lower level of from 10 to 12 grams.

Anemia.—When there is a marked deficiency in the number of red blood cells and/or the amount of hemoglobin, the condition is known as anemia (*a*, without; *aima,* blood). The blood is then unable to unite with the required amount of oxygen (anoxemia) and as a result active muscles do not receive all the oxygen needed in their catabolism; this decreases the liberation of energy. Anemic persons are for this reason deficient in physical strength, exhibit great shortness of breath, and speedily fatigue; their power of resistance to adverse conditions is lessened; mental work is difficult. Such conditions are observed, e.g., in hookworm infestation and in malaria.

D. Life History of the Red Blood Cells

Destruction of the Red Blood Cells.—Like all cells, the corpuscles grow old and decrepit. When they have reached a certain stage, they are broken into fragments in the blood stream. The whole corpuscle or its fragments are disposed of by phagocytosis of the macrophages (see p. 156), especially in the red bone marrow and spleen (Fig. 219). In these macrophages (*macros,* large; *phagein,* to eat) the red blood cells are chemically destroyed and the hemoglobin set free. The hemoglobin is broken up into globin and heme, and this last compound is still further decomposed into iron and a product known as bilirubin. The bilirubin is carried to the liver to be excreted with the bile, and thereby gives the bile its golden yellow color. The iron is stored in the liver, spleen, and **red bone marrow,** and is used again in the formation of new corpuscles. As to the extent to which the spleen participates in the destruction of the red blood cells there is at present much controversy.

That the destruction of the red blood cells and the decomposition of the hemoglobin can take place in many other tissues of our body is evidenced by the discoloration of a bruised part. In a bruise the blood escapes from the ruptured blood vessels and the gradual destruction of the hemoglobin gives rise to a series of compounds which cause the many shades of blue, green, and yellow.

How long the red blood cells live is not definitely known. It is generally placed at from three to eight weeks. From the amount of bile pigments excreted, it has been calculated that from 500 million to one and a half billion are destroyed daily.

Formation of Red Corpuscles.—As the number of corpuscles is fairly constant, a new supply must be made each day. In the fetus the liver and spleen are the chief centers for the formation of the red blood cells (hemopoiesis). But gradually this function is taken over by the red bone marrow. In the young child all bone marrow is red, but in the adult the marrow in the shaft of the long bones (femur, humerus, e.g.) is transformed into white, or fat, marrow. In the ribs, sternum, certain bones of the skull, and in the ends (epiphyses) of the long bones we find red marrow. In the red marrow certain large colorless cells, the erythroblasts (*blastos*, a germ) acquire the pigment heme, lose their nuclei, and are then poured into the circulation. The hemoglobin is, most likely, made by the bone marrow, although some contend that the liver may play a part in this.

It is generally stated that in an emergency, as in severe hemorrhage, the liver and spleen may again take up the hemopoietic function. The extirpation of the spleen leads to temporary anemia. By some this is attributed to the loss of a considerable amount of stored-up iron; others hold that the spleen plays a more important function. In the following section we shall speak of the substances and agencies concerned in the formation of red blood cells.

Hemorrhagic Anemia.—In a laboratory animal anemia may be established by repeated bleeding. This the body strives to counteract in three ways:

1. Absorption of Tissue Fluid.—Immediately after the hemorrhage there is an influx of water and salts from the lymph spaces

and vessels into the blood. As we shall see in another chapter, this is necessary in order to keep up circulation. By this inpouring of water, the blood is much diluted, and the specific gravity and the red blood cell count are reduced. Incidentally it may be noted that this migration of water also explains the great thirst experienced after an extensive hemorrhage.

2. THE SPLEEN.—The loss of a large volume of blood is followed by a marked contraction of the spleen. The muscles in the spleen capsule are stimulated by the lack of oxygen and by a demand for more oxygen carriers, as in severe muscular work, carbon monoxide poisoning, asphyxiation, and living at high altitude. This organ must be looked upon as a *storehouse for red cells,* and by its constriction a large number of previously noncirculating red cells are thrown into the blood stream.

3. RED BONE MARROW.—Soon the activity of the red bone marrow is greatly increased. The red marrow in the long bones which is normally confined to the epiphyses encroaches upon, and replaces, the fat marrow in the shaft. The stimulating agency is, no doubt, the decreased oxygen tension in the blood. The amount of iron normally present in the marrow is decreased.

4. THE SPLEEN AND LIVER are said to resume their hemopoietic function.

Several weeks may elapse before the blood count is normal. Whipple found that the nature of the diet has little influence on the formation of red blood cells, except that the eating of liver or kidney markedly increased it and that milk, in this respect, is the poorest possible food.

Nutritional Anemia.—Inasmuch as iron is the characteristic and functionally indispensable component of hemoglobin and as iron is gradually eliminated from the body by the kidneys and alimentary canal, it is obvious that a diet deficient in this element must tend to anemia. Now, milk contains merely a trace of iron (0.0002 per cent), and it is therefore not surprising that young rabbits or rats on a diet of whole milk soon show a marked decrease in the hemoglobin content of the blood. This nutritional anemia was found by Elvehjem and his co-workers not to be amenable, as we might expect, to the administration of iron; but the addition of iron oxide plus a minute quantity of copper sulfate to the milk was followed within six weeks by an increase in hemoglobin from the low anemic level of 2.7 grams hemoglobin per 100 c.c. of blood to 13.3 grams.

As to the specific rôle of these two elements, it was found that with the addition of iron salt only to the ration of milk the amount of iron deposited in the liver and spleen was greatly increased, although the amount of hemoglobin was not affected; if now the iron was discontinued, the administration of copper sulfate led to a mobilization of the stored iron in the liver and spleen and to an increase in the hemoglobin. It has been suggested that the copper aids in the conversion of the absorbed iron into hemoglobin. As both iron and copper are found in very insufficient quantities in milk, used as an exclusive diet this food may lead to anemia. The ordinary diet, however, contains sufficient amounts of both elements.

Pernicious Anemia.—This form of anemia interests us because until recently it was inevitably fatal and because of the brilliantly successful experiments conducted by physiologists and physicians to stay its ravages. Based upon the above-described liver-feeding experiments, it was discovered that the daily consumption of one-fourth to one-half pound of liver caused the blood count to approximate the normal with astonishing rapidity. Subsequent to this,

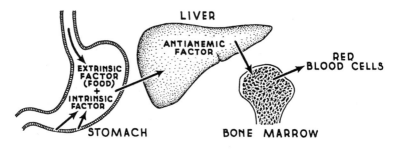

Fig. 71.—To illustrate the anti-anemic factor.

Sturgis and Isaacs found that dried hog stomach has the same beneficial effect as liver. Castle, in 1929, discovered that very favorable results are obtained by feeding the patient beef muscle which had been digested by normal human gastric juice, but not when the beef had been acted upon by the gastric juice of a person ill with pernicious anemia. There are, therefore, two factors concerned: an extrinsic factor found in the food and an intrinsic factor made in the pyloric end of the stomach (see Fig. 71) and perhaps in the duodenum. Here are located certain peculiar cells, sometimes referred to as the pyloric gland organ; these cells are absent in case of pernicious anemia. As to the nature of these two factors nothing can be definitely said. By their interaction an anti-anemic agent, known as hemopoietin,* is formed; this is carried to, and stored in, the liver, to be transferred to the blood-forming organs as needed. The anti-

*Hem-o-poi-e′-tin.

anemic principle has been isolated from the liver. It relieves the anemic condition but offers no cure; consequently the treatment must be continued indefinitely.

The utilization of the iron in the food and its functions in the animal body will be dealt with in Chap. XX.

E. Hemolysis and Crenation

Hemolysis.—Hemoglobin is readily soluble in dilute salt solutions and, therefore, in the plasma; but notwithstanding this solubility the hemoglobin remains in the red blood corpuscle. By various means we are able to drive the pigment out of the corpuscle. When a drop of blood is placed on a glass slide and diluted with four or five drops of physiologic salt solution (0.9 per cent NaCl), we are not able to see through it; the mixture is opaque. But a drop of blood diluted with four or five drops of distilled water or 0.3 per cent sodium chloride solution becomes transparent because these media, in a manner to be described presently, liberate the hemoglobin which then dissolves in the surrounding water; this solution of hemoglobin is transparent. It is generally believed that the red blood cell is a saclike structure. The plasma membrane, which encloses the more or less fluid material composed of water, salts, hemoglobin, etc., possesses a certain degree of semipermeability which allows some substances (water, urea, ammonia salts, glucose, amino acids) to pass through, but bars other compounds, such as hemoglobin and sodium, potassium, calcium, and magnesium ions. The fluid material enclosed in the membrane exerts an osmotic pressure equal to that of the plasma, or a 0.9 per cent NaCl solution.

On placing the corpuscles in pure water or in a 0.3 per cent NaCl solution, the greater osmotic pressure in the cell draws the water from the surrounding medium and thereby increases the volume of the cell. This either stretches the membrane and thus increases the permeability to such an extent that the hemoglobin molecule is able to pass out into the surrounding fluid, or the internal pressure ruptures the membrane and the cell contents escape. This process is called laking the blood, or more specifically, *osmotic hemolysis*. From the above it is evident that in supplementing a reduced volume of blood, as in hemorrhage, a salt solution isosmotic with the blood must be used—a 0.9 per cent NaCl. Although the red blood cell has an osmotic pressure equivalent to that of a 0.9 per cent NaCl solution, extensive hemolysis does not take place until the pressure of the surrounding fluid is reduced to that of a 0.47 per cent NaCl solution, for a certain amount of water must enter the cell before the pressure is sufficiently great to rupture the membrane. Some corpuscles become laked at a little higher and some at a lower osmotic pressure (0.35 per cent NaCl); this depends, it seems, upon the age of the corpuscle whose membrane becomes weaker with age; thereby the fragility of the cell is increased.

Crenation.—When blood is placed in a solution of greater osmotic pressure than that of a 0.9 per cent NaCl solution, water leaves the corpuscles; as a result the cells shrink and shrivel—a condition known as *crenation,* Fig. 72.

Corpuscles placed in a solution of urea or ammonium chloride having an osmotic pressure greater than that of a 0.9 per cent NaCl solution do not undergo crenation, but are hemolyzed. As the protoplast of the corpuscle is not injured, we must conclude that the membrane is permeable to the molecules of these substances and, therefore, their solutions behave like distilled water.

1   2   3   4   5

Fig. 72.—*1,* Normal red blood corpuscle; *2, 3, 4,* and *5,* various stages of crenation.

Fig. 73.—Hemin crystals. (Frey.)

CHEMICAL HEMOLYSIS.—Laked blood can also be produced by fat-dissolving agents, such as ether and chloroform, which by dissolving the lecithin destroy the integrity of the membrane and liberate the hemoglobin. Alcohol, bile salts, saponin, and snake and spider venom also have hemolytic power. Freezing and thawing may lake the blood. The toxins produced by certain bacteria, and the parasitic organism of malaria (which enters and destroys the red blood cells) are also able to cause hemolysis.* The liberated hemoglobin is either transformed into bilirubin by the spleen (p. 360) and excreted with the bile by the liver, or it is treated as a foreign protein and rapidly eliminated by the kidneys.

*In this connection the paragraph on lysins, p. 165, should be read.

Carbon monoxide, a gas found in ordinary illuminating gas, in the fumes escaping from leaking coal stoves and furnaces, and in the exhaust from gas engines, by its great affinity for hemoglobin expels the oxygen from the oxyhemoglobin. The tissues not receiving any oxygen are asphyxiated, and death may result. The compound formed by the union of CO and hemoglobin is known as carboxyhemoglobin and has a very bright red color.

Hemin Crystals.—When hemoglobin or dry blood is heated with a few drops of glacial acetic acid, and, if necessary, a small crystal of NaCl, there are formed yellowish, microscopic crystals, called hemin, or Teichmann's crystals, Fig. 73. These crystals of hemin, which is the hydrochloride of heme, are very characteristic of blood and, therefore, furnish us with a *reliable and delicate test for blood*. However, this test does not enable us to differentiate between the blood of man and that of the lower animals.

V. THE WHITE BLOOD CORPUSCLES OR LEUCOCYTES

Classification.—According to their size, granules, staining reactions, and the number and shape of their nuclei, the leucocytes are divided into the following classes:

1. *Granular Leucocytes, or Granulocytes* (subdivided into neutrophil, *E*, Plate I, eosinophil, *F*, and basophil or mast cells, *G*). These are the most numerous, constituting 70 to 73 per cent of all the leucocytes; their number increases in many infectious diseases.

2. *Lymphocytes.*—These nongranular leucocytes, *C*, are the next most abundant—20 to 25 per cent. They have about the same size as the red blood cells.

3. *Monocytes, D,* are considerably larger than the lymphocytes, are also nongranular and constitute about 4 per cent of the total number of leucocytes.

Function.—The salient feature of the neutrophilic granulocytes and monocytes is their power of ameboid movement and of phagocytosis. Their amebic power enables them to pass through the walls of the capillaries and into the tissue spaces. This process is known as diapedesis (*dia,* through; *pedao,* to leap), for which reason they are sometimes called the wandering cells. The cause of the diapedesis of the white blood corpuscles when an infection has taken place is generally sought in chemotactic, or chemotropic, influence. When a capillary tube filled with physiologic salt solution is introduced beneath the skin of a frog, nothing noteworthy takes place. But a tube filled with a solution of the extract of bacteria soon swarms with leucocytes. The diffusion through the tissue spaces and capillary walls of the bacterial compounds or of substances formed by the destruction of tissue seems to orientate the leucocytes so that by their ameboid movement they are brought to the source of the diffusion. This is known as positive chemotaxis or chemotropism (*tropos,* turning). A tube filled with quinine repells the leucocytes—negative chemotaxis. It is generally held that the leucocytes perform their functions only after they have left the blood stream, that is, in the tissues. This function is largely a matter of engulfing various forms of particulate matter. It is by **phagocytosis** that the granulocytes and the monocytes defend the body against invading bacteria, for after being ingested the microorganisms are digested by the ferments present in the white blood cells. Normally the ability of these cells to engulf bacteria is not very great; but in case of an infectious disease there are formed certain substances, known as *opsonins,* by which the bacteria seem to be prepared to be phagocytosed by the granulocytes. It may be noted that the action of the opsonin is specific; that is, it prepares only that kind of bacterium to which the blood has been rendered immune.

The phagocytic function of the leucocytes and, in general, the resistance that the body offers to the onslaught of the bacteria is lessened by several factors, among which we may mention exposure to extreme heat or cold, starvation, worry, loss of sleep, local infections (of teeth, tonsils, etc.), and wasting diseases, such as diabetes and cancer, and alcoholism. The function of those leucocytes which do not exhibit ameboid movements is not well understood.

Many other functions have been ascribed to the leucocytes, among which we briefly mention:

1. They are said to aid in fat absorption from the intestines.

2. Under proper conditions they produce immune bodies (to ''fix'' or neutralize toxins) and bacteriolysins for the extracellular destruction of bacteria.

3. They aid in the repair of injured tissue. Carrel discovered that the lymphocytes produce from the food material found in the plasma certain substances, called *trephones,* needed by the regenerating connective and epithelial tissues for repairing damages sustained.

Macrophages.—Many cells other than the white blood cells possess the power of phagocytosis; collectively they are called macrophages. Some are fixed cells and therefore incapable of ameboid movement; they are frequently called histiocytes (*histos,* tissue) or ''resting wandering'' cells. Other macrophages have the power both of ameboid movement and phagocytosis. The free and fixed phagocytic macrophages are found in many locations: in loose connective tissue, the spleen pulp, the liver where certain forms are known as the Kupffer cells, bone marrow, lymph nodes, and the alveoli of the lungs.

The granulocytes, monocytes, and macrophages engulf not only bacteria but almost any other particulate matter of small dimensions. When a tissue has been broken down to a certain extent by a pathologic process, these cells engulf and remove the cellular detritus. This also happens in the metamorphosis in lower animals, as in the absorption of the tail of a tadpole. The worn-out red blood cells or the fragments of their disintegration also are thus disposed of.

The number of leucocytes is stated at from 5,000 to 7,000 per cu. mm., but the number is quite variable. The number is greatly increased by strenuous physical exercise (as high as 35,000), in certain emotional stresses, and in pain. This increase, known as activity leucocytosis, is only an apparent increase; it is due to the washing of the corpuscles out of stagnant pools into the active circulation. A real increase, called inflammatory leucocytosis, occurs during infectious diseases; the importance of this is evident.

Life History of the White Blood Corpuscles.—It is not known where these cells are destroyed, and in regard to their formation there is also some uncertainty. We may briefly state:

1. The lymphocytes and monocytes are made in lymphoid (adenoid) tissue of the lymphatic glands, tonsils, spleen, thymus, etc.

2. The granulocytes are formed in the red bone marrow. According to some investigators, all the various forms of colorless blood cells are derived from one common form, but most authors hold that the individual forms have separate and independent origins and also distinct functions.

VI. PLATELETS OR THROMBOCYTES

The platelets, or thrombocytes, are generally regarded as spherical or oval bodies, 3 micromillimeters in diameter, nucleated, and capable of ameboid movements, Plate I, *A*. The number is stated at about 500,000 per cu. mm. They play a very important part in the coagulation of the blood, as is shown by the fact that the coagulability varies as the number of platelets. When there is a great diminution of these bodies, the blood coagulates slowly. On leaving the blood vessels, they rapidly agglutinate, or clump, and break to pieces. It is generally held that the platelets are formed in the red bone marrow, but Howell has presented evidence for their formation in the lungs.

VII. COAGULATION

It is a familiar fact that shortly after the blood leaves the blood vessels it undergoes a marked change which we call clotting, or coagulation. The clotting of blood escaping from a ruptured vessel is of the greatest importance in stemming a hemorrhage.

A. Formation of Fibrin

If a drop of freshly drawn blood is placed upon a slide and observed with a microscope, it will be found that delicate threads, or fibrils, are rapidly formed throughout the whole drop. When a beaker of freshly drawn blood stands for a few minutes, a meshwork of these fibrils entangles the red blood corpuscles and encloses the liquid part of the blood; the whole volume of blood is jellylike and clings to the walls of the vessel, so that the dish may be inverted without the contents being spilled. Soon this jelly begins to shrink and to press out of itself a slightly yellowish fluid; the shrinkage continues for some time, forming more and more of the fluid. This fluid is called *serum,* and the solid floating in the serum is called the clot, or coagulum. Suppose that instead of letting the blood stand quietly in a dish, we whip it with a bunch of rods or wires, or with our fingers. Instead of obtaining one solid lump, the wires become covered with a mass of stringy material having a red color; the vessel contains a liquid known as *defibrinated blood.* On washing the stringy material thoroughly in a stream of water, a white fibrous material is obtained which, by the Millon test (p. 327), can readily be proved to be a protein. This protein is known as *fibrin.* As there is no fibrin in the blood, two questions present themselves: What is the origin of the fibrin and what causes its appearance?

B. Source of Fibrin

The red and white blood cells contribute no material to the fibrin; for after their removal the remaining fluid can be caused to coagulate. The fibrin must, therefore, originate from some of the proteins of the plasma, namely, serum albumin, serum globulin, and fibrinogen. Various proteins in solution can be separated from each other by dissolving in the solution a certain quantity of neutral salts, such as sodium chloride, ammonium sulfate, or magnesium sulfate. In this manner the fibrinogen is obtained in a fairly pure condition. The precipitated fibrinogen can be redissolved in a dilute salt solution and under proper conditions will coagulate; that is, the fibrinogen, which was soluble in the dilute salt solution, is rendered insoluble. It is this transforming of a soluble into an insoluble protein that constitutes the important changes in the coagulation of any protein material. *Coagulation of the blood is the changing of the soluble fibrinogen into the insoluble fibrin.*

C. Factors in Coagulation

Although much has been learned concerning the mechanism of blood coagulation, our knowledge is still far from complete. Blood coagulation is an exceedingly complex phenomenon in which several factors are involved and which can be accelerated or retarded in many ways. We shall very briefly state Howell's theory. This, however, is only one of a score of theories which have been proposed, and objections have been raised against it; but our space is too limited for any discussion.

Coagulation may be considered as a twofold process: (1) the formation of an active agent, and (2) the activity of this agent by which fibrin is formed. According to Howell's theory, the blood normally contains five ingredients concerned in coagulation, namely, fibrinogen, prothrombin, antiprothrombin, calcium salts, and platelets. In the circulating blood the antiprothrombin is united with the prothrombin; this renders this last-named substance inactive. On leaving the blood vessels, the platelets break up and thereby liberate a material called thromboplastin; this unites with, or neutralizes, the antiprothrombin and thereby liberates the prothrombin. By the action of the calcium salts the prothrombin is converted into the active agent known as thrombin (*thrombus,* clot). This constitutes the first phase of coagulation. The real coagulation consists of the action of thrombin (also known as the fibrin ferment) upon the fibrinogen; by this the fibrinogen is rendered insoluble and forms fibrin.

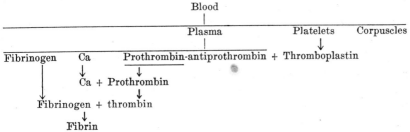

Vitamin K.—Another factor recently added to the already complex process of coagulation is the influence of vitamin K. It was discovered that certain animals, e.g., the chick, placed on a diet free of this vitamin show a great deficiency in prothrombin and therefore in the coagulability of the blood. Supplying these animals with the vitamin restored the prothrombin to its normal amount.

Prothrombin is manufactured by the liver, but this seems to be impossible in the absence of vitamin K. This conclusion is based

upon the following: in obstructive jaundice, which is associated with
a decreased coagulability of the blood, the bile made by the liver
cannot enter the intestine. Here the bile is needed for the absorption
of fats and fat-soluble substances (p. 361) from the intestines into
the blood. Vitamin K is a fat-soluble substance and therefore cannot
be absorbed in jaundice; this is now regarded as the cause of frequent fatal hemorrhages seen in new-born babies. Man and certain
animals do not require this vitamin in their food; it is made for them
by the bacterial action in the intestines. Substances having activities
similar to vitamin K and soluble in water have been prepared synthetically.

Coagulation time is the length of time required for coagulation
to set in after the blood has left the vessel. This varies somewhat
in different individuals, but five minutes may be regarded as the average. It sometimes happens that the blood clots in the usual length
of time, but the clot is too soft (lacking in firmness) to adhere to
the bleeding surface. It is then necessary to determine the *bleeding
time* by puncturing the skin and applying to it at regular intervals
a piece of filter paper and noting the length of time elapsing before
the paper is no longer stained with blood. The average bleeding
time is about 2½ minutes.

The Prevention of Coagulation.—It is sometimes desirable, for
experimental or practical purposes, to delay or prevent coagulation.
Of the various methods we may mention the following:

1. Cooling the blood to near the freezing point. This, no doubt,
inhibits the union of the various agents in the formation of thrombin.

2. By the precipitation of calcium salts, for example, by sodium
oxalate. If the blood flowing from a severed vessel is caught in a
solution of sodium oxalate, it remains liquid indefinitely. By adding
to such oxalated blood, or oxalated plasma, a quantity of calcium
chloride a little greater than that needed to offset any excess of sodium oxalate previously added, coagulation sets in very promptly.
Sodium citrate has much the same effect. In the indirect method of
blood transfusion, the blood of the donor is prevented from clotting
by adding a small quantity of sodium citrate solution before it is introduced into the recipient.

3. Hirudin.—From the head of a leech a substance, hirudin, can
be extracted which prevents coagulation of dog's blood for twenty-
four hours; hirudin is regarded by some as antithrombin which in-
activates the thrombin as soon as it is formed. Some snake venoms
act in a similar manner.

4. HEPARIN.—From the liver Howell obtained a very effective anticoagulating substance, heparin. This he regards as identical with antiprothrombin, and prevents the formation of thrombin. Some hold that heparin also has antithrombin activity.

5. ROUGH SURFACE.—One of the most striking factors favoring coagulation is the contact of the blood with a rough surface. If blood is collected, with due precautions, into a paraffined dish and covered with a layer of oil, coagulation is prevented for a considerable length of time. A drop of this blood taken out and thrown upon a rough surface coagulates immediately. It is supposed that the smooth surface prevents the breaking up of the platelets and hence the formation of thrombin is delayed.

Stopping a Hemorrhage.—It must be evident that bleeding can be stopped in two distinct ways:

A. By the coagulation of the blood a plug may be formed which prevents the escape of the blood. The process may be hastened by:

1. Contact of the blood with a rough surface; hence placing a sterile towel or piece of bandage on the wound aids in stopping the flow of blood.
2. A moderately high temperature. Applying cloths wrung out in hot physiologic salt solution to the bleeding (oozing) surface is a great aid in stopping the hemorrhage.
3. By the local application of thromboplastic material found in tissue juices.
4. Seegers has prepared a thrombin of great potency. Sprayed onto a profusely bleeding surface, it caused a cessation of bleeding in 5 seconds, or less.

B. Bleeding may be controlled by preventing, or at least lessening, the flow of blood to the injured vessel. This can be done by:

5. The local application of adrenalin which, as we shall see subsequently, causes the blood vessels to constrict (pp. 231 and 488).
6. When the bleeding is too violent for the clotted blood to remain in place, packing and tight bandaging may occlude the bleeding vessels and furnish a nidus for the coagulation. Bleeding from large severed vessels which cannot be controlled by coagulation must be checked by hemostats or ligatures.

Intravascular Coagulation or Thrombosis.—That coagulation can take place in the body during life is demonstrated by introducing a foreign body, e.g., a rough needle or thread into the blood vessel: a coagulum is formed upon the object. Or when a blood vessel in the

body is crushed or injured by bacteria so as to damage the endothelium, the rough surface thereby created may cause a clot to be
formed on the wall of the vessel during life. Such a clot, known as
a *thrombus,* may remain attached to the walls of the vessels or to
the valves and block the blood stream. The thrombus may break loose
(*embolus*) and be carried to a distant part of the body there to interfere with the circulation of the blood. These emboli may also be
slowly absorbed (dissolved).

As to why coagulation normally does not take place in the vascular system, several views have been expressed, depending largely on
which theory of coagulation is favored. Eagle lays great stress on
the preservation of the platelets. According to his view, the platelets
in the normal circulating blood are stable and do not liberate thromboplastin; no anticoagulating agency is necessary. Howell, on the
other hand, holds that the always present antiprothrombin prevents
the liberation of prothrombin by any small amount of thromboplastin
which may be formed by the limited breaking up of platelets in the
circulating blood. It is only in the shed blood that enough thromboplastin is liberated to offset the inhibiting influence of the antibody.

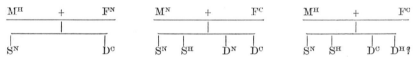

Fig. 74.—Diagram to illustrate the inheritance of hemophilia. M = male;
F = female; S = son; D = daughter; H = hemophiliac; C = carrier; N = normal.

Hemophilia is the abnormal condition in which the coagulation
time and/or the bleeding time are very much prolonged. In this condition bleeding about the teeth, into the stomach, etc., may take place.
It may also be responsible for the appearance of blue and black areas
when the skin has been but slightly bruised. In a hemophiliac, or
bleeder, a trivial cut may result in serious bleeding. The cause of
hemophilia is generally said to lie in the too great stability of the
platelets which prevents the liberation of thromboplastin. Various
treatments for hemophilia have been suggested. Some have advocated
the use of the venom of certain vipers. Purified thrombin has been
used with good results.

Hemophilia is hereditary and, although females are very seldom,
if ever, bleeders, the disease is transmitted only through the mother
to her sons. A hemophilic man marrying a nonhemophilic woman
will therefore have no hemophilic children, but the daughters will
be carriers of this disease and transmit it to half of their sons, and
half of their daughters will be carriers—see Fig. 74.

VIII. ANTIBODIES

Bacteria, molds, and protozoa on entering the body may cause harm either by the formation and liberation of poisonous compounds, generally known as toxins, or by the actual destruction of the cells and tissues of the body; as examples of the former we may mention diphtheria and smallpox, of the latter, leprosy. To defend itself against the onslaught of these microorganisms the body employs two distinct methods: the cellular and the humoral. The cellular method we discussed briefly in our study of the leucocytes. By the humoral method we understand the formation of antibodies which enable the animal to cope not only with the invading microorganisms and their toxins but also with various poisonous substances, such as foreign proteins, which may have entered the body.

When a sublethal (*lethum,* death) dose of diphtheria toxin is injected, the animal recovers and is then able to withstand a larger amount than the first dose administered; each subsequent dose gives the animal power to withstand a greater amount of poison. This constitutes *active immunity* and is due to the antitoxin which the inoculated animal has formed and which unites with the toxin, thereby causing it to become inactive. The blood, or serum, of this animal when injected into another animal will confer upon it a *passive immunity* toward diphtheria toxin.

The agencies which the animal produces in response to the inoculation with certain foreign substances and cells are collectively known as *antibodies,* and the substances which induce the formation of the antibodies are called *antigens.* There are perhaps only two general kinds of antigens; namely, foreign cells (especially bacteria) and foreign proteins; but for the sake of clearness we shall add the toxins. The antibodies are of four kinds (at least as far as action is concerned): agglutinins, lysins, precipitins, and antitoxins. When the antigen is a foreign cell, the antibodies formed are agglutins and lysins; the inoculation with a foreign protein causes the formation of a precipitin; to the introduction of a toxin the animal responds with the production of an antitoxin.

Antibodies are not present in the normal animal; they are the result of exposure of the organism to antigens. Their activities are collectively spoken of as immunologic reactions. It is only by their activity that we know them; in this respect they are similar to enzymes. Like the enzymes, the antibodies are very specific in their actions, as we shall see presently. We may now treat briefly of each of these antibodies.[*]

a. Precipitins.—When an animal receives several injections of an egg albumin solution, a few days elapsing between the successive injections, the serum of this animal acquires the power to precipitate egg albumin. A drop or two of the serum added to the albumin solution causes a rapid precipitation of the albumin. The agent in the blood causing this is called a precipitin, and its action is specific; e.g., if the egg albumin was obtained from the egg of a hen, the serum precipitates the albumin of the hen's egg but not that of any other egg.

In this manner precipitins may be made for various proteins that are foreign to the blood of the animal. Tchistovitch discovered that the serum of an animal previously inoculated with the blood (or serum) of another animal had the power to cause precipitation of the protein in the serum of the second animal. This action, like the above, is quite specific. If, therefore, a rabbit receives an injection of human blood or serum, there develops in the rabbit blood a precipitin which can be used, within certain limitations, for detecting human blood. Such antihuman immune serum caused 100 per cent precipitation in 34 specimens of human blood; also 100 per cent in the blood of anthropoid apes (8 specimens); only 92 per cent in the blood of common monkeys and none in that of lemurs or animals lower in the scale.

b. Agglutinins.—The addition of serum from a person recovering from typhoid causes clumping of typhoid bacilli; the germs are said to agglutinate. The agglutinins are also specific and hence the above reaction, called Widal's test, is a means of diagnosing typhoid fever, and for detecting typhoid carriers.

The blood of one individual may cause agglutination of the red blood cells of another. This is of extreme importance in the transfusion of blood, for the clumping of the corpuscles may block the flow of the blood in the capillaries (embolism). Consequently the blood of the donor must be tested for its compatibility with the blood of the recipient. In this respect it has been found there are four blood groups, called AB, A, B, and O. These letters designate the agglutinogens present on the red blood cells of each respective group. Absolute safety in a blood transfusion can be assured only if the donor's and the recipient's blood are of the same group. Since these agglutinogens are an inheritable characteristic, the blood groups have been used in forensic medicine, e.g., in establishing a child's paternity. However, this blood typing can only show either that a given man may be the father of the child, or could not possibly be.

c. **Antitoxins.**—We have already seen that the inoculation with certain pathogenic bacteria (diphtheria, e.g.) leads to the formation in the animal's blood of an antitoxin which is able to counteract the toxin formed by the bacteria. The antitoxin can be isolated (although more or less contaminated with proteins) from the serum of the immune animal and its injection into another animal renders this animal immune against the toxin. The action of the antitoxin is highly specific.

Antitoxins can be formed for many poisons such as ricin (from castor oil bean), snake and spider venoms, and tetanus toxin. These toxins are among the most poisonous substances known; e.g., it is stated that 0.23 milligram (0.0035 grain) of tetanin is the lethal dose for a man. We may compare this to strychnine, the fatal dose of which is from 30 to 100 milligrams. By some, these toxins are regarded as proteins or bodies closely allied to proteins. It is generally held that alcoholic indulgence decreases the formation of antibodies and thereby lowers the resistance power of the body.

The injection of a very minute dose of a certain toxin is frequently employed to determine the susceptibility of an individual to this particular disease. Thus, in the Schick test for diphtheria, one-fiftieth of the minimal lethal dose in 1 cubic centimeter of a 0.9 per cent sodium chloride solution is injected subcutaneously; susceptibility to diphtheria is indicated by an area of inflammation at the point of injection within twenty-four hours. It is stated that 60 per cent of children between the ages of six months and three years show a positive Schick test. Similar to this, we have the Dick test for scarlet fever.

A child not having active immunity to diphtheria, as shown by the Schick test, may acquire immunity by two or three injections of toxin-antitoxin. In this preparation the antitoxin is just a little less than that necessary to neutralize the toxin and thereby stimulates the production of antitoxin in the body of the child.

d. **Lysins or Cytotoxins.**—If the serum of dog's blood is mixed with the blood of a guinea pig, the red blood corpuscles of the guinea pig become laked (hemolysis). When the dog's serum is injected into the blood vessels of a guinea pig, hemolysis also occurs and this is followed by the excretion of hemoglobin by the kidneys (hemoglobinuria). Normal guinea pig's serum has no hemolytic action on the blood cells of a rabbit. But if the guinea pig during the course of ten or twelve days receives three or four injections of about 4 c.c. of defibrinated rabbit's blood, the blood of the guinea pig acquires the power to destroy the rabbit's corpuscles. The agent causing the destruction of a foreign cell is known as a lysin, or cytolysin.

When the foreign cell is a red blood corpuscle, the lysin is specifically called a hemolysin. When the two animals whose bloods are acting upon each other are of a different species, the process is known as heterolysis; if they are of the same species, it is called isolysis or homolysis. When the serum of an animal destroys its own corpuscles, we speak of it as autolysis. The animal body can also acquire the power to destroy bacteria, the lysin in this case being known as a bacteriolysin. It is the development of the bacteriolysins that renders vaccination a protective inoculation against bacterial diseases such as typhoid fever. The vaccine used for this purpose is composed of the highly attenuated organisms of the disease. Although causing but a very slight pathologic reaction in the patient, the vaccine is capable of stimulating the formation of antibodies.

e. **Anaphylaxis.**—The injection of a single dose of horse serum into a rabbit may have no ill results. But if a week or two later the rabbit receives another injection, grave results and even death may follow. This great increase in the susceptibility to what otherwise may be regarded as a harmless substance is known as anaphylaxis (*ana,* against; *phylaxis,* guarding). The foreign substance calling forth the anaphylaxis is of a protein nature. The profound disturbances following the second injection are sometimes spoken of as anaphylactic shock (low blood pressure, heart and respiratory failure). Such shock has been observed in the use of antitoxins. The cause of the shock is obscure; it seems as if the rapid formation of toxins after the second injection may be responsible. The anaphylaxis reaction is specific.

Upon this principle is based the tuberculin test for tuberculosis. The introduction of this foreign material derived from the tubercle bacilli causes inflammation and fever in a tuberculous cow, but not in the normal animal. In 1929 Anderson isolated from the tubercle bacilli a hitherto unknown sugar the injection of which has very little effect upon the normal animal but proves fatal, in from four to five hours, to one having tuberculosis. The animal afflicted with tuberculosis has gradually acquired a great sensitiveness toward certain chemical compounds manufactured by or in the bacteria. The exceedingly small quantity of foreign protein necessary to bring about this state of anaphylaxis can be appreciated when we are told that 0.00,000,005 gm. of egg albumin may sensitize an animal to a subsequent dose of this protein.

Some individuals are naturally hypersensitive to certain foreign substances, and as this seems to run in families it is generally held that a disposition to such sensitization is inherited. Most of us are familiar with the hives and rashes experienced by certain individuals on indulging in some particular food (strawberries, sea foods, eggs, etc.) for which they have an idiosyncrasy; other individuals suffer attacks of dyspepsia or cardiac disturbances. And still more common are the asthma and hay fever caused by the proteins of pollen, dandruff, feathers, dust, etc., entering the body by way of the respiratory passages. This is frequently referred to as *allergy* (*allos,* other; *ergon,* energy). Some investigators hold that the lack of vitamins and, in other instances, focal infections play an important part. In a manner similar to the tuberculin test, it is now frequently possible to determine the particular protein (from pollen or other sources) to which the victim of hay fever is hypersensitive.

CHAPTER IX

THE MECHANICAL FACTORS OF BLOOD CIRCULATION

I. INTRODUCTION

The blood, as we have learned in the last chapter, performs functions, such as the carrying of foods to the various organs of the body and the collecting of waste products from the cells. It is only as the blood circulates from one part of the body to another that these functions can be performed. The discovery of the circulation of the blood is generally attributed to Harvey (1628), although the passage of the blood through the capillaries was not seen until four years after his death, when, in 1661, Malpighi first observed the capillaries of a frog's lungs.

The Cause of Circulation.—The movement of a fluid, whether it be air, water, or blood, depends upon the establishment of an **inequality of pressure.** For example, if the circular rubber tube, in Fig. 75, nearly filled with water, lies on the table, there is no movement of the water in the tube because the pressure is the same at all points. But suppose that with the hand we exert pressure at the point a; the pressure is now greater at a than at b or c and the water flows from a in both directions, until the pressure at b and c is again equal to that at a. If the hand is withdrawn from a, the pressure at a becomes less than at b and c, and the water returns to a. Let us next suppose that at c there is situated a valve, so constructed that it opens up toward a and, therefore allows the water to flow from c to a but not in the reverse direction; we may imagine another valve at b so placed that the water can flow from a to b. If pressure is exerted at a, the greater pressure here causes the valve at c to close while the valve at b is opened and the liquid moves from a to b; this increase of pressure is communicated to every point of the tube so that finally all points again attain the same pressure. Removal of the hand from a decreases the pressure at a, and the high pressure beyond b and c will tend to move the fluid back to a. But the fluid going toward b closes the valve at b; the fluid going toward c opens the valve at c with the result that the water moves from c to a. When next the hand presses upon a, the fluid moves again to b and from *b* around the tube to *a*. Thus we have established, by a rhythmically acting force and the existence of a couple of valves, a circulation.

To obtain proper circulation of blood in the vascular system, four factors are indispensable:

1. A rhythmically beating heart to generate the necessary pressure.

2. A proper condition of the blood vessels; without this an active heart would be of no avail.

3. An adequate amount of blood.

4. An adequate mechanism for insuring unidirectional flow.

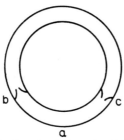

Fig. 75.—Diagram to illustrate the circulation of a fluid. *b* and *c* valves; *a*, point of pressure applied.

II. ANATOMY OF THE CIRCULATORY SYSTEM

The Heart.—The circulatory, or vascular, system is composed of the heart and the various blood vessels: arteries, arterioles, capillaries, venules, and veins. The heart is a hollow muscular organ, in the walls of which we can distinguish three coats: the endocardium, the myocardium, and the epicardium. The innermost layer, or endocardium, is a thin layer of connective tissue fibers and smooth muscle cells, covered with a layer of squamous endothelial cells; this coat is reflected over the valves of the heart. The myocardium forms the bulk of the muscular wall and is covered externally by the epicardium, a serous membrane, which is reflected at the upper portion of the heart to form a sac, the pericardium (page 203), covering the heart.

In mammals the heart is divided into four cavities: the right auricle (or atrium), the right ventricle, the left auricle, and the left ventricle (see Fig. 78). In fact, we may speak of the mammal as having two hearts, a right and a left heart, each composed of an auricle and a ventricle; but these two hearts are anatomically so intimately united that they are generally regarded as constituting one organ.

The auricular walls are thin and feel flabby to the touch, those of the ventricles are much thicker and firmer; especially is this true of the walls of the left ventricle which may be from 3 to 5 times as thick, and, therefore, 3 to 5 times as powerful as those of the right ventricle. Between the auricles and ventricles are placed valves; the *bicuspid*, or *mitral valve,* on the left, and the *tricuspid valve* on the right (see Figs. 76 and 77). The bicuspid, or mitral, valve is composed of two

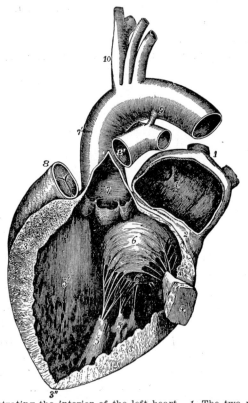

Fig. 76.—Illustrating the interior of the left heart. *1,* The two right pulmonary veins emptying into the left auricle. *1'*, laid open (the two left pulmonary veins are not shown); *2,* external groove between the auricle and ventricle; *3,* the ventricular wall cut across; *3",* the apex; *5,* papillary muscles; *5'* septum between the two ventricles; *6,* mitral valve with *6',* the chordæ tendineæ; *7,* the mouth of the aorta with the three flaps of the semilunar valves; *7',* the aorta from the arch of which springs, *10,* the innominate artery to the right of which is seen the left common carotid and the left subclavian artery; *8,* pulmonary artery arising from the right ventricle and showing the semilunar valves; *8',* continuation of the pulmonary artery; *9,* remnant of the fetal ductus arteriosus. (Allen Thompson.)

flaps of connective tissue, while the tricuspid has three flaps, or cusps, which open up into the ventricles. These valves open when blood passes through the auricle into the ventricle, but close during the contraction of the ventricle. To prevent a bulging of these valves into the auricle thereby nullifying their function, there are attached to the borders of the valves (Figs. 76 and 77) many small but strong cords, the *chordae tendineae,* whose other ends are attached to fleshy columns, papillary muscles, of the ventricular wall, Fig. 77, *4';* by the contraction of these muscles the cords are tightened during the contraction of the ventricle.

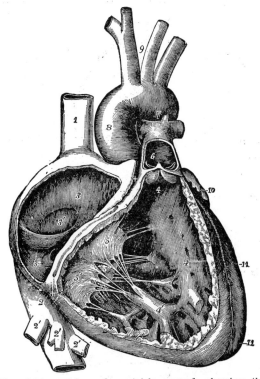

Fig. 77.—The right auricle and ventricle opened, showing their interior. *1,* superior vena cava; *2,* inferior vena cava; *2',* hepatic veins; *3,* right auricle; *3",* is placed close to the aperture of the coronary vein; + +, placed in the auriculoventricular groove, where a narrow portion of the adjacent walls of the auricle and ventricle has been preserved; *4, 4,* cavity of the right ventricle, the upper figure is immediately below the semilunar valves; *4'.* large musculus papillaris; *5, 5', 5",* tricuspid valve; *6,* placed in the interior of the pulmonary artery; *8,* arch of the aorta; *9,* placed between the innominate and left carotid arteries; *10,* appendix of the left auricle; *11, 11,* the outside of the left ventricle, the lower figures near the apex. Note the chordæ tendineæ stretching from the tricuspid valve, *5, 5',* and *5",* to the musculus papillaris, *4';* *7,* the remnant of the ductus arteriosus. (Allen Thompson.)

The Blood Vessels.—The tubes leading into the auricles carry the blood to the heart and are called veins; the superior and inferior venae cavae convey the blood from the body in general to the right auricle; the four pulmonary veins take the blood from the lungs to the left auricle. From the ventricles spring tubes, known as arteries, that carry the blood away from the heart; the aorta, *Ao* in Fig. 78, arises from the left ventricle, and the pulmonary artery, from the right ventricle. At the opening of these arteries are found the semi-lunar (*semi*, half; *luna*, moon) valves which, by opening up into the arteries only, prevent the blood from flowing back into the ventricles (Figs. 76, 77, and 78). The arteries split into many branches each smaller than the parent stem; this multiplication of vessels continues until microscopic vessels, the capillaries, are ob-

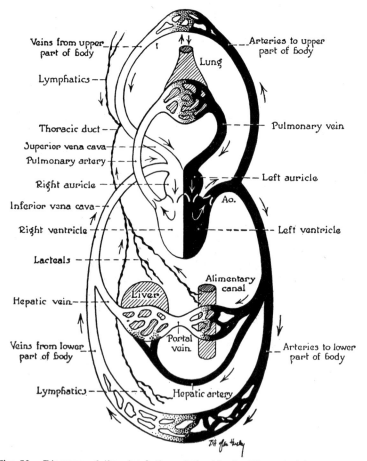

Fig. 78.—Diagram of the circulation of the blood. The arterial, or oxygenated, blood is shown in black; the venous blood, in white. The lymphatics are black knotty lines. (Pettibone's Physiological Chemistry, The C. V. Mosby Co.)

tained, which exist in countless numbers in practically every tissue of the body. The capillaries reunite to form larger tubes (venules), and these in turn unite until finally they form the large veins opening into the auricles.

The wall of the artery is considerably thicker and stronger than that of the corresponding vein; this arrangement is necessary as the pressure in an artery is always greater than that in a vein. The arterial wall (Figs. 79 and 80) may be considered as made up of three coats.

1. *The inner coat,* or *tunica interna,* contains elastic connective tissue. Its innermost layer is formed by squamous epithelial cells (endothelium) and by its smoothness reduces the resistance encountered by the flowing blood.

2. *The tunica media,* the thickest coat, is composed of smooth muscle fibers, mostly circularly arranged, and of yellow elastic fibers. This coat constitutes the active part of the artery, for by the muscles the size of the vessel is regulated and the amount of blood supplied to the organ controlled. The elastic tissue enables the artery to adapt itself passively to the change in the volume of blood.

3. *The tunica externa* is composed chiefly of white fibrous connective tissue. Being inelastic and tough, it limits the distention of the artery and gives it strength.

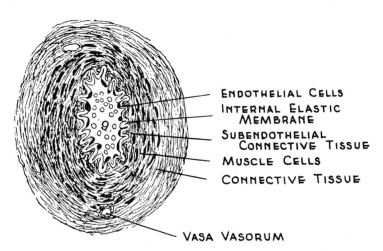

Fig. 79.—Cross section of medium-sized artery. (Bates.)

In the veins the muscle and elastic tissue are less, and the white connective (inelastic) tissue more, developed. For this reason veins are less extensible and elastic than arteries. In distinction to the arteries, the veins, especially those of the extremities, are well supplied with valves which prevent the regurgitation of the blood into the capillaries.

It is of prime importance to bear in mind that the blood performs its function of nourishing the tissues while it is passing through the capillaries and at no other place (see Chap. XII). The function of the other and far more conspicuous parts, i.e., heart, arteries, and veins, is subservient to that of the capillaries; and the study of the circulation concerns itself almost entirely with the wonderful regulation of the activities of the heart and blood vessels in order that an amount of blood sufficient for the nutritional demands of the body may be efficiently supplied to the capillaries.

Systemic and Pulmonary Circulations.—Each side of the heart, the right and the left heart, has its own circulation. The circuit from the left ventricle, Fig. 78, through the aorta, the systemic capillaries throughout the whole body, and the superior and inferior venae cavae to the right auricle is known as the *greater,* or *systemic, circulation.* The lesser, or *pulmonary, circulation* starts in the right ventricle from which springs the pulmonary artery which gives rise to the pulmonary, or lung, capillaries; these unite to form the four

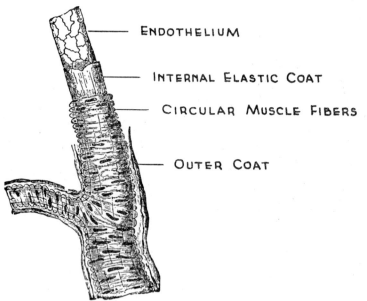

ENDOTHELIUM

INTERNAL ELASTIC COAT

CIRCULAR MUSCLE FIBERS

OUTER COAT

Fig. 80.—Coats of a small artery. (Landois and Stirling.)

pulmonary veins which connect with the left auricle. Many of these vessels and their connections with the heart are shown in Figs. 76 and 77.

In its passage through the lungs the blood acquires oxygen and loses some of its carbon dioxide; thus oxygenated the blood becomes arterial (shown as black in Fig. 78) and as such it is returned to the left heart. In the systemic capillaries the arterial blood loses some oxygen and acquires carbon dioxide, thereby becoming venous; this is returned to the right heart, to be sent by it to the lungs.

Systole and Diastole.—By the contraction of the muscle fibers of the auricle or ventricle, the size of the cavity is reduced and any fluid in the cavity is squeezed upon, that is, it is put under pressure and will be driven from the cavity. When the musculature of the heart relaxes, the cavities increase in size and the pressure in the cavity is decreased; this allows blood to enter. The contraction of the walls of a heart cavity is called *systole* and its relaxation, *diastole.** In the action of the heart, the auricles contract first; by this auricular systole the blood is driven through the open auriculoventricular valves (bicuspid and tricuspid, Fig. 78) into the ventricles. This is followed by the auricular diastole which allows the blood from the veins to flow into the empty auricles. Almost simultaneous with the beginning of the auricular diastole, the ventricular systole takes place. The contraction of the muscles of the ventricle puts the blood under a considerable pressure, and, by first closing the auriculoventricular valves and then opening the semilunar valves, forces the blood into the arteries. The contraction of the ventricle is followed by its diastole, which results in the closing of the semilunar valves in the arteries and the opening of the auriculoventricular valves. For details of the function of the heart valves see pages 201 and 202.

III. PRESSURE, CURRENT, AND VELOCITY

Law of Pressure.—Suppose that the tank in Fig. 81 is filled to the line *b* with water, and that the opening at *o* is closed. According to the law of hydrostatics, the water in the small tubes *d*, *e*, *f*, and *g* will stand at the same level as in the tank. Let us suppose that the horizontal tube *ao* is of uniform bore and, therefore, offers the same amount of resistance at all points to a fluid moving through it. If now *o* is opened wide, the water in the vertical tubes will fall to the heights indicated by the figures *1, 2, 3,* and *4.* It will be noticed that these levels can be connected by a straight line which extends from the outlet *o* to the tank, striking the tank at level *h*. Next let us cause the opening at *o* to be quite narrow, that is, let us increase the resistance that the water encounters in getting out of the tube. As a result the levels of the water in the vertical tubes will be higher, and the line joining them will strike the tank at level *j.*

The force which causes the water to flow out of the tank is the pressure of the column of water, *ab*, in the tank; this may be termed the *head of pressure.* Some of this force is consumed, i.e., transformed into heat, by the resistance (friction) which the water must overcome.

*Systole, sys′-to-lē ; diastole, dī-ăs′-to-lē.

The amount of the force thus used up, when *o* is wide open, is indicated by *ah;* that is, of the total head of pressure, *ab,* the part *ah* was needed to overcome the resistance, for which reason it is called the *resistance,* or *lateral, pressure.* The amount of the lateral pressure at any point along the horizontal tube is indicated by the height to which the water rises in the vertical tube placed upon the horizontal tube at the point in question. The remainder of the head of pressure, *hb,* is the pressure that has not been consumed by the fluid

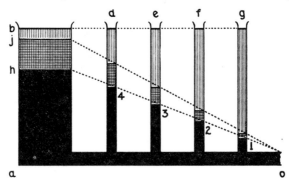

Fig. 81.—Diagram to illustrate head of pressure, lateral pressure, and velocity pressure. (For description, see text.

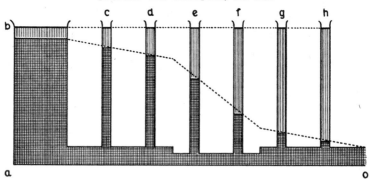

Fig. 82.—Diagram to illustrate variations in lateral pressure due to increased peripheral resistance. For description, see text.

in overcoming the resistance and hence is the force that is left in the fluid as it escapes from *o;* therefore, this may be called the *velocity pressure.* When the resistance is increased at *o* by narrowing the opening, the lateral, or resistance, pressure is increased to *aj* and the velocity pressure is decreased to *jb.*

It will be noticed from the diagram that the *fall* in pressure along the horizontal tube, as shown by the levels in the vertical tubes, is constant. This is due to the fact that the resistance at any one point of the horizontal tube is the same as at all other points. But suppose that, as shown in Fig. 82, the tube is narrowed between the points *e* and *f* so that the resistance is greater here than at *c* or *g*. The levels of the water in the vertical tubes will now not show a gradual and uniform fall of the lateral pressure along the horizontal tube, but the grade of fall will be far greater where the resistance is greater, that is, the fall of pressure will be more pronounced between *d* and *g* than between *c* and *d*, or between *g* and *h*. Moreover, because of the narrowing of the tube the level of the water in the vertical tube at *d* is much higher than it would be if the bore of the horizontal tube were constant. Now, the height of the level of the water in the vertical tube *d* indicates the lateral pressure at this point; hence:

1. The lateral pressure of a moving fluid at any given point varies directly with the amount of resistance between this point and the outlet.

2. The fall of pressure between any two given points is the greater, the greater the resistance between these two points.

It must also be evident that, as shown in Fig. 81, we are able to increase the velocity pressure in two ways. First, we may increase the head of pressure by putting more water in the tank so that the level now stands at some distance above *b*. By this the velocity pressure is increased, but as is well known, the resistance which a moving body encounters varies directly with the velocity with which it moves; consequently, the increase in the velocity causes the resistance, or lateral, pressure also to be increased. How much the lateral pressure and how much the velocity pressure are each increased by an increase in the head of pressure is a matter we need not consider in detail; suffice it to state that, if the head of pressure is reduced, the lateral pressure is decreased less than the velocity pressure, while increasing the head of pressure causes a greater increase in the velocity pressure than in the lateral pressure.

Law of Current.—From Fig. 82 it is evident that no matter what variations there may be in the size of the cross section of the tube *ao*, the amount of fluid passing any one given point of the system in a unit of time must be the same as that passing any other point in that system. For example, if one pint of water passes the wide part, *d*, in one minute, the same amount must pass by the narrow part, *e*, in the same length of time, i.e., *the volume flow* is the same.

Law of Velocity.—The velocity, or the distance a certain particle of fluid travels in a unit of time, varies directly as the pressure. Increasing the height of the water in the tank in Fig. 81 increases the velocity at every point along the tube *ao*. From the law of current it follows that the velocity is greater between *e* and *f* (Fig.

82) than at any other point; hence, **the velocity varies inversely as the cross section of the bed of the stream.** Again, it is well known that the velocity varies inversely as the viscosity of the fluid; an increase in the number of corpuscles is associated with a greater viscosity.

IV. BLOOD PRESSURE

We may now apply these principles and facts to the movements of the blood. In the circulatory system the head of pressure is represented by the force exerted by the contracting cardiac muscle. The energy so imparted to the blood is nearly all spent in overcoming the resistance that the blood meets in passing through the arteries, capillaries, and veins.

The amount of pressure is measured in the laboratory by means of an apparatus called the *manometer*. There are many forms of manometers; we shall describe one commonly used in animal experimentation, the mercury manometer. This consists primarily of a U-tube partly filled with mercury, C_1 and C_2 in Fig. 83. To one limb of the tube, C_1, is affixed, by means of a rubber tube, a pressure bottle, *P.B.* This same limb of the manometer is also attached by a thick-walled rubber tube to an arterial cannula, *C*. In the other limb of the manometer, C_2, is placed a float of hard rubber of such size that it snugly fits the bore of the tube without experiencing much friction when moved up or down. Into this float is fixed a stiff vertical wire, which in turn holds in place a horizontal arm to which is attached a stylus which writes on the kymograph. To use this apparatus we proceed as follows: A carotid artery of an anesthetized animal is exposed for a distance of one or two inches. A tight ligature is placed upon the distal (cephalic) end of the exposed segment. An artery clip is applied an inch or so towards the heart, from the ligature. Between the ligature and the clip, a V-shaped cut is made in the wall of the artery and into the opening is inserted the arterial cannula, *C*, of the manometer. If now the clip be removed from the artery, the blood from the heart will surge into the rubber tube and into the proximal limb of the manometer and, exercising pressure upon the mercury, will force the mercury down on this side and up on the other. The difference between the levels of the two mercury columns expresses the amount of blood pressure in, say, millimeters of mercury; as for example, 160 mm. Hg. But if the blood were to flow into the manometer or its tubes, coagulation would very speedily set in, and thereby terminate the experiment. To prevent this, previous to inserting the cannula into the artery, the bottle, *P.B.*, is filled with a 6 per cent solution of sodium citrate (p. 160). The rubber tubing is removed from arm C_1, of the manometer, and this arm is filled with sodium citrate solution by use of a medicine dropper. With all pinchcocks open, the system is filled with the solution by applying light pressure to the bulb. Next, we connect the filled system to arm C_1, close P_3 and P_4, and apply pressure until the difference between the mercury columns, C_1 and C_2 is equal to the estimated blood pressure of the animal; then P_2 is closed. When the

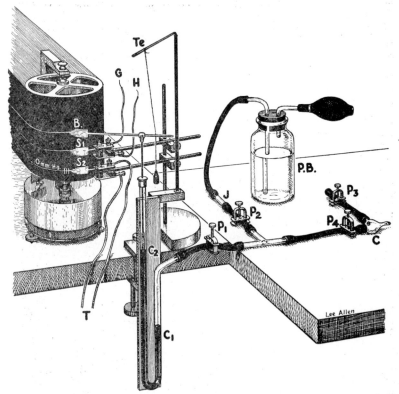

Fig. 83.—Apparatus for measuring directly the blood pressure by means of the mercury manometer.

cannula, C, has been securely tied in the artery, P_4 is opened and the clip removed from the artery. The blood forces itself against the column of sodium citrate and thus exerts its pressure against the mercury column. In this manner the coagulation of the blood is prevented and no blood is lost.

Arterial Blood Pressure.—The level of the mercury in the manometer does not remain stationary, but shows oscillations corresponding to the rhythmical action of the heart. At each systole the blood pressure is increased and the float rises; during the diastole the pressure falls. These rises and falls in pressure are recorded by the stylus on a kymograph, as seen in Fig. 84. The larger and less numerous curves in this tracing are caused by the inspiration and expiration. The more numerous but less marked rises and falls represent the maximum or *systolic pressure,* and the minimum, or *diastolic, pressure,* respectively. In an adult human being, the systolic pressure in the

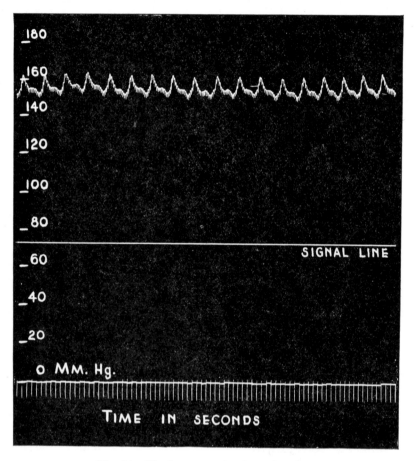

Fig. 84.—Blood pressure tracings of a dog.

branchial artery in the upper arm is about 120 mm. Hg; the diastolic, about 80. The difference between these two pressures is termed the *pulse pressure.* The details of this must be deferred till later pages.

The arterial blood pressure varies with:

1. The energy output of the heart (rate, force, and amount of blood discharged).

2. The elasticity of the arteries.

3. The amount of peripheral resistance.

4. The volume of the circulating blood (decreased immediately after a hemorrhage).

5. The viscosity of the blood (increase in corpuscular elements and in colloids in the plasma raises the viscosity).

We may here note that the amount of blood pressure bears no relation to the size of the animal; for example, the blood pressure of a rat is about the same as that of a man, and that of a dog is frequently higher.

Capillary Blood Pressure.—As the blood flows from the larger to the smaller arteries, a certain amount of the energy imparted to the blood by the contraction of the left ventricle is lost by the friction encountered. The smaller the diameter of the tubes, the greater the resistance; it is chiefly in the arterioles and to a lesser extent in the capillaries that the blood loses most of its energy. As the veins offer but a small amount of resistance, the pressure of the blood in the capillaries is low, averaging, let us say, 20 mm. Hg.

To determine capillary pressure, a very fine capillary tube filled with a fluid under a certain amount of pressure is introduced into the blood capillary. If the pressure of the fluid is the same as that of the blood in the capillary, the blood enters and recedes from the tube with each heartbeat. The capillary blood pressure varies so largely in the different parts of the body and in the same capillary under different conditions (some of these will be discussed in subsequent pages) that no definite value can be assigned to it. Generally it is estimated at from 10 to 30 mm. Hg.

Venous Blood Pressure.—As the blood courses from the capillaries through the veins to the heart, the blood pressure falls more and more, but the slope of the fall becomes less and less steep (see Fig. 85). In the large veins near the heart the blood pressure may be found to be negative, that is, when the cannula of the manometer is inserted into the vein, the mercury will not be forced up into the distal limb, Fig. 83, but will be sucked, or aspirated, into the proximal limb. In other words, the atmospheric pressure upon the mercury in the distal limb is greater than the pressure which the blood in the large vein exerts upon the mercury in the proximal limb. When such a vein is opened, the air may rush (be sucked) into the vein and cause great harm by embolism.

The pressure of the blood in the veins is not only much less than in the arteries, but here, and also in the capillaries, the pressure is steady, that is, it does not undergo rhythmical fluctuations depending on the rhythmical action of the heart. The reason for this we shall discuss when we deal with the elasticity of the blood vessels. The venous pressure may, therefore, be stated to be from plus 30 to minus 5-15 mm. Hg. In the arm or hand held at the level of the heart it has been found to be about 6 mm. Hg, being a little lower in early youth and a little higher in old age.

V. BLOOD FLOW

Velocity of Flow.—The large aorta soon breaks up into smaller vessels, and these, in turn, into still smaller ones. While the branches thus formed may individually be smaller than the parent vessel, collectively the bed formed by them is larger. Each capillary is a

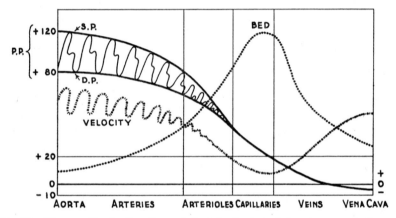

Fig. 85.—Diagram illustrating the variations in the bed of the stream, velocity and pressure in the arteries, arterioles, capillaries, and veins.

minute tube (0.5 to 1.0 mm. long and 0.01 mm. wide) but the combined area of the capillary bed of the systemic circulation is estimated at from four to eight hundred times that of the aorta. Hence, in the aorta we must look for the fastest, and in the capillaries for the slowest, flow, Fig. 85. A vein is generally a little larger than its corresponding artery, and venous flow is, therefore, a little slower than that in the arteries. In various ways it has been determined that the blood in the carotid artery flows with a velocity of from 200 or 300 mm. per second.

The capillary circulation can be studied microscopically in the web or tongue of a frog by transmitting the light directly through the structure. A very cursory examination of the frog's web shows that in general the flow is not pulsating but uniform (see next section). The diameter varies from one capillary to another, but in an open vessel, the elliptical red blood cells pass through in single file, Fig. 86. It may also be noticed that in the smaller arterioles the spherical white blood cells, because of their lighter weight, travel in the slower current near the walls of the vessels. The velocity of the capillary flow varies from 0.5 to 1.0 mm. per second. As the blood leaves the capillaries and courses through the veins, the bed becomes gradually smaller, and the velocity increases.

The Volume Flow.—The volume of blood flowing through any given artery in a unit of time can be found by means of Ludwig's stromuhr or some modification of it. It is of interest to note how

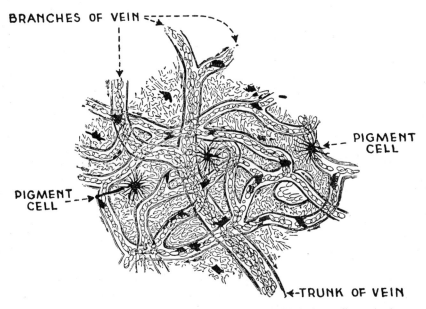

BRANCHES OF VEIN

PIGMENT CELL

PIGMENT CELL

-TRUNK OF VEIN

Fig. 86.—Capillaries in web of frog's foot. (Modified from Carpenter.)

much this varies from one organ to another; thus, per 100 grams of tissue the flow through the stomach wall was found to be 21 c.c. per minute; for the brain, 136; for the kidney, 150; and for the thyroid gland, 560. As we shall learn in a subsequent chapter, the quantity of blood passing through an organ is greatly increased or decreased according to the need for blood by the organ.

It is obvious that the enormous size of the capillary bed as compared with that of the aorta must cause the volume flow in each capillary (amount of blood discharged in a unit of time) to be exceedingly small. If the length of the capillary is taken as 1 mm. and the velocity of flow as 1 mm. per second, the quantity of blood passing through the capillary in this length of time is equivalent to the volume of the capillary; this can be found by the formula for the volume of a cylinder: $r^2 \pi h$. Assuming that the radius of the capillary is one-half of the diameter of a red blood cell (0.004 mm.), the volume becomes 0.00,005 cu. mm. or 0.00,000,005 c.c. If one drop of blood measures $\frac{1}{15}$ c.c., it requires approximately 15 days for a drop of blood to pass through a capillary.

Character of the Flow.—Because of the rhythmical contraction of the heart, the flow of the blood in the artery is pulsating; during the systole the velocity of flow in the carotid artery of a horse was found to be 520 mm. per second; this decreased to 150 mm. during the diastole. When, therefore, an artery is severed, the blood spurts in distinct gushes; from a cut vein, on the other hand, the blood flows with a steady stream. In capillaries and veins the flow is said to be uniform.

The cause of this change of the rhythmical, or pulsating, flow in the artery to a uniform flow in the capillaries and veins is based upon the elasticity of the arterial walls and a great peripheral resistance. This can be demonstrated by means of a rigid and an elastic tube. Suppose that by means of a bulb, or pump, we force water intermittently into a glass tube; let this tube be provided with a very narrow outlet. The first amount of water discharged by the bulb into the tube will perhaps not completely fill the tube and, if the outlet is held a little higher than the bulb, none of the water will issue from it. The second discharge from the bulb is just sufficient, let us say, to fill the tube. The third discharge will push a column of water out of the tube; this outflow stops when no more water is discharged by the bulb, to be resumed by the next action of the bulb; in other words, the outflow is intermittent. Now let us substitute a rubber tube, very extensible and elastic; it is also provided with a narrow outlet. When the tube has been filled by the first two contractions of the bulb, the third contraction will not exert all its force in pushing the column of water out of the tube, but the pressure exerted by the contracting bulb upon the water will cause the extensible rubber walls to stretch. In this manner room is provided for most of the newly ejected fluid, only a portion being forced out during the contraction of the bulb. When the bulb now stops sending any more water, the elastic walls, having been distended, continue to squeeze upon the water and force it in a continual stream out of the exit. If the rubber tube is not provided with a narrow opening, the water will escape as quickly as it is put into it by the bulb; the extensibility and elasticity of the tube are not called into play, and, consequently, the outflow must be intermittent. Hence, two factors are concerned in the production of this uniform flow in the capillaries and veins: first, great peripheral resistance in the capillaries and, second, elasticity of the arteries. It is very evident that the exchange of material between the blood and the cells is aided by constant flow in the capillaries.

We may here call attention to two other advantages derived from the elasticity of the arterial wall. First, the heart may miss a beat or two without appreciably disturbing the capillary circulation. Several minutes after the heart has ceased to beat, the opening of a vein may cause bleeding, for which reason the arteries are often found empty after death (*arteria*, windpipe). Second, it eases the work of the heart. Although the blood is discharged from the ventricle during the systole, the work done by the heart is distributed over the whole cardiac cycle, i.e., the systole and diastole combined. Were the vessels inelastic, the blood stream would come to a standstill immediately after each systole, and the next heartbeat would have to overcome the inertia of the stationary blood.

It should, however, be borne in mind that the flow in a capillary or vein does not proceed at an absolutely uniform and regular rate; a few minutes' observation of the capillary circulation will demonstrate that the capillary flow may be very irregular, now going quite fast and now stopping altogether. But the rhythmicity (or pulse) so characteristic of the arterial flow, is generally lacking in the capillaries. In the veins also there are many factors that tend either to increase or decrease the velocity of the flow; some of these will be considered a little later on.

Pulse.—The elasticity of the arteries gives rise to another phenomenon with which we are acquainted, namely, the pulse. With every systole of the left ventricle the heart discharges a certain quantity of the blood into the aorta; this quantity, variable but generally estimated at 50 to 100 c.c., is termed the *systolic output, stroke volume,* or *pulse volume.* When the left ventricle forces this blood into the aorta, the blood pressure in the aorta, *a,* Fig. 87, is markedly increased above that found a little lower down the vessels, at, say *b.* This sudden increase in pressure causes the wall of the aorta at *a* to distend, but as the walls are elastic this inequality spreads from *a* to *b;* that is, the dilation goes down at *a* and up at *b* and in this manner in the form of a wave, spreads over the whole arterial system. When the finger is placed upon an artery, this increase of pressure and the resultant dilation are felt; we say we feel the pulse. It is the same phenomenon that we considered when we spoke of the alternation of the systolic and diastolic pressures, and of the rhythmical increase and decrease in the velocity of the blood flow in the artery. All these rhythmical phenomena are caused by the rhythmical action of the heart and spread from the aorta toward the capillaries. In the smaller tubes this wave of increased pressure, velocity, and dilation of the vessel is gradually extinguished so that in the capillaries the blood pressure and velocity are not rhythmical. The pulse wave must not be confused with the flow of blood. While the velocity of the flow in an artery is, let us say, 100 to 500 mm. per second, the pulse wave in this length of time travels from 6 to 9 meters. By means of a piece of apparatus known as a sphygmograph a tracing of the radial pulse can be obtained, Fig. 88.

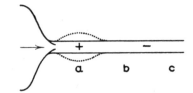

Fig. 87.—Diagram illustrating the formation of the pulse.

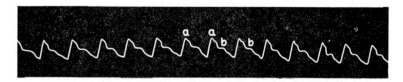

Fig. 88.—A sphygmogram, or pulse tracing.

THE PLETHYSMOGRAPH.—When the pulse wave strikes any part of the body, say, the arm, finger, or kidney, the amount of blood in that part is increased and the volume of the organ will also be increased. To determine this we employ a piece of apparatus called a plethysmograph, the form of which depends upon the organ to be investigated. In Fig. 89 we have one adapted for the arm. The arm of an individual is inserted in the cylindrical vessel, and the connection between the arm and the edge of the vessel made airtight by means of a broad piece of rubber. The interior of the plethysmograph is connected by means of a tube with a tambour. The tambour consists of a metal box, the top of which is covered by a rubber membrane upon which rests a writing lever. If, for any reason, the volume of the arm is increased, the pressure in the cylinder is increased; this is communicated by a rubber tube to the tambour causing the lever to be thrown upward; when the volume of the arm decreases, the lever goes down. Such a change in the volume of the arm occurs when the pulse wave enters the arteries of this organ.

This increase in the volume of the blood vessels is also seen in the throbbing pain of an aching tooth or an inflamed finger. The blood vessels of the parts affected are much dilated and by pressing upon the nerve endings in the immediate neighborhood give rise to pain. The still further enlargement of the blood vessel by the pulse wave causes more pressure on the nerves, and the pain is augmented. Raising the inflamed part above the level of the heart, if possible, drains the blood away from it; in consequence the nerves are less pressed upon and the pain subsides.

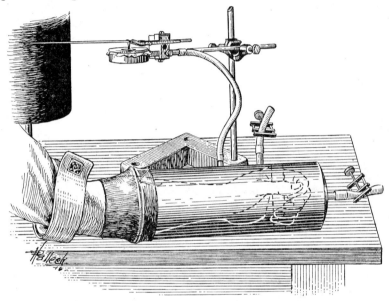

Fig. 89.—The plethysmograph. (Jackson: Experimental Pharmacology and Materia Medica, The C. V. Mosby Co.)

Blood Pressure and Blood Flow.—From the above discussion we may conclude that *augmenting the cardiac force increases both the velocity and the pressure, and an increase in the resistance causes an increase in the pressure but a decrease in the volume flow.* It should be borne in mind that while blood flow is indispensable for the nutrition of the tissue, the blood pressure is of importance only as it generates the flow. The least amount of pressure required to bring this about is for the best of the animal economy.

The facts we have thus far learned concerning the amount and nature of the blood pressure, the blood flow in the various vessels, and the size of the bed may be summarized in the diagram shown in Fig. 85.

VI. SECONDARY AIDS IN VENOUS CIRCULATION

The main force which drives the blood along the veins and back to the heart is the pressure of the blood behind it in the capillaries; hence the muscular energy of the left ventricle is the driving force. In addition to this, there are auxiliary factors that sometimes play an important part. Among these we may mention:

Influence of Respiration on Circulation.—That respiration has an influence on the blood pressure can be gathered from the blood pressure tracing in Fig. 84 which very definitely shows two sorts of curves: first, the less pronounced and more numerous cardiac curves and, second, the less numerous curves. If the respiration of the animal is watched while the blood pressure is being registered, it will be seen that these latter curves have the same periodicity as the respiration of the animal. The exact relation between these two phenomena is by no means clear, and it seems very likely that many factors, especially the rate, depth, and nature of respiration, may materially modify it. Without going into the details too much, we may give the following statement which is perhaps the more commonly accepted view of the matter.

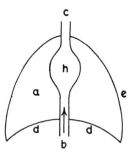

Fig. 90.—To illustrate effect of respiration on circulation. For description, see text.

If the respiration of the animal is not too fast, it is generally found that during inspiration the blood pressure rises, and during the expiration it falls. The rise and fall do not perhaps strictly correspond with the inspiration and expiration, but such is the general effect. The cause of this increase of blood pressure during inspiration can best be understood by reference to Fig. 90. This figure represents a longitudinal section of the thoracic cavity, *a*, in which are located the large blood vessels such as the vein, *c*, draining the capillaries of the head and *b* carrying the blood from the abdomen to the right auricle, *h*. In it are located also the lungs, but we do not need to consider them in this connection. During inspiration the chest wall, *e,* is expanded and, *d,* the diaphragm (the floor of the cavity) is moved down. Let us suppose that this inspiratory effort takes place with both mouth and nose closed, so that no air can enter the thoracic cavity. As the chest cavity is enlarged, the intrathoracic pressure in *a* must become less. Now, the intrathoracic pressure exerts its force upon all organs situated in the thorax. It will be remembered that veins have much thinner walls than arteries and that, therefore, any external force affects the blood in veins far more than that in arteries. The reduction of the intrathoracic pressure during inspiration reduces the external force playing upon the veins and auricles, and these cavities will thereby be allowed to distend. By so doing they exert a suction upon the blood in the veins of the head and abdomen; that is, the difference of pressure between points *h* and *b* and between points *h* and *c* in Fig. 90 becomes greater, and hence the blood streams with a great velocity from *b* and *c* toward *h*. In addition to this, we have during inspiration the descent of the diaphragm by which the pressure upon the organs of the abdomen is increased; this tends to squeeze the blood in the abdominal veins, *b,* toward the heart. These veins empty into the right auricle from which the blood passes into the right ventricle, and, as a result of this, the amount of blood sent through the lungs to the left heart is increased. Because of the greater filling of the left ventricle, this cavity discharges more blood into the aorta, thereby raising the arterial blood pressure. However, it should be borne in mind that the capacity of the pulmonary blood vessels is very great, and that during inspiration the lessened pressure in the thorax allows the numerous pulmonary vessels to dilate and thus take up a considerable amount of blood. This tends to lessen the flow toward the left auricle during the first period of inspiration and thereby lower the systemic blood pressure. But if the rate of respiration is not too fast, this decrease in blood pressure is followed, as above described, by an increase.

From the foregoing it must be clear that the increase of intrathoracic pressure during the first part of expiration squeezes a large amount of blood out of the distended pulmonary vessels to the left heart and thereby increases the systemic blood pressure; but this increased intrathoracic pressure also tends to retard the flow of the venous blood toward the heart, thereby lessening the diastolic intake of the left ventricle and reducing the aortic blood pressure. This is especially seen when, with the air passages closed, powerful expiratory efforts are made (Valsalva's experiment), or when one blows forcibly through a narrow tube; due to the marked decreased filling of the heart the systolic pressure may fall sufficiently low to abolish the radial pulse and even to cause unconsciousness. The stagnation and the lack of aeration of the blood account for the bluish discoloration (cyanosis) of the face, in the above experiments. When after such an experiment the respiratory passages are opened, the decrease in the intrathoracic pressure permits a tremendous rush of blood to the right auricle; as a result the diastolic intake of the left ventricle is very largely augmented and the force exerted may increase the systolic blood pressure in the systemic arteries to as much as 250 mm. Hg. Conditions similar to Valsalva's experiment are met with in any muscular effort associated with a closed glottis and a fixed thorax; we find this, for example, in rowing, the lifting of heavy weights, coughing, and straining at stool. The high systolic pressure resulting from such activities may prove very harmful to individuals with sclerotic (hardened) blood vessels.

"**Milking**" **Action of the Muscles.**—The venous circulation is greatly aided by the rhythmical contraction of skeletal muscles. When these muscles contract, the veins in and near the muscles are squeezed upon and, because of the valves found in the veins, the blood can be forced only toward the heart. When next the muscles relax, the veins open up and the blood from the capillaries flows more rapidly into the almost empty veins. By this milking action the muscles function as auxiliary venous hearts. In addition to aiding the flow of the venous blood, this same process accelerates the flow of the lymph from the exercised parts of the body—see Chap. XII. The improved nourishment of the tissue hereby brought about is one of the many reasons why rhythmical exercises have such beneficial effects upon circulation.

The valuable influence of rhythmic muscular action in contrast with that of static, or constant, contractions can readily be seen in the following manner: Stand erect for two or three minutes and note the prominent condition of the veins of the feet; also note that they feel hard to the touch. On taking a few steps, a great change in these veins will be seen. This matter will be referred to when we study the influence of gravity on the circulation.

Belonging to the same class as the above, we have the influence of the contraction of the muscles found in the walls of the alimentary canal (peristalsis) by which the venous circulation through these organs is accelerated. The rhythmical contractions of the spleen and of the villi of the intestines have the same effect. In this connection we may also refer to massage by which the flow of blood from a muscle may be increased to three times the usual quantity.

VII. CIRCULATION TIME

By the total circulation time is meant the time required for a drop of blood to make a complete circuit through the vascular system. For example: let us inject into the jugular vein (in the neck) a solution of methylene blue and note the time of its appearance in the carotid artery. This time indicates how long it takes for a given corpuscle to travel through the right heart, the pulmonary circuit, and the left heart and into the carotid artery. In man the pulmonary circulation time has been estimated at about 15 seconds, and that of the systemic at from 20 to 25.

If the stroke volume be placed at 75 c.c., the heartbeat at 70 per minute, and the total volume of blood in the body at 5,000 c.c., all the blood passes through the left ventricle in a little less than one minute. Because of the greatly increased heart rate and stroke volume this time is much less in severe muscle work.

VIII. THE AURICLES, OR ATRIA

We have seen that the walls of the auricles are very thin compared with those of the ventricle; from this we would gather that the pressure generated by them must also be much less, and direct observations on animals confirm this. The maximum pressure in the left auricle is somewhere from 10 to 15 mm. Hg, while that of the left ventricle is from 110 to 150. Neither is there a great amount of energy necessary, for the resistance that the blood encounters in passing from the auricle into the ventricle is but slight. We may, therefore, state that the primary function of the auricle is not to generate pressure.

We shall presently learn that the auricular systole is very much shorter than that of the ventricle; in this lies the principal use of the auricle. Let us suppose that the pulmonary veins emptied directly into the left ventricle, the auricle being absent. With each ventricular systole, the flow of blood in the veins would come to a standstill until the ventricle again dilated. This would cause the venous flow to be pulsatile and, as a result, the capillary flow would also be intermittent; as we have seen, this would be highly unfavorable to the performance of the functions of the blood in the capillaries. But with an auricle whose systole lasts but 0.1 second this retardation in the velocity of the flow in the veins (which is in part the cause of the so-called venous pulse) is almost negligible. Because of its short systole, the auricle remains open during its long diastole seven-eighths of the time and thereby it serves well as *a reservoir for the blood coming to the heart.*

IX. THE PULMONARY OR LESSER CIRCULATION

The lesser, or pulmonary, circulation is characterized principally by the fact that the pressure in the pulmonary vessels is much less than that in the systemic vessels. The pressure in the pulmonary artery is estimated at about $\frac{1}{5}$ of that found in the aorta. This accounts for the relative size of the musculature of the left and the right ventricles. The reason that a much smaller force is required to send blood through the pulmonary than through the systemic circuit is, no doubt, the smaller amount of resistance encountered in the pulmonary circuit.

X. BLOOD PRESSURE IN MAN

The blood pressure in a human being is determined by the *sphygmomanometer,* of which there are several makes but all of which depend upon the same principle. Suppose that while the pulse is being felt at the wrist, the upper arm is encircled by a bandage. The tighter the bandage is pulled, the feebler the pulse will become, until finally when the external force applied to the arm is sufficiently great to block the artery, the pulse wave cannot pass. In a common form of sphygmomanometer a rubber bag, about five inches wide and nine inches long, is applied to the bare upper arm of the patient and is held in position by a strip of strong inelastic cloth wound around the arm (Fig. 91). This armlet has two openings; one of these is connected with some apparatus for forcing air into it (an inflating bulb); the other opening is connected with a mercury or aneroid manometer to indicate the amount of pressure in the armlet.

To determine the pressure two methods are in common use: the palpatory and the auscultatory. In the latter method the bell of the stethoscope, Fig. 91, is placed over the brachial artery just in front of the bend of the elbow and as close to the armlet as possible. Without any pressure in the armlet no sounds are heard, but when the pressure has been raised to a sufficient height a clear but not loud sound is heard with each heartbeat; on raising the pressure still further, the sound disappears. If now the pressure is very slowly reduced, the sound reappears; this denotes the systolic pressure. On further very gradual decompression a point is reached at which the sound is reduced and becomes less distinct; but at a slightly lower level it undergoes rather a marked change in that it becomes more of a snapping sound. On still further reducing the pressure this sharp snapping sound changes quite abruptly into a muffled sound; this point indicates the diastolic pressure. The difference between the

systolic and the diastolic pressure is called the *pulse pressure*. In
the palpatory method, the pressure in the armlet is raised sufficiently
to obliterate the radial pulse. On slowly decreasing the pressure, the
pulse reappears; this indicates the systolic pressure.

As to the meaning of these three pressures, we may briefly state
the following: The diastolic pressure indicates the load to which the
arteries are subjected because of the resistance which the blood encounters in passing from the left ventricle to the right auricle. It
is the amount of pressure which must be overcome by the systole

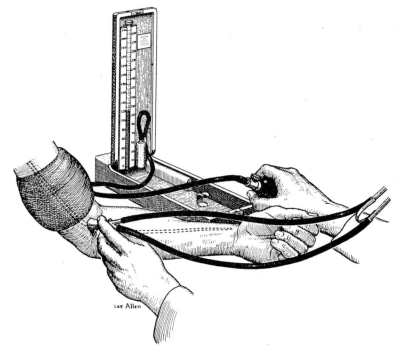

Fig. 91.—The sphygmomanometer. Note the relative position of the instrument,
subject, and operator.

of the left ventricle before the valves are opened and before any
blood can be discharged into the aorta. Whenever the vessels offer
greater resistance, the diastolic pressure is increased; *this pressure
may therefore be said to represent the condition or state of the blood
vessels* and for this reason its determination is of such great moment.
The systolic pressure represents the driving force of the left ventricle
or the amount of work it does in overcoming the resistance of the
vessels. The pulse pressure is the excess of the amount of work the
heart does over and above that needed to open the aortic valves; to
a certain extent it represents the "useful propulsive force" of the
heart.

Basal Blood Pressure.—As the blood pressure varies from one individual to another and in the same individual under different circumstances, one cannot speak of a normal blood pressure; but it is permissible to use the term, *normal range,* of blood pressure. The pressure obtaining with the body perfectly at rest and the mind at ease is known as the basal blood pressure. While the basal pressure is constant in any given individual, in different individuals it varies with many factors among which we may mention the following:

1. AGE.—At the age of five years, the systolic pressure is about 90 mm. Hg; this gradually increases as shown in Table VII, which

TABLE VII

AGE	SYSTOLIC	DIASTOLIC	PULSE PRESSURE
10	103	70	33
20	120	80	40
30	123	82	41
40	126	84	42
50	130	86	44
60	135	89	46

gives the average basal blood pressure based on 250,000 determinations for males (after Hunter and Frost).

The normal range of the systolic pressure for any age extends from 10 mm. above to 10 below, that for the diastolic from 5 mm. above to 10 below the values given in Table VII. A systolic pressure above 150 or a diastolic pressure above 100 mm. Hg is generally regarded as abnormally high.

2. SEX.—In the female both systolic and diastolic pressures are generally about 5 to 10 mm. lower than in the male.

3. BODY WEIGHT.—Overweight is generally associated with a higher blood pressure and underweight with a lower pressure. Hunter and Rogers, who collected pressure readings of 62,000 men and 5,000 women, also came to this conclusion. A reduction in blood pressure is generally observed when by proper dieting the body weight becomes more nearly normal.

CHAPTER X

THE HEART

Our study of the blood circulation has thus far been confined to the mechanical factors which govern the flow of any liquid in a closed system of tubes with a central pump. But the amount of blood needed by any organ in a unit of time varies with the degree of activity of the body and with the changing conditions of the environment. To meet these needs efficiently, the work of the heart and the condition of the vessels must be closely regulated. In this chapter we shall concern ourselves with the activity of the heart and its regulation.

I. ORIGIN AND TRANSMISSION OF THE HEART IMPULSE

Origin of the Heartbeat.—The relation between the skeletal muscles and the central nervous system is so intimate and the action of these muscles is so thoroughly controlled by, and is so dependent upon, the impulses coming from the brain and cord that severing the connection between them causes a complete and permanent cessation of the activity of the muscles—motor paralysis. Therefore, an excised frog muscle exhibits no sign of action unless we stimulate it artificially. In this respect the cardiac muscle is very different. The heart is connected with the central nervous system by means of two nerves, the vagus and the cervical sympathetic. When in a frog these nerves are cut, or when the whole heart is excised, the heart goes on beating. Evidently the origin of the beat does not lie in the central nervous system. We, therefore, say that the heart action is automatic, meaning thereby that for its action the heart is not dependent upon impulses carried to it from other parts of the body.

The frog's heart, Fig. 92, is composed of four chambers: a sinus venosus into which the three systemic veins (venae cavae) empty; a right auricle which receives the venous blood from the sinus venosus and sends it into the ventricle; a left auricle which receives the oxygenated blood from the pulmonary veins and delivers this to the same ventricle. The ventricle, it will be noticed, receives both reduced, or venous, and oxygenated, or arterial, blood; the mixed blood is sent to all parts of the body, including the lungs.

In a cooled frog's heart it is easy to observe that the sequence of the contraction is: sinus venosus, auricles, ventricle, aortic bulb, or truncus arteriosus. The last named part is a contractile portion (Fig. 92) of what corresponds to the aorta in the mammalian heart. It seems, therefore, that the impulse causing the contraction of the musculature is generated in the sinus venosus. This view is substantiated by the fact that if the sinus venosus only is cooled, the whole heart beats more slowly; cooling the ventricle has not this effect. From the sinus the impulse spreads through the auricles, into the ventricle, and finally into the bulb. But on entering each succeeding part, there is a retardation of the impulse so that the auricles contract after the sinus, and the contraction of the ventricle follows that of the auricles. The sinus beats first because its irritability to

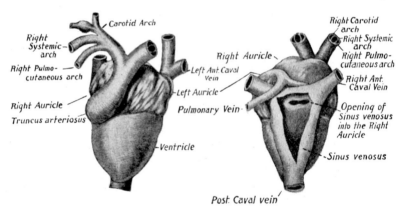

Fig. 92.—The anatomy of the frog's heart. (Jackson: Experimental Pharmacology and Materia Medica, The C. V. Mosby Co.)

the "inner stimulus" is greater than that of any other part. It is held by some that the heart (perhaps the sinus venosus or the sino-auricular node—see infra) manufactures a chemical compound, a *heart hormone,* which is the direct stimulus for the heart muscle. Because of the long refractory period (see p. 207) this constant stimulus must result in rhythmical contractions.

The Sino-Auricular Node.—In the mammalian heart are found two small masses of a peculiar tissue ("neuromuscular" tissue). One of these collections lies in the wall of the right auricle near the mouth of the superior vena cava; this is called the sino-auricular node and corresponds embryologically to the sinus venosus of the hearts of lower vertebrates. Another node, situated a short distance from the sino-auricular node and known as the auriculoventricular node, gives rise to a bundle of fibers (the *auriculoventricular* *bundle,* or the bundle of His) which passes downward and pierces the fibrous ring between the auricles and the ventricles (Fig. 93) ; after splitting into two branches it passes along the septum between the two ventricles and ultimately breaks up into many fibers which make connections with the ventricular muscle fibers.

The generally accepted view of the origin and conduction of the impulse may be stated in a few words. The impulse is generated in the sino-auricular node, from which it spreads to and through the muscle fibers of the auricles and causes the auricular systole; by the muscle fibers the impulse is conveyed to the auriculoventricular node. From this node the impulse is carried by the auriculoven-

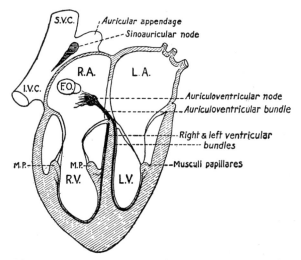

Fig. 93.—Diagram illustrating the conducting material of the mammalian heart. *F.O.,* foramen ovale ; *i.v.c.,* inferior vena cava ; *s.v.c.,* superior vena cava. (Macleod: Physiology, The C. V. Mosby Co.)

tricular bundle to the ventricles. The conductivity of the auriculoventricular node is low; this brings about a delay which allows the auricle sufficient time to finish its contraction before the systole of the ventricle begins—a necessary arrangement for properly coordinated heart action. The conduction by the auriculoventricular bundle is so fast that all the muscle fibers of the ventricles receive the impulse almost simultaneously (coordination); the advantage of this is apparent.

Although in the frog's heart the sinus venosus and in the mammalian heart the sino-auricular node must be regarded as the *pacemaker* of the heartbeat, by proper experiment it can be shown that all the various parts of the heart possess a certain degree of automaticity.

If the sinus venosus of a frog's heart is cut away from the auricles, the sinus continues its usual beat, but the activity of the auricles and ventricle ceases for a certain length of time. After a lapse of from 10 to 30 minutes these cavities resume their beat which is, however, at a slower rate than that of the sinus; in this the auricles always beat before the ventricle. If now a section is made between the auricles and the ventricle, the former continue their beat and after a long period of quiescence the ventricle may resume a very slow beat. The lower part of the ventricle severed from the rest of the heart never beats spontaneously, although it responds to artificial stimulation. These facts furnish a beautiful illustration of the gradual decrease in irritability and automaticity of the different parts of the heart, from the sinus to the apex.

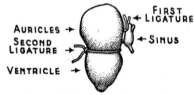

Fig. 94.—To illustrate the position of the first and second Stannius ligatures.

Heart Block.—The delay which the impulse encounters in passing from the auricles into the ventricle can be exaggerated, in the frog's heart, by applying pressure at the auriculoventricular groove. This may be done either by a ligature (known as Stannius' ligature—see Fig. 94) or by a specially constructed clamp, the Gaskell clamp. If the pressure is sufficiently great, no impulse can pass and the ventricle ceases to beat; after a certain length of time it may initiate its own beat which bears no relation to the auricular beat. If the pressure is not sufficiently great for this, only every second, third, or fourth impulse from the auricles will pass into the ventricle and hence the auricle makes two, three, or more beats to every ventricular beat. The same experiment can be made with the mammalian heart by pressure applied to the auriculoventricular bundle, Fig. 95. In certain pathologic conditions the conductivity of this bundle is reduced, and the ventricle beats less frequently than the auricle. Digitalis, frequently employed to "strengthen" the heart, reduces the conductivity of the auriculoventricular node or bundle and thereby lessens the number of impulses coming to it from the right auricle, which in these conditions is vastly accelerated. This increases the length of the filling period of the ventricles, affords the heart an opportunity for rest, and thus enables it to contract with greater strength, regularity, and efficiency.

Fibrillation or Delirium Cordis.—Normally the various muscle fibers of the ventricle contract in an orderly, or coordinate, manner, so that by their united action the pressure in the cavity is increased and the blood expelled. When a faradic current is applied to the heart for a few seconds, the fibers no longer act coordinately, some contracting before others and relaxing while the latter are in contraction. This is known as fibrillation, or delirium cordis. Because of the lack of harmonious action, in fibrillation of the ventricle no blood is discharged and circulation fails. In man ventricular fibrillation is usually irreversible and therefore fatal. Since the auricle is not absolutely necessary for the charging of the ventricle, auricular fibrillation may be compatible with life; it may also pass off. Auricular fibrillation may be detected by means of the electrocardiogram (see below). Fibrillation may be caused by the passage of a strong electric current through the body (electrocution), by mechanical stimulation(e.g., rough handling) of the heart, or by interference with the coronary circulation (see page 208). We may here state that electric currents may also interfere with the work of the respiratory center and thereby stop breathing; in such cases artificial respiration should be resorted to.

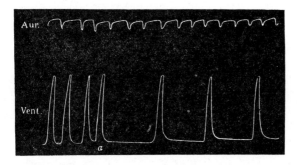

Fig. 95.—Curve illustrating the heart block produced at *a* by applying a clamp at the auriculoventricular junction. (Brubaker.)

The Electrocardiogram.—It will be recalled that the formation and propagation of an impulse (or wave of excitation) in a nerve or muscle are associated with changes in the electric potential which can be detected by a suitable galvanometer. This also applies to the heart. For this purpose the right arm and the left leg, the left and the right arms, or the left arm and left leg make contact with suitable electrodes. From these electrodes the currents are conducted to a galvanometer. A record thus obtained is known as an electrocardiogram.

From Fig. 96, which is a normal electrocardiogram, it will be noticed that, in the three heartbeats recorded, a number of larger and smaller waves occur. These waves are due to changes in the electric potential of the heart as the excitation wave, which always precedes the contraction itself, spreads from the sino-auricular node to the apex. The impulse, we have seen, is not conducted by all parts of the heart at the same speed. To determine which particular wave of the electrocardiogram is associated with a certain phase of cardiac activity, an electrocardiogram is obtained at the same time as the record of the auricular and ventricular pressures. Attention may be called to two or three points generally agreed upon.

The P-wave just precedes the contraction of the auricle and may therefore be regarded as the wave of excitation of this structure. The R-wave occurs immediately before the contraction of the ventricle; the excitation of this part is said by some to continue from R to T, and T may be considered as indicating the end of the ventricular systole. The distance between P and R indicates the interval (delay) between the auricular and the ventricular excitation. As to the cause of the other waves, Q and S, there is much doubt. Certain cardiac disturbances, especially those concerned with the generation and transmission of the impulse or wave of excitation, alter these electric waves in a characteristic manner, for which reason the electrocardiogram is of great diagnostic value.

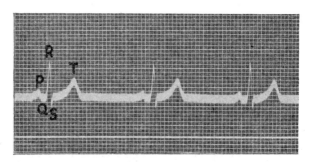

Fig. 96.—The normal electrocardiogram.

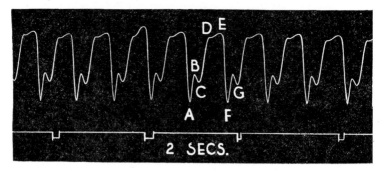

Fig. 97.—Tracing of frog's heartbeat. *AB*, auricular systole; *BC*, the first part of the auricular diastole which is completed at *F*; *CDE*, the ventricular systole; *EF*, the first part of the ventricular diastole which is completed at *G*.

II. CARDIAC ACTIVITY

Cardiac Cycle.—To follow more readily the activity of the heart, we have recourse to a kymographic record. To obtain this we proceed as follows:

The brain of the frog being destroyed, the heart is exposed and a small hook is inserted in the thick fleshy apex of the ventricle. This hook is fastened by means of a thread, to a lever the movement of which is recorded on the kymograph. In this manner the tracing in Fig. 97 was obtained. The auricular systole causes the lever to rise from *A* to *B*. The auricular diastole begins at *B;* in the tracing this is interrupted by the ventricular systole, and lasts till *F*. The contraction of the ventricle begins at *C* and is completed at *E;* here the ventricular diastole begins, and continues to *G*. The length of time consumed by each of these four phases in the action of the human heart, beating at the rate of 70 per minute, is approximately as follows:

Auricular systole	0.1 sec.	0.862
Auricular diastole	0.762 sec.	
Ventricular systole	0.379 sec.	0.862
Ventricular diastole	0.483 sec.	

From these values we may note the very short time occupied by the auricular systole, this being about one-fourth of the time taken by the ventricular systole and less than one-seventh of that of the auricular diastole; the importance of this we have spoken of on p. 191. It will also be noticed that the diastole, or resting period, of the ventricle is, at the rate of 70 beats per minute, about 25 per cent longer than the systole, or active period; this insures plenty of rest. But when the rate of the heart is greatly increased, the diastole is cut short far more than the systole.

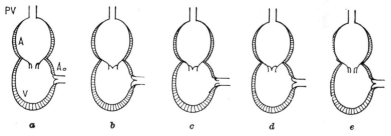

Fig. 98.—Illustrating the sequence of the opening and closing of the heart valves during systole, *b* and *c*, and during diastole, *d* and *e*, of *V*, the ventricle, *a*, the resting state of the heart; *A*, the auricle; *Ao*, the aorta or the pulmonary artery; *PV*, pulmonary veins.

Cardiac Valves.—In order that the energy expended by the contraction of the ventricle shall efficiently cause the blood to circulate and not to be regurgitated, the valves of the heart (see pp. 170 and 171) must operate properly. The opening and the closing of a valve are determined by the difference between the pressures applied to it from opposite sides.

To understand the order in which the various valves of the heart open and close, it is necessary to bear in mind that the pressure in the auricle never rises very high and that arteries are always quite well filled and, therefore, constantly show a considerable amount of pressure. During the systole of the ventricle the pressure in this cavity is higher than anywhere else in the vascular system; during its diastole it falls even below that in the auricle.

Let us begin with the completely dilated and resting state of the ventricle (its diastasis); the pressure in the aorta or in the pulmonary artery is much greater than in their corresponding ventricle and in consequence the semilunar valves are closed (Fig. 98, *a*); at this time the gradually rising pressure in this cavity causes the changes in the valves shown in *b* and *c*. The gradual reduction in ventricular pressure during the diastole and its results upon the valves are indicated in *d* and *a*. We may summarize:

Ven. Systole: 1. Closing of the auriculoventricular valves, Fig. 98, *b*.
             2. Opening of the semilunar valves, *c*.
Ven. Diastole: 3. Closing of the semilunar valves, *d*.
             4. Opening of the auriculoventricular valves, *a*.

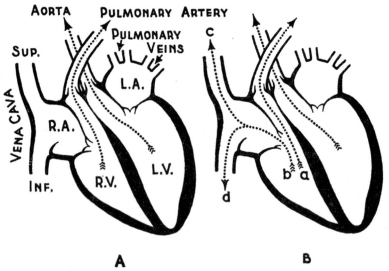

Fig. 99.—To illustrate tricuspid regurgitation. For description, see text.

The endocardium of the valves is frequently the seat of inflammation caused by the toxins from infected teeth and tonsils, by infectious diseases, such as scarlet fever and diphtheria, and especially should we mention the so-called rheumatic pains ("growing pains") in children. In the healing of these inflammations, adhesions of neighboring portions of the valves or the puckering of the valves by the formation of scar tissue (inelastic connective tissue) may prevent the proper closing of the valves (incompetent, or insufficient valves), and regurgitation ensues. The results of an insufficient valve of the heart may be far-reaching, as the following may illustrate.

Normally the full force of the ventricular systole is directed to the emptying of the blood into the pulmonary artery; this is indicated in Fig. 99, *A*, by the dotted line leading from the right ventricle into the pulmonary artery. But in tricuspid insufficiency, as shown in Fig. 99, *B*, while a portion of the blood, *a*, follows the normal pathway, another portion, *b*, regurgitates into and partly fills the right auricle. This impedes the flow of venous blood from the venae cavae, *c* and *d*, into the auricle and thereby increases the volume and the pressure of the blood in the systemic veins. The damming of the venous flow must sooner or later cause an engorgement of the capillaries, a reduction in capillary circulation (passive congestion), and an interference with tissue nutrition.

Pericardium.—The heart is held in place by the pericardium, a strong and inextensible double membrane, one layer of which is closely applied to the myocardium and forms the epicardium spoken of on page 169. The outer, or parietal, layer forms a loose sac around the heart and is firmly attached to the large blood vessels at the base of the heart and to the central tendon of the diaphragm. Between the two layers of the pericardium is the pericardial cavity in which is found a small amount of fluid (lymph) by which the heart and the membrane are kept moist; this lessens the friction that the heart experiences in its movements. Normally the amount of this fluid is very small, just enough, we may say, to moisten the surfaces.

In certain diseases of the heart the amount of pericardial fluid may increase greatly, from an ounce to even a pint; this may interfere with the proper functioning of the heart. The inelasticity of the pericardium no doubt prevents acute dilation of the heart. But with a continual excessive pressure within the pericardium, as in the above described effusion and in hypertrophy of the heart, this membrane undergoes considerable stretching. Whether this also takes place during long-continued strenuous muscle work, when a large volume of blood is returned to the heart, is a controversial problem.

The Apex Beat or Cardiac Impulse.—It is a familiar fact that with every heartbeat one may feel a thumping by placing the finger in the fourth or fifth intercostal space and about one or two inches to the left of the sternum. The cause or causes of this beat are somewhat obscure, but two factors seem to play the major part: first, the hardening of the heart muscle, and second, a change in the shape of the heart from that of a flattened cone during diastole to that of a rounded cone; this causes the heart to press more firmly against the chest wall. In persons over twenty years of age, the apex beat becomes feebler because of the greater expansion of the thorax.

Heart Sounds.—The beating of the heart is associated with the production of two distinct sounds. By noting the apex beat, it can be determined that one of the sounds is heard during the systole of the ventricle, while the other takes place during the diastole. For this reason they are sometimes called the systolic sound and the diastolic sound, but they are more commonly spoken of as the first and the second sounds. The first, or systolic, sound is of longer duration and lower pitch than the second. The pause between the first and the second sounds is shorter than that following the second sound. The first sound is heard best if the bell of the stethoscope is placed over the fifth left intercostal space, or apex beat; for the second sound the stethoscope should be placed over the second right costal cartilage (for the aortic valve closure) or over the second left cartilage (for closure of the pulmonary valve).

The cause of these sounds has given rise to much discussion; the commonly accepted idea is as follows: During the ventricular systole the auriculoventricular valves are suddenly thrown into rapid vibration, which, by being communicated to the blood, heart muscle, and thoracic wall, can be heard if the ear or, better, a stethoscope is placed on the thoracic wall. Moreover, it has been found that a skeletal muscle during its contractions produces a sound or noise; this can readily be demonstrated in the following manner. When one winks quickly and energetically, a dull rumbling sound is heard in the ears. This sound is not caused by the eyelids or their muscles, but by an extremely small muscle found in the middle ear, the stapedius muscle; the innervation of the eyelid muscles is generally associated with a simultaneous innervation of the stapedius muscle. Again, if a stethoscope is placed on the contracting muscles of the arm, a sound is heard. When the ventricular musculature contracts, a similar rumbling noise is produced which fuses with the sound caused by the vibrations of the closing auriculoventricular valves.

The second, or diastolic, sound is caused by the vibration of the closing semilunar valves. When the strength of the heartbeat is increased, the first sound is accentuated; an increase in the aortic blood pressure has this effect on the second sound. If in a beating heart the auriculoventricular valves are prevented from closing, the higher pitched part of the first sound disappears but the lower rumbling part persists.

In abnormal conditions of the valves, the regurgitation of the blood is accompanied by peculiar murmurs. Another cause of these extra sounds is stenosis (narrowing) of the outlet between the auricles and the ventricles or between the ventricles and the aorta or pulmonary artery. From this it will appear how important these sounds are in the investigations of the heart and its valves.

All or None.—From our study of the skeletal muscle we have learned that the extent of the contraction is, within limits, proportional to the strength of the stimulus; that is, the stronger the electric shock, the more forcible the contraction. In the heart this matter is quite different. If a frog's heart is brought to rest (by a ligature applied between the sinus and the auricles, Fig. 94) and is then stimulated at half-minute intervals, the extent of the contraction remains the same for any strength of adequate stimulus; there is no summation. The heart, as a whole, follows the law of all or none, as shown is Fig. 100.

It will be recalled that this holds true also for the individual fibers of a skeletal muscle, although the muscle as a whole is capable of graded contractions. The reason for this difference lies in the relation of the muscle fibers to each other. In a skeletal muscle the

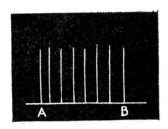

Fig. 100.—Illustrating the all-or-none phenomenon of the heart. Gradually increasing strength of stimuli from *A*, the minimal, to *B*. (Francis, Knowlton and Tuttle: Textbook of Anatomy and Physiology, The C. V. Mosby Co.)

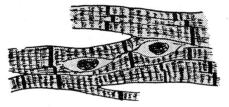

Fig. 101.—Cardiac muscle. (Hewer: Histology, The C. V. Mosby Co.)

individual fibers are isolated from each other by a sarcolemma; in the heart the imperfectly cross striated fibers by their anastomosis, Fig. 101, are brought into intimate contact with each other which permits the impulse to spread from one fiber to another throughout the whole auricle or ventricle. Hence, the contraction of any chamber of the heart is always maximal under stated conditions.

The Law of the Heart.—When in the preceding paragraph we stated that the heartbeat is always maximal, we do not mean to imply that the beats are always equally powerful. Common observation leads us to a different conclusion. But under a given condition the law of all or none holds true. The condition of the heart, however, may vary and thereby bring about either a stronger or a feebler beat. We may study one of these conditions.

The reader, no doubt, will remember that, within limits, an increase in the load applied to a skeletal muscle increases the force with which the muscle contracts on stimulation. In this respect the cardiac muscle resembles the skeletal muscle. When, for certain reasons, the return of venous blood to the heart is increased, the diastolic filling of the left ventricle (via the pulmonary circuit) is also increased; this causes a stretching of the musculature of the ventricle, and the force of the beat is augmented. In other words, the initial length of the muscle fiber determines the force of the contraction. This is known as *Starling's Law of the Heart.*

As illustrations of this law we may recall the following from our previous discussion. Muscular work by its "milking" action forces a larger volume of blood to the right heart; the stretching of its fibers enables the right ventricle to discharge the extra load of blood and thereby prevent the engorgement of the systemic veins and a rise in venous blood pressure, conditions likely to produce great damage (p. 263). The left ventricle receiving the extra blood behaves in the same manner; this increases the force and the stroke volume of the left ventricle, the systolic blood pressure, and the total volume of blood sent throughout the body.

The same principle is also demonstrated in certain abnormal conditions of the circulatory system. Thus, in aortic regurgitation there is a backing up of the blood through the insufficient semilunar valves and a greater filling of the left ventricle. This stretching of the muscle fibers results in an increased force exerted by the heart. If this condition persists for a long time, the extra work done by the heart may lead to hypertrophy of the left ventricle. We may state parenthetically that this hypertrophy is not due to multiplication of the fibers, but to an increase in the size of the fibers already present. If the ventricular musculature can move this extra blood, a proper circulation is maintained; the heart is then said to have compensated for the defect, and the individual may carry on the usual duties of life. But if extra muscular work is attempted, the increase in the venous blood returned by the muscles to the already well-filled venæ cavæ may cause so large an increase in the diastolic filling that the ventricle is unable to move the load; that is, *the ventricle fails to discharge into the aorta an amount of blood sufficient to supply the necessary oxygen to, and remove the waste products from, the muscles; breathlessness and great fatigue are soon experienced.* The same happens, without muscular exertion, when the valvular defect and the venous stagnation become progressively greater; the compensation is then said to be broken, and cardiac failure results.

The above conditions exist whenever the power of the heart muscle is greatly reduced. The weakened state may be the result of toxins formed in pneumonia, diphtheria (especially in young people), recurrent tonsillitis, influenza, typhoid, syphilis, rheumatic fevers, infected teeth, or tuberculosis, or from the excessive use of tobacco or alcohol. Again, the blood flow through the coronary system (p. 208) is greatly impeded by the sclerotic condition of these vessels, in consequence of which the heart muscle is deprived of its nutrition, and degeneration sets in. The heart may also be insufficiently nourished in anemia, or because of the lack of proper food.

Starling's law of the heart is also operative in the opposite condition of that spoken of above, namely, that of reduced diastolic intake and lessened stretching of the muscle fibers. This is seen after a hemorrhage; the heart beats feebly but with sufficient force to overcome the much reduced diastolic pressure.

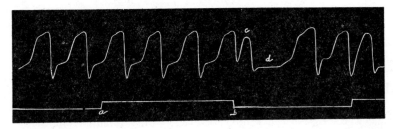

Fig. 102.—Tracing of the frog's heartbeat, showing at *a*, the refractory period, at *c*, the extrasystole, and at *d*, the compensatory pause. Single faradic shocks were thrown into the heart at *a* and *b*. Note the extra contraction near the end of the tracing.

In summary: *every heart has its margin of adaptation, or reserve power, above that necessary for the generation of a basal blood pressure.* In a normal individual the reserve power of the heart is surprisingly large, but in a weak, or so-called "low-toned," heart this margin is so limited that the generation of even a small increase in blood pressure beyond the basal is difficult or impossible (see also pp. 250 and 308).

The Refractory Period.—If the beating heart be stimulated with a single electric shock during its contraction, the heart is not affected by it; the irritability of the heart during its systole is so greatly reduced that the stimulation is without result. This is illustrated in Fig. 102, in which the frog's heart was stimulated at *a*, during the systole of the ventricle. The tracing shows that the heart continued with its usual rhythm. It will be recalled that this period of reduced irritability of a tissue during its activity is known as the refractory period. On the other hand, when the stimulation was

thrown in at *b,* during the diastole of the heart, the heart proved to
be irritable, for the stimulation was followed by a hurried contraction, *c.* This is known as the *extrasystole,* better stated, a premature
contraction, and is followed by a lengthened pause, *d,* the *compensatory pause.* The human heart sometimes gives these premature beats
which are then followed by a compensatory pause. Because of the
long refractory period, the heart, unlike the skeletal muscle, cannot
be thrown into complete tetanus.

Staircase.—Like the skeletal muscles, the quiescent heart when
stimulated with electric shocks of constant strength in fairly rapid
succession, say, one every three or four seconds, shows the "staircase" phenomenon, Fig. 103.

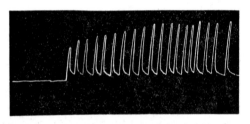

Fig. 103.—The staircase phenomenon of the heart.

Coronary Circulation.—The cardiac tissue is supplied with blood
by two arteries, the coronary arteries, which spring from the aorta,
penetrate into the tissue of the heart walls, and break up into capillaries around the muscle cells. The blood from these capillaries is
collected by the coronary veins and brought to the right auricle.

It is held by most investigators that the pressure exerted upon
the coronary vessels by the hardening of the heart wall squeezes
some of the blood out of these vessels during the first part of the
systole, but during the remainder of the systolic period the intake
into the coronary arteries ceases. During the diastole the relaxed
state of the heart muscle allows blood to flow freely through the
coronary vessels; hence the diastolic period may be regarded as the
"feeding" period of the cardiac muscle. Now, we have learned that
an increase in the heart rate is associated with a proportionately
greater shortening of the length of the diastolic than that of the
systolic period. From this it is evident that it may be possible for a
fast beating heart to receive an inadequate amount of nutrition, unless
the shortening of the diastole is compensated by an increase in the
mean arterial pressure which forces more blood through the coronary
system in a unit of time. During muscle work and digestion the
coronary flow is increased.

When a branch of a coronary artery is occluded by a thrombus (generally due to the sclerotic condition of the artery—see p. 239) the insufficient supply of oxygen to the heart muscle may cause agonizing pain—angina pectoris. Other abnormal conditions, e.g., anemia or a low diastolic pressure due to aortic regurgitation, may interfere with an adequate supply of oxygen to the heart muscle; it can therefore be readily seen that under these circumstances any bodily condition calling for increased cardiac activity may precipitate an attack of angina pectoris. The ingestion of too much food sometimes has this result, and is not infrequently called "acute indigestion." In more severe obstruction of the coronary circulation ventricular fibrillation may set in and cause sudden death.

Energy Supply for the Heart.—From the work of Evans and others it appears that cardiac muscle derives its energy only to a limited extent from glucose directly; the oxidation of lactic acid, produced from glucose by other organs of the body, serves as the chief source of energy. The heart very soon succumbs to lack of oxygen. It will be recalled that skeletal muscles can incur an oxygen debt represented by 0.3 per cent of lactic acid; but when this acid accumulates in the heart to the extent of 0.07 per cent, heart block may occur and cardiac activity becomes irregular and soon ceases. It was also found that, within limits, the mechanical efficiency increased as the work done was increased; in other words, as the heart was called upon to do more work, the conditions of the mechanism for the utilization of the liberated energy became more favorable. On the other hand, a failing heart has a lowered efficiency.

FUNCTION OF THE INORGANIC SALTS.—The heart muscle for its nourishment must be supplied not only with organic materials, such as proteins and sugars, from which it obtains energy, but also with inorganic salts. If a strip of the ventricle of a turtle's heart is immersed in a 0.7 per cent sodium chloride solution, it begins to beat and continues its activity for a long time. But finally the beat becomes feebler and feebler. If now there is added to the sodium chloride solution a few drops of a calcium chloride solution, the strength of the beat is increased. By much experimentation it has been found that the heart beats best when it is supplied with the chlorides of sodium, potassium, and calcium. A solution containing the salts in the most favorable concentration for the frog's heart is Ringer's solution having the following composition:

$$100.0 \text{ c.c. of } 0.6\% \text{ NaCl.}$$
$$1.0 \text{ c.c. of } 1.0\% \text{ CaCl}_2.$$
$$0.75 \text{ c.c. of } 1.0\% \text{ KCl.}$$

To this there may be added 1 c.c. of 1 per cent of sodium bicarbonate. If the potassium chloride is too concentrated, the heart muscle relaxes freely and may stop in diastole; potassium salts favor the diastole of the heart. Calcium chloride, on the other hand, aids the systole, and excess of it causes systolic arrest, Fig. 104. A heart brought to rest by calcium chloride may be started again by potassium chloride. The sodium chloride not only supplies the necessary osmotic pressure, but may be said to be indispensable for the origin of the heartbeat, for an excised heart placed in a cane sugar solution of the proper osmotic pressure soon ceases to beat; the beat is restored by the addition of a small amount of sodium chloride. These experiments teach us the great importance of the part played by the inorganic materials. This is true not only of the heart, for all protoplasmic structures must have certain salts at their disposal in order to do their work well.

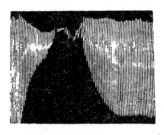

Fig. 104.—Tracing showing the effect of excess calcium salt in the Ringer's solution with which the frog's heart was perfused.

To maintain the beat of the excised mammalian heart, the coronary system is perfused with an oxygenated salt solution having the proper osmotic pressure, hydrogen ion concentration, and temperature. To this solution (0.9 per cent NaCl plus the necessary KCl and $CaCl_2$) is added a small amount of glucose. By keeping the pulmonary circulation intact with the excised heart (a ''lung-heart preparation''), the activity of a rabbit's heart can be maintained for several hours and even a human heart shortly after death has been caused to beat again.

Rate of Heartbeat.—The rate of the heartbeat under different conditions and in different persons varies so very largely that we cannot talk about a normal pulse rate. What we may call the usual rate in a normal adult, under ordinary conditions, is between 65 and 75 per minute. Some of the more common factors causing variations are:

1. AGE.—At birth the rate may be as high as 130 to 150 per minute; with increase in years the rate gradually decreases; however, in extreme old age there may be an increase.

At birth	140
1 year	120
10 years	90
Adult	70

2. Size.—The great difference in the rate of the heart of the young and the adult is not due to the difference of age, but to difference in the size of the body. A small animal always has a higher pulse rate than a larger animal; compare the pulse rate of a mouse, about 1,000, with that of an elephant, 28.

3. Sex.—Sex influences the rate, women having from 5 to 10 beats more per minute. It is possible that a difference in size plays a part in sex difference. It should also be remembered that in women and children the rate is more susceptible to variations than in men.

4. Body Position.—Position of the body causes a variation in most people, the rate being from 5 to 10 more in the erect than in the reclining position. The more robust the person, the smaller is this variation; in certain diseases the difference may be as great as 30 to 40 beats.

5. Individual Variations.—There are marked individual variations. Perfectly normal persons with pulse rates of from 120 to 130 and others with a rate between 30 and 40 per minute have been known.

6. Physical Training.—In individuals who are well trained physically the resting pulse is frequently found to be no more than 50 to 60 per minute.

7. Other Factors.—The rate is increased by: (a) muscle work (therefore decreased during sleep); (b) high body temperature (fever); (c) eating; (d) warm bath; (e) hot drink; (f) high altitude.

III. CONTROL OF THE HEART

The function of the heart is to discharge, with adequate force, an amount of blood sufficient for the metabolic needs of the body. The amount discharged in a unit of time is determined by the stroke volume and the rate of heartbeat. As the demand for blood varies from moment to moment, it is evident that the rate, force, and systolic output of the heart must be governed in accordance. This control is both neural and humoral.

The Vagus.—We have seen that the origin of the heartbeat is not dependent upon the central nervous system. But it is a fact, proved by everyday observation, that the state of mind or body can modify the action of the heart. The heart is connected with the central nervous system by means of two nerves, the vagus and the cervical sympathetic. From the brain there issue twelve pairs of cranial nerves (see Fig. 291); of these the vagus, or pneumogastric nerve, forms the tenth pair. The vagus springs from the lowest portion of the brain, known as the medulla oblongata, which may be looked upon as the connection between the brain and the spinal cord (see Figs. 266 and 277). This nerve is very widely distributed, sending branches to the heart, lungs, trachea, esophagus, stomach, pancreas, gallbladder, intestines, etc.; it is, therefore, one of the most important nerves in the body. The endings of the efferent fibers of the vagus in the heart are found in the sino-auricular and the auriculoventricular nodes.

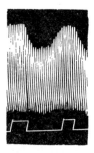

Fig. 105.—Vagal inhibition showing a decrease in the force of the beat without any change in the rate.

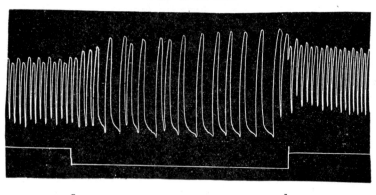

a   b

Fig. 106.—Tracing of the heartbeat of the turtle. From *a* to *b* the vagus nerve was stimulated with weak stimuli. Note the decrease in rate but not in force.

Cardiac Inhibition.—In an animal the vagus nerve may be exposed without any great difficulty. Under the influence of an anesthetic the skin in the neck, a little to either side of the larynx, is slit open; the structures immediately below the skin are pushed aside, and the carotid artery is brought to view. Alongside this vessel lies a large nerve trunk, the vagus. When the vagus on one side is cut, there is usually little or no result, but if both vagi be severed, there is a marked cardiac acceleration, Fig. 111. Stimulation of the vagus nerve may cause either a decrease in the rate, as shown in Fig. 106, or in the force without affecting the rate (Fig. 105), or a complete cessation of the heartbeat, as shown in Fig. 107. This slowing or stoppage of the heart is called cardiac inhibition. It will also be noticed in Fig. 107 that notwithstanding the continued stimulation of the vagus (up to *d*), the heart resumes its beat at *b*. This phenomenon is known as the escape from inhibition or vagal escape. This is also well illustrated in Fig. 109. The beats immediately following the inhibition are more forcible than those before the vagus was stimulated.

Cardiac Inhibition and Blood Pressure.—It is evident that a marked decrease in the activity of the heart must soon be followed by a considerable fall in the blood pressure. In Fig. 108 we see the blood pressure tracing of a dog (carotid artery); at *A* the vagus nerve was stimulated; as a result the blood pressure fell immediately to less than half its previous value. Here also we notice that the escape from inhibition restores circulation to its normal state.

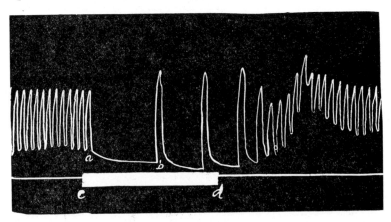

Fig. 107.—Tracing of the heartbeat of a turtle. From *c* and *d* the vagus nerve was stimulated with strong stimuli. Note escape from inhibition at *b* and the augmented beats following the inhibition.

The fall in blood pressure, due to inhibition of the heart, causes a decrease in the flow of the blood, and, as a result, the tissues are not well supplied with oxygen, and the carbon dioxide is not properly removed. This interferes with the functions of the various organs of the body, but the organ that feels this effect most speedily and severely is the central nervous system. Especially is this true of the activity of the cerebrum, the large anterior portion of the brain (see Figs. 266 and 277), which is the seat of psychic functions. These functions depend, in some manner or other, upon the continued normal activity of the cerebral cells; if these cells, either because of the want of oxygen or by poisoning due to the accumulation of carbon dioxide, cease to be active, the mental functions also are in abeyance. Hence, severe cardiac inhibition in a human being causes loss of consciousness (fainting, or syncope; see p. 650).

Cardiac Inhibitory Center.—The inhibitory fibers of the vagus nerve spring from the medulla; the particular spot where they or-

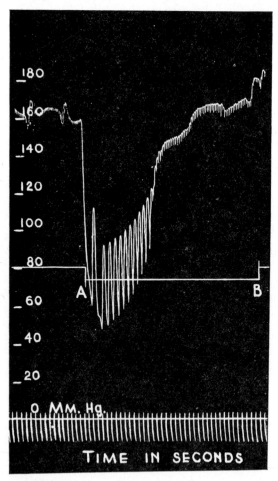

Fig. 108.—The influence of vagal stimulation upon blood pressure in a dog. From *A* to *B* the vagus was stimulated. Note the immediate and severe drop in blood pressure, the escape from inhibition, the subsequent acceleration of the heartbeat, and a greater than normal blood pressure.

iginate is known as the *cardiac inhibitory center*. It is here that these fibers come in contact with afferent nerve fibers to complete the reflex arc. The center can be influenced: (1) reflexly by impulses over the afferent nerves from the sensory surfaces of the body and (2) by impulses from the higher brain centers.

Reflex Cardiac Inhibition.—It frequently happens that the stimulation of a sensory nerve in our body is followed by a perceptible slowing of the heart; in fact, the heart may be slowed to such an extent as to cause fainting. No doubt, we can all recall instances of this sort, such as the fainting caused by a blow on the abdomen. Here the sensory nerves of the stomach and intestines are mechanically stimulated, impulses pass up the cord to the medulla; in the cardio-inhibitory center the impulses are transferred to the vagus nerve and thus to the heart. This experiment can be demonstrated in the frog by tapping the exposed intestines with the handle of a scalpel and watching the slowing of the heart. If in this experiment the medulla is destroyed or if the vagus nerves are cut, the action does not take place because the reflex arc has been broken.

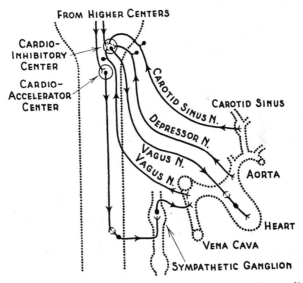

Fig. 109.—Diagram illustrating the influence exercised over the cardio-inhibitory center by the afferent nerves from the cardio-vascular sensory area.

Other instances of reflex slowing of the heart are experienced in acute dyspepsia, inflammation of the peritoneum, pain in the middle ear, etc. It has been supposed that, in some instances, death brought about by plunging into cold water may be caused in this manner. The inhalation of irritating fumes may stimulate the sensory nerves of the trachea or lungs and thereby reflexly stop the heart.

The afferent nerves from three areas, collectively known as the CARDIOVASCULAR SENSORY REGION, are of particular interest. These areas are: (1) the aorta, (2) the carotid sinus, (3) the venae cavae and right auricle.

1. AORTIC REFLEX.—When one vagus nerve is cut and its central end (connected with the brain) is stimulated, the impulse carried to the cardio-inhibitory center is returned to the heart by way of the other, still intact, vagus nerve. Sectioning the second vagus abolishes this reflex. The vagus nerve is a mixed nerve, that is, it contains both afferent and efferent fibers. The efferent fibers for the vascular system carry the impulses for inhibition to the heart. The afferent fibers which have their endings in the arch of the aorta, Fig. 109, make synaptic connections with the neurons in the cardiac inhibitory center. These fibers are stimulated by the stretching of the aortic wall when the blood pressure rises above a certain height; this results in reflex cardiac inhibition and thus prevents an abnormally high blood pressure and safeguards the heart against excessive strain.

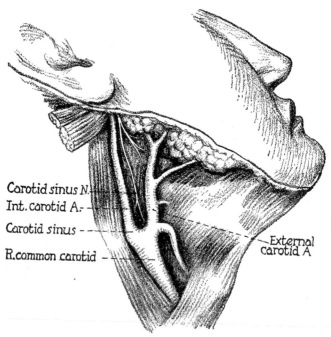

Fig. 110.—Dissection showing the carotid sinus and neighboring structures. (McGuigan: Applied Pharmacology, The C. V. Mosby Co.)

2. THE CAROTID SINUS.—From the arch of the aorta, Fig. 77, *8*, spring three large arteries: the innominate, the left common carotid, and the left subclavian artery. The innominate artery gives rise to the right common carotid. The common carotid arteries, Fig. 110, divide into the internal carotid (which supplies part of the blood to the brain) and the external carotid arteries. Upon the internal carotid artery and near its origin from the common carotid is found

a small pocket, known as the carotid sinus. The walls of this sinus are supplied with an afferent nerve, the carotid sinus nerve.

When the walls of the sinus are distended by increased internal pressure the rate of the heartbeat is diminished. The mechanically stimulated sensory nerves from the sinus excite the cardio-inhibitory center to greater activity. This can also be done by electric stimulation, and in some individuals external pressure is also effective. On the other hand, if the blood pressure in the sinus is decreased by external pressure upon the common carotid, Fig. 110, the heart is accelerated because of the lack of excitatory impulses transmitted from the sinus to the inhibitory center.

3. THE VENAE CAVAE AND RIGHT AURICLE.—The afferent fibers originating in the venae cavae, Fig. 109, and in the right auricle are stimulated by distention of these cavities due to increased venous blood pressure. Contrary to what we found true for the distention of the aorta, this causes an inhibition of the cardiac inhibitory center and in consequence the heart is accelerated. This is known as the *Bainbridge reflex*. The importance of this is seen in muscle work. We have learned that the milking action of rhythmically contracting muscles causes a large volume of blood to be forced into the veins and the right auricle. To prevent an accumulation of blood in the veins from impeding the capillary circulation (venous congestion), the blood must be more quickly moved from the right to the left heart and into the aorta; hence the necessity for inhibiting the cardiac inhibitory center. The reflex inhibitory mechanism discussed in the preceding paragraphs and the Bainbridge reflex are in constant operation and by the mutual check they exert upon each other the rate of the heart is governed to meet the demands for the amount of blood needed by the body (consult Fig. 109). And as a result it is generally true that the rate of the heartbeat varies inversely with the blood pressure (Marey's law).

When the blood pressure is very low, as after a severe hemorrhage, the vagal restraint over the heart is no longer exercised and the heart rate is much accelerated. In this condition no great force of heartbeat is necessary (Starling's law of the heart), but the small amount of blood left in the vessels must be sent as quickly, and used as often, as possible.

Tonic Action of the Vagus.—As sectioning of both vagus nerves causes cardiac acceleration (Fig. 111), we must conclude that the cardio-inhibitory center has a tonic, or constant, inhibiting influence on the heart; that is, the rate and force of the heart are, under normal conditions, constantly held in check. The vagus may be regarded as the "brake" of the heart, which may be more firmly or less firmly applied as occasion demands. While, as we have seen, certain states of mind and body cause the center to be more active and the brakes to work more strongly, other conditions take the brakes off. For example, certain gastric disturbances inhibit the inhibitory center and palpitation of the heart results. The tonicity of the center is due, no doubt, to afferent impulses originating in the different parts of the body, especially from the aorta and carotid sinus.

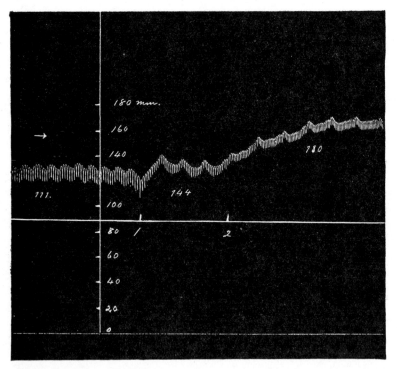

Fig. 111.—To show the effect of section of the two vagi in the dog upon the rate of heartbeat and the blood pressure: 1 marks the section of the vagus on the right side; 2, section of the second vagus. The numerals on the vertical mark the blood pressures; the numerals on the blood pressure record give the rate of heartbeats. (Dawson.)

Influence of Higher Brain Centers.—That emotions have a pronounced effect upon the heart is well known. By the activity of the cerebral cells concerned with mental conditions, impulses are sent to the cardio-inhibitory center. Some emotional states accelerate the heart rate, but others, especially those which are painful and highly disagreeable, may cause inhibition even to the point of complete heart failure and may result in fainting.

The Neurohumoral Theory and Inhibition.—From our study of the nerve impulse, it will be recalled that it is quite generally held that the transfer of the wave of excitation from one histologic structure to another is brought about by the formation or liberation of a chemical compound between the two structures (p. 136). The following investigation concerning cardiac inhibitions signally substantiates this theory.

The heart, *a*, in Fig. 112, is supplied from a reservoir of physiologic salt solution which is forced by the contraction of this heart through a tube leading into the heart of another animal. When the vagus nerve of the first heart is stimulated, not only the donor's heart, *a*, but also, after the lapse of a certain length of time, the heart, *b*, is

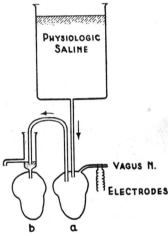

Fig. 112.—Diagram of apparatus by which the heart, *b*, is perfused with the fluid which has circulated through heart, *a*. (After Bain.)

slowed down. The inhibition of the second heart must have been caused by a chemical compound, a vagal substance, formed in heart *a* by the stimulation of its vagus nerve. In experiments on guinea pigs, it has been found that stimulation of the maternal vagus induces a slowing of the heart of the fetus. The vagal substance is generally held to be acetylcholine, a compound formed by the union of choline and acetic acid. Applied to the exposed heart, acetylcholine brings about cardiac inhibition which, similar to the inhibition produced by vagus stimulation, is abolished by the application of atropine. This property of acetylcholine is one of the most delicate tests for its presence; 1/1,000,000 milligram, it is stated, can be detected. It is very rapidly destroyed by the blood and tissues of the body by a ferment called cholinesterase. In our study of the nervous system, especially of the autonomic system, we shall have occasion to speak more fully about acetylcholine and other physiologically related compounds.

Action of Chemical Compounds.—The cardio-inhibitory mechanism, which includes the endings of the vagus nerve in the heart as well as the nerve fibers and the center, is readily affected by certain drugs. Atropine, the poisonous alkaloid of the deadly nightshade, makes the heart beat faster because it neutralizes the action of acetylcholine generated by the vagal endings in the heart. The result of its action is therefore similar to that of cutting of both vagus nerves. Muscarin, the toxic principle of poisonous mushrooms, stimulates the vagus endings and thereby slows the heart to a complete standstill. A heart arrested by muscarin, acetylcholine, or pilocarpine may be revived by atropine.

The Cardiac Accelerator.—The other nerve to the heart is the cervical sympathetic. Stimulation of this nerve, Fig. 113, may cause an increase in the rate or force of the heartbeat, for which reason it is called the cardiac augmentor or accelerator. It is supposed that this nerve plays a less important part in regulating the action of the heart than the vagus. The quickening of the heart during muscle work is said not to take place when the sympathetic is cut.

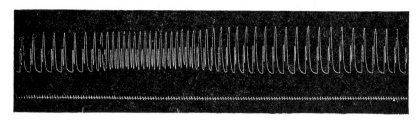

Fig. 113.—Tracing of the frog's heart, showing the effect of stimulation of the sympathetic nerve. (Brodie.)

By some it is maintained that a cardiac acceleratory center is located in the medulla; if so, it is highly probable that a reciprocal relation exists between it and the cardiac inhibitory center. For example, it is possible that in the Bainbridge reflex there is not only an inhibition of the inhibitory center but also a stimulation of the acceleratory center. It is also conceivable that certain mental conditions may cause acceleration of the heart by stimulating the center of the cervical sympathetic, as well as by inhibiting the cardio-inhibitory center. If both nerves exert a tonic influence, as some suppose, the rate of the heartbeat must be the algebraic sum of their combined influences.

Adrenalin, the internal secretion of the adrenal glands, exerts a powerful stimulating action upon all structures innervated by the sympathetic nervous system (see Chap. XXIII). Injected into the blood stream, or directly into the heart, adrenalin greatly accelerates the heartbeat. The augmented heart action following stimulation of the cervical sympathetic is due to the production in the heart of an adrenalin-like compound; this was demonstrated by showing that the fluid passing through the heart during the period of sympathetic nerve stimulation was capable of causing inhibition of the muscles of the stomach (p. 382).

CHAPTER XI

VASOMOTOR CONTROL

I. NECESSITY FOR VASOMOTOR REGULATION

Capacity of the Blood Vessels.—It will be recalled that the circulation of the blood depends not only upon the rhythmical activity of the heart, but also upon a certain condition of the blood vessels. To illustrate this, no better experiment can be made than the following: Let us take two frogs, *A* and *B;* of *A* we destroy the brain, and of *B,* both brain and spinal cord. On exposing the hearts, without loss of blood, it is noticed that both are beating at approximately the same rate. When the web of the hind leg is examined, it is found that in *A* there is a brisk circulation through the vessels of the web, but in *B* there is no flow at all. Closer inspection of the hearts will reveal a marked difference. While both hearts are beating, the heart of *A* during its diastole swells up with blood and assumes a bright red color, and during the systole the ventricle becomes very pale. The heart of frog *B* has the same color throughout the whole cardiac cycle; in other words, the diastolic flushing and the systolic paling do not take place. The heart of *A* is receiving and sending blood and hence there is a circulation; but the other heart is not receiving any blood and, therefore, not sending any, and, as a consequence, there is no circulation in the body. This lack of circulation cannot be sought in the heart, for it is doing its duty. When the abdominal wall is cut open and the blood vessels on the surface of the stomach and elsewhere are examined, another striking difference is seen. In frog *A,* with only the brain destroyed, these vessels are small and very few of the branches can be detected; in *B,* on the other hand, the blood vessels in the abdominal organs are much larger, and the smaller branches, invisible in *A,* can be clearly discerned. And here lies the secret of the lack of circulation in the second frog; all, or nearly all, of the blood of frog *B* has collected in the abdominal vessels, and none is returning to the heart.

Intravascular Hemorrhage.—Compared with the amount of blood in them, the blood vessels of an animal are very large; all the blood, in fact, can be held and stored away in the blood vessels of the abdomen. Sometimes this happens, as in frog *B* spoken of above, and we say that *the animal has bled to death in his own blood vessels*—intravascular hemorrhage. The blood stagnates in these large vessels, none returns to the heart, and the animal dies of intravascular hemorrhage. If these blood vessels are so large, or, stated in other terms, if the amount of blood is so small, how can there ever be any circulation? The answer is, under normal conditions all the vessels never assume simultaneously their maximum size, for reasons we shall now consider. In this chapter we shall also discover how the body derives the greatest amount of good out of the small quantity of blood.

II. NERVOUS CONTROL

Vasomotor Nerves.—Blood vessels are supplied with smooth muscle fibers arranged in two layers (Figs. 79 and 80): (1) the circular muscles, in which the fibers are arranged around the lumen; these are more abundant than (2) the longitudinal fibers which run parallel with the lumen of the artery. It is the circular muscles which are of great interest to us. By their contraction the lumen becomes smaller and, therefore, the capacity of the arteries is decreased, while their relaxation has the opposite effect. These muscles are especially abundant in the smaller arteries and arterioles where the bed of the vascular system is very large. Like the heart, they are under the control of the central nervous system, with which they are connected by means of nerves.

Claude Bernard, in 1851, was the first to discover these nerves. In the rabbit the vagus and the cervical sympathetic nerves lie as two distinct nerves alongside the carotid artery. In an albino (white) rabbit the blood vessels in the ear can be seen very readily, especially when the ear is held up to the light. Claude Bernard exposed the left cervical sympathetic in an albino rabbit, and, on cutting it, he noticed that the blood vessels in the left ear were much larger than those in the other ear; that is, the blood vessels on the left side had dilated. As a result of the greater volume of the blood flowing through it, the left ear had a redder color and was warmer than its mate. The cervical sympathetic must, therefore, exercise some influence on the circular muscle fibers of these blood vessels: this is corroborated by the fact that stimulation of the peripheral end (the end toward the ear) causes the vessels to become smaller. An efferent nerve which governs the vascular muscles is termed a vasomotor nerve, and, if the stimulation of the vasomotor nerve causes a constriction of the vessels, it is called a *vasoconstrictor nerve*.

The opposite sort of nerve was also discovered by Claude Bernard. The submaxillary salivary gland (Fig. 164) is supplied with a nerve called the chorda tympani, a branch of the seventh cranial, or facial, nerve. When this nerve is stimulated, the blood vessels of the gland dilate; hence, there are *vasodilator* fibers in this nerve. It must also be clear that the dilation of a blood vessel may be brought about either by inhibiting the action of the constrictor or by stimulation of the dilator nerve.

A. The Vasoconstrictor Mechanism

1. VASOCONSTRICTOR NERVES

From our discussion in Chapter IX of the mechanics of circulation it can readily be seen that the constriction of the smaller arteries and arterioles of a certain organ must cause:

a. An increase in the peripheral resistance.

b. An increase in the blood pressure on the heart side of the constriction (see Fig. 114).

c. A decrease in the amount of blood flowing through the artery and its capillaries. If the part is a superficial part, such as the skin, a blanching and a lowering of temperature result.

d. A decrease in the volume of the organ, as less blood is supplied to the organ. This can be ascertained, it will be recalled, by means of the plethysmograph, Fig. 89.

e. A lowering of the pressure in the veins draining this part.

If the organ concerned is a relatively small organ, the constriction of its vessels has little or no effect on the general blood pressure. Even when the area of vascular constriction is large, this may still be true, for, as we shall see a little later on, a constriction in one large area is normally associated with a vascular dilation in some other part of the body. And while the dilation of an artery causes a greater volume of blood to be sent through the part of the body supplied by this artery, if a large number of arterioles dilate simultaneously, the increase in the size of the bed and the lowering of the peripheral resistance are so great that a lesser volume of blood is sent; in fact, as we have shown above, there may be no circulation at all.

2. VASOCONSTRICTOR CENTER

The vasoconstrictor nerves belong to the sympathetic division of the autonomic nervous system (p. 82). The fibers from the nerve cell bodies in the vasoconstrictor center of the medulla oblongata (Fig. 115) pass down, and end at various levels in, the spinal cord. Here synaptic connections are made with preganglionic fibers of the sympathetic nervous system. These fibers terminate in a sympathetic ganglion where connections are made with the postganglionic fibers. The postganglionic fibers transmit the impulses to the blood vessels.

Plate II.—Illustration showing the appearance of the blood vessels in the ears of a white
rabbit. "To show the contrast between the constricted vessels still connected with the vasoconstrictor center (left ear) and the control dilated vessels that have been disconnected from
that center (right ear). Drawing made late in the experiment when the animal was apparently
in a state of deep shock. The strong vasoconstriction in the left ear was replaced by a wide
dilatation as soon as the connection of this ear with the vasomotor center was severed." (From
Selig and Joseph: Journal of Laboratory and Clinical Medicine, 1: 283, 1916.) This illustration
shows the continued marked activity of the vasoconstrictor center in the *ears* of animals when
they are apparently "in a state of deep shock." (Jackson: Experimental Pharmacology and
Materia Medica, The C. V. Mosby Co.)

The blood vessels of the skin and of the abdominal organs are especially well supplied with vasoconstrictor nerves. Those for the many large abdominal blood vessels run in the splanchnic nerves and have their cell bodies in the middle and lower part of the thoracic region of the spinal cord.

The vasoconstrictor center is influenced (*a*) reflexly by afferent impulses over sensory nerves (*b*) by the activity of higher brain centers, and (*c*) chemically by the condition of the blood.

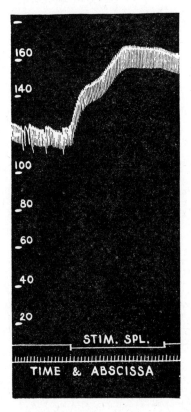

Fig. 114.—Curve showing the effect of stimulation of the left splanchnic nerve on blood pressure. (Macleod.)

a. **Reflex Vasoconstriction.**—An everyday example of reflex constriction or dilation of blood vessels is seen in the paling of the skin in cold, and the flushing in warm weather. When one hand is placed in ice water, the temperature of the other hand is lowered. The stimulation of the sense organ, Fig. 115, stimulates the "cold" nerves; these convey the impulse to the vasoconstrictor center which transmits it to the blood vessels of both hands. On the other hand,

the stimulation of the "heat" nerves of the skin causes the vasoconstrictor center to be more or less inhibited, and the superficial vessels
dilate.   To this may be due to the enervation resulting from exposing
the body to hot baths and to intense sunlight.   The stimulation of
the bare arms or neck by a cold draught may cause constriction of the
vessels of the pharynx and nasal mucosa.

Sensory nerves, such as the above-described "cold" nerves, are
spoken of as *pressor nerves,* because reflexly, that is, by way of the
vasoconstrictor center, they cause an increase of the blood pressure
in the vessels concerned.   Sensory nerves, like the "heat" nerves
of the skin, which produce a fall in the blood pressure, by reflexly

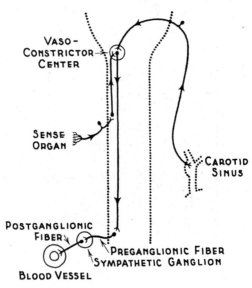

Fig. 115.—Diagram showing the influence of the carotid sinus on the vasoconstrictor center.

causing a dilation of the vessels, are called *depressor nerves.*   It
should be borne in mind that vasomotor nerves are efferent, and
that pressor and depressor nerves are afferent nerves.   Pressor and
depressor nerve fibers are found in almost every sensory nerve.   For
example, stimulation of the sciatic nerve with feeble faradic shocks,
once per second, causes a dilation of the vessels and a fall in blood
pressure; on the other hand, greater frequency of stimulation is
followed by a constriction (as shown by the plethysmograph) and a
rise in pressure.   In general, we may say that all strong or painful
stimulation of any afferent nerve results in a higher blood pressure;
these are therefore pressor nerves.   To this last statement, however,

we must make two exceptions, namely, the cardiac depressor and the afferent nerves from the carotid sinus, which we shall now discuss.

THE AORTIC OR CARDIAC DEPRESSOR.—It will be recalled that in the wall of the aorta are found sensory nerve fibers of the vagus nerve. In the rabbit these fibers form an independent nerve lying alongside the vagus, but in most animals (dogs, e.g.) the afferent (depressor) and the efferent (inhibitory) fibers are found in a common nerve trunk.   When the depressor fibers are stimulated by distention of the aortic wall, there is, in addition to the cardiac inhibition studied in the preceding chapter, a marked fall in the blood pressure due to the dilation of the blood vessels, Fig. 116.   That this last result is not merely due to a slowing of the heart can be demonstrated in a dog by first cutting both vagi and then stimulating the central end of one nerve; the usual fall in pressure results although the heart

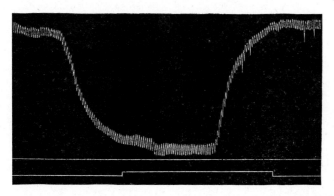

b   *a*
Fig. 116.—Tracing showing the fall in blood pressure caused by stimulation of the depressor from *a* to *b*. Record to be read from right to left. (Macleod, after Bayliss.)

is not affected. By this neural mechanism an excessively high blood pressure caused by abnormal vasoconstriction can be avoided and thus the heart is safeguarded against too great a load.   It should be noted, however, that in muscular work the blood pressure rises in spite of this depressor mechanism, and the heart rate is much accelerated; in a healthy heart this works no injury.

THE CAROTID SINUS.—In the previous chapter we discussed the location and nerve supply of this area (see Figs. 109 and 110).   Similar to the depressor nerve endings in the aorta, the nerve endings in the sinus are normally stimulated by the distention of the walls of the sinus by the blood pressure.   The impulse thereby created is carried by afferent nerves to the cardiac inhibitory center and the vasoconstrictor center.   The first mentioned center is stimulated, and the heart rate is reduced; the vasoconstrictor center is inhibited, and the blood vessels become dilated; and, as a result, the blood pressure is reduced. This is beautifully shown by experiments of which Fig. 117 is a record. In this experiment the common carotid arteries were clamped so as not to allow any blood to flow into the sinus. The pressure in the femoral artery rose to 280 mm. Hg. When at the point *b* the clip on one of the carotids is removed, the sinus wall is stretched, and as a result the vasoconstrictor center is inhibited and the blood pressure drops to 210 mm. Removal, at *c,* of the clip on the other carotid is followed by a drop of the femoral blood pressure to 180 mm. Hg. If previous to the removal of the clips the afferent nerves from the sinuses (Fig. 110) are severed, the removal of the clips at *d* and *e,* Fig. 117, has no effect on blood pressure.

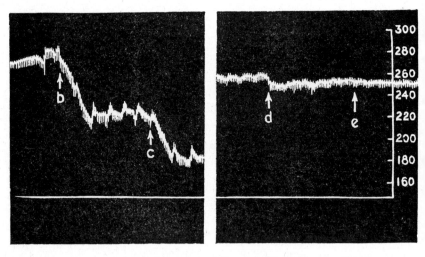

Fig. 117.—Illustrating the effect of carotid sinus stimulation on blood pressure. For explanation, see text. (C. Heymans.)

External pressure applied to the carotid artery may also lower blood pressure; persons with hypersensitive sinuses should, for this reason, avoid tight collars, and bending the head far backward as in looking up.

SPINAL CENTERS AND PERIPHERAL ACTION.—As described in a previous section, the neurons of the vasoconstrictor center in the medulla, Fig. 115, send their axons to the preganglionic neurons which have their cell bodies in the spinal cord. These second neurons are indirectly connected with the blood vessels. The cutting of the spinal cord in the lower cervical region separates all the blood vessels from the medullary center and their dilation causes a tremendous fall in blood pressure; however, if the animal survives, the pressure gradually rises. This must be attributed to the subsidiary spinal centers which, in the absence of the controlling impulses from the chief medullary center, acquire a certain amount of independent activity, for, if now the cord is destroyed, the blood vessels again dilate and the blood pressure falls. Cutting a vasoconstrictor nerve causes the muscles in the vessel wall to relax completely. Eventually, however, the arterioles and capillaries may regain their normal caliber; the cause of this is an unsettled question.

b. Influence of Higher Brain Centers.—The activity of the vasoconstrictor center is readily modified by mental conditions; of this we have such common illustrations as the blushing of shame and the pallor of fear, the first being a dilation, and the second, a constriction, of the blood vessels of the face. Strong emotions may cause inhibition of the vasoconstrictor center to such a degree that the resulting dilation of the vessels leads to syncope, or fainting. In other acute mental strains and emotional stresses the blood pressure may become abnormally high. But whether a continued state of mind, e.g., worry or sorrow, can for any length of time affect the caliber of the vessels is doubtful. Because of emotional influences upon both the heart and the blood vessels the first two or three blood pressure readings from an individual not familiar with the procedure may not be very reliable. By enclosing the spleen or a part of the liver of an animal in a plethysmograph, it has been shown that emotional excitement may decrease the size of these organs, due to vasoconstriction.

B. Venomotor Nerves

It has been shown that certain veins, e.g., the portal and mesenteric veins, are supplied with nerves whose stimulation results in a diminution of the caliber of these vessels.

C. Vasodilators

We have seen that dilation of blood vessels can be induced by the stimulation of certain afferent nerves, as, for example, the depressor of the aorta. This reflex vasodilation could be the result either of the inhibition of the vasoconstrictor center or of the stimulation of a vasodilator center which functions solely in sending dilating impulses to the blood vessels. The large fall in blood pressure following the stimulation of the afferent nerve from the aorta or carotid sinus is an illustration of the former method. But it will be recalled that the stimulation of certain efferent nerves causes dilation of the vessels supplied by these nerves; this can be understood only on the supposition that vasodilator centers are present. There is some evidence for the existence of a chief vasodilator center in the medulla. However, we may note that, in distinction from the constrictors, the vasodilator nerves have a limited distribution and their action is therefore more local; that is, instead of controlling the blood pressure in general and affecting the distribution of blood over large areas and many organs of the body, they govern the local demand of a small part or of a single organ. We find dilators especially supplied to the glands where a large quantity of blood for a relatively short length of time is wanted. It is perhaps well to hold that subsidiary dilator centers are located in the various parts of the central nervous system, each one governing a limited part of the body closely related to it; thus, a vasodilator center for the vessels of the salivary glands is perhaps located in the medulla oblongata and that for the sexual organs, in the sacral region of the spinal cord. Such a local vasodilator center can be influenced reflexly and emotionally and is active only when the part of the body innervated by this particular center is in need of more blood because of increased activity. For instance, the stimulation of the gustatory nerves during eating reflexly evokes a dilation of the vessels of the salivary glands; certain emotions have the same effect upon the center governing the vessels of the sex organs.

III. CHEMICAL CONTROL

Many substances are known to increase or decrease blood pressure by influencing the vasomotor mechanism. Some of these are produced in the body. We may discuss a few of them.

Carbon Dioxide.—The carbon dioxide of the blood stimulates the vasoconstrictor center, hence the great increase in blood pressure during the early stages of asphyxiation. We may call attention to the very high blood pressure which follows cardiac inhibition, as illustrated in Fig. 108. During the inhibition there is a temporary asphyxiation, and the accumulation of CO_2 in the blood stimulates the vasoconstrictor center and, it is claimed, also the heart itself.

On the other hand, it is a matter of common observation that over-ventilation of the lungs, as by voluntary deep inspiration and expiration for a period of 3 or 4 minutes, brings about a feeling of giddiness. By some it is held that the expulsion of a large amount of CO_2 from the blood by the overventilation deprives the vasoconstrictor center of its proper stimulation and as a consequence vasodilation and a fall in blood pressure take place; this lessens the cerebral circulation.

Adrenalin.—Just above the kidneys lie the adrenals, or suprarenal glands, Fig. 219. The medullary part of these glands secretes a hormone, adrenalin, which on being injected into the blood stream causes a tremendous rise in the blood pressure. From Fig. 118 it will be seen that the pressure rises very quickly after the injection of the adrenalin and also that this high pressure is maintained for but a brief length of time. Locally applied adrenalin stimulates the nerve endings in the arterial wall, for which reason it is used in minor operations on the eye, nose, etc., to stop hemorrhage in small vessels.

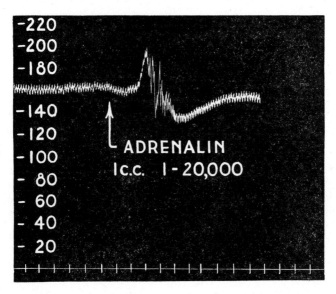

Fig. 118.—Illustrating the effect of the injection of adrenalin on blood pressure. (Courtesy of Dr. E. G. Gross.)

Cannon has laid great stress upon emotional states influencing the amount of adrenalin formed (see Chap. XXIII). He found that when a cat becomes anxious or is in great fright or rage, the amount of adrenalin in the blood is increased. It is possible, according to Cannon, that in rage the changed distribution of the blood (due to the great constriction of the abdominal vessels), the increased action of the heart, and the rise in blood pressure, are brought about by this increased formation of adrenalin.

Pituitrin.—From the pituitary body, or hypophysis, of the brain (see Figs. 279 and 291) an internal secretion is obtained which on injection into the blood stream increases blood pressure. The rise in pressure is not as great as that obtained with adrenalin, but it lasts much longer.

Lactic Acid.—It will be recalled that lactic acid is produced during muscular work. This acid decreases vascular tonus and therefore may produce a local dilation during functional activity and thereby increase the blood supply to the muscles.

Histamine.—This compound is found in many of the tissues, especially in the lungs and the mucosa of the stomach and intestines. It causes a marked dilation of the capillaries and arterioles. We shall consider this more in detail in Chapter XII.

Ephedrin.—This has an effect similar to that of adrenalin, Fig. 119. For its constricting action it is much used in bad colds and hay fever. When applied locally as a spray or ''drops'' or when inhaled it causes an immediate shrinkage of the congested blood vessels of the nasal mucosa; this effect persists for two or three hours. The opening of the nasal passages by the constriction of the vessels leads to freer and more comfortable breathing.

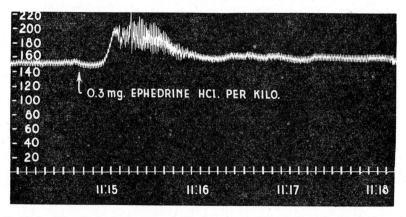

Fig. 119.—The effect of ephedrine on blood pressure. (Courtesy of Dr. E. G. Gross.)

Chloroform greatly depresses the activity of the vasoconstrictor center; this constitutes one of the dangers in the use of this drug. *Ether* has generally no effect on this center. *Nicotine,* according to Sollmann, causes powerful stimulation of the vasoconstrictor center, but excessive smoking may lower blood pressure considerably. *Alcohol* dilates the blood vessels, acting as a depressant on the vasomotor center; especially are the cutaneous vessels dilated, which accounts for the warmth felt after taking alcohol on a cold day.

IV. TONICITY OF THE VASOMOTOR MECHANISM

The vasoconstrictor center is constantly discharging impulses to the blood vessels, maintaining thereby a tonic contraction of their muscles and a continual arterial constriction; this activity of the vascular system is spoken of as *vasomotor,* or *arterial, tonus.* The existence of such a tonic influence by this center has been demonstrated by severing the physiologic connection between the center and a large number of blood vessels, as can be done, for example, by cutting the splanchnic nerves which innervate the abdominal vessels.

This always results in a very extensive fall in blood pressure because of the loss of the tonicity of the muscles in the walls of the blood vessels. *Upon this arterial tonus depends very largely the amount of blood pressure; in fact, as we have seen from the experiments on frogs, circulation itself is made possible by means of it.* The tonic action of the vasoconstrictor system is due largely, if not entirely, to (*a*) the constant stream of afferent impulses from the various sensory surfaces to the vasoconstrictor center, and (*b*) the chemical stimulation by compounds (hormones, waste products) formed in the body. Which of these two factors plays the predominating part is a matter of dispute. Our discussion of the influence of the lack and of the accumulation of carbon dioxide in the blood lends support to the view that this waste product, or H ions, play an important rôle in maintaining the vasomotor tonus.

V. RECIPROCAL CARDIOVASCULAR CONTROL

Coordination Between Heart and Vessels.—In order that the tissues may be adequately supplied with blood and at the least expenditure of cardiac energy, a close correlation must exist between the nervous mechanism governing the heart and that controlling the size of the blood vessels. We have seen that a decrease in the heart rate or in the stroke volume, which tends to lower the general blood pressure, is associated with a compensatory constriction of the vessels; this is brought about by the carotid sinus which in this manner provides a sufficient amount of blood to the brain. This mechanism may, however, establish a vicious circle: for example, a failing heart is no longer able to maintain the usual blood pressure; this induces a constriction of the blood vessels and thereby places a still heavier burden upon the already overtaxed heart.

On the other hand, a general increase in blood pressure causes reflexly (by the aortic and carotid sinus mechanism) a decrease in cardiac activity. When the blood pressure is reduced by relaxation of the vessels or by hemorrhage, the rate of the heart is increased. Again, when the venous return to the heart is augmented, the Bainbridge reflex causes an acceleration of the heart output and thereby prevents an excessive distention of the veins and a high capillary blood pressure.

Reciprocal Vasomotor Control.—The various parts of the vascular mechanism, exclusive of the heart, also bear a reciprocal relation to each other. When the cutaneous vessels are constricted under the influence of cold, those of the abdominal area dilate, and vice versa (see p. 245). Again, we find a reciprocal relationship between the blood vessels of the muscles and those of the splanchnic area. During severe physical work the muscles must be supplied with a greater volume of blood in order that the increased metabolism may be carried on. To accomplish this, the arterioles and capillaries of the active muscles dilate and a compensatory constriction takes place in the splanchnic area; the cutaneous vessels may also participate in this constriction, at least until the excessive heat produced by the muscle work renders it necessary to increase the cutaneous circulation in order to prevent an excessive rise in body temperature.

From these discussions the importance of impulses originating in the cardiovascular sensory area in controlling the cardio-inhibitory and the vasoconstrictor centers must be apparent. It is largely by this mechanism that the amount of blood discharged by the heart in a unit of time (i.e., the circulating blood volume) and the amount of peripheral resistance (as determined by the condition of the blood vessels) are regulated.

VI. CAPILLARY ACTIVITY*

Independent Activity.—It has been known for some time that capillaries, under certain conditions, constrict and dilate. That the capillaries play an active part in these changes and are not merely passively influenced by the blood pressure and the flow in the arterioles and venules is evident from the following facts: In viewing a certain field of a frog's tongue or web, a capillary, previously closed and empty, may be seen to dilate and fill with blood; at the same time other capillaries fed by the same arteriole and drained by the same venule undergo no change. Again, an individual capillary can be made, by mechanical stimulation, to dilate, and such dilation may begin at the venous end of the capillary. This contractility is said to reside in the endothelial cells themselves.

Control of Capillaries.—The capillary constriction and dilation seem to be under the influence of two distinct forces: chemical and nervous. It has been proved conclusively that oxygen causes their constriction, and acids, such as carbonic acid (from CO_2 and H_2O) and lactic acid, bring about dilation. Gaskell found that in a dilution as great as 1:15,000 lactic acid has a dilating effect. In the following chapter we shall have occasion to discuss the action of these and certain other compounds more fully.

It is generally conceded that the capillaries are also influenced by impulses over the sympathetic nerves. For example, by micro-

---

*The function of the capillaries in the exchange of materials between the blood and the tissues is dealt with in Chap. XII.

scopic observation it has been shown that the pallor of the face during emotions is due to capillary constriction.

Similar to the arteries, the capillaries exhibit a certain amount of tonus, or constant contraction, which, as we shall see subsequently, is imperative in view of the large capacity of these vessels. Krogh maintains that this may be due very largely to the stimulating influence of pituitrin; Dale attributes it to adrenalin. Hooker contends that the general tonicity of the capillaries throughout the body is brought about by the nerve impulses over the sympathetic nerves, and that their dilation, which is generally a local affair determined by the needs of a particular tissue or organ for an increased blood supply, is mediated by chemical stimuli, among which we may list carbonic and lactic acid. The presence of these metabolites, produced by the activity of the organ, is indicative of the necessity of a larger blood supply. When this need has been filled, either the tonic activity of the sympathetic nerves, or the chemical stimulation by a surplus of oxygen, leads to the reduction in the size of the capillaries until such time as the tissue by its increased activity shall again demand a greater volume of blood. The loss of the capillary tonicity will be reviewed more fully under the heading of Shock.

Mechanical Stimulation.—Most of us have observed that drawing a blunt instrument across the skin leaves a temporary white or red mark. This is known as a *tache*.* When the instrument is drawn lightly over the surface of the arm a white line makes its appearance after the lapse of from 15 to 20 seconds and disappears in about 3 or 4 minutes. The line is due to the absence of blood along the pathway described by the instrument. That this emptying of the vessels is caused by the active and independent constriction of the capillaries which are mechanically stimulated is borne out by the fact that the same effect is obtained when the circulation has been stopped by a sufficiently tight bandage around the upper arm.

With a slightly greater pressure, the tache is a red line lasting for a considerable time and bordered on both sides by a white line which may speedily disappear. In this instance the stronger pressure caused capillary dilation in the immediate neighborhood of the pressure. Very strong mechanical stimulation gives rise to a general reddening around the stimulated area; this is due to dilation of the arterioles. Because of the augmented circulation, the temperature of the skin is raised. We shall refer to this matter in our study of lymph formation.

Hyperemia, or Congestion.—On removing the hand which has been held in warm water for some time, we readily notice the bright red color and a certain amount of swelling and warmth. These changes are indications of an increased blood supply to the capillaries beyond the usual amount. This is an illustration of a condi-

---

*Tache (tahsh) = spot.

tion known as hyperemia (*hyper,* above or more; *haima,* blood), or congestion. Hyperemia may be brought about in two ways:

1. ACTIVE, OR ARTERIAL, HYPEREMIA.--This form of hyperemia is caused by the dilation of arterioles and capillaries in a *restricted* area. As a result, the amount of blood in, and coursing through, the capillaries is largely increased. Active hyperemia may be functional or inflammatory. The former is brought about by chemical stimulation by metabolic products normally arising in the body and favors the exchange of materials between the blood and the tissues. In inflammatory hyperemia the stimulating agencies are produced by injury of any form to the cells. These substances also greatly increase the permeability of the capillary wall and will be spoken of in connection with the subject of lymph formation (Chap. XII). The capillary dilation and the increased permeability of the wall give rise to the four cardinal symptoms of inflammation: color, heat, swelling, and pain. If the vascular dilation is marked and widespread throughout the body, the condition is known as shock (see Chap. XII).

2. PASSIVE, OR VENOUS, HYPEREMIA.—Whenever there is an interference with the passage of blood from the capillaries and into the venules, the capillaries become engorged with blood and blood pressure is greatly increased. This constitutes passive hyperemia and may be readily illustrated by tying a string around a finger. In this condition the blood stagnates and soon the oxyhemoglobin loses all its oxygen and the resultant reduced hemoglobin, as seen through the skin, appears blue (cyanosis). It is evident that the supply of food and oxygen to the tissue is cut off; this soon leads to serious cellular changes.

VII. HYPERTENSION AND ARTERIOSCLEROSIS

These two terms, popularly called "high blood pressure" and "hardened arteries," respectively, are so very common at the present time that a few remarks concerning them may not be amiss. At the outset it must be realized that, although these two conditions are frequently found simultaneously in an individual, they are not identical, for the one may be present without the other. Contrary to the general opinion that a high blood pressure is always and only associated with advanced age, in 650 school children Dawson found 8 per cent having a pressure in excess of 130 mm. of Hg. Among 5,122 male students at the University of Minnesota 9 per cent showed, by repeated examinations over a period of three years, a systolic pressure above 140 mm. of Hg. On the other hand, some elderly people have no higher pressure than young adults. What constitutes hypertension? It is difficult to draw a sharp line between so-called "normal" pressure and high pressure, but perhaps it is best to regard a pressure of 140 mm. Hg systolic and 100 diastolic pressure as the dividing line. Few subjects in physiology and pathology are of greater importance than that of hypertension. In fact, it has been stated that hypertension is more destructive than cancer, tuberculosis, or syphilis. When we realize the disastrous results of high blood pressure and arteriosclerosis (see p. 239) and that, according to Robinson and Bruser, at least 40 per cent of adults are actually or incipiently hypertensive, this statement may not be exaggerated.

From our study of pressure and resistance, it logically follows that a high blood pressure must be associated with unusually great peripheral resistance. When we inquire into the cause of this increased resistance offered by the arterioles, we meet with such divergent opinions that nothing seems certain except that *"a constitutional predisposition plays a dominating rôle in a large percentage of patients."* Ayman found that when both parents showed hypertension, the incidence of high blood pressure in the children reached 45.3 per cent; in contrast with this, the percentage was but 3.1 in those families in which the parents had normal blood pressures. Thacker, examining 15,000 students, also came to this conclusion. Evidently, a hereditary factor is involved. But it must be borne in mind that a human being does not inherit tendencies, predispositions, or traits; only two things are bequeathed to us by our forebears: chemical composition and physical structure of matter. What has gone amiss in a person with this so-called "constitutional predisposition" for hypertension? Does the defect lie in the arteries themselves or are more remote organs which indirectly affect the arteries at fault? Of the host of suggestions made, we can only briefly examine a few.

1. It will be recalled that the individual's emotional states exert no small influence on blood pressure. Some writers lay stress on the high-strung, nervous temperament of the average American and his high pressure mode of living. But Weiss found that among 30,000 applicants for life insurance the business men and those engaged in the learned professions exhibited no higher blood pressure than that of farmers and others leading less emotional lives.

2. Obesity is very frequently associated with a high blood pressure; especially is this true for women after the menopause. Persons of stocky type with short body, broad thick neck, and a tendency to obesity are more prone to exhibit hypertension. But a causal relation between obesity and hypertension has never been demonstrated.

3. A few years ago hypertension was thought to be linked with a high protein diet (meat, fish, eggs, etc.), but Eskimos, although consumers of large amounts of animal foods rich in proteins, are said not to be subject to hypertension to any great extent.

4. Overactivity of certain glands, such as the adrenals and the pituitary (Chap. XXIII), which normally secrete hormones having pressor effects, has also been regarded by some as a causative agent.

5. From the above speculations which throw very little light upon the question, we may turn to more recent experimental work. The belief was quite general that a relation existed between high blood pressure and faulty kidney function. By some it was held that the retention of waste products, especially the nitrogenous, exerted a toxic influence on the arteries. This claim, however, could not be fully established. The experiments of Goldblatt and many other investigators have thrown much light upon this. We may briefly state the results of these investigations.

When in an animal the circulation to one kidney is reduced by means of a clamp applied to the renal vein, in the course of a few weeks a high blood pressure develops. This is not due to the toxic influence of waste products, for these are properly eliminated. As cutting the spinal cord brings no abatement, the high pressure is not neural in origin. After much search it was discovered that the blood contains a compound, called renin (made by the kidney?), which by the interaction of a second constituent of the blood forms a compound having powerful vasopressor properties. This last material, called **hypertensin** or **angiotonin,** is always present in the blood in case of renal hypertension and is responsible for the rise in both the systolic and diastolic pressures.

Normally there is formed in the body, especially in the kidneys, a substance having destructive action upon hypertensin, for which reason it is designated as **hypertensinase.** It is conceivable that the damaged kidney fails to manufacture a sufficient amount of this destroying agent to keep the hypertensin in check; at any rate, curtailing the blood flow through the kidney results in upsetting the balance between the formation and the destruction of hypertensin; this results in a high blood pressure of humoral origin.

Whether these facts are adequate to explain the origin of hypertension in all cases is a question. Some believe that many cases of hypertension are not renal in origin; others maintain that all cases of hypertension of long duration are always accompanied by kidney lesion.

ARTERIOSCLEROSIS.—Frequently it happens that the arteries under-go degenerative changes because of the depositing of either a fatty material, known as cholesterol, in the intima (inner coat) or of calcium salts in the media of the arterial wall. Elastic connective tissue may also be replaced by inelastic fibers (scar tissue). By these processes the arterial wall becomes thickened and loses its elasticity; the lumen may be considerably narrowed; and the depositing of calcium and magnesium salts may result in great rigidity and brittleness—arteriosclerosis (*skleros*, hard). Arteriosclerosis is generally associated with old age, but it is not rare to find the vessels of a younger individual more or less sclerotic; and in some cases ripe old age is attained without hardening of the blood vessels.

RESULTS OF HYPERTENSION.—Progressive hypertension may prove disastrous. As the diastolic pressure gradually rises, the extra work thrown upon the heart causes it to undergo hypertrophy; so long as the heart can maintain a sufficiently high systolic pressure, a good general circulation obtains. A still further rise in the diastolic pressure due to the increasingly great peripheral resistance, may finally render it impossible for the heart to deliver the proper systolic output and, as a result, the blood pressure falls—heart failure.

Normally a blood vessel has a high tensile strength; by this we mean that to rupture a vessel a very great internal force is required. For example, Volkmann found that the carotid arteries of a goat could withstand a pressure of 2,250 mm. Hg, which is at least fourteen times the normal blood pressure. No normal blood vessel therefore ever ruptures. But when an artery has undergone the above-discussed changes, the breaking point may be reduced and any sudden increase in the blood pressure may cause rupture. If the vessels of the cerebral hemispheres are concerned (apoplexy), very great damage may be done to the mental and neuromuscular life (paralysis) of the individual, because of the destruction of brain cells and fibers; frequently this proves fatal.

All the arteries of the body do not suffer simultaneously or to the same extent. The increased resistance offered by a certain narrowed artery may lead to a poor supply of blood to the organ involved; this, in turn, leads to inadequate nutrition and the function and structure of the organ suffer greatly. If the artery under consideration supplies the stomach or intestines, indigestion and impaired nutrition of the whole body are the results. Gradual loss of memory, or of some other psychic function, frequently attends the sclerosis of a cerebral vessel. Heart failure is very frequently due to an insufficient nutrition to the heart musculature because of sclerosis of the coronary arteries. From these considerations it can readily be seen why it is frequently stated that a person is as old as his blood vessels. The longer we succeed in maintaining the physical and physiologic integrity of the arteries, the longer the tissues receive their adequate nutrition; this lays the foundation for normal activity. The physiologic age of any organ, and of the body as a whole, is measured by its capacity to do work.

From the above it is evident that people afflicted with arteriosclerosis should lead a quiet life physically (although performing the amount of work their condition warrants), mentally, and especially emotionally. They should eat sparingly, sleep and rest abundantly, have proper elimination of wastes by kidneys and bowels, and harbor no infections in teeth, tonsils, gallbladder, etc.

As to the causes of these degenerative changes in the arteries there is much debate and little certainty. Perhaps many factors play a part. Some maintain that continued hypertension may bring about the structural, or organic, disturbances known as arteriosclerosis. By some authors much stress has been laid upon infectious and other diseases, such as recurrent tonsillitis, scarlet fever, diphtheria, gout, rheumatism, and nephritis. Especially may we here mention syphilis, concerning which Osler and Churchman say: ''On no system does the virus of the disease fall with greater intensity in all stages than on the blood vessels; it is safe to say that through the arteries syphilis kills more than through any other channel.''

VIII. HYPOTENSION

Not infrequently we meet with people who have what is generally looked upon as a very low blood pressure, or hypotension. As to what pressure constitutes hypotension we can give no definite answer, for, as elsewhere, the normal gradually merges into the abnormal. It is generally held that in an adult a systolic pressure below 100 and a diastolic below 60 mm. must be regarded as hypotension.

Whether a low blood pressure works detrimentally cannot be stated offhand. In many people a low pressure seems normal and is compatible with physical endurance and vitality. When we recall that volume circulation but not blood pressure, per se, determines the amount of nutrition supplied to the tissues and which therefore limits the extent of tissue activity, it is not surprising to learn that competent investigators conclude that a systolic pressure of 100 mm. Hg in a person forty years of age is desirable and favors longevity.

A low blood pressure is frequently the result of toxins of wasting and infectious diseases (measles, scarlet fever, diphtheria, tuberculosis, etc.). These toxins are held responsible either for weakening the heart or reducing the arterial and capillary tonus. From the microorganisms found in decaying human teeth, tonsils, and prostatic secretion, products have been obtained which, on being injected into rabbits, lowered the blood pressure.

Extremely low blood pressures are encountered in various conditions collectively known as shock. As this is frequently associated with excessive formation of tissue fluid, we shall take up this subject in the next chapter.

IX. CEREBRAL CIRCULATION

The brain is more directly dependent upon a constant supply of oxygen than any other organ of the body. In dogs the total cessation of blood flow for twenty minutes is fatal to the higher cerebral

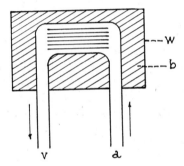

Fig. 120.—Diagram illustrating circulation through the brain.

cells, and in man fainting results from more than a momentary stoppage of the oxygen supply. It is therefore not surprising to learn that the brain is very liberally supplied with blood by the two internal carotids and the two vertebral arteries. It is a question whether the amount of blood in the brain at any given time can be increased by the activity of vasomotor nerves innervating the cerebral vessels. The anatomic relation of these vessels to the neighboring structures makes this supposition very unlikely. The brain vessels are imbedded, we may say, in the incompressible brain tissue which is lodged in a bony cavity, the walls of which are rigid. We may picture this as shown in Fig. 120, in which *a* is an artery and *v* a vein of the brain, *b;* between these two vessels we have the arterioles and capillaries, and around the brain, the rigid wall *w*. When a small opening is made in the wall, the brain matter can be seen to swell out and pulsate with each heartbeat and with each respiration. In fact, this is the cause of the pulsations we observe on the head of a young child (the fontanels), the skull acting as a plethys-mograph for the brain. But when no opening in the skull exists, the brain matter cannot swell out, and the only way the pulse in the artery can make an impression upon the brain matter is by forcing as much blood out of the cranium as enters through the artery. The shock that the brain receives with each pulse is transmitted through its substance to the walls of the veins, causing the flow of blood from these veins to be more or less pulsating. From this it must be clear that the dilation of the arteries would narrow the veins, and thus the volume of the blood in the brain would remain constant. It is, therefore, not possible to dilate the cerebral arteries and thus in-crease the amount of blood in the brain; but what may be increased is the velocity of the blood flowing through the brain. This increase in blood flow is brought about by increasing the resistance offered the blood in other parts of the body by the constriction of the vessels in these parts. The amount of blood passing in a unit of time through the brain is therefore determined not, as in active muscles or glands, by the dilation of its vessels, but by the general blood pressure and by the relative amount of resistance offered by the cranial and the extracranial vessels. So far as supplying the brain with oxygen and nourishment is concerned, it will be seen that the re-sults are identical; for it is not the absolute volume of blood in the brain at any given time, but the amount of blood flowing through the cerebral vessels in a unit of time that determines the amount of nourishment supplied.

From this description it can be readily understood why a heavy meal may make mental work difficult. The blood vessels of the ali-mentary canal, being much dilated, retain a large volume of blood, and the velocity of flow through the brain is lessened. For perhaps somewhat similar reasons it is difficult to go to sleep under certain conditions. Whatever the cause or causes of sleep may be, a liberal supply of blood through the brain favors mental activity and there-fore hinders sleep. If the blood can be drawn away from the brain, sleep may be induced, as, for example, by eating a small amount of food, or by a hot foot bath.

For similar reasons we find it difficult to exert ourselves mentally in an extremely warm room. If working in shirt sleeves favors mus-cular work, it may under certain circumstances also help the flow of thought. That the higher civilizations flourish in the temperate zone is no doubt due to many factors, but we do not need to stretch our imagination very far to see how the influence of climate upon the circulation might play an important part.

It is now generally conceded that the cerebral blood vessels are innervated by vasomotor nerves. Even though we grant that the volume of blood in the brain cannot be increased because of the inability of the vessels to expand, yet one might see some use of vasomotor nerves. When we are mentally active, our whole brain is not equally active in all its parts. When we listen to a lecture, that part of the brain where auditory impressions are received and elaborated is more active than the area where visual sensations are recorded; on reading a book, the reverse is true. While there is no experimental evidence in the matter, yet it would not be contrary to the general plan of the circulatory system to suppose that the active part of the brain has its blood vessels dilated while the inactive part is deprived of some of its blood. In this manner the distribution of the blood in the brain would be regulated according to the needs of the individual parts, without increasing the total volume of blood in the whole organ.

From our discussion it is evident that any increase in the pressure in the cranium must exert its force upon the cerebral blood vessels and, if sufficiently great, obliterate their lumen and thus cause cerebral anemia. Now we have learned that anemia of the medulla stimulates the vasoconstrictor center; this results in a higher systemic blood pressure, which, by overtopping the increased intracranial pressure, may be able to force an amount of blood through the cerebral vessels sufficient to maintain the life of the brain cells. Among the conditions bringing about an increase in the intracranial pressure, we may mention the presence of a foreign body—a blood clot or tumor—or the compression of the brain by fracture of the skull.

X. FACTORS INFLUENCING CIRCULATION

A. Hemorrhage and Blood Pressure

Without the proper activity of the vasomotor system circulation is greatly impaired, if not impossible. How efficient this mechanism is can be judged from the fact that, although there is a relatively small amount of blood in the vessels, an animal can lose about one-tenth of its blood without lowering blood pressure to any great extent. Many factors play a part in bringing this about.

1. A fall in blood pressure due to the hemorrhage reduces the activity of the depressor nerves of both the aorta and the carotid sinus, and as a result the vasoconstrictor center is more, and the cardiac inhibitory center less, active. The greater constriction of the arteries and the acceleration of the heart are able, under these conditions, to maintain the circulation.

2. During the hemorrhage the secretion of adrenalin by the adrenal glands is increased; this also aids in the constriction of the blood vessels and in increasing cardiac activity.

3. We shall learn in our study of respiration that the conditions obtaining during a hemorrhage also bring about increased respiration, which, as we have seen, may very favorably affect circulation. It is evident, therefore, that the body makes every effort to use to its fullest extent what little blood remains.

4. In addition to these measures, we shall learn in the next chapter how the tissue fluid is drawn from the lymph spaces and the tissues themselves into the blood stream, a method by which the volume of blood is quickly augmented.

5. By the contraction of the muscles in the spleen, a large number of red blood cells normally stored in this organ are forced in the blood stream.

Blood Banks; Plasma Banks.—When there is a serious shortage of red blood cells so that a sufficient amount of oxygen cannot be carried to the tissues, no matter how efficient the circulation may be, transfusion of whole blood (plasma and corpuscles) is necessary. But in many cases of hemorrhage and shock life is threatened not because of the loss of oxygen carriers but because of the lack of a sufficient amount of fluid to carry on circulation. To prevent death, it is necessary to inject into the blood vessels some inert fluid. For this purpose a physiologic salt solution or a physiologic saline containing a viscid substance, such as gum arabic, has been used. The last, because of the slight colloidal osmotic pressure of the gum, is superior to the pure saline solution. But it was soon discovered that blood transfusion was the most efficient method.

In transfusion of blood, care must be exercised that the blood of the donor and that of the host are not inimical toward each other. In such transfusions about 500 c.c. of blood may be taken from the donor without any serious results; this volume of blood is restored in about six hours and the number of corpuscles becomes normal within two months. According to Brewer, the minimal safe interval for such large donations is three months for men and four months for women.

In many cases of hemorrhage or shock the individual has a sufficient number of blood cells and, therefore, whole blood transfusion is not required. Indeed, the injection of plasma, obtained by the removal of the blood cells, may be more efficient. Hemorrhages and shock, whether in civilian or military life, are of an emergency nature. Proper donors are not always at hand. This led Shanow, a Russian investigator, to study methods for the collections and preservation of blood. At first whole blood collected from donors was mixed with a suitable preserving solution and stored at a temperature from 4° to 6° C. Even with these precautions blood could not be kept for more than 10 days. It was subsequently found that plasma, properly treated and kept at 10° to 20° C. was good after 6 or 7 months' storage. Frozen plasma at –15° to –20° C. remains good indefinitely. Recently dried plasma (quite comparable to dried milk) has been used; this keeps indefinitely without any special care. By this 1,000 c.c. of blood are reduced to 8 c.c.

B. Activity and the Distribution of the Blood

A working organ needs more nourishment and, therefore, a larger blood supply than a resting organ. In order to let the small quantity of blood in our vessels do the largest amount of work, we shunt the blood stream from one part of the body to another, as occasion may demand. For example, when the skeletal muscles of our body become very active and need a larger volume of blood, the blood vessels in these muscles dilate; at the same time the abdominal vessels are constricted. By this arrangement the blood pressure is kept fairly constant and the muscles obtain this greater volume of blood without changing the resistance which the heart has to overcome in maintaining an adequate circulation. A very heavy meal on a hot day, when a very large amount of blood circulates through the skin, may not be well digested. For the same reason, a hot bath may interfere with digestion.

If the blood vessels were of a constant size, they would have to be large enough to carry a maximum amount of blood to any organ during its greatest activity. This would demand an extremely large amount of blood, and a large heart, needing much food. It will, therefore, be seen that the vasomotor system is a system for efficiency, the greatest results being obtained with least expenditure of energy; hence it is a system of economy.

C. External Temperature and Distribution of Blood

It is well known that the color and temperature of the skin vary with the amount of heat produced in the body by muscular exercise and with the temperature of the environment. The dilated state of the cutaneous arterioles and capillaries during physical work or on a warm day causes a relatively large volume of blood to circulate through the skin thus affording the body an opportunity to throw off a larger amount of heat. The reverse holds true during inactivity and in cooler weather. It is one of the foremost functions of the vasomotor system to regulate the amount of heat dissipated by the skin.

But it is not sufficient on a warm day to dilate the vessels of the skin. It will be recalled that the volume of the blood in the body is small compared with the capacity of the vessels; therefore a marked cutaneous dilation, associated with a great decrease in peripheral resistance, may be followed by a fall in blood pressure sufficiently great to impede circulation seriously. It is therefore necessary that this should be counteracted, and so it is. There are two great vascular tracts in the body closely governed by vasomotor nerves: the cutaneous area and the abdominal, or splanchnic, area (governed by the splanchnic nerve). These two areas stand in a reciprocal relationship toward each other; that is to say, a dilation in the one is normally accompanied by a constriction in the other, and vice versa. When the vasomotor center is stimulated by impulses from the cutaneous heat nerves and sends impulses to the cutaneous vessels for dilation, impulses are brought to the abdominal vessels for constriction. On a cold day the process is reversed.

In certain instances the collapsing of individuals in hot weather has been attributed to failure of this reciprocal mechanism to operate properly. On the other hand, sudden exposure to cold causes a marked cutaneous constriction with its resultant increase in peripheral resistance. Were this not counteracted by the dilation in the splanchnic area, the high blood pressure might result disastrously in those individuals in whom the vessels have lost to a large extent their tensile strength.

D. Position of Body; Gravity

A moment's reflection will show that the position of the body must influence the distribution of the blood. In the reclining position gravity plays but a negligible part, for none of the various parts of the body is either much above or below the level of the heart. But in the erect position, the blood tends to settle to the lower parts of the body, the abdomen and legs. To see this effect of gravity, one has merely to observe the condition of the skin and the superficial veins on the back of the hand. When the hand is raised high above the head, the skin is paler and the veins far less swollen than when the hand is allowed to hang down. It is stated that this effect of gravity makes itself felt very powerfully in such an animal as the hutch rabbit, for if this animal is suspended by the ears, he dies of cerebral anemia. In this position gravity draws so much blood into the large blood vessels of the abdomen that the head is deprived of blood. Applying a tight bandage around the abdomen is said to prevent the death of the animal.

Now, gravity tends to do the same in our body. During the first 10 seconds of standing the systolic pressure falls from 5 to 40 mm.

Hg, and were it not for a counteracting mechanism fainting would result. The rushing of the blood to the abdomen and lower limbs decreases the blood pressure in the carotid sinuses. This decreases the impulses for inhibition to the vasoconstrictor center and for excitation to the cardiac inhibitory center; as a result more vasoconstriction takes place and the heart rate is speeded up. By this the accumulation of the blood in the abdominal organs is prevented and circulation goes on without any great effect upon the blood pressure, with but little or no increase in the rate of the heartbeat, and no significant decrease in cardiac output.

Such is the state of things in a robust person in whom the vasomotor tonus and the tonus of the skeletal muscles are in good condition. But in a person with a poor vasomotor tone and with the skeletal muscles more or less relaxed, this compensatory act to offset the effect of gravity may fail. It frequently happens that an individual who has spent many days or weeks in bed, or who has had a wasting illness, faints on trying to arise or on being lifted into an erect position—*gravity shock*. Because of the action of poisons, lack of proper food, or a long period of inactivity, the vasoconstrictor center in the medulla is less irritable than normally. On the individual's arising from the reclining position, gravity draws some of the blood to the abdomen; but the resulting loss of blood does not stimulate the vasomotor center and no impulses are sent to the splanchnic blood vessels for constriction; in consequence of this, these vessels, by the influx of blood, keep on dilating, and the head becomes more and more anemic until finally the cerebral circulation is so feeble that the mental functions can no longer be maintained. Or, if the condition is not so grave as this, the partial fall of blood pressure may only cause a great increase in the rapidity of the heart (for it is generally true that the rate of the heartbeat varies inversely as the blood pressure) and the person feels more or less dizzy.

In the erect position, there rests in the veins of the lower extremities a column of blood reaching from the feet up to the level of the heart. This column of blood exercises hydrostatic pressure upon the walls of these veins and the force of the moving blood must overcome this hydrostatic pressure in order to reach the heart. It is evident, therefore, that in the erect position more force is required than in the reclining position. This extra driving force is not derived from the action of the heart, but from the secondary aids afforded by the respiratory movements and, more especially, by the rhythmical contraction of the muscles of the legs. Without these contractions the return of blood from the lower portions of the body is very slow, and, if the motionless standing be long continued, fainting may result even in a normal subject.

In this connection, we may call attention to another factor, namely, the proper muscle tonus in the abdominal wall. If these muscles have poor tonus (as in bed-ridden patients), the wall is flabby and the size of the abdominal cavity increased; this enables more blood to lodge in this part, to the detriment of circulation. A constant slouching posture of body in standing or sitting weakens these muscles and may cause stagnation of blood in the liver, intestines, and other abdominal organs. This congestion results in lack of proper circulation through the brain and other parts of the body which seriously interferes with the activity of these organs. It is, therefore, important that the abdominal muscles should be strengthened by proper exercise; especially is this urgent in persons of sedentary occupations.

We may summarize the factors by which we counteract the effect of gravity:

(1) increased vasomotor tonus
(2) increased cardiac activity
(3) the "milking" action of skeletal muscles
(4) the auxiliary action of the respiratory pump
(5) the tonicity of the muscles of the abdominal wall.

VARICOSE VEINS.—When the blood flowing through a vein meets with a large amount of resistance so that more or less stagnation takes place, a varicose vein is likely to result. As is well known, the superficial veins of the legs are especially liable to this disturbance, and we find it particularly in those individuals who stand for long periods at a time (motormen, typesetters, etc.). People who walk a great deal are rarely afflicted. In standing, the hydrostatic pressure tends to dilate the veins; the column of blood in the vein is not properly renewed (because of lack of the "milking" action of rhythmical exercise) and the nutrition of the walls of the vein is impaired; sooner or later the wall degenerates, the lumen widens, and the vein becomes very tortuous.

In straining efforts, as in lifting heavy weights, the pressure in the abdomen is increased. A short breath is taken, the glottis (the slit between the vocal cords) is closed; by the contraction of the muscles of expiration of thorax and abdomen, pressure is exerted upon the contents of both cavities. The increased abdominal pressure impedes the return of venous blood from the lower parts of the body. Therefore, straining efforts should be avoided by persons with inherited weak and thin-walled veins. External pressure upon these superficial veins, as by tight garters, may also aid in the formation of varicose leg veins. Straining at stool is frequently responsible for the varicosity of the veins of the rectum, a condition known as hemorrhoids, or piles.

E. Muscular Work*

The increased demand during muscular activity for food and oxygen and for the removal of waste products is met by increased functioning of many organs; among these the first and most obvious is an increase in the volume of blood flowing through the muscle. Krogh calculated that the volume of blood circulating through an active muscle of a guinea pig is 275 times greater than that supplied to the same muscle at rest. Our study must concern itself with the methods by which this is brought about.

a. The heart rate is increased during muscular activity by means of the Bainbridge reflex. As a result of the "milking" action of the rhythmically contracting muscles and the increase in the activity of the respiratory pump, the venous return to the right auricle is greatly increased. By way of afferent vagus nerve fibers this increased filling of the right auricle inhibits the cardiac inhibitory center and, as a result, the heart is accelerated. This acceleration outlasts the period of work for a certain length of time.

It is here that we find a marked difference between the "well-trained" heart and the heart of an untrained individual. Not only is the increase in rate far greater for the untrained, but the length of time the acceleration continues after the work has stopped is much longer. Thus: five minutes after performing a certain piece of work the pulse rate of the trained was almost normal, but that of the untrained was 30 per cent higher than in the resting state. The longer the work is continued (as in races) the longer will it take the heart to regain its original beat (one or more hours), but in this case also the rate of the trained heart subsides far more speedily than that of the untrained. This, then, may be used as a test to determine whether the heart is weak or strong and whether an individual may safely perform a certain piece of physical work.

b. The Stroke Volume.—From the greater diastolic intake by the right auricle spoken of above, it is evident that the stroke volume of the left ventricle must also be increased. As both the rate and the stroke volume are increased, it is evident that the output per minute is also augmented. In a certain experiment the minute vol-

---

*The effects of muscular work on the circulation of the blood can not be fully dealt with until the subject of Respiration has been discussed; see p. 306.

ume was increased from five liters in the resting state to thirty liters during severe work—an increase of 600 per cent. As the volume of blood in the body is about 5 liters, this entire quantity of blood must have circulated through the left ventricle six times per minute, a notable feat for a pump weighing about 12 ounces. The increase in the cardiac output, which is the most important factor in the adjustment of the circulation to the increased needs of the body, is brought about by the greater diastolic filling. If the left heart cannot dispose of the large volume of blood brought to it, there is venous stagnation and cyanosis sets in; this is often seen in persons attempting to do physical work for which they are not fit. The increase in the minute volume in the physically fit is obtained with a smaller increase in the rate of heartbeat than in the untrained individual.

c. **The force of the heartbeat** is increased, due to the greater stretching of the ventricle by its augmented diastolic intake (Starling's law).

Speaking of trained and untrained hearts, we may add that a trained heart has a comparatively large amount of reserve strength which may be utilized in case of extraordinary demand. It is self-evident that this is desirable for all persons, so that they may be able to meet emergencies of a physical nature or those originating from pathologic conditions. Many a patient succumbs because of a lack of sufficient cardiac reserve.

The chronic effect of exercise on the heart has created considerable interest. There is good reason to believe that the muscle cells of the heart respond to exercise in a manner similar to skeletal muscle cells. If this is true, increased demands on the heart cause an increase in heart size. It is a well-known fact that animals which do much work generally have a larger heart in relation to body weight than those that lead a less active life. For example: in the thoroughbred greyhound the heart weight is 17.3 grams per kilogram of body weight; in mongrels this ratio is 7.98. But whether this also holds true for athletic and nonathletic human beings is a moot point. Eyster holds that no hypertrophy in man or experimental animals takes place as the result of extreme physical work so long as the heart is normal. Steinhaus, however, is inclined to believe that functional hypertrophy of the heart does take place in some individuals.

d. **Cardiac Nutrition.**—To enable the heart to accomplish this extra work, its nutrition must be increased. This is made possible by the dilation of the coronary vessels (p. 208) which are held by some authors to receive vasodilator fibers from the sympathetic nervous

system and constrictors from the vagus nerve. As to the excitatory
agent for the dilation of these arteries, many ideas have been advanced: the increased secretion of adrenalin (see below) or the
formation of acetylcholine, hydrogen ions, or a histamin-like compound during the work. Whatever the cause may be, it was found
that the coronary flow in an animal was increased from the usual
140 c.c. per minute to 800 c.c. during a certain piece of muscle work.

e. **Blood Pressure.**—Such a large increase in minute volume can
not fail to influence the blood pressure. Even before the physical
work is actually begun, there may be a preliminary rise in pressure
(*AB,* Fig. 121) caused, no doubt, by the psychic influence on the circulatory apparatus. Very soon after beginning the work, the systolic
pressure rises considerably, *BC;* this may last from five to twenty-
five minutes. As the work is continued the pressure falls, *CD,* gradu-

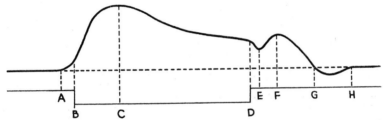

Fig. 121.—Curve illustrating the effect of muscle work on blood pres sure (see
text).

ally, but generally does not reach the resting systolic pressure. Immediately after the work there is for a few seconds a decided fall in
the systolic pressure, *DE.* This is due to the fact that the "milking"
action of the muscles ceases and the heart receives a smaller quantity
of blood. After this adjustment, the pressure again rises for a brief
space of time above the resting pressure, to gradually descend to normal, and not infrequently, a little below normal. The venous pressure
also rises during physical work.

The increase in systolic pressure is proportional to the severity of
the exercise, while diastolic pressure changes but little. However,
because the cardiorespiratory adjustments necessary to increase the
supply of blood and oxygen to the muscles are more quickly and adequately made in the trained individual, the blood pressure neither
rises so quickly nor so high as it does in the untrained, for a given
amount of work. Furthermore, in the untrained man the return of
the pressure to normal after cessation of the work requires a greater
length of time than in the trained. Fatigue reduces the systolic,
diastolic, and pulse pressure.

Certain kinds of work (rowing; lifting heavy weights) have a powerful influence on blood pressure. There is the mechanical effect which the straining of the muscles of the arms, shoulders, and lower extremities has upon the blood vessels (especially the veins) found in these parts; by this the vessels may be to a greater or lesser extent squeezed shut. McCurdy showed how the lifting of weights, varying from 240 to 550 pounds, caused the pressure to rise, on the average, from the normal 111 to 180 mm. Hg.

f. Distribution of the Blood.—That the extra supply of blood sent by the heart may do the largest amount of good, it is to a great extent shunted to the organs needing it in the following manner:

1. During vigorous exercise the blood vessels of the abdominal organs are constricted; this accounts partly for the increase in blood pressure (*B* to *C* in Fig. 121). It is for this reason that digestion may be seriously delayed by physical work, and that a full stomach is incompatible with strenuous exercise. This constriction may also involve the renal arteries and cause the scant secretion of urine at this time.

2. The arterioles to the active muscles dilate very greatly, thereby insuring a good supply of blood to the capillaries.

3. There is a tremendous dilation of the capillaries. Krogh states that while he found only 200 open capillaries in one square millimeter of inactive muscle tissue, the number increased to 2,500 during activity, and all the capillaries were wider than in the resting muscle. The dilation of the capillaries is, no doubt, brought about by the increased hydrogen-ion concentration due to the formation of carbon dioxide and lactic acid. Some hold that histamin, a very active dilator of the capillaries, may be responsible.

4. Due to the "milking" action of the rhythmically contracting muscles, the venous blood is more forcibly and speedily removed from the muscle. Thus the capillary blood pressure is kept low so that the arterial blood in the arterioles finds very little resistance to its entrance into the capillaries and the blood is sent hastily to the heart to be returned to the lungs for oxygenation.

5. Soon after the work is begun, there is a marked dilation of cutaneous blood vessels. This is to a certain extent responsible for the fall in blood pressure at *CD* in Fig. 121 and aids largely in the elimination of heat from the body.

CHAPTER XII

CAPILLARIES AND TISSUE FLUID FORMATION

I. THE INTERNAL MEDIUM

The cells of the body are highly specialized, and, for their protection, most of them are withdrawn from the stimulating or deleterious influences of the external environment to which the body as a whole is subject. Upon this environment, however, the cells are dependent for all materials necessary for the construction and repair of protoplasm and for the production of energy. In order that the cells may obtain these substances from, and return their waste products to, the environment, the body is supplied with a common carrier traveling between the cells and the environment, namely, the blood. All materials acquired by a cell are obtained from the blood and into it all cellular products find their way.

But the blood does not make direct contact with the cells, for this fluid, as blood, remains within the capillaries; moreover, the capillaries are not in contact with the cells. Between the capillaries and the cells, and between the various cells are found spaces, generally known as tissue, or lymph, spaces, Fig. 69. These spaces vary much in shape and size; most of them are microscopic but some are very large. The serous cavities, such as the pericardial and pleural spaces, may be regarded as lymph spaces.

As the blood flows through the capillaries, certain substances, such as water, salts, glucose, amino acids, etc., pass through the capillary wall into the surrounding spaces; the fluid filling these spaces is known as *tissue fluid,* also very frequently referred to as lymph. Into this fluid are cast the waste products formed by cellular activity. Being constantly bathed by the tissue fluid, the cells of our body may, with truth, be called aquatic cells, and the tissue fluid constitutes their environment, or internal medium.

Composition of Lymph.—In lymph we find essentially the same ingredients as in blood plasma, but the percentage of the substances present is not necessarily the same in the two fluids. Lymph contains practically no red blood cells and has for this reason a very low specific gravity (1.015); the number of lymphocytes varies considerably. The amount of protein in real tissue fluid as found in the limbs is perhaps 0.5 to 1 per cent and that in the lymph in the thoracic duct, 2 to 4 per cent (compare with 6 to 8 per cent in plasma). Because of the presence of fibrinogen, lymph has the power to coagulate. The salts and glucose have about the same concentration as in plasma.

The lymph conveyed from the intestine to the thoracic duct by lymph vessels known as lacteals (see Fig. 172) is called chyle; during the process of absorption of food it is rich in fat. The fluid in the ventricles and canals of the central nervous system and between its coverings is known as *cerebrospinal fluid*. We may also mention the pericardial fluid, the peritoneal fluid, the humors of the eye, the lymph found in the canals of the inner ear; all these perform special functions. Differing much from true lymph, there is the synovial fluid found in the joints; it contains a viscous mucinlike substance. The amount of synovial fluid is increased by inflammation of the joints.

Because of the high degree of specialization of the body cells, the physical and chemical properties and the quantity of the tissue fluid must be kept as nearly constant as possible. Changes in tissue fluid may be due to:

1. The addition of materials from the blood.
2. The removal of substances from the tissue fluid and their consumption by the cells.
3. The addition of cellular products, e.g., waste products and hormones.
4. The removal of substances by excretion.

To maintain, under these conditions, the constancy of the tissue fluid demands the closest coordination of the various factors concerned in its formation and removal. We may now study some of these factors.

II. TISSUE FLUID FORMATION

Transudation; Filtration.—The passage of the material from the capillaries through the capillary wall and into the tissue spaces is known as transudation and is generally regarded as primarily a process of ultrafiltration. At this time it may be well for the reader briefly to review the factors, discussed in Chap. IV, which are concerned in the translocation of substances in solution. In viewing transudation as a matter of filtration, two things must be considered: a membrane serving as a filter and the force or forces which cause substances to pass through it.

A. Capillaries in Tissue Fluid Formation

a. Permeability of the Capillary Wall.—To serve as a filter, the wall must possess a certain degree of permeability and impermeability, for no filtration is ever accomplished with a membrane that does not restrain some things from passing through it. The wall is exceedingly thin, being composed of a single layer of flat endothelial cells and therefore not more, and sometimes less, than one micromillimeter ($\frac{1}{25,000}$ inch) in thickness. Under the usual conditions the capillary wall is permeable to water and crystalloids (glucose, salts, urea, amino acids, lactic acid); indeed, for these the capillary wall is more permeable than any other membrane. But, as the capillary wall (protoplasm) itself is a colloid, it is only slightly permeable to the protein colloids of the plasma.

Capillary permeability varies from one organ to another. Capillaries of the muscles have perhaps the least, those of the intestine, more, and those of the liver, the greatest degree of permeability. This may cause the lymph coming from the two last-named organs to contain more proteins than that from the body in general. It is also held that the permeability of the venous end of the capillary is greater than that of the arterial end. Again, the permeability of any given capillary varies with many conditions, such as, temperature, the constriction or dilation of the capillary, and the chemical nature of the fluid on the one or the other side of the membrane.

b. Proximity of the Capillaries to the Cells.—The capillaries may be fittingly regarded as the feeders of the cells, and it is highly desirable that no cell be far removed from its base of supply. To obtain this condition, the capillaries must be exceedingly numerous, and so Krogh found them to be. This observer calculates that the capillaries in the human body, if placed end to end, would form a tube 62,000 miles long. As each capillary is but one millimeter in length, the number of capillaries is beyond comprehension. How closely the capillaries and the muscle cells are situated to each other may be gathered from the fact that in a cross section of a muscle each square millimeter of muscle tissue is supplied with approximately 2,500 capillaries (1,562,500 per square inch). The food and oxygen, therefore, do not need to travel far from the capillary to reach the muscle fiber.

c. Surface.—The extent of surface offered by a filter to the fluid to be filtered plays an important part. In this respect also the capillaries serve admirably, for the surface of the 62,000 mile tube spoken of above has an area of 67,000 square feet (1½ acres). It has been calculated that 1 c.c. ($\frac{1}{28}$ ounce) of blood is exposed to a capillary surface of 7,300 square cm., or 8 square feet.

B. Forces in Tissue Fluid Formation

a. Capillary Blood Pressure.—The chief factor concerned in forcing the fluid of the blood into the tissue spaces is the blood pressure in the capillaries; the greater this pressure, the greater the filtration and the greater the amount of lymph formed. It must, however, be apparent that were it not for restraining forces, the blood pressure would squeeze all the plasma through the capillary wall in about ten seconds. This would have two disastrous results: (*a*) It would rob the blood stream of all its water and leave the corpuscles high and dry in the vessels and unable to move; all circulation in these vessels would come to a standstill—*stasis.* (*b*) The amount of tissue fluid formed would be so great as to cause destructive pressure upon the cells. To prevent this calamity, there are two opposing factors: the osmotic pressure of the colloids (proteins) of the blood, and the pressure of the tissue fluid in the tissue spaces.

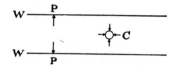

Fig. 122.—To illustrate the forces concerned in lymph formation. *w*, capillary wall; *p*, blood pressure; *c*, colloidal particle exerting its colloidal osmotic pressure. See text.

b. Restraining Factors.—On page 70 we drew attention to the small but definite amount of osmotic pressure exerted by colloids. Let us call this a water-drawing power. As the plasma proteins pass with great difficulty and only to a very limited extent through the capillary wall, they oppose the blood pressure and thus prevent the unrestrained filtration of the plasma into the tissue spaces. The water with its dissolved solids is subject to the capillary blood pressure, *P* in Fig. 122, which tends to squeeze it through the capillary wall, *W;* the colloidal proteins, *C*, attracting the water tend to prevent its escape from the vessels. It is apparent, therefore, that: Filtration Pressure = Blood Pressure – Colloidal Osmotic Pressure. The amount of colloidal osmotic pressure is determined by the amount of proteins in the plasma. Whatever increases the blood pressure in the capillaries or decreases the colloidal osmotic pressure increases the filtration pressure. If these two opposing forces just balance each other, no water exchange between the blood and the tissue fluid takes place; and if the osmotic pressure of the proteins is greater than the capillary blood pressure, the tissue fluid is drawn into the capillaries (absorption). As to the quantitative values of these factors no definite statement can be made, since they vary from time to time and from place to place. For the sake of example, we may place the capillary blood pressure at 32 mm. Hg and the colloidal osmotic pressure at 27; this leaves 5 mm. Hg as the *effective filtration pressure.*

The fluid in the tissue spaces exerts a certain amount of hydrostatic pressure which counteracts the filtration effect of the blood pressure. But as the small amount of proteins in the tissue fluid exert a water-drawing power in opposite direction to, and of approximately the same magnitude as, that of the hydrostatic pressure of tissue fluid, we may, for our purpose, leave them out of consideration.

c. Diffusion Pressure.—A second factor playing a part in the passage of materials through the capillary wall either in one or the other direction is diffusion pressure. If the concentration of, say, glucose, in the tissue fluid is lessened by the increased consumption of the sugar by the cells, its greater concentration in the blood will cause it to diffuse through the capillary wall, irrespective of hydrostatic pressure. On the other hand, if the concentration of the waste products in the cell rises above that in the tissue fluid, diffusion takes place so that finally these products are taken up by the capillaries.

d. Osmotic Pressure.—A third factor which influences the passage of water from the blood or cells into the tissue fluid is osmotic pressure. Normally intracellular and extracellular fluids (i.e., the tissue fluid) are in osmotic equilibrium. Any increase or decrease in the osmotic pressure of the tissue fluid must affect the cells. For example: if much salt is eaten, it freely enters the blood and tissue fluid. But as the protoplast of the cells is impermeable to NaCl, the salt remains in the tissue fluid and increases its osmotic pressure; this draws water from the cells into the tissue fluid and causes, among other disturbances, great thirst.

III. REMOVAL OF TISSUE FLUID

In order that the tissue spaces shall not become surcharged with liquid and thereby exert injurious pressure upon the cells, the materials not needed by the cells, whether derived from the blood or from the cells, must be constantly drained away. Two channels are provided for this: the blood capillaries and the lymph vessels.

a. Absorption by the Capillaries.—In Fig. 123 let *a* represent one of the smallest arterioles (which, together with the smallest venules, *v*, some investigators consider as part of the capillary system), *b* is the arterial end and *c,* the venous end of a capillary; *v* represents a venule. As the blood enters the capillary, *b,* the above-quoted values for the blood pressure and colloidal osmotic pressure hold good and filtration, *l,* occurs. In its passage along the capillary, from *b* to *c,* the blood loses by filtration some of its fluid; this reduces the blood pressure and increases the concentration and therefore also the colloidal osmotic pressure of the plasma proteins. The blood pressure is further reduced by the friction the blood encounters in moving from *b* to *c*. These changes cause the colloidal osmotic pressure to exceed the blood pressure, and as a result at the venous end of the capillary, *c,* fluid from the tissue spaces is drawn into the blood, *k*. In this way a constant circulation of tissue fluid is brought about and, excepting as noted below, excessive accumulation of tissue fluid is prevented. It will be seen that materials move out of the blood stream by hydrostatic pressure and into it by colloidal osmotic pressure.

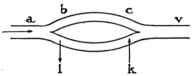

Fig. 123.—Diagram illustrating the filtration, *l,* at the arterial end of the capillary, *b,* and the absorption, *k,* at the venous end *c; a,* arteriole; *v,* venule.

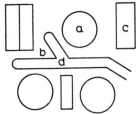

Fig. 124.—Illustrating the relation between the cell, *c,* the blood capillaries, *a,* the tissue spaces, *b,* and the lymph vessels, *d.*

b. Lymph Vessels.—The second route for draining the tissue fluid from the tissue spaces is by means of the lymph vessels, or lymphatics. It is now held that in all these spaces there is found a very delicate system of tubes, the lymph capillaries. We may picture this relationship by means of a simple diagram, as in Fig. 124. In this figure *a* is the cross-section of a blood capillary; *c* is a cell of the tissues; the space between the cells and the blood capillary is marked *b,* and in this space we find the lymph capillary, *d,* composed of but one layer of flat broad endothelial cells. The fluid from the tissue spaces, *b,* may find its way into the lymph capillaries, *d,* and by the forces to be discussed presently be moved onward toward the heart. Similar to the blood capillaries, the lymph capillaries also serve to maintain the constancy of the composition and volume of the tissue fluid.

The lymph capillaries communicate freely with each other and by their union form larger and larger vessels. Although considerably thinner, the walls of these larger lymph vessels resemble those of the veins, being composed of an inner layer of endothelial cells, a muscle layer, and an outer layer of connective tissue.   The lymph vessels are abundantly supplied with valves which cause them to assume a beaded appearance, as shown in Fig. 125.   The lymph vessels from the lower limbs and the organs of the abdomen unite to form the largest lymph vessel in the body, *the thoracic duct,* which, after being joined by the lymphatics of the left arm and left side of head, neck, and thorax, empties its contents into the left subclavian vein, Figs. 78 and 173.   The lymph from the right side of the head, neck, and thorax and from the right arm is discharged into the right subclavian vein.

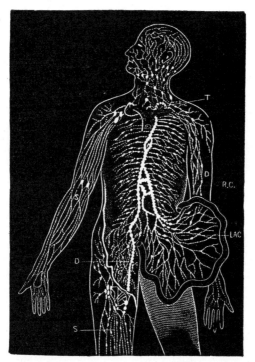

Fig. 125.—Lymphatics of the body. *S,* the superficial and *D,* the deeper lymph vessels; *LAC,* the lacteals in the mesentery of the intestines; *RC,* the receptaculum chyli, above which is the thoracic duct which empties, at *T,* into the left sub-clavian vein. Note the numerous lymph glands, or nodes. (Yeo.)

During the inactive condition of an organ, all the tissue fluid is returned directly into the blood capillaries; it is only when there is an excessive formation of tissue fluid that any appreciable amount finds its way into the lymph vessels to be carried to the large veins of the thorax.   The latter route has well been called "an emergency spillway."   The drainage from the intestine and liver forms an exception to the above statement.

IV. TISSUE ACTIVITY AND LYMPH FORMATION

The activity of an organ being reduced to a minimum, the formation of tissue fluid is very limited. Most of this is reabsorbed into the capillary stream, and in consequence the amount of lymph flowing through the larger lymph vessels of a quiescent muscle or limb is practically nil. As a working organ needs more food and oxygen and produces more waste products than a resting organ, an increased interchange between the blood, lymph, and cell must take place. As a result, more of the tissue fluid is discharged into the lymph vessels, and there is a greater flow of lymph from the active organ. However, even then, the volume of lymph discharged is not very great. This increased exchange between blood, tissue fluid, and cells is brought about chiefly by four factors:

a. **Circulatory Changes.**—The capillary system forms an exceedingly capacious set of tubes, the bed of which is estimated at from 400 to 1,000 times as large as that of the aorta. Considering the small amount of blood in the entire vascular system, it must be evident that all these capillaries are not filled at the same time. In a cross section of one square millimeter of a resting muscle Krogh found 200 open capillaries; in an active muscle the count was 2,500. The vessels are also considerably dilated during work.

During the inactive condition of the tissue, the capillary is maintained in a tonic state of contraction, brought about perhaps by hormones (pituitrin, e.g.) manufactured in the body. This constriction may be so severe as to close entirely many of the capillaries, as related above. But as no living organ is ever absolutely inactive (muscles exhibit tonus), some of the capillaries are relaxed to admit an amount of blood sufficient for nourishment during usual inactivity. It is conceivable that this constriction or dilation alternates from one set of capillaries to another according to the needs of the various parts of the organ. During increased muscular activity the lack of oxygen and the changes in the pH value of the blood (by CO_2 or lactic acid) may cause an inhibition of the usual constricted state of the capillaries. It has been shown that the concentration of histamine, which is a powerful dilator of capillaries, is greater in the venous than in the arterial blood of an active muscle; it has been suggested that this compound may aid in the capillary dilation during muscular activity.

All the neural and chemical regulations of cardiac activity and of the conditions of the blood vessels by which blood pressure, rate of flow, and volume flow are altered, exist for but one purpose, namely, to supply the capillaries with an amount of blood sufficient to meet the varying metabolic demands of the tissues. The increased amount of blood under slightly greater pressure coupled with the increased capillary filtration bed, brings about a greater filtration.

b. Permeability Changes.—The dilation of the capillaries by the metabolites discussed in the previous paragraph causes a stretching and thinning of the capillary wall. It is conceivable that to a limited extent this may increase the permeability; but whether, aside from this mechanical method, the metabolites as chemical agents increase the permeability is doubtful.

c. Diffusion and d. Osmotic Changes.—During activity of a muscle the large food molecule (glycogen, e.g.) is split into a large number of smaller molecules. This has a threefold result: (*1*) It increases the osmotic pressure in the cell and causes water with its dissolved food to be drawn from the tissue fluid into the cell. (*2*) The decreased concentration of the glucose and other foods in the cell allows the more concentrated food in the tissue fluid to diffuse into the cell. (*3*) The increased concentration of the waste products in the cells sets up a diffusion of these products into the tissue fluid.

The changes in the tissue fluid resulting from the above-discussed transferences result in: (*1*) a diffusion of the more concentrated wastes in the tissue fluid into the capillaries; (*2*) a diffusion of the food molecules in the blood into the tissue fluid. In this manner the muscles are properly supplied with food (including oxygen) and the waste products effectively removed.

V. EDEMA

Injury to the Capillary Wall.—Many changes in the capillary circulation and in the formation of tissue fluid are held to be due to damage to the capillary wall. This can be experimentally observed as follows: When the web of a frog's foot is stretched and exposed to the air so that it dries, or is subjected to extreme heat, cold, or irritating substances, such as alcohol, croton oil, chloroform, etc., microscopic investigation shows many changes in the circulation. After a possible initial increase in the velocity and rate of flow, due to the dilation of the vessels, the flow is gradually slowed down until, finally, it ceases altogether, with the capillaries heaped full of red blood cells. This cessation of the flow is called *stasis*. The above-named agencies render the capillary wall more permeable and the plasma is squeezed through with greater ease and in larger quantities. The amount of plasma thus forced through may be so great and may take place so rapidly that none remains in the capillaries; this causes the blood corpuscles to fill these vessels, blocking the circulation. It is, therefore, very necessary that the exposed tissues of an animal be kept moist by means of a physically and chemically inert solution, and, in case of the warm-blooded animals, the tissues must be kept at the body temperature. During the process of stasis, the leucocytes, Fig. 126, can be seen to force their way by ameboid movement through the wall of the capillary, and gather in the surrounding tissue.

Local Edema.—When in the above experiment, the formation of tissue fluid is so great that its drainage, either directly into the blood capillaries or by the lymphatic vessels, cannot keep pace with it, the tissue fluid accumulates in the part of the body affected and causes this part to be swollen and enlarged, a condition known as

Fig. 126.—Small vessel of the frog's mesentery showing leucocytes in the act of passing through the wall, *a;* some have already left the vessel, *b.*   (Frey.)

edema, or dropsy. Such a phenomenon may be very localized, as in the wheal resulting from the lash of a whip, the blisters raised by manual labor on hands unaccustomed to work, the great redness and blistering of the skin after exposure to intense light. We may also mention the rashes and hives resulting in some individuals from the eating of certain foods (allergy). The redness is, of course, the outward token of a great dilation and hyperemia of the capillaries; the swelling (a local edema) is brought about by an excessive amount of tissue fluid formation made possible by the increased permeability of the capillary wall to such an extent as to enable the plasma proteins to pass into the tissue fluid. As a result, the increased colloidal osmotic pressure of the tissue fluid decreases the re-absorption of this fluid into the blood stream and leads to its accumulation in the **tissue** spaces.

A drop of histamine pricked into the skin causes a redness and wheal similar to that observed on mechanical injury of the skin. Histamine is found in nearly all tissues. It has been argued that extreme mechanical, chemical, or photic stimulation releases the histamine and thereby causes a dilation of capillaries and an increase in permeability. Histamine is a capillary poison. According to Zinsser, anaphylaxis (p. 166) has its primary cause in the increased permeability of the capillary endothelium. As adrenalin is a powerful constrictor of the arterioles and, therefore, antagonizes the action of histamine, it is used in allergy for reducing the vasodilation and the local edema.

Edema and Blood Pressure.—The more the capillary pressure exceeds the colloidal osmotic pressure, the greater is the filtration pressure and the lymph formation. The most effective way to increase capillary blood pressure is to obstruct the venous outflow. It will be recalled (p. 236) that in a severe case this causes venous, or passive, congestion with a high pressure and a sluggish flow. We have in a previous chapter indicated how lesion of the cardiac valves may cause a high venous blood pressure (Fig. 99). We have also seen that in the erect position of the body gravity impedes the return of the venous blood from the feet and legs to the heart. This increases the capillary blood pressure and, because of the increased filtration, as much as 300 c.c. of fluid may be lost by the blood in one-half hour; this causes the feet to swell. Pressure with the finger upon these parts leaves an imprint—pitting.

Edema and Colloidal Osmotic Pressure of the Blood.—Since the effective filtration pressure is equal to the capillary pressure minus the colloidal osmotic pressure of the blood proteins, it is apparent that any decrease in the proteins is associated with an increase in the filtration pressure. When the normal percentage of the plasma proteins (6 to 8 per cent) falls to about 4 per cent, edema ensues. This occurs in nephritis, a kidney disturbance in which large amounts of the blood proteins are excreted in the urine (albuminuria). During World War I the people of Central Europe suffered partial starvation, and edema was prevalent. Some authorities hold that this *nutritional, or war, edema* was due to the want of sufficient proteins in the diet; others attribute it to the lack of vitamins.

VI. SHOCK

Shock.—So many meanings have been assigned to this well-known term that it has become almost meaningless. We shall limit it to those conditions in which there is a marked depression of circulation which interferes with the proper functioning of the body and, in severe cases, may result in death. Many circulatory disturbances (aside from cardiac failure, incompetence of valves, etc.) are known as shock; these are generally designated in accordance with the manner of their origin, e.g., neural, gravitational, hemorrhagic, anaphylactic (allergic), toxic, traumatic, and surgical shock. In the following paragraphs the term ''shock'' refers only to the last two mentioned forms.

Most of us are acquainted with the fact that shock frequently follows severe mechanical injury (especially great laceration of muscles) and surgical operations, even though very little blood has been lost. The symptoms are pallor and coldness of the skin, frequently accompanied with cyanosis (blueness) of ears and fingers, a feeble but rapid pulse, shallow and rapid breathing, and, to a greater or lesser extent, mental collapse. All of these are indicative of a great fall in blood pressure. This reduction in pressure could be due to a disturbance in any one of the three necessary elements in circulation: cardiac failure, loss of vasomotor tonus, or a reduction in blood volume. That the heart is not at fault is shown by the very rapid, though less forceful beat (Starling's law); the second factor has also been ruled out. It is now generally conceded that the cause of the fall in pressure must be sought in a decreased volume of blood in the vascular system; this view is substantiated by the fact that the cavities of the heart and the blood vessels are but poorly filled. We have already intimated that the loss of blood is not due to extravascular hemorrhage. As the concentration of the corpuscles in the remaining blood is high, it may be safely concluded that the loss of blood is due to the escape of plasma from the blood vessels. As to the cause of the escape of plasma, we may briefly state one of several views that have been suggested. It will be recalled that mechanical damage to the capillary wall is associated with a capillary dilation and an increased permeability. This allows a greater transudation of fluid from the blood stream into the tissues. If the action is local, a wheal is formed. It will be noticed that this is but exaggeration of what normally takes place in an active tissue. But if the damage to the capillaries is quite extensive, the loss of plasma may be sufficiently great to bring about anoxemia which, in turn, leads to a more widespread capillary dilation and an increase in permeability. As this condition progresses, more and more plasma is lost, less blood returns to the heart, and a fall in blood pressure results.

According to this view, the factors concerned in the normal formation of tissue fluid are also the cause of traumatic or surgical shock. A wheal is ''shock in miniature,'' and both are exaggerations of normal processes.

From the above discussion it is clear that to combat shock, the lost fluid must be replaced by transfusions. Preliminary to this, it is well to place the patient in such position as to aid the feeble circulation, especially the cerebral circulation. His body and mind (if he is conscious) should be kept at ease; the administration of liquids is highly desirable (but never to an unconscious person); and he should be kept warm. The latter treatment, it is now held, is frequently overdone. In shock there is a great dearth of oxygen in the tissues; therefore the metabolic rate should not be increased. If the body (not the skin) temperature is normal, do not apply heat, as this will increase the anoxemia.

VII. HEMORRHAGE AND LYMPH

The reverse of the above process is seen in an extensive hemorrhage. The volume of the blood and the pressure are considerably decreased, but the osmotic pressure of the proteins in the plasma remains normal. When the latter pressure exceeds the capillary blood pressure, fluid is drawn from the tissue spaces into the capillaries. It is by this means that an adequate blood volume is maintained and circulation made possible.

VIII. THE FLOW OF LYMPH

The velocity of the lymph flow is very slow. In the thoracic duct the average velocity is about 4 mm. per second. The total lymph discharged by the duct was found by Munk to be from 1,200 to 2,280 c.c. per day. When compared with the volume of blood carried by the aorta—about 5,000 c.c. per minute—the quantity of lymph is exceedingly small. The pressure of the lymph is also very low. As no special organs for the propulsion of lymph obtain, the flow is dependent upon external forces, among which we may discuss the following:

1. In general we may say that whatever increases the flow of the blood in the veins also aids the lymph flow. Among the various factors we have noted the "milking" action of skeletal muscles. No lymph flows from the resting leg of a dog; but in muscular activity the rhythmical contraction of the muscles squeezes out the lymph and a considerable flow takes place. This may be counted as one of the benefits derived from physical exercise.

2. Aspiration by the thorax during respiration.

3. The massaging of the body and passive movements of the limbs act upon the flow of the lymph and venous blood in much the same manner as the rhythmical contraction of the muscles. The fatigue after work is lessened by massage, for it removes more speedily the waste products (fatigue substances) from the tissues. Massaging a bruised part may prevent the accumulation of lymph which generally takes place and causes the part to swell.

IX. THE LYMPH NODES

In the course of the lymph vessels there are inserted at frequent intervals, as can be seen in Fig. 125, little round or oval masses varying in size, the largest having the dimensions of a bean. In certain localities of the body, these little swellings, known as lymph nodes, or glands, are very abundant, as in the neck, axilla, groin, and in the mesentery. Their functions, so far as they are known with any degree of certainty, may be stated as follows:

1. They form lymphocytes, for the lymph leaving the node is richer in these cells than that which enters. This function they have in common with the other structures composed of what is known as lymphoid, or adenoid, tissue, such as the tonsils and spleen, as also the more or less scattered patches of this tissue found in the mucous membrane of the intestines (solitary glands and Peyer's patches) and of the respiratory tract.

2. The nodes serve as filters for the lymph.

(a) The nodes of the respiratory tract may become pigmented with particles of carbon, as in the case of miners.

(b) The nodes remove bacteria from the lymph. When an infection by bacteria takes place in a certain part of the body, the infection frequently spreads by way of the lymphatic system. As the lymph moves from the infected area toward the heart, the germs are retained by the nodes, and thus prevented from entering the blood stream. In the nodes the bacteria may, to a certain extent, be destroyed, but if they gain the upper hand, the nodes, in consequence of the toxins produced by the bacteria, may enlarge. A well-known example of this is the enlargement of the nodes of the neck, in case of tuberculosis. The cervical nodes may become infected through the tonsils, ear, nose, or decaying teeth. The bubo (the inflammation and swelling of the nodes in the groin due to gonorrheal or syphilitic infection) furnishes another example. When these nodes, loaded with bacteria and their products, are unable any longer to cope with the situation and break down, the infection spreads and septicemia (*sepsis*, putrefaction) results.

Some investigators have seen in the spleen a defense of the body against bacterial infection, for after its removal the animal is incapable of being immunized against the toxin of tetanus. The splenic cells have been shown to possess the power to withdraw other toxins from the circulation.

CHAPTER XIII

GAS EXCHANGE: RESPIRATION

For the maintenance of its life, the body must be supplied with a large number of different substances, but it is a matter of common observation that the most fundamental and *the most urgent need is a continual supply of oxygen.* Of almost equal importance is the constant elimination of the waste product, CO_2. "Breathing is living." Although a muscle obtains its energy directly from various substances, nevertheless, "oxygen winds up the vital clock." The body is liberally supplied with reserves of energy-furnishing materials, such as carbohydrates, fats, and, to a lesser extent, proteins. But, as the oxygen lies at its very door, there is no need to provide the body with stores of oxygen. Hence, the oxygen, without which the above-named reserves would be of no value, must be furnished from the environment in a continual, uninterrupted stream. And as the power of the body to defend itself against the poisonous effects of CO_2 is exceedingly limited, this waste product must be removed almost as fast as it is formed. The exchange of gases between the organism and its environment is called respiration. To bring the oxygen from the environment to the cells and to return the carbon dioxide to the environment, the middleman, blood, is necessary as a carrier of these gases.

The pulmonary, or lung, capillaries are almost in direct contact with the air in the lungs, and the exceedingly thin walls of these blood vessels readily permit the oxygen from the air to pass into the blood and the carbon dioxide of the blood, into the air. This exchange by which the blood gains oxygen and loses some carbon dioxide transforms the venous into arterial blood and is known as *pulmonary* or *external respiration.* In the systemic capillaries the blood parts with some of its oxygen and gains carbon dioxide from the tissues. This changes the arterial into venous blood and is called the *internal respiration.*

That the exchange of the gases between the air and the blood may continue, it is evident that the air in the lungs must be renewed. This renewal, by which the old air, robbed of some of its oxygen and laden with carbon dioxide, is expelled from the lungs and by which fresh air is introduced, is also called respiration; a better and more distinctive term for this process is pulmonary ventilation.

I. PULMONARY VENTILATION

The mechanism by which pulmonary ventilation is brought about comprises: (1) the respiratory tract, and (2) the respiratory muscles. The respiratory tract is, broadly speaking, a tubular structure which includes the nose, pharynx, trachea, bronchi, and the lungs proper, Fig. 127.

Mucosa.—Many tubular organs in the body have their inner surfaces lined with a membrane, known as the mucosa, or mucous membrane. The structure of this membrane differs in the various organs, but the part that is common to all these membranes is the outermost layer, the epithelium. This is formed in some places of a single layer of pavement, or squamous, epithelial cells (Fig. 7); in other regions

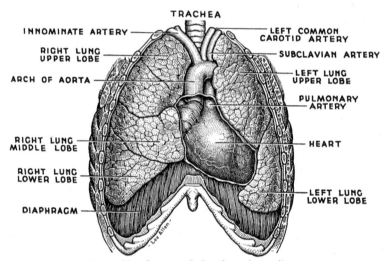

Fig. 127.—Organs of the thoracic cavity.

it is columnar, Fig. 8, and in many parts of the respiratory tract these columnar cells are ciliated (Fig. 9). Beneath the epithelium there is a layer of connective tissue (areolar, or frequently lymphoid, as in the tonsils) which binds the epithelium to the next layer, the muscularis mucosa, in which are found bundles of plain muscle fibers. The mucosa is well supplied with blood vessels (note the mucosa of the nostrils of a running horse), and the capillaries lie just beneath the epithelial cells. In the mucosa small glands are frequently found which pour a viscid fluid, mucus, onto the surface; or the columnar epithelial cells themselves secrete this fluid. In the upper part of the respiratory tract this mucus serves to catch a great deal of the inhaled dust and bacteria; by means of the cilia, the mucus with the entangled dust is propelled toward the pharynx and is then swallowed.

A. Functions of the Nose

1. The nose informs us of the presence of noxious gases, provided they stimulate the olfactory or the trigeminal nerve. The deadly gas, carbon monoxide, CO, has no odor.

2. Certain bones of the skull, as the superior maxillary, the frontal, etc., contain cavities, or sinuses; we speak of the frontal sinus, located behind the eyebrow, and the maxillary sinus (or the antrum of High-more) in the cheek bone. These sinuses, lined with ciliated mucous membrane, open up into the nasal cavities. Infection of these sinuses, sinusitis, coupled with incomplete drainage (especially true for the maxillary sinuses) may give rise, by the pressure of the confined pus, to severe pain and may eventually involve the eyes or brain. Into the nasal cavities, or fossae, open the nasal ducts, which convey the tears

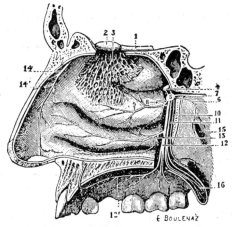

Fig. 128.—The nasal cavities. *1*, olfactory tract; *2*, olfactory bulb; *3*, branches of olfactory nerve; *6*, pharyngeal nerve; *8*, *9*, sphenopalatine; *10*, *11*, *12*, palatine nerves with *13*, nasal branch; *14*, termination of ethmoidal nerve; *15*, opening of Eustachian tube; *16*, vault of palate. (Testut.)

from the inner angle of the eyes to the nose. The second function of the nose may, therefore, be stated to be the draining of the secretions of the sinuses and of the lacrimal glands. The value of these sinuses consists in reducing the weight of the skull and in acting as resonators for the voice.

3. By passing through the hairs at the entrance of the nose and more especially through the narrow passages formed by the three turbinate bones (see Fig. 128), the inspired air is prepared for the lungs, in that the nose warms, moistens, and filters it. Many of the bacteria of the inspired air are caught in the mucus which bathes the mucous membrane; and by the action of the cilia of the nasal pas-sage, upper pharynx, trachea, bronchi, and bronchioles (except the

very smallest), the mucus, inhaled bacteria, and dust are moved outward. Some of the dust and bacteria are taken up by the lymph tissue of the respiratory tubes and brought to the lymph nodes.

The inhalation of metal and mineral dust is especially injurious to the respiratory tract because of the sharpness and cutting action of this form of dust, and is, therefore, a great predisposing factor in pulmonary diseases such as bronchitis, asthma, tuberculosis, pneumonia, etc. It is stated that among the Cornish tin miners 68 per cent of all the sick are consumptives and that among glass cutters and grindstone makers the percentage may run as high as 80 and 90 per cent. Among the other occupations that are for this reason very harmful we may mention pottery making, cotton spinning and allied trades, the grinding and polishing of metals of all sorts, working in hard woods, and the preparing of hides and feathers. The depositing of sand particles in the lungs is known as silicosis (*silex*, flint); in the same manner we speak of the blackened condition of the coal miner's lungs as anthracosis.

Mouth-Breathing.—Increased resistance offered to the flow of the air through the nasal passages leads to mouth-breathing. This resistance may be due to a too great development of the turbinate bones, or the bony septum which divides the nasal passage into the two fossae may be deflected or bent to one side. Again, the mucous membrane may be swollen; especially do we find marked hypertrophy of the adenoid (connective) tissue, a trouble which constitutes the well-known "adenoids." Mouth-breathing affects the jaws, the hard palate becomes narrow and highly arched, and the lower jaw may recede so that the upper incisor teeth project beyond the lower. Even the chest may not be developed properly because of inadequate expansion.

How largely mouth-breathing may affect the health of the individual is seen from a report by Wotzilka who found that of 100 tuberculous men and women 45 were unable to breathe normally through the nose; of 100 nontuberculous people only 13 were mouth-breathers. The reason for this is partly due, no doubt, to the greater number of bacteria that find entrance into the lungs when the person breathes through his mouth. Even in normal breathing some germs pass by the mucus and cilia of the nasal and bronchial tubes, but it is easily seen that this number must be vastly increased by mouth-breathing. In such conditions the tonsils are also exposed to the direct attack of bacteria. By surgical operation the cause for mouth-breathing can generally be removed.

"Cold."—Closely related to the functions of the nose in respiration is the subject of "colds." A cold in the head, rhinitis, pharyngitis, and laryngitis are caused by infections. It is the almost unanimous opinion of people that taking a cold is ushered in by exposure to cold. While we may state at the outset that mere exposure to cold does not bring on a cold, as is well illustrated by Arctic explorers who seldom, if ever, catch cold, yet it is so frequently true that unaccustomed exposure to cold precedes the catching of a cold, that some causal relation seems to exist. We are familiar with the fact, as above stated, that merely exposing oneself to the cold may do no harm whatever. As long as we are walking briskly or otherwise muscularly active, no degree of cold injures us. It is when we sit quietly in a cold room without being sufficiently protected by clothing, and more especially when the body experiences the continual chilling caused by the drying of our clothes, wet with rain or perspiration, that we are most liable to take a cold, provided that the infective agency is present.

To relieve a cold, according to Long, two or three days in bed, a mild laxative, and a moderate amount of water intake is the best course. Not much reliance is to be put in certain diets, in vitamins A, B_1, B_2, C, D, and niacin, or in ultraviolet light; neither has the degree of "hardness" or "softness" of the individual any influence. It is claimed bacterial vaccines are of some benefit. "At present the only prophylaxis against colds is the avoidance of contact with infected people."

Generally a "cold" is perhaps not anything very serious; certainly most people look upon it as such. But it should always be borne in mind that it may be a source of danger. The local inflammation of the nasal mucosa may spread to the eustachian tube (which connects the pharynx with the middle ear; see Sense Organs) and even to the middle ear and seriously interfere with hearing. The sinuses of the cranial bones may also become involved. Having a cold may lower the vitality of the body so as to lay it open to other diseases.

B. The Lungs

The position of the lungs in the thoracic cavity and their relation to the other organs may be seen in Fig. 127. The lungs may be regarded as great ramifications of the windpipe, or trachea. The trachea, Figs. 127 and 129, splits into two large bronchi; these, in turn, split into smaller and smaller branches until finally the smallest branches (bronchioles) form little dilated end pockets named infundibula, Fig. 130. The walls of the infundibula are dilated to form the alveoli, 4. As the branches of the air tubes become smaller and smaller, the walls become simpler and thinner in structure, until in the walls of the alveoli we find only flattened epithelial cells (Fig. 7) supported by a thin layer of elastic connective tissue. Closely applied to this respiratory epithelium is a dense network of capillaries, Fig. 131; it is in these capillaries that the aeration of the blood takes place.

The blood supply for the lungs is obtained from two sources; the pulmonary and the bronchial artery. The pulmonary artery, from the right ventricle, carries the venous blood to the lungs; the oxygenated, or arterial, blood is returned to the left auricle by the four pulmonary veins; this is the functional circulation of the lungs. The bronchial arteries, springing from the thoracic aorta, supply arterial blood to the lungs for the nourishment of these organs.

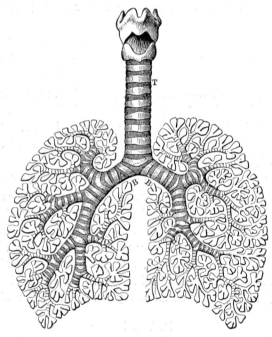

Fig. 129.—Respiratory tract. *T*, trachea with larynx; *B*, bronchi. (Dalton.)

Each lung is surrounded by a double serous membrane, called the pleura, Fig. 132. That part of the membrane applied to the lungs is the visceral pleura; that which lines the thoracic cavity is the parietal pleura. The space between these two layers is known as the pleural cavity. In the normal condition this cavity is only potential; the two layers are closely applied to each other, being separated only by a very thin layer of a lubricating fluid (lymph), secreted by the pleura itself. In pleurisy these membranes are inflamed and, as a result, much lymph may collect in the pleural sac. Or, the thoracic wall being punctured, air may enter into it (see Pneumothorax); sometimes blood finds its way into the cavity. In all these conditions the lungs will be pressed upon and breathing may be seriously interfered with. The lungs, each enclosed in its pleura, are suspended from the trachea in an air-tight box, the thoracic cavity. The walls of this cavity, formed by the ribs, sternum, and diaphragm, are more or less movable, and by their movement the capacity of the thorax is altered.

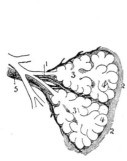

Fig. 130.

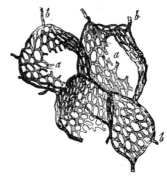

Fig. 131.

Fig. 130.—Two primary lobules of the lungs. *1*, Bronchial tube. *2*, A pair of primary lobules connected with fibroelastic tissue. *3*, Infundibulum (ultimate lobule) with, *4*, the air cells, or alveoli. *5*, Branches of the pulmonary artery and vein. (Leidy.)

Fig. 131.—Capillary network of air cells. (Frey.)

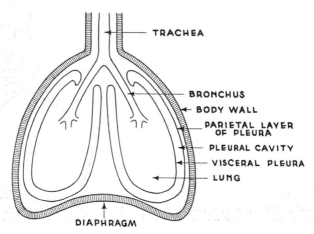

TRACHEA

BRONCHUS

BODY WALL

PARIETAL LAYER OF PLEURA

PLEURAL CAVITY

VISCERAL PLEURA

LUNG

DIAPHRAGM

Fig. 132.—Diagram of the thorax to show position of the pleura and pleural cavity.

Inspiration.—By the expansion of the thoracic wall the chest cavity is enlarged; this results in a decrease of the air pressure in the lungs and, because of the greater atmospheric pressure, the air rushes into the lungs, which, being elastic bags, distend and follow the thoracic wall. This constitutes *inspiration*. During *expiration* the chest wall assumes its former position and the cavity is reduced; as a result the pressure in the lungs becomes greater than the atmospheric pressure and the air rushes out of the lungs.

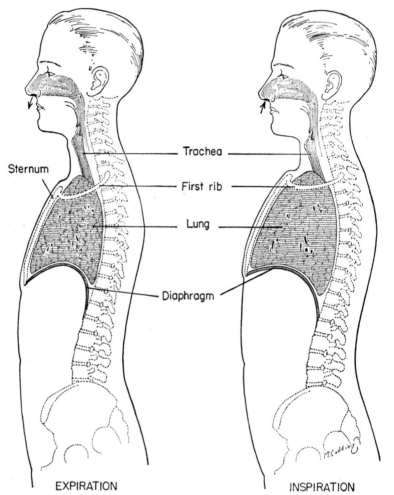

Fig. 133.—To illustrate the enlargement of the thorax by diaphragmatic and costal breathing. (Turner and McHose: Effective Living, The C. V. Mosby Co.)

The enlargement of the thoracic cavity during inspiration is produced by:

1. THE DIAPHRAGM.—The diaphragm is a dome-shaped muscular sheet between the thorax and the abdomen. When its radial muscle fibers contract, the diaphragm is flattened more or less, and thereby enlarges the longitudinal diameter of the chest and reduces the air pressure in the lungs (Fig. 133). The descent of the diaphragm

increases the pressure in the abdomen; this causes the abdominal wall to be pushed forward. The muscles of the diaphragm are innervated by the *phrenic nerves*, originating from the 3rd and 4th

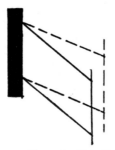

Fig. 134.—To illustrate the position of   ribs, sternum, and spinal column.

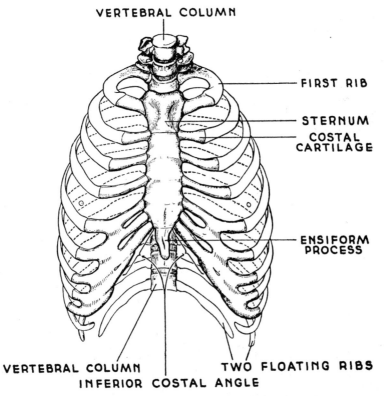

VERTEBRAL COLUMN

FIRST RIB

STERNUM

COSTAL CARTILAGE

ENSIFORM PROCESS

VERTEBRAL COLUMN

INFERIOR COSTAL ANGLE

TWO FLOATING RIBS

Fig. 135.—The skeleton framework of the thorax.

cervical segments of the spinal cord; cutting one of these nerves paralyzes the corresponding half of the diaphragm. The diaphragm is the chief muscle of inspiration; during forced breathing as much as 60 per cent of the inhaled air finds room because of the contraction of this muscle.

2. The chest cavity is enlarged also by the raising of the ribs. The upward rotation of the ribs not only elevates the sternum but, as the ribs slant downward and forward, also pushes it forward (see Fig. 134), thereby increasing the anteroposterior diameter of the chest (Fig. 133). The raising of the ribs also increases the lateral diameter, for the ribs which form the wall of the thorax vary in size, each rib being larger than the one just above it, Fig. 135. This raising is brought about by many muscles among which we may mention:

(a) The external intercostals (Fig. 136, A).

(b) The scaleni, from the transverse processes of the cervical vertebrae to the first and second ribs.

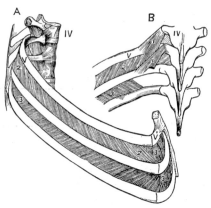

Fig. 136.—Illustrating three of the ribs with the external intercostal muscles, *2;* the internal intercostal muscles, *3;* and the levatores costarum, *1.* A, lateral and B, posterior view. (Cloquet.)

(c) The levatores costarum, from the transverse processes of the seventh cervical and first to eleventh thoracic vertebrae, to the nearest rib below (Fig. 136, B).

(d) Sternocleidomastoideus, from the mastoid process of the skull to the sternum and the clavicle.

(e) Pectoralis minor, from the coracoid process of the scapula to the second, third, fourth, and fifth ribs.

(f) Serratus posticus superior, from the spinous processes of lower cervical and upper thoracic vertebrae to the second, third, fourth, and fifth ribs.

Expiration is either passive or active. During quiet respiration no muscular contraction is needed to bring the chest wall to its resting position, for the elasticity of the tissues (costal cartilages, the abdominal wall, etc.) and the weight of the structures (the whole thoracic wall when we assume the erect position) are sufficient to bring about this result. During forced, or labored, respiration, as occurs in muscular work, expiration is a powerful muscular process in which the following muscles may take a part:

1. By the contraction of the external and internal obliquus, rectus, and transversus muscles of the abdominal wall the pressure in the abdomen is increased and the diaphragm forced upward.

2. The internal intercostal muscles, Fig. 136, *A,* are attached to the lower edge of one rib and the upper edge of the next lower rib. As the fibers slant downward and backward, by their contraction the ribs are lowered, and the sternum pulled down and in.

3. The serratus posticus inferior (from the spinous processes of the lower two dorsal and upper two or three lumbar vertebrae to the four lower ribs).

4. The quadratus lumborum (from the crest of the ilium to the lowest rib) also depresses the ribs.

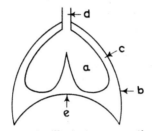

Fig. 137.—Diagram to illustrate pneumothorax. See text.

Pulmonary Pressure.—By alternate expansion and constriction of the chest cavity the pressure in the lungs is decreased and increased respectively. The extent of the changes in pressure depends upon the rapidity and extent of the action of the respiratory muscles, and, more especially, upon the amount of resistance the air encounters in finding its way into or out of the lungs. Thus, during quiet inspiration, the pulmonary pressure falls but 4 or 5 mm. Hg, but during labored inspiration the decrease is from 5 to 10 mm., and with the air passages closed this can be reduced 30 to 70 mm. Similarly, during quiet expiration the pressure is seldom increased by more than 2 or 3 mm., but with the air passages closed the expiratory muscles are able to generate a pulmonary pressure 40 to 100 mm. Hg greater than the atmospheric pressure.

The lungs in their expansion and constriction are purely passive. In the adult these highly elastic lungs are smaller than the thoracic cavity in which they are placed, with the result that, because of the air pressure in them, they are always in a distended condition, even when the chest cavity is reduced to a minimum. The lungs (*a*, Fig. 137) tend to collapse (because of their elasticity) but the thoracic wall, *b*, in which they are inclosed is rigid and does not follow the shrinking lungs, hence a partial vacuum is created in the pleural cavity, *c*. The pressure in the pleural cavity, called intrathoracic pressure, is negative to the extent that the elasticity of the lungs causes them to collapse; this is generally stated at about 5 mm. below atmospheric pressure, when the chest wall is at rest. The negative pressure (suction) in the pleural cavity prevents further collapse of the lungs. When the chest wall is opened, the inrush of the air causes the pressure in the pleural cavity to become equal to the atmospheric pressure and therefore equal to that in the lungs; as the force restraining the collapsing of the lungs has been removed, by their elasticity the lungs collapse. This condition is called *pneumothorax* (*pneuma*, air). In case the pneumothorax exists on one side, the other side of the thorax continues the function of respiration. If the wound in the chest heals over so as to prevent any further entrance of air, the air inclosed in the cavity is absorbed by the blood and tissues, and, as the intrathoracic pressure falls, the lung expands.

Pneumothorax is sometimes induced surgically by the injection of nitrogen gas into the pleural cavity, as in tuberculosis and in lobar pneumonia, to immobilize the lung; this insures complete rest, prevents extension of the disease, and favors healing. In the newborn child, before the first breath has been taken, the lungs are totally collapsed—*atelectasis**—due to the adhesion of the walls of the bronchioles and alveoli; this causes them to sink when excised and placed in water. During inspiration the apical portions do not expand as freely and fully as the rest of the lungs. To this is generally attributed the fact that these parts are so frequently the first to be involved in tuberculosis.

During coughing, vomiting, and straining at stool, the individual takes a deep breath and then closes the glottis (the slit between the vocal cords in the larynx); this imprisons the air in the lungs. By the powerful and steady contraction of the muscles in the wall of the abdomen, a great pressure is exerted upon the contents of this cavity; by it the venous blood is squeezed toward the heart, but at the same time the flow in the arteries is impeded. The intra-abdominal pressure tends to force the diaphragm upward; this, however, is largely prevented by the closed glottis and the contraction of the muscles of expiration. As a result the intrathoracic and pulmonary pressures are also increased. This prevents the return of the venous blood from the head and other parts of the body; evidence of this is seen in the stagnation of blood in the superficial vessels of the face, which may result in cyanosis. When next the glottis is opened, the

---

*ăt-e-lec′-ta-sis.

escaping air reduces the intrathoracic pressure and allows a great rush of venous blood to the right heart. When this large amount of blood reaches the left heart, the large systolic output and strongly contracting ventricle may raise the arterial blood pressure to an extent which may be dangerous to an individual with arteriosclerosis or a weakened heart. Somewhat similar conditions exist during any sustained effort, such as the lifting of heavy weights.

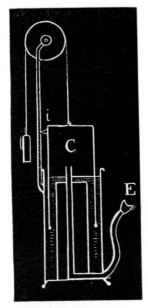

Fig. 138.—Spirometer.

Amount of Air Respired.—The volume of air that can be taken into or forced out of the lungs can be measured by a spirometer. Fig. 138 shows Hutchinson's spirometer. By means of the mouthpiece, *E*, the subject either inhales air from or exhales into the tank, *C*, which is suspended by a cord and pulley over an outer tank filled with water. The amount of air inhaled or exhaled is shown by the indicator, *i*. The amount of air we respire, with varying depths of respiration, is described in the following terms:

1. TIDAL AIR.—The amount of air breathed out during quiet expiration. The average for adults is about 500 c.c.

2. COMPLEMENTAL AIR.—This is the amount that can be breathed in over and above tidal air by the deepest inspiration. Its volume is about 2,000 c.c.

3. SUPPLEMENTAL AIR.—This amount, about 1,500 c.c., can be exhaled by the most forceful expiration after a quiet expiration.

4. VITAL CAPACITY.—This is the volume of air expired by the most forcible expiration after the most complete inspiration. It represents the total movable air in the lungs. In 164 normal students the amount varied from 2,450 to 6,200 c.c. If the vital capacity is stated in terms of body surface area, the average for a normal man is 2.64 liters per square meter of surface area; for a woman, 2.09 (see pp. 442 and 443).

5. RESIDUAL AIR.—Even after the most forcible expiration there remains a quantity of residual air estimated at about 1,500 c.c.

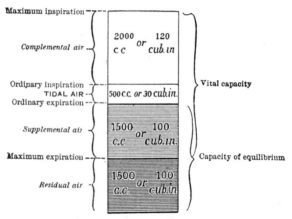

Fig. 139.—Diagram showing the relation of the various volumes of air inhaled and exhaled. (Waller.)

The relation of these volumes and the extent of the inspiratory and expiratory movements are shown in Fig. 139.

Of the 500 c.c. taken in by quiet inspiration about 150 c.c. remain in the nose, trachea, bronchi, etc., where no exchange of gases takes place; this is called the *"dead space."*

Vital capacity varies with many factors, some of which we shall consider briefly. From birth to maturity there is a gradual increase in the vital capacity; because of the stiffening of the chest wall the vital capacity may decrease materially in old age and thereby lessen the ability to carry on vigorous muscular work. That body position is a factor to be considered is shown by the fact that an individual with a vital capacity of 4.3 liters in a standing position experiences a reduction of as much as 0.68 liters when in a prone position. It is for this reason that patients with labored breathing cannot breathe as well in a prone as in a sitting or standing position. Physical exercise and occupations in which there is a demand for increased pulmonary ventilation increase vital capacity; occupations conducive to shallow breathing have the opposite effect. In fact, by practicing deep breathing the capacity of the lungs may be materially increased.

Thoracic Index.—Much importance has been attached to the measurement and capacity of the chest. Hutchinson lays great stress upon the thoracic index by which is meant the quotient of the anteroposterior diameter (at the nipple line) divided by the lateral diameter. In a normal, healthy chest the former diameter is about 67 per cent of the latter; in this chest the vital capacity may be as much as 50 per cent greater than in one with a higher index. By stretching the chest muscles, tree or ladder climbing favors the flattening of the chest. An individual with a flat chest is less prone to tuberculosis than one with a deep (large anteroposterior diameter) and narrow chest, having a higher index.

Rate of Respiration.—The usual rate in the adult is generally stated from 13 to 18 per minute, but this number is subject to great variations. It is increased by muscular exertion, greater body temperature, and certain mental conditions. In women the rate is from 2 to 4 per minute greater. The cause of this higher rate in women and in children no doubt lies in the smaller size of the body. The rate varies with the age:

At birth_____from 40 to 70 per minute.
5 years_____about 25 per minute.
15 years_____about 20 per minute.
30 years_____about 16 per minute.

It is also influenced by the position of the body:

Reclining_____13 per minute.
Sitting_____18 per minute.
Standing_____22 per minute.

The rate is much affected by certain conditions of the blood which will be discussed later. Sleep decreases the rate by as much as 25 per cent.

Ventilation Rate.—The amount of air passing into and out of the lungs in a unit of time is determined by the rate and the depth of breathing. The following terms are frequently employed in describing the rate and depth of respiration: eupnea (*eu,* well) is quiet breathing; hyperpnea is increased breathing (as in muscular exercise); dyspnea (*dys,* bad) is very labored and excessive breathing associated with discomfort and distress; apnea is the temporary cessation of breathing. The conditions in which we find these various types of breathing and their causes will be discussed in a subsequent part.

Rhythm of Respiration.—By means of a pneumograph and a tambour the movements of the chest wall can be recorded. The reader will find a description of this apparatus and its use in any laboratory manual. From the curve obtained, Fig. 140, we learn that the expiratory phase, from *b* to *c* is a little longer than the inspiratory, from *a* to *b*, and that while a short pause may take place at the end of each expiration (expiratory pause, at *c*), there is normally no inspiratory pause at *b*. The ratio of respiration to heartbeat is as 1:4 or 1:5. Although in normal life the rate of either the

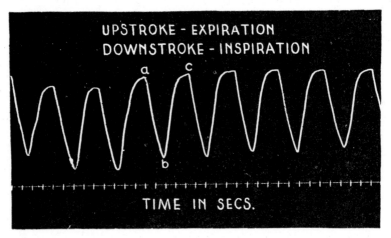

Fig. 140.—Pneumograph tracing of the respiratory movements in man. *ab*, inspiration; *bc*, expiration.

heart action or the respiration may be increased or decreased, such a close relation exists between these two processes that the above ratio is very constant; in pathologic conditions it may vary.

Respiratory Sounds.—The movement of the air through the air passages and into the lungs causes two sounds:

1. *Bronchial,* or *tubular, sound.* This is a blowing sound originating at the glottis and is heard, in health, only over the trachea and large bronchi, both during inspiration and expiration. When the lungs are consolidated, as in pneumonia, this sound is conducted by the solid lungs to other parts.

2. The *vesicular murmur* is a much softer, and a breezy sound and is heard only during inspiration over the whole lung. It is supposed

to be due to the distention of the alveoli with air. Hence this sound is absent when the alveoli do not function, as in tuberculosis and pneumonia.

II. CHEMISTRY OF RESPIRATION

Respiration is the exchange of gases between the organism and its environment, the blood acting as the "middleman" between the tissues and the outer world. We may, therefore, look for changes in the air as it passes into and out of the lungs, and for changes in the blood as it circulates through the lungs and through the tissues.

A. External Respiration

The changes the air undergoes in its passage through the lungs may be studied by comparing the inspired with the expired air:

1. The gases found in the inspired and expired air are:

TABLE VIII

	OXYGEN	CARBON DIOXIDE	NITROGEN	ARGON, ETC.
Inspired air	21%	0.04%	78%	1%
Expired air	16%	4.00%	78%	1%

2. At room temperature the expired air is 90 per cent saturated with water vapor; the amount of vapor in the inspired air is variable but generally much less than that found in the expired air. In this manner we lose about 400 c.c. of water per day; the evaporation of this water entails a loss of heat.

3. The expired air may contain traces of ammonia, sulfureted hydrogen, hydrogen, and other gases formed in the intestines, where they are absorbed by the blood and, on reaching the lungs, are exhaled.

4. Expired air is nearly always warmer than the inspired.

5. Some have supposed that the expired air contains, besides the carbon dioxide, deleterious substances ("crowd poison") which cause the evil results of rebreathing the vitiated air. This idea, however, is not supported by experimental evidence.

Room Ventilation.—It is a well-known fact that crowding a number of people into an unventilated room for any length of time soon causes great discomfort, and ventilation is resorted to. Why is ventilation necessary? Knowing the changes in the oxygen and carbon dioxide content of the breathed air, and the great necessity for oxygen, and the poisonous effects of carbon dioxide, a ready answer to our question might be found in saying that oxygen must be brought into the room and carbon dioxide must be removed. And this was formerly regarded as summing up the needs of ventilation. How far this is from the truth the following will show.

1. That it is not the decrease in the amount of oxygen in the air of a room that brings about the need for ventilation is seen from the following fact: On a mountain of 4,000 meters the air pressure is 450 mm. Hg* and hence the oxygen pressure is only 450/760, or about ⅗ of what it is at sea level. Thus, instead of an oxygen pressure of 160 mm. Hg (21 per cent of 760 mm. Hg), there is a pressure of only 95 mm. Hg (21 per cent of 450 mm. Hg); this is equivalent to an atmosphere, at sea level, containing 12 or 13 per cent oxygen. Yet people find little difficulty in living at this altitude. Now, the oxygen content of the worst ventilated schoolroom is never lessened by more than 1 per cent (7.6 mm. Hg oxygen pressure).

We may approach this problem from another angle. To produce by the oxidation of food 5 calories of heat requires about 1,000 c.c. (or one liter) of oxygen. An adult at rest (basal metabolism) produces about 1,800 calories per day. The oxygen required for this is 360 liters, or approximately 12 cubic feet. This amount of oxygen is found in 60 cu. ft. of air. Consequently, the oxygen in a room measuring 10 by 10 by 9 feet is sufficient for almost eight days.

2. Workmen in bottling works sometimes breathe air containing from 0.4 to 1.0 per cent carbon dioxide without apparent detriment to their health. It is only when the percentage of carbon dioxide reaches from 2 to 4 per cent that respiration is markedly increased; when the amount reaches 6 per cent, mental confusion occurs. Compared with this, the carbon dioxide occurring in the most crowded and worst ventilated rooms is of no account.

3. We stated that it is held by some that the lungs throw off a poisonous product which causes the headache, drowsiness, and general discomfort felt on rebreathing the stale air. This material was also held responsible for the foul odor so often observed in such rooms. Many experiments have been made to determine whether the expired air really contains such deleterious substances. By condensing the water vapor of the exhaled air and injecting it into an animal, it has been found by some that the animal experienced bad effects; others claim that such injections have no special results. It is now quite generally accepted that the expired air does not contain any poisonous substances aside from the carbon dioxide. The foul odor can be attributed to the lack of cleanliness of the person, the clothing, or the room.

---

*At sea level the atmospheric pressure is 760 mm. Hg.

4. Experiments by Leonard Hill show that the first demand for fresh air is not due to any chemical change and has nothing to do with the lungs. Eight students were placed in a small air-tight chamber (three cubic meters) and remained there until the oxygen content was 16 per cent and the carbon dioxide 3.5 per cent. The air was very warm and moist, and at this time they experienced great discomfort. This discomfort was greatly relieved by starting an electric fan which set the air in motion and thereby cooled the men. At the time great discomfort was felt, one of the party breathed the outside air through a tube, but he experienced no relief; on the other hand an outsider, breathing the inside air through a tube, experienced no bad effects. The discomfort was, therefore, caused not primarily by the rebreathing of the vitiated air and its effect upon the respiratory processes or upon the gaseous composition of the blood, but by those qualities of the air that stimulate the cutaneous nerves and play an important part in the maintenance of the body temperature. *We feel the need for ventilation when the air has lost its cooling power.*

Closely related to the problem of ventilation is the spreading of infection. The overcrowding of rooms, schools and halls greatly increases the danger of infections, especially by the droplets of moisture ejected from the mouth and nose during coughing, sneezing, and forcible speaking. Germs survive considerably longer in moist than in dry air. Haldane concludes that *decreasing the bacteria population in the air is about the only reason for keeping windows open in cold weather.*

B. Internal Respiration

We have learned that in its passage through the pulmonary capillaries the venous blood, by losing some of its CO_2 and taking on an additional amount of oxygen, is made arterial. That this change occurs in the lungs can be verified by comparing the color of the blood in the right auricle with that in the left. The gas exchange during pulmonary respiration is greatly facilitated by the following:

1. All the blood in the body passes through the lung capillaries in one minute; during severe work this does not require more than 10 or 15 seconds. Through these capillaries the red blood cells pass single file.

2. The astonishingly large number of red blood cells (which are the carriers of the oxygen) and their exceedingly large amount of surface (see p. 148) favor the rapid taking in of oxygen.

3. The respiratory epithelium and the capillary wall which separate the blood from the air have a combined thickness of not more than 0.004 mm. (0.00,016 inch); through this membrane the gases pass with great rapidity.

4. The alveoli of the lungs have an area of about 250 square yards and the area of the capillaries found in the walls of the alveoli is estimated at 100 square yards; over this is distributed 900 c.c. of blood. The depth of this layer of blood is equal to the diameter of one corpuscle; as a consequence every corpuscle is in very close proximity to the alveolar air.

As the lungs are never completely emptied even during forced breathing, the gas exchange in the lung takes place continuously.

The above facts make it clear why a person having a deficient amount of hemoglobin or lacking the usual amount of functioning lung tissue may be able to obtain a sufficient quantity of oxygen during the resting condition of the body but immediately exhibits the symptoms of breathlessness on slight exertion.

Amount of Gases in the Blood.—To understand the forces by which the oxygen and carbon dioxide are moved from or into the blood during its passage through the pulmonary and systemic capillaries, it is necessary that we consider the extent to which these gases are present, the amount of pressure they exert in the blood and how they are held by the blood. The per cent by volume of the gases is stated in Table IX.

TABLE IX

	OXYGEN	CARBON DIOXIDE	NITROGEN
Arterial blood	20%	50%	1 to 2%
Venous blood	15%	55%	1 to 2%

Oxygen of the Blood.—From every 100 c.c. of arterial blood there can be expelled 20 c.c. of oxygen and 40 c.c. of carbon dioxide. These are very large figures when we compare them with the quantity of these gases that can be absorbed by water. By shaking 100 c.c. of water, at 40° C., with pure oxygen under 760 mm. Hg (one atmosphere) pressure, there are dissolved 2.31 c.c. of oxygen. If, instead of pure oxygen, the ordinary air is used, only about $\frac{1}{5}$ of 2.31 or 0.46 c.c. is dissolved, for the amount of gas dissolved in a liquid depends upon the partial pressure of that gas, and the oxygen forms $\frac{1}{5}$ of the atmosphere.

As there always remains in the lungs a considerable amount of residual air, the air in the alveoli has less oxygen and more CO_2 than the inhaled air. The composition of the alveolar air and the pressure of the gases present are given in Table X.

TABLE X

ALVEOLAR AIR	% BY VOLUME	PARTIAL PRESSURE		
Oxygen	13.0	13 /100 × 760 =	98.8	mm. Hg
Carbon dioxide	5.5	5.5/100 × 760 =	41.8	mm. Hg
Nitrogen	79.5	79.5/100 × 760 =	604.2	mm. Hg

If 100 c.c. of water were exposed, at 40° C., to the alveolar air, the amount of oxygen absorbed from this air would be 98.8/760 of 2.31 c.c., or about 0.33 c.c. But 100 c.c. of blood under the same conditions take on almost 20 c.c. of oxygen. It is, therefore, very evident that by far the largest amount of oxygen must be held in the blood in some other way than by physical solution. This is ac-

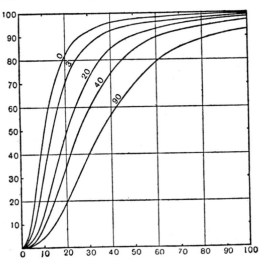

Fig. 141.—The abscissae indicate the pressure of oxygen in the air to which the blood is exposed; the ordinates show the percentage to which the blood is saturated with oxygen; the numbers on the curves give the percentage of CO_2 present in the blood. (Macleod: *Physiology in Modern Medicine; after Barcroft.*)

complished by the hemoglobin of the red blood corpuscle. The ability of hemoglobin to unite with such a large amount of oxygen and the rapidity with which this union takes place fit it admirably for the function of oxygen carrier. But to serve the tissues, it must also readily liberate the oxygen, and, from an economical point of view, the amount of oxygen set free should be in accordance with the demand for oxygen by the tissues. The following shows how well this rôle is played by the hemoglobin.

When blood at body temperature is exposed, as it is in the lungs, to an atmosphere of oxygen at about 100 mm. Hg pressure, 96 per cent of its hemoglobin becomes loaded with oxygen; that is, the blood is practically saturated. This is illustrated in Fig. 141, where the curve marked "40" shows the per cent saturation of the hemo-globin when the amount of CO_2 in the blood is 40 per cent. The abscissae (numbers along the base line) indicate the mm. Hg pres-sure of the oxygen in the air to which the hemoglobin is exposed; the ordinates on the left-hand side of the figure show the percentage of the hemoglobin combined with oxygen (per cent saturation). When the oxygen pressure is 100 mm. of Hg, the amount of oxygen absorbed by the blood is 96 per cent of saturation, and the tension of the oxygen in this blood is 100 mm. Hg. By the tension of a gas in a liquid we mean the force by which it tends to escape from the liquid; it is measured by the pressure that the same kind of gas in the air above the liquid must have in order to prevent the escape of the gas from the liquid.

The arterial blood with 20 per cent oxygen at a pressure of about 100 mm. Hg leaves the lungs and is sent to the tissues in which the pressure, or tension, of the oxygen is always low. The greater the activity of a tissue, the lower the tension; in a resting muscle and, therefore, in the tissue fluid bathing the capillaries, it is estimated at about 20 mm. Hg. As a result of this difference in oxygen ten-sion, some of the oxygen passes from the blood to the tissues; the rapidity with which the capillary stream flows does not permit a complete equalization of oxygen pressure between the blood and the muscle. Hence the venous blood leaving the muscle contains about 15 c.c. oxygen at a tension of 40 mm. Now it will be seen from Fig. 141 that at this tension, the oxygen saturation of blood is 75 per cent; i.e., the blood in the systemic capillaries contains 75 per cent of all the oxygen it can hold and has liberated therefore 96 minus 75, or 21, per cent. We see, therefore, that very little oxygen is set free from the blood when the tension remains above 40 mm.

But let us suppose that the muscles are contracting vigorously; they consume all the oxygen available, and the tension of the oxygen is reduced to zero. Curve "40" of Fig. 141 shows that as the ten-sion falls below 40 mm., the percentage saturation drops very fast, that is, the liberation of the oxygen takes place to a very great ex-tent; in fact, at 10 mm. tension, the percentage of oxygen in the blood is only 6 per cent of that originally found in the arterial blood.

The liberation of oxygen from the oxyhemoglobin is materially as-sisted by the presence of the CO_2. By the aid of Fig. 141 let us com-pare the amount of oxygen liberated from the arterial blood when the amount of CO_2 in the blood is (a) 3 per cent and (b) 40 per cent. In (a), as shown by the curve marked "3," the blood, containing 3 per cent CO_2, is almost saturated (100 per cent) with oxygen at 100 mm. Hg oxygen pressure (alveolar air), but its saturation is

educed to about 93 per cent when the oxygen pressure in the surrounding medium (tissues) falls to 40 mm.; that is, the blood loses
100 minus 93, or 7 per cent, of its oxygen. Since the blood contains
20 c.c. of oxygen at 100 mm. Hg (alveolar) oxygen pressure, this 7
per cent loss is equal to 1.4 c.c.; this amount of oxygen can therefore pass from the blood to the tissues. In (b) the percentage volume of CO_2 is 40 instead of 3; the blood, at an oxygen pressure of
40 mm., is but 75 per cent saturated; that is, there is a liberation
of 96 minus 75, or 21 per cent of its original oxygen, which is 4.2 c.c.
In other words, three times as much oxygen passes from the blood
to the tissues. Even when the oxygen pressure in the tissues is
reduced to 20 mm., the blood containing 3 per cent CO_2 liberates
only 100 minus 70, or 30 per cent of its oxygen; with a carbon dioxide content of 40 per cent the same blood under the same conditions liberates 96 minus 35, or 61 per cent.

The more severe the muscle work, the less is the oxygen pressure
in the medium surrounding the blood, and the greater is the amount
of CO_2 entering the blood; as discussed above, both these factors
favor the dissociation of the oxyhemoglobin. In addition to these,
muscle activity is always associated with an increase in temperature,
and at a higher temperature the oxyhemoglobin surrenders its oxygen more freely. We have, therefore, a most wonderful chemical
regulation by which the supply of oxygen to a tissue is controlled by
the needs of the tissue.

Carbon Dioxide of the Blood.—When 100 c.c. of water is exposed
to an atmosphere of CO_2 having a pressure of 60 mm., it dissolves
about 10 c.c. of gas; but the blood exposed to CO_2 under this tension
in the tissues absorbs as much as 50 to 55 c.c. From this we may
conclude that only a small part of the total quantity of the gas is
carried in solution. To understand how the blood can hold from
50 to 55 per cent by volume of CO_2, we must consider the characteristics of solutions of CO_2 and carbonates, and the behavior of the
red blood cells.

1. Carbon dioxide passed through water unites with the water to
form carbonic acid—H_2CO_3. But, it is well known that when a strong
solution of carbonic acid (under pressure) is exposed to the air, the
acid breaks up into CO_2 and H_2O. This is seen in the uncorking of
any carbonated drink. We may express this reversible action:

$$CO_2 + H_2O \rightleftarrows H_2CO_3.$$

2. Being an acid, the H_2CO_3 can unite with bases to form salts;
of these the sodium carbonate—Na_2CO_3—and bicarbonate—$NaHCO_3$
—are familiar examples.

3. When a solution of sodium or potassium bicarbonate is subjected to the vacuum of an air pump, the following reaction takes place:

$$2 \text{ NaHCO}_3 \rightarrow \text{Na}_2\text{CO}_3 + \text{H}_2\text{O} + \text{CO}_2$$

in which, it will be seen, part of the CO_2 is liberated and the other part is more firmly held as sodium carbonate, Na_2CO_3. To drive off all the CO_2 an acid must be added:

$$\text{Na}_2\text{CO}_3 + 2\text{HCl} = 2 \text{ NaCl} + \text{H}_2\text{CO}_3 ;$$
$$\text{H}_2\text{CO}_3 \rightarrow \text{H}_2\text{O} + \text{CO}_2.$$

4. By subjecting plasma to a vacuum, only a part of the CO_2 is set free, but the addition of an acid removes all the CO_2; therefore, some of the gas in the plasma must be held as bicarbonate. If, instead of plasma, the whole blood (plasma plus corpuscles) is used, all the CO_2 is liberated without the addition of an acid; from this we must conclude that the red blood corpuscles behave as an acid.

5. The uniting of CO_2 with water to form H_2CO_3 and the breaking up of the acid into the gas and water take place very slowly. It was found that the red blood cells contain an enzyme, carbonic anhydrase, which accelerates both processes tremendously.

6. Proteins, as we shall learn in a subsequent chapter, are able to play the part of weak acids and can, therefore, unite with bases to form protein salts. We may symbolize the acid hemoglobin as HHb, and oxyhemoglobin, $HHbO_2$. The acid hydrogen from HHb can be replaced by a base, say, potassium or sodium, and thereby yield the potassium or sodium salt of hemoglobin: KHb or NaHb.

Let us now trace the CO_2 from the time of its formation in the cells to its expulsion into the external air. Because of its continual formation, the percentage and pressure of the CO_2 are greater in the cells than in the tissue fluids and blood; as a result the gas diffuses from the cells into these fluids. In the blood it speedily, under the influence of carbonic anhydrase, unites with water to form H_2CO_3; this acid can unite with any base available. As hemoglobin is a very weak acid, the carbonic acid takes the base from the protein salt:

$$\text{H}_2\text{CO}_3 + \text{KHb} \rightarrow \text{KHCO}_3 + \text{HHb}.$$

This enables the blood to carry a large amount of CO_2.

In addition to this, it has recently been shown that the hemoglobin molecule is able to unite directly with carbon dioxide, and form a compound known as *carbhemoglobin*. According to this view, in the carrying of CO_2 the red blood cells serve three functions:

(a) They contain the carbonic anhydrase; (b) the hemoglobin unites directly with CO_2; (c) the hemoglobin supplies a base for the formation of bicarbonate. In these ways the blood carries a large amount of CO_2 which is distributed: 5 per cent in solution in the water of the blood, from 8 to 10 per cent as carbhemoglobin, and the remainder as bicarbonates.

On arriving at the lungs the reduced hemoglobin of the venous blood takes on oxygen to form oxyhemoglobin. Now oxyhemoglobin is a stronger acid than reduced hemoglobin and takes the base away from the bicarbonate.

$$HHbO_2 + KHCO_3 \rightarrow KHbO_2 + H_2CO_3.$$

By the action of the carbonic anhydrase the H_2CO_3 is rapidly broken up into H_2O and CO_2. This greatly increases the pressure of the CO_2 in the plasma and causes it to diffuse into the alveolar air where the CO_2 pressure and percentage are constantly kept low by pulmonary ventilation. Moreover, the conversion of HHb into $KHbO_2$ lessens its power to hold the CO_2 directly united with it; as a result the carbhemoglobin is broken up and the CO_2 liberated. On arriving at the tissues a part of the $KHbO_2$ surrenders its oxygen to the cells; the resultant reduced KHb surrenders its base to the H_2CO_3 to form bicarbonate, as already described.

Exchange of Gases in the Lungs and in the Tissues.—When two gases are separated from each other by a moist membrane which is permeable to both gases, the gases will diffuse through the membrane until the concentration of the gases is the same on both sides of the membrane. If the pressure of the oxygen in the lungs is greater than the tension of this gas in venous blood, more oxygen passes from the lungs through the respiratory epithelium and the capillary wall and into the blood stream than passes in the opposite direction. If the tension of the carbon dioxide is greater in venous blood than in the alveoli of the lungs, this gas passes from the blood into the lungs. As to the exchange of gases between the arterial blood and the tissues, the same process of reasoning holds good. The tissues are practically devoid of free oxygen and consequently its pressure may be stated as zero. On the other hand, as the tissues are constantly producing carbon dioxide, the pressure of this gas is considerable. The pressures (tension) of the oxygen and carbon dioxide in arterial and venous blood, in the lungs, and in tissues are given in Table XI. The direction of the flow of the gases is also indicated.

TABLE XI

	ALVEOLAR AIR		VENOUS BLOOD	ARTERIAL BLOOD		TISSUES
Oxygen	100 mm. Hg	→	40	100	→	0 to 35
Carbon dioxide	40	←	50	40	←	40 to 60

The nitrogen in the blood is held in physical solution only and plays no part in the metabolism of the body.

III. TISSUE OR CELL RESPIRATION

The oxygen absorbed by the blood in the lungs is used in the body to oxide organic compounds, such as fat and sugar, in which process carbon dioxide is formed. This oxidation does not take place in the lungs; for the blood leaving the lungs is richer in oxygen and poorer in CO_2 than that arriving. Neither does it occur in the blood, for the blood in coursing from the lungs to and through the heart and to the tissues loses none of the oxygen nor does it gain any carbon dioxide. But in its short stay (about one second) in the systemic capillaries, it suffers a loss of about 5 per cent oxygen and acquires an equal volume of carbon dioxide. Because of its corpuscles, the blood must be regarded as a living tissue, and as such, no doubt, consumes oxygen and produces carbon dioxide, but the quantities involved are of little significance compared with the total gas changes occurring in the blood. The blood is not the consumer but only the carrier of oxygen. It is in the various tissues (muscles, glands, etc.) that we must seek for true respiration; that is, the consumption of oxygen and the production of carbon dioxide take place in the cells.

Oxidations and Oxygen Supply.—It is a well-known fact that in a furnace fire the amount of oxidation is directly proportional to the amount of oxygen supplied; under a forced draught a more intense fire is obtained, more heat is liberated and, other factors remaining constant, more work can be performed by the engine. In the animal body matters stand quite differently, for here an increase in the amount of oxygen supplied, provided a minimum amount necessary to carry on the function is given, does not influence the intensity of the oxidation, and neither, therefore, the activity of the organ. For example, in an atmosphere of pure oxygen the amount of the oxidations in the animal body is no greater than when the ordinary air is breathed. In other words, **the activity of the tissue determines the amount of oxygen consumed by the tissue,** but the amount of oxygen supplied does not determine the activity of the tissue (provided a minimum of oxygen is supplied). Indeed, in pure oxygen an animal develops pulmonary lesions (inflammation, edema, consolidation), and death takes place in two or three days. Barach states that life continues normally in an atmosphere containing no more than 70 per cent oxygen. On the other hand, Hill found that human life is possible in an atmosphere containing such a low percentage of oxygen that a match was unable to burn.

If, in addition to the above facts, it be borne in mind that the arterial blood under the usual conditions of breathing is 96 per cent saturated with oxygen and that therefore we are unable to any appreciable extent to increase this amount, it is readily seen that deep breathing, when the body is inactive, cannot be of great systemic benefit. It can be readily understood that in anemia oxygen therapy is of very little, if any, benefit. Other factors than the greater supply of oxygen must be responsible for any good obtained from a sojourn in the country as compared with that in the crowded city. However, if the oxygen concentration in the blood falls below the required level (anoxemia; *a,* without; oxygen; *aima,* blood) when ordinary air is respired, breathing of a higher concentration may in certain instances be of great value. For example, when the available alveolar surface for the absorption of oxygen is greatly reduced (as in pneumonia and pulmonary edema), the higher the concentration of the oxygen in contact with the functioning surface, the more oxygen will enter the blood. For this purpose the air in an oxygen tent contains 40 to 50 per cent oxygen and, for reasons we shall consider presently, about 4 or 5 per cent CO_2.

Nature of the Oxidations.—We may call attention to another striking difference between the oxidations in the animal tissues and those generally observed outside the body. The foodstuffs are relatively stable substances; a lump of sugar, starch, or fat is not oxidized in the air at a temperature of the body (37° C.). In order that these substances may be burned they must be heated to several hundred degrees (kindling temperature); in the animal body these substances are completely transformed into water and carbon dioxide at a temperature of 37° or 38° C. It is true, by the use of strong oxidizing reagents (Fehling's solution) the sugars can be oxidized at relatively low temperatures, but the tissues in our body are not supplied with such strong reagents, being practically neutral fluids. Inasmuch as foods have no affinity for molecular oxygen, to bring about their oxidation either the oxygen or the oxidizable material, or both must be prepared.

The activation of the food and of the oxygen are brought about by a series of chemical reactions in which three distinct classes of enzymes participate. Before discussing these enzymes, it may be well to call attention to the word, oxidation. While the original meaning of this word is the union of oxygen with another material, at present it may be defined as increasing the proportion of oxygen in a molecule. If, for example, one or more hydrogen atoms are removed from a compound (a process properly termed *dehydrogenation*) the proportion of oxygen in the compound is increased, and oxidation is said to have taken place, although actually no oxygen was added. On the other hand, by the addition of hydrogen to a molecule the proportion of oxygen is decreased; this process is called reduction.*

1. Food Activators.—Enzymes which activate the food molecule for the reception of oxygen do so by the withdrawal of hydrogen from the food molecule. These enzymes, known as *dehydrogenases*, have been found in practically all plant and animal cells.

2. Oxygen Activators.—Even after the food molecule has been prepared by the dehydrogenases, it is still unable to take up the molecular oxygen found in the tissue fluids; oxygen also must be activated. This is accomplished by another class of enzymes generally spoken of as *oxidases*. Oxidases are also known as the *respiratory ferment*, or Warburg's respiratory ferment. It is present in all cells which use oxygen in their metabolism, and its concentration in the cell is the greater, the more intense the oxidation and activity taking place in the tissue. Oxidases contain iron and are derivatives of the pigment, heme, which is the characteristic part of hemoglobin and is concerned with oxygen transportation in the blood.

3. Intermediate Carriers.—The oxidase, which has combined with the molecular oxygen of the blood and tissue fluid, does not directly deliver its oxygen to the activated food molecule. This transfer is accomplished by means of another and more complicated series of chemical reactions. In the cells of all aerobic organisms is found a pigment called *cytochrome*. Similar to the above described respiratory ferment, it is closely related to the heme of the hemoglobin, and its concentration in a tissue runs parallel with the activity of that tissue. The cytochrome can be oxidized and reduced. The activation of the food causes the loss of hydrogen on the part of the food; this hydrogen is taken up by the cytochrome. Functioning as a hydrogen acceptor, it becomes reduced cytochrome. This later substance can be oxidized, but not by molecular oxygen. However, the molecular oxygen which the oxidase has taken up and activated can be transferred to the reduced cytochrome. This active oxygen carried by the cytochrome can be received by the activated food molecule. Still other enzymes, e.g., peroxidase and catalase, may be concerned in the oxidation-reduction reactions in the tissues. For the part they play the reader is referred to the larger texts.

We may, however, mention a yellow pigment found in nearly all, if not all, cells and which seems to function in cell respiration; this pigment is known as flavin (*flavus*, yellow) or flavoprotein. Its exact rôle in this complex dehydrogenase—intermediate carrier—oxidase system is not well understood. Perhaps it acts as an intermediate carrier (similar to cytochrome), but differs from this last-named substance in that it can directly unite with molecular (not activated) oxygen. It may be of interest to learn that flavin is derived from vitamin B_2 (see p. 467).

Certain very poisonous compounds, the cyanides, have a great affinity for iron compounds. In the animal body they cause an almost total cessation of the oxidations in the tissues. The cyanides bring about this reaction by uniting with the iron of the above-discussed enzymes, thereby preventing the oxidation of the intermediate carrier, cytochrome. If to a tissue poisoned in this manner there is

*This concept of oxidation and reduction is not antagonistic to the more modern idea that oxidation is the withdrawal of electrons from a molecule.

added a substance which can be reversibly oxidized and reduced, the cell respiration is restored to a certain extent. Such a compound is the dye, methylene blue,*
which has been actually used in combating the effects of cyanide poisoning in man.

IV. REGULATION OF PULMONARY VENTILATION

Innervation.—The muscles by which the expansion and contraction of the chest are brought about are striated, or skeletal, muscles.
Their action, like that of all skeletal muscles, depends upon nerve

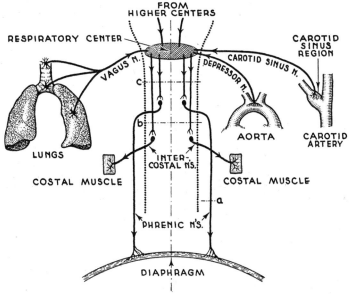

Fig. 142.—Schema to illustrate the respiratory center and its afferent nerves from
sensory surfaces and its efferent nerve to the respiratory muscles.

impulses brought to them from the central nervous system. If one
of the phrenic nerves, which innervate the diaphragm, is cut, as indicated at *a*, Fig. 142, that side of the diaphragm is paralyzed. When
the spinal cord is cut at, say, the seventh cervical vertebra, *b*, the
costal respiration ceases while that of the diaphragm goes on. The
intercostal muscles for costal respiration are innervated by the intercostal nerves springing from the spinal cord below the cervical
region. We may, therefore, conclude that these nerves receive their
impulses from a point in the central nervous system lying higher
than the cut made at *b*. This is also borne out by the fact that the
section at *b* does not interfere with diaphragmatic breathing, seeing

*On being reduced (by the addition of hydrogen to its molecule) the methylene
blue loses its color (methylene white). This latter substance by uniting with
oxygen (and thereby losing its previously acquired hydrogen in the form of H_2O)
is transformed into methylene blue (oxidation).

that the phrenic nerves originate from the third and fourth cervical spinal nerves. If now a section of the cord is made at the first or second cervical vertebra, c, the diaphragmatic as well as the costal breathing stops. This indicates that the point of the central nervous system which controls these muscles lies above this section also. By making other sections, the French physiologist, Flourens, concluded that the point of innervation lies in the medulla (see Figs. 277 and 291); this area is called the *respiratory center*. Upon its activity depends all respiration and for this reason breaking of the neck is fatal. In anterior poliomyelitis (infantile paralysis) the efferent fibers are rendered functionless and respiratory movements cease.

The Respiratory Center.—The cells of the respiratory center are situated bilaterally in the medulla. The cells of each side innervate chiefly the respiratory muscles of the corresponding side. The center actually consists of an inspiratory and an expiratory part. The activity of the respiratory center is influenced by: A, the condition of the blood and B, the nervous system.

A. Chemical Regulation by the Condition of the Blood

The respiratory center is affected by the oxygen and the carbon dioxide content of the blood, and by the pH and temperature of the blood.

a. **Oxygen Content.**—As it is absolutely necessary that the animal body be supplied with oxygen, we might surmise that a diminution of oxygen in the blood would quickly stimulate the respiratory center so as to cause increased ventilation of the lungs and better aeration of the blood. This idea was quite generally held until more recent work, especially that of Haldane, showed that the amount of oxygen in the inspired air may be decreased until only 13 per cent is present without affecting respiration. Indeed, it is possible to lessen the amount of oxygen to such an extent that unconsciousness may result without respiration having been much influenced. We shall refer to this again in subsequent pages.

b. **The accumulation of carbon dioxide** in the blood is one of the most potent stimulations for the respiratory center. From Zuntz's work we quote the following:

TABLE XII

COMPOSITION OF INSPIRED AIR	AIR RESPIRED PER MINUTE
Normal air (21% oxygen plus 0.03% CO_2)	8,100 c.c.
Air containing 10% oxygen plus 0.03% CO_2	8,700 c.c.
Air containing 18% oxygen plus 3% CO_2	11,326 c.c.
Air containing 18% oxygen plus 11% CO_2	32,464 c.c.

From Table XII it will be noticed that a decrease in the inspired oxygen from the normal 21 per cent to 10 per cent caused an increase in the ventilation of the lungs equal to only 7.5 per cent. But an increase of 3 per cent carbon dioxide in the inspired air was followed by 30 per cent increase in the ventilation of the lungs. In fact, asphyxiation from lack of oxygen, but without an increase in CO_2 causes paralysis of the center and produces unconsciousness without pain or distress.

It is, however, not primarily the amount of carbon dioxide in the inspired air, but the tension of this gas in the alveoli of the lungs that is the important factor. In his investigations Haldane found that an increase of 1.5 mm. pressure in the tension of the alveolar carbon dioxide causes the amount of air passing through the lungs to be doubled. In fact, increasing and decreasing of the rate and depth of respiration are under ordinary circumstances caused by changes in the tension of CO_2; by changes in the respiratory movements the amount of carbon dioxide in the alveolar air is almost a constant quantity. This is shown in Table XIII taken from Haldane.

TABLE XIII

% CO_2 IN INSPIRED AIR	RATE OF RESPIRATION	DEPTH OF RESPIRATION	% CO_2 IN ALVEOLAR AIR
0.04	14	673	5.6
2.02	15	864	5.6
3.07	15	1216	5.5
5.14	19	1771	6.2

Two or three facts are to be observed. First, an increase of carbon dioxide in the inspired air from the normal 0.04 per cent to 2 per cent had little or no effect upon the rate but increased the depth of respiration considerably. Second, even as much as 3 per cent carbon dioxide in the inhaled air (about 100 times the usual quantity) did not cause the amount (5.5 per cent) of this gas in the alveoli of the lungs to be increased. By the increased depth of respiration the exchange of air in the lungs was sufficient to keep the percentage of carbon dioxide in the lungs at the usual level. When, however, the air contained as much as 5 per cent carbon dioxide, notwithstanding the very great increase in both rate and depth of respiration, the percentage of. carbon dioxide in the alveolar air was increased. It goes without saying that seldom, if ever, does a human being breathe air containing such large quantities of this gas.

There is a constant striving on the part of our body to keep the carbon dioxide tension of the alveolar air constant. This is brought about by the stimulation of the respiratory center by the increased carbon dioxide tension in the arterial blood and occurs whenever the percentage of CO_2 in the alveolar air becomes so great that it is impossible for the blood to lose a sufficient quantity of carbon dioxide. Under usual conditions, this method of regulating respiration also maintains the proper oxygen content of the blood.

The ventilation rate is ordinarily regulated so as to maintain a constant concentration (5.5 per cent) of CO_2 in the alveolar air. But by forced breathing for a period of 3 or 4 minutes, the CO_2 concentration of alveolar air is decreased to as little as 3 per cent. The influence of this upon the respiratory center is shown by the following experiment. After normal quiet respiration was registered, Fig. 143, overventilation of the lungs was performed for four minutes (not shown in the tracing). It will be seen that this thorough ven-

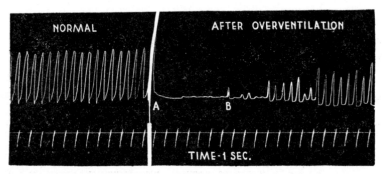

Fig. 143.—Respiratory tracing (dog) to show apnea, from *A* to *B*, after a period of overventilation (not shown in the tracing).

tilation is followed, at *A*, by a period of apnea; at *B* a feeble respiratory movement took place but normal respiration did not begin for several seconds. Voluntary deep breathing may cause disturbances in consciousness and cannot be maintained for any great length of time, for the fatigue which sets in is overpowering. The feeling of dizziness following a period of voluntary overventilation of the lungs has been attributed to two factors: a fall in blood pressure (p. 229) which lessens cerebral circulation, or a decrease in the liberation of oxygen from oxyhemoglobin because of the great reduction of CO_2 in the blood (see p. 288). If an individual breathes from and into a paper sack closely applied to the face, the excessive breathing is followed by neither apnea nor respiratory fatigue. We may, therefore, conclude that the apnea and the inability voluntarily to carry on deep respirations are due to changes in the gases of the blood.

To demonstrate the importance of carbon dioxide as a respiratory stimulus and the slight effect of lack of oxygen, Haldane made the following experiment. A person breathed into and out of a rubber bag, the carbon dioxide being allowed to accumulate; a very severe hyperpnea set in when the carbon dioxide reached 5.6 per cent, at which time the oxygen content was still 14.8 per cent. In a second case, the carbon dioxide of the air in the rubber bag was absorbed by lime water; now the individual could maintain his normal breathing for a much greater length of time and no hyperpnea set in because of the lack of CO_2 in the blood *(acapnia)*; the subject, however, became cyanotic owing to the lack of oxygen which had dropped to 8 per cent. In fact, when the experiment was continued a little longer, the individual passed into apnea (no breathing) and, because of the want of oxygen, unconsciousness resulted. Before this took place, the breathing of a little carbon dioxide again brought on the usual rhythm of respiration.

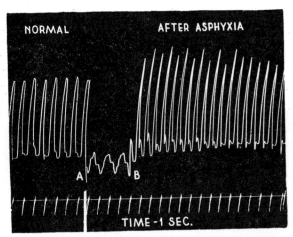

Fig. 144.—Tracing (dog) to show the effect of asphyxia by closing the trachea cannula at *A*. The cannula was opened at *B*.

The effect of increasing the CO_2 content of the blood on respiration is shown in Fig. 144. Following a period of normal breathing, asphyxia was caused in a dog by closing the trachea cannula at *A* for two minutes. At *B* the cannula was opened; the increase in the rate and depth of respiration is very evident. This influence of carbon dioxide may explain, in part, the rapid onset of hyperpnea in muscle work. Muscle work is always associated with the production of carbon dioxide, and its absorption by the blood increases the tension of this gas in the venous blood. Such blood in passing through the lungs loses a part of its carbon dioxide, but with the usual ventilation of the lungs the residual carbon dioxide is no doubt a trifle greater than when no extra muscle work is being done.

Because of its powerful effect as a respiratory excitant, Henderson has used carbon dioxide in the resuscitation of people overcome by carbon monoxide. Diluting the concentrated oxygen used in artificial ventilation of the lungs with as much as 7 per cent CO_2 has been found very advantageous in re-establishing the patient's own breathing. This procedure has also proved beneficial after ether anesthesia, in case of drowning, and in establishing the respiration in the newborn.

c. **Respiration and the Acid-Base Balance.**—In a previous chapter (p. 145) we have spoken of the hydrogen ion concentration of the blood; this concentration is expressed either as the cH or its reciprocal, the pH. As the only free acid in the blood is carbonic acid—H_2CO_3, formed by the union of CO_2 and H_2O—and as sodium bicarbonate is the important alkali, the pH is determined by the relative amount of each of these present or by the ratio $\dfrac{H_2CO_3}{NaHCO_3}$. The carbonic acid of the blood is equivalent to 0.0015 molar solution, while the concentration of the bicarbonate is 0.03 m; the ratio of these two in the blood is therefore ½0. The above ratio represents the acid-base balance of the blood and is equal to pH 7.4.

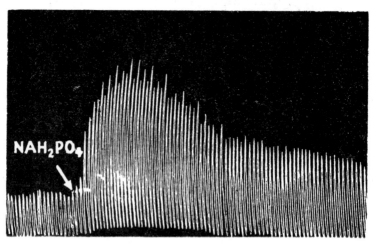

Fig. 145.—Showing the effect of injection of NaH₂PO₄ upon respiration.

An increase in the carbon dioxide content of the blood, under otherwise constant conditions, increases the value of the ratio above ½0 and therefore decreases the pH. Such an increase, known as *acidosis,* can be brought about in many ways: by decreasing the elimination of CO_2 by the lungs (as by voluntarily holding the breath); by breathing air rich in CO_2; by the inability of the heart to adequately supply oxygen to the tissues; or by a decrease in the alkali reserve. In muscle work the lactic acid acting upon the

$NaHCO_3$ forms sodium lactate and carbonic acid and thus causes acidosis by increasing the acid and decreasing the alkaline reserve; this state, however, is transient, for the carbonic acid is got rid of as CO_2 by the lungs, and any acid salts that may arise in this process are eliminated by the kidneys. In whatever manner it may be produced, acidosis results in increased stimulation of the respiratory center. This is well illustrated in Fig. 145 which shows the powerful effect of the injection of a small amount of NaH_2PO_4. The resultant increased pulmonary ventilation causes a fall in the carbon dioxide content of the alveolar air. As will be explained on page 517, it also results in an increase in the acidity of the urine and an increased excretion of ammonium salts. As we have previously noted, a high degree of acidosis is accompanied by coma. A pH below 6.9 is incompatible with life.

An increase in pH of the blood can be produced by voluntarily forced pulmonary ventilation by which the CO_2 and, therefore, the carbonic acid, in the blood are decreased (alkalosis). In severe cases a pH 7.8 value may obtain; this is accompanied with tetany and an increased excretion of alkaline salts by the kidneys. The function of the respiratory center, accordingly, is to maintain the pH value of the blood by discharging more or less of the CO_2 of the blood. The increased pulmonary ventilation during muscle work does not produce alkalosis because of the increased formation of various acids.

d. We may here note that **the temperature of the blood** also influences the activity of the respiratory center; the increased respiration in fevers must be attributed to a certain extent to this factor.

B. Nervous Regulation

It is a familiar fact that one's respiration may be much altered by the stimulation of certain sensory nerves. The deep and audible gasping following a plunge into cold water, and the sneeze produced by the inhalation of pepper or by a bright light falling into the eyes are well-known examples.

The gentle stimulation of almost any sensory nerve, excepting nerves from the abdominal viscera, may increase respiration. In narcotic poisoning, the respiratory center may be kept going by stimulating the skin, as by hitting with a wet towel or by applying faradic shocks. The stimulation of the sciatic nerve in a dog powerfully increases respiration, as is shown in Fig. 146. Another example of this reflex effect upon respiration is seen in the coughing resulting from food, or even saliva, being swallowed "the wrong way." The food, instead of going down the esophagus, tends to go through the trachea; however, on arriving at the larynx (voice box), the superior laryngeal nerve is stimulated and the work of the respiratory center is so modified that inspiration is checked immediately and coughing, a modified form of violent expiration, takes place. From *a* to *b* in the respiratory tracing shown in Fig. 147 the laryngeal nerves of an anesthetized dog were stimulated by the introduction of a swab of cotton into the trachea; it will be noticed that a cessation of respiration in the expiratory phase followed immediately. Swallowing is normally associated with an inhibition of respiration, due to the stimulation of the glossopharyngeal nerves by the food.

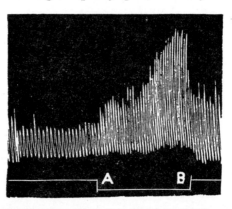

Fig. 146.—Effect of stimulation (from *A* to *B*) of the sciatic nerve on respiration.

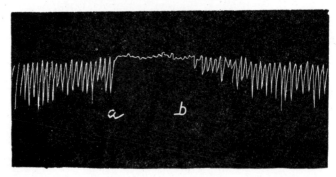

Fig. 147.—Respiratory curve (dog) showing the effects of stimulation, *ab*, of the sensory nerves of the trachea. The upstrokes represent expiration.

While many afferent nerves can influence the respiratory center, most of these are only occasionally active. There are, however, two afferent nerves that constantly modify respiration: the vagus nerve and the nerve from the carotid sinus.

The Vagus Nerve.—The afferent fibers for the respiratory tract are found in the vagus nerve. These fibers pass up the spinal cord to end in the respiratory center in the medulla, Fig. 142. The center is not dependent for its action upon impulses brought to it over the vagi nerves, for the sectioning of these nerves does not stop respiration; however, the rate and depth of respiration are profoundly influenced, as can be seen in Fig. 148. At *A* in this tracing the right

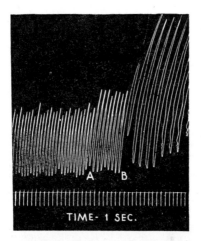

Fig. 148.—Respiratory tracing (dog) to illustrate the effect of cutting the right vagus nerve at *A*, and a few moments later the left nerve at *B*. Note the marked decrease in rate and increase in depth of respiration.

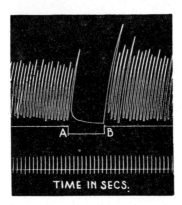

Fig. 149.—Respiratory tracing to illustrate the effect of vagal stimulation from *A* to *B*. Note the slight increase in depth of respiration immediately after the stimulation.

vagus nerve in a dog was cut; the result was very slight. At *B* the other vagus nerve was cut and immediately a decrease in the rate and a corresponding increase in the depth of respiration followed. Starling gives the following results of cutting both vagi in a rabbit. Before cutting the nerve the animal made 72 respirations per minute, and took in 19 c.c. with each respiration, hence the total ventilation of the lungs per minute was 1,368 c.c.; after the sectioning of the nerves the rate was 45 while the depth of each inspiration was increased to 29 c.c., making the total ventilation 1,305 c.c. per minute. It will be noticed that while the rate was reduced almost 40 per cent, the depth of respiration was increased about in the same proportion, so that the total ventilation of the lungs remained constant. From this experiment we may conclude that the total amount of air respired is not determined by the vagus nerve, but the vagus nerve determines (by checking further inflation) by how many inspiratory movements of a certain depth this quantity of air shall pass through the lungs.

Fig. 150.—Tracing showing the effects upon respiration (dog) when the trachea is closed at the end of expiration, *a*. The downstroke represents inspiration. Note the exaggerated inspirations. At *b* the trachea was opened.

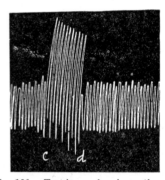

Fig. 151.—Tracing showing the effect upon respiration (dog) when the trachea is closed at the end of inspiration, *c*. The upstroke represents expiration. Note the greatly increased expiratory efforts. At *d* the trachea was opened.

Stimulation of the central end of the cut vagus frequently results in a cessation of breathing as shown in Fig. 149. The effect, however, depends largely upon the nature of the stimulation; it is generally stated that stimulation with a very weak electric current increases the expiratory movements; stronger stimulation results in increased inspiratory efforts. For this reason it is supposed by some that the vagus contains both inspiratory and expiratory afferent fibers; the former are stimulated by the deflated, and the latter by the inflated or stretched state of the lungs. In Fig. 150 the trachea cannula through which an anesthetized dog was breathing was suddenly closed, at *a*, at the very end of a normal expiration; as a result, powerful inspiratory efforts (down strokes) were immediately made and these continued during the entire time of the closure of the trachea. On the other hand, the powerful expiratory efforts (up strokes) made when the trachea cannula was closed at the end of a normal inspiration, at c in Fig. 151, are very noticeable.

The vagus also contains efferent, or motor, fibers which supply the muscles of the bronchi and bronchioles. By the stimulation of these fibers the muscles of the air tubes are thrown into activity and the lumen of these tubes is diminished; as a result, the air in passing into and out of the lung encounters more resistance. This is generally held to be the condition of affairs in asthma, in which the spasm of the bronchial muscles is responsible for the difficult and labored breathing. Such constriction can be brought about reflexly by stimulating the nasal mucosa. The bronchial muscles receive inhibitory impulses from the sympathetic nervous system.

Carotid Sinus.—Other important afferent impulses for the respiratory center are generated in the carotid sinus (Fig. 142). It has been found by Heymans and other workers that a great deficiency of oxygen in the blood causes increased respiration; this failed to take place when the afferent nerves from the carotid sinus were severed. An excess of carbon dioxide also acts as an excitor of the sinus, but to a much less extent than the lack of oxygen.

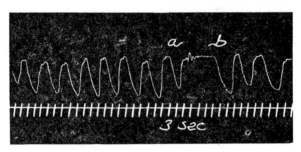

Fig. 152.—Respiratory tracing of an individual attempting to thread a fine needle; note the cessation of breathing during this period, from a to b.

The Influence of Higher Nerve Centers.—It is common knowledge that mental conditions influence respiration; as an illustration of this we may mention the inhibition which extreme concentration of one's attention may exercise (see Fig. 152). Being absorbed in the reading of an exciting story, we say we forget to breathe. The intense activity of the cerebral cells has a depressing effect upon the respiratory center thereby causing shallow and slow breathing. This leads to an accumulation of carbon dioxide in the blood, and after a while the stimulating effect of this product is so great that it breaks through the inhibitory influences coming from the cerebral hemispheres; the result is a deep inspiration followed by a deep, audible expiration—a sigh.

Other examples of the influence of the mind upon respiration are seen in what may be termed the psychic cough and the "contagiousness" of yawning. Respiration can be voluntarily increased or inhibited, but this control is also limited by the chemical stimulation of the respiratory center and the carotid sinus.

During the process of attention, when the receptors are adjusted for the best reception of stimuli, respiration is altered. This is seen during acts such as shooting a gun, hitting a golf ball, or starting a sprint. As a part of the preparation for such acts, the individual takes a deep breath and holds it until after the performance, when respiration again becomes normal.

V. CONDITIONS AFFECTING RESPIRATION

Muscular Work.—The influence of work upon gaseous metabolism has been investigated, for example, by letting the individual breathe from and into a gas bag which is constantly supplied with a measured amount of oxygen; the exhaled carbon dioxide is absorbed by soda lime or similar chemical. We may note the following changes produced by walking at the rate of eight kilometers (5 miles) per hour:

a. The amount of air respired increased from about 7 liters per minute in the resting condition to almost 50 liters. The first deep breathing experienced at, or even before, the beginning of the work is due to the mental conditions always associated with effort. Impulses descending from the cerebrum to the muscles radiate to the respiratory center. How muscle activity increases the lung ventilation we have already considered. Because of the better adjustment of the circulatory-respiratory mechanism to the needs of the active muscles and because the work is performed more efficiently, the increase in pulmonary ventilation for a given amount of work is less in the trained than in the untrained individual.

b. The oxygen consumption increased from the resting 320 c.c. to 2,500 c.c. per minute.

c. The CO_2 production increased from 260 c.c. to 2,300 c.c. per minute. But because of the increased lung ventilation, the CO_2 content of the alveolar air is not changed by moderate exercise; however, as the exercise becomes more strenuous, the CO_2 per cent in the alveolar air may rise to as high as 7 per cent.

d. During rest the muscles take 4 c.c. of oxygen from the 20 c.c. present in each 100 c.c. of blood. Hence, in its resting state the muscles consume ⅕ or 0.2 of the available oxygen; this is called *the coefficient of oxygen utilization*. During work the oxygen utilization may be increased to 0.4. We have seen (Fig. 141) that an increase in the carbon dioxide concentration in the blood during work hastens the dissociation of the oxyhemoglobin; the liberation of the oxygen is also favored by the local rise in temperature in the active muscle; as a consequence more oxygen is available in a unit of time.

e. In studying the chemical changes in a muscle we learned that the splitting of the glycogen molecule gives rise to lactic acid, which, in part, is oxidized and, in part, is reconstructed into glycogen. When the work is moderate the amount of acid is but slightly increased and although the oxygen intake at first lags somewhat, it soon becomes sufficient to oxidize the acid produced; at this stage, known as the "steady state," the production of lactic acid and the consumption of oxygen are balanced, Fig. 153. But in a sudden and severe spurt of work, the lactic acid production is so greatly increased that its disposal lags behind its production, because of the lack of a sufficient supply of oxygen; consequently at the cessation

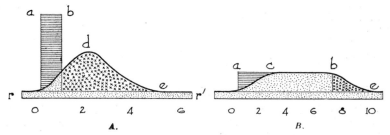

Fig. 153.—Illustrating the "oxygen debt" in *A*, severe work of brief duration and in *B*, moderate work of longer duration. The stippled area represents lactic acid production and an equal oxygen consumption; *rr'*, resting period; *ab*, working period; the shaded areas represent the excessive production of lactic acid, or oxygen debt, which is paid by extra oxidation shown by the areas containing the small crosses. The area below the heavy curved line shows the oxygen consumption; the part *cb*, represents the "steady state"; the abscissas denote minutes. (After Macleod.)

of the work there still remains a certain quantity of lactic acid to be oxidized. The amount of oxygen necessary for this constitutes the so-called *oxygen debt* of muscle work, and the hyperpnea following the muscular work is related to the payment of the debt. For example, Hill found that running in place for a certain duration caused an oxygen debt of 18.6 liters. The greater the oxygen debt, the longer is the period of hyperpnea following the work. In the above instance, the recovery period (for paying the oxygen debt) was eighty-seven minutes.

The extent of the oxygen debt, under constant conditions of work, depends upon the oxygen delivery. During rest the difference between the oxygen content of arterial and that of venous blood is about 4 volumes per cent. The greater the bodily activity, other conditions remaining constant, the greater this arterio-venous oxygen difference; when this difference exceeds a certain value, the lactic acid accumulates and the oxygen debt increases proportionately. How soon this point is reached depends, among other factors, upon:

1. OXYGEN-CARRYING CAPACITY OF THE BLOOD.—In an anemic person, the arterio-venous oxygen difference becomes pronounced very quickly, which accounts for his shortness of breath and incapacity for sustained work. In the normal individual, it has been demonstrated that exercise causes an acute increase per cubic millimeter of all the formed elements of the blood, the extent of the increase depending on the severity of the exercise. This is due to a washing out of the more or less stagnant blood pools in the body and also by the contraction of the spleen. By this, however, the number of corpuscles in the body is not augmented. After long periods of training, there is an actual increase in the number of erythrocytes per unit volume of circulating blood. This chronic increase is attributed to a persistent oxygen want, as is the case in individuals living at high altitudes.

2. CAPILLARY ADJUSTMENT.—As we have seen (p. 252) during the activity of a muscle, a large number of previously closed capillaries is opened up and, as the result of the increased flow of blood, the arterio-venous oxygen difference is decreased.

3. MINUTE VOLUME OF THE HEART.—It will be recalled that both the stroke volume and the minute volume of the heart are increased during muscle work; the greater these increases, the greater will be the oxygen delivery. So urgent for the active animal is this oxygen delivery that it has been well said that "one of the most fundamental physiological adjustments" is the adjustment of the volume of the blood discharged by the heart to the amount of oxygen consumed and carbon dioxide produced. The efficiency of the heart, that is, how well it serves the body, can be gauged by the difference between the oxygen content of the arterial and that of the venous blood. When the heart is pumping efficiently, this oxygen difference is small. In general we may state: *the efficiency of the heart is measured in terms of "the volume of the blood it can pump in relation to the oxygen requirements of the body."*

Because of a greater power of the heart to adjust itself, the oxygen debt in moderate exercise in the well-trained person is less, and the respiration is restored to the normal resting state sooner, than in the untrained person. As a result of strenuous work a well-trained person can contract a greater oxygen debt than the untrained. We may also notice that this adjustment in the trained person is made more by an increase in the stroke volume and less by augmentation in the heart rate than in the untrained.

The power of the heart to adjust its work to the oxygen needs of the body, is inversely related to the distress experienced. When this distress, even in moderate work, is greatly exaggerated and continues not only throughout the work but also for an abnormally long period after the cessation of the work, the condition is known as **effort syndrome**; such individuals are said to have an *irritable heart*. This syndrome is characterized by great dyspnea, a very marked increase in the pulse rate and blood pressure, palpitation of the heart, pain in the region of the heart, exhaustion, dizziness, and even fainting. Frequently the valves or the myocardium of the heart have been impaired by infectious diseases. Again, it may be a matter of a weak heart due to the entire lack of exercise; in such cases graded exercises are very useful. Obviously, a decrease in the alkali reserve or the curtailing of the gas exchange in the pulmonary epithelium (as in certain forms of "gassing") is associated with effort syndrome.

The cause of getting one's *second wind* is not very well understood. When it occurs, the organs of circulation and respiration, the skin, and other organs have adjusted themselves better to the increased demands of the active muscles. Some lay stress on a reduction in the hydrogen ions of the blood by the better disposal of the lactic acid and by better circulation. Second wind is acquired more readily and with less discomfort by the trained than by the untrained.

Irrespirable Gases.—These we may divide into three classes:

a. The inert gases which in themselves have no effect upon the body; such are hydrogen, nitrogen, and the "firedamp" (methane—CH_4) of mines. They cause ill effects or death only when the amount of the gases in the inspired air is so great as to exclude the necessary amount of oxygen.

b. Gases which cause spasmodic closure of the glottis (the opening between the vocal cords); they kill, therefore, by strangulation. Among these are ammonia, sulfur dioxide, and chlorine.

c. The gases which work injury because they rob the blood of its oxygen; especially does this apply to carbon monoxide. As the affinity of this gas for hemoglobin is about 300 times as great as that of oxygen for hemoglobin, the carbon monoxide drives the oxygen from the oxyhemoglobin and forms the rather stable compound carboxyhemoglobin. This decreases the oxygen-carrying capacity of the blood and, in consequence, the tissues undergo oxygen starvation.

Carbon monoxide is found in the "afterdamp" in mines, in the exhaust gases of gas engines (automobiles), in illuminating gases (water gas and coal gas), and in the fumes from leaking stoves, furnaces and flues. In a concentration of 0.03 per cent (3 parts CO in 10,000 of air) CO shows its deleterious effects. Air containing 0.4 per cent may prove fatal if respired for a sufficient length of time; and in a concentration of 2 to 4 per cent death occurs in five to ten minutes.

Small animals and children have a relatively greater respiratory exchange in proportion to the size of the body than larger animals, and are more quickly overcome. For this reason mice or canaries are carried by rescue crews in mines. Death by carbon monoxide and the after effects, in case of recovery, are due to lack of oxygen. In small amounts it is not a protoplasmic poison and, therefore, if it is possible to increase sufficiently the oxygen held in physical solution by the plasma, the animal survives. Mosso found that a mouse kept in oxygen having a pressure of two atmospheres is not killed by even 50 per cent of carbon monoxide. Recovery from carbon monoxide poisoning is frequently accompanied by great disturbances in the functions of the nervous system, such as blindness, loss of power of speech, etc.

Attention has been called to the fact that the addition of 7 per cent of carbon dioxide to the oxygen used for resuscitation has proved very beneficial. As deprivation of oxygen for about ten minutes causes irremediable damage to many of the higher nerve centers, artificial respiration (see infra) should in all cases be instituted without a moment's delay. It should also be noted that carbon monoxide gives no warning whatever of the approaching asphyxia. The victim, according to the Harvard Fatigue Laboratory reports, showed no decrease in his skill, even though practically ready to collapse.

Pressure Changes.—a. That increased oxygen pressure has no effect on the rate of metabolism and that a concentration above 70 per cent causes inflammation of the lungs has been discussed in previous pages.

b. Decreased oxygen pressure is without effect unless the amount in the air is reduced to 10 or 12 per cent, when it causes a lack of oxygen in the blood, *anoxemia*, and may cause asphyxiation of the cells.

c. If the total barometric pressure falls, as on the mountains, there may develop mountain sickness (vertigo, nausea, weakness, increased respiration, heart rate, and minute volume, etc.), which, if severe, may cause symptoms of heart failure. The cause, most likely, is the diminished oxygen pressure. If the ascent is made not too hurriedly, the body gradually adapts itself and by more active lung ventilation and an increase in the number of red blood cells, the tissues are properly supplied with oxygen. At 5,000 meters altitude, the amount of oxygen in the blood is reduced from the normal about 96 per cent to about 75 per cent saturation and this appears to be the highest that man, without being protected, can reach. The high altitude attained by aviators creates many problems as to atmospheric pressure and its effect on man. The lack of oxygen in the tissues (anoxia) which occurs at high altitude flying cannot be compensated by man, and therefore must be avoided.*

d. Increased atmospheric pressure is not encountered except by divers and caisson workers. The high pressure of the air in which they work causes a great volume of the gases of the air, chiefly oxygen and nitrogen, to be dissolved in the blood. As long as the workmen remain in this high air pressure no particular distressing symptoms are experienced. But on suddenly passing from the high pressure to the ordinary air, the extra gases dissolved in the plasma can no longer be held in solution and make their appearance as bubbles in the blood. These bubbles clog the capillaries and lead to anemia of the tissues; this results in many disturbances, such as muscle and joint pains and paralysis (diver's palsy). By passing from the caisson through air locks, the decompression is made very gradually; this allows time for the dissolved gases (chiefly nitrogen) to be discharged by the lungs.

VI. MODIFIED FORMS OF RESPIRATION

1. COUGHING. In coughing there is first an inspiration generally of greater amplitude than normal. Next, the glottis is closed and the muscles of expiration, especially those of the abdomen, contract forcibly causing a great increase in the pulmonary pressure. When a certain amount of pressure has been obtained, the vocal cords part and the imprisoned air escapes with a rush, taking with it movable matter, such as mucus, food crumbs, etc. Coughing is generally a reflex act and the stimulations for it may be obtained from the back part of the mouth, lower parts of the respiratory tract, the pleura, skin (cold draught), stomach, etc. There is also a psychic cough; hearing another person cough is very likely to cause a desire on our part to cough.

2. SNEEZING is a violent expiration, the air being sent through the nose, the contraction of the anterior fauces shutting off the mouth cavity. It can be brought about by stimulation of the fifth cranial nerve in the nose, by a bright light thrown into the eyes, etc.

---

*Armstrong, Harry G., Principles and Practice of Aviation Medicine, 1939. The Williams and Wilkins Co., Baltimore.

3. HICCOUGH is caused by a spasmodic contraction of the diaphragm the sudden inspiration thus produced being cut short by the closure of the glottis. It is generally found in irritation of the stomach, and is frequently seen in young children after the overfilling of that organ

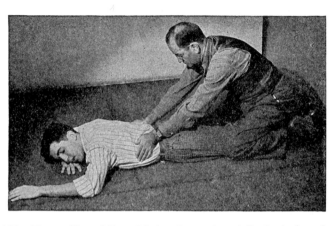

Fig. 154.—The position of the subject and operator at the beginning of artificial respiration. (Figs. 154, 155 and 156 from Francis, Knowlton and Tuttle: Textbook of Anatomy and Physiology, The C. V. Mosby Co.)

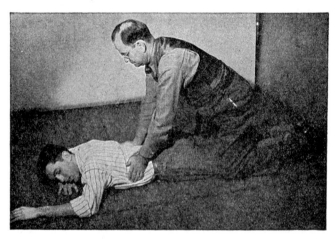

Fig. 155.—From the position assumed in Fig. 154, the operator swings slowly forward, with the arms held straight, so that his body weight applies the pressure to the subject.

4. SNORING is caused by the vibration of the soft palate and is generally found when the sleeper breathes through his mouth.

5. DYSPNEA is extremely labored breathing. From our study of the blood, circulation, and respiration, it must be evident that dyspnea can be produced in the following ways:

A. Mechanical impediment to expansion of the lungs as in:
  (a) Strangulation;
  (b) Excess of liquid or gas in abdomen;
  (c) Postnasal growths.
B. Lessened absorbing power of the lungs as in:
  (a) Pneumonia (inflammation of respiratory surface);
  (b) Tuberculosis.
C. Abnormal conditions of the blood:
  (a) Accumulation of carbon dioxide;
  (b) Lack of oxygen (anoxemia);
  (c) Loss of blood;
  (d) Lessened alkalinity (acidosis);
  (e) Higher temperature.

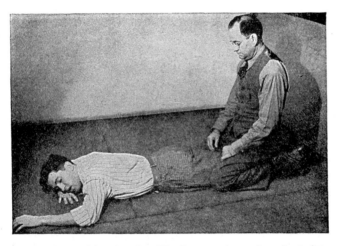

Fig. 156.—From the position in Fig. 155, the operator swings back immediately, removing the pressure completely.

D. Abnormal circulation causing loss of blood pressure:
  (a) Loss of vasomotor tone;
  (b) Lessened heart action;
  (c) Insufficiency of the heart valves;
  (d) Loss of blood.

Artificial Respiration.—In order to save the life of an individual it sometimes is necessary to institute artificial respiration. Such conditions exist, for example, in a person overcome by carbon monoxide or electric shock, and in case of drowning. Whenever the respiration has ceased for a short length of time but it is thought that life may not be extinct, artificial respiration should be practiced.

There are several methods of manual artificial respiration. Schaefer's, or the prone, method (Figs. 154, 155, and 156) ''consists in laying the subject in the prone position, preferably on the ground, with a thick folded garment underneath the chest and epigastrium; extend the arms forward. The operator puts himself athwart or at the side of the subject facing his head, and places his hands on each side over the lower part of the back (lowest rib). He then slowly throws the weight of his body forward, to bear upon his own arms, and thus presses upon the thorax of the subject and forces air out of the lungs. This being effected, he relaxes the pressure by bringing his own body up again to a more erect position, but without moving his hands.'' Repeat this regularly from 12 to 15 times a minute. It is held that respiration is restored more effectively by manual artificial respiration than by mechanical means (pulmotors, e.g.).

Fetal Respiration.—The fetus derives its oxygen from the blood of the mother, and to it surrenders the carbon dioxide; but it must be understood that the blood of the mother never enters the blood vessels of the fetus. In the placenta (see Chapter **XXXI**) the blood of the mother and of the fetus are separated from each other by a membrane through which the various food materials pass from the maternal blood to the fetal blood, and the waste products produced by the fetus pass in the opposite direction. The placenta is, therefore, for the fetus the organ of absorption, respiration and excretion. Consequently, the fetal blood in the umbilical arteries going to the placenta is venous (like that in the pulmonary artery of the adult) while that returning to the fetus by way of the umbilical vein is arterial.

The cause of the first breath in the newborn has been attributed to two sources: first, to the increasing amount of carbon dioxide in the blood; and second, to cutaneous stimulation, both mechanical and thermal. Perhaps the latter is of greater importance.

The respiration of the newborn is much faster and likely to be less regular than in the adult. The young child or animal can also withstand the lack of oxygen better than the adult.

Cutaneous Respiration.—It is sometimes stated that the skin is an organ of excretion and absorption in that we lose carbon dioxide and gain oxygen by means of it. But when we learn that we excrete about 9 grams of carbon dioxide a day by this channel, while we lose about 900 grams by means of the lungs, the value of the skin as an organ for excreting carbon dioxide becomes insignificant. It is stated that the amount of oxygen absorbed by the skin is still less than that of the carbon dioxide excreted.

CHAPTER XIV

FOODS

The animal body performs work, as all mechanisms do, at the expense of energy. We have learned that the energy thus expended is derived from the potential energy of the foods and that in performing its functions the protoplasm undergoes more or less wear and tear which must be made good by the ingestion of food. This gives us a basis for a definition of the term food. A food is a substance which

1. Supplies the body with energy or
2. Furnishes the body with material for growth, for repairing the waste the body has sustained, or for the production of hormones, enzymes, etc.
3. Supplies the body, in very minute quantities, with materials which exercise a tremendous influence upon the various organs; these are the vitamins.

It is necessary to add to this a fourth clause. There are substances that can furnish the body with energy which nevertheless must not be included among the foods. We have reference to such compounds as alcohol. The alcohol ingested is burned in the body, and the heat thus generated can be used for maintaining the body temperature and perhaps for doing muscular work. But, even in comparatively small amounts, alcohol has deleterious effects and, therefore, cannot be properly regarded as a food. Hence we must add:

4. In the quantity consumed, the substance has no direct harmful influence on the body.

Foodstuffs.—The foods of a civilized man are many and complex, but the real nourishing materials in all the varieties of foods may be divided into five classes of substances which have been called the foodstuffs, or alimentary principles:

1. Carbohydrates ⎫ non-nitrogenous ⎫
2. Fats   ⎬   ⎬ organic.
3. Proteins   nitrogenous ⎭
4. Inorganic foodstuffs—water and salts.
5. Vitamins.

Flavors and Condiments.—Our foods contain, in small quantities, other substances which are not true foods, seeing that they supply neither energy nor material for repair; we have reference to the condiments (mustard, pepper, etc.) and to the materials (flavors), already present in the foods, that give the foods their distinctive tastes. The taste of a piece of meat, for example, has nothing to do with the real food found in the meat but is due largely to the so-called extractives which may be removed by heating the meat in a large amount of water. Most of the food is still found in the taste-less, cooked meat, and the water contains the tasty materials; hence meat extracts have very little food value although, like the spices, they are of some use (p. 353).

I. CARBOHYDRATES

Composition.—The carbohydrates are chemical compounds composed of carbon, hydrogen, and oxygen. The molecule always contains six, or a multiple of six, atoms of carbon; and the ratio of the hydrogen atoms to the oxygen atoms is always 2:1.

Classification.—We may divide the carbohydrates into three classes: monosaccharides, disaccharides, polysaccharides.

1. THE MONOSACCHARIDES.—These are sometimes called the simple sugars and have the formula $C_6H_{12}O_6$. There are three important members of this group: dextrose, also known as glucose, or grape sugar; levulose, fructose, or fruit sugar; and galactose. These sugars are sweet to the taste, neutral in reaction, crystallizable, soluble in water, and are readily dialyzable. They can undergo alcoholic fermentation (see Chap II). Glucose and levulose are found in many fruits, seeds, and the roots of plants and in honey. Glucose is found in the blood (about 0.1 per cent) and in the tissues of the body.

Detection of Sugars.—To detect the presence of sugar and to determine the amount present in a fluid, we may employ one of several methods. The one commonly used is known as Benedict's test.* When the blue Benedict's solution is heated with sugar, a reddish precipitate is formed, which settles to the bottom of the test tube. Sugar at the high temperature takes oxygen away from the copper salt found in Benedict's solution; we therefore say the solution has been reduced.

2. THE DISACCHARIDES are the double sugars which we may regard as being formed by the union of two molecules of a monosaccharide with the subsequent loss of one molecule of water:

$$C_6H_{12}O_6 + C_6H_{12}O_6 = C_{12}H_{24}O_{12}.$$

This product minus H_2O gives $C_{12}H_{22}O_{11}$, the general formula for a disaccharide. There are three disaccharides:

> Cane sugar composed of glucose and levulose,
> Maltose composed of two molecules of glucose,
> Lactose composed of glucose and galactose.

---

*For the details of this and other tests see Laboratory Experiments in Physiology by W. D. Zoethout, The C. V. Mosby Co., 1943.

In a similar way we obtain secondary propyl alcohol:

$$CH_3 - HCOH - CH_3$$

On oxidizing the same group of the ethyl alcohol once more ethyl aldehyde is formed:

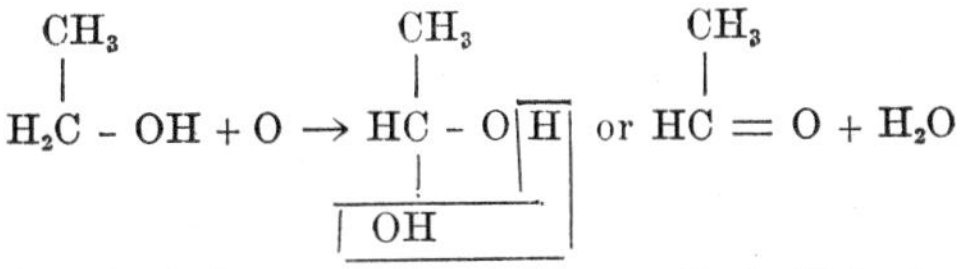

$$CH_3 \qquad CH_3 \qquad CH_3$$
$$H_2C - OH + O \rightarrow HC - O\overline{|H|} \text{ or } HC = O + H_2O$$
$$\overline{| OH}$$

ethyl alcohol   ethyl aldehyde

A single molecule may contain two or more alcohol groups, thus:

$$CH_2OH \qquad\qquad\qquad CH_2OH$$
$$\qquad\qquad\qquad\qquad\qquad CHOH$$
$$CH_2OH \qquad\qquad\qquad CH_2OH$$
glycol   glycerol
(a diatomic alcohol)   (a triatomic alcohol)

When six carbon atoms are present and all the groups are oxidized a hexatomic alcohol of the following composition is obtained:

$$CH_2OH$$
$$(CHOH)_4$$
$$CH_2OH$$

If now one of the end groups is still further oxidized the CH_2OH group is transformed into the aldehyde group, CHO, and the above formula becomes:

$$CH_2OH$$
$$(CHOH)_4$$
$$O = CH$$

This is the formula for dextrose, the simplest carbohydrate generally spoken of in human physiology. On the other hand, if in the above hexatomic alcohol one of the secondary alcohol groups, CHOH, is oxidized we obtain a ketone (containing the C = O group) and the formula becomes:

$$CH_2OH$$
$$C = O$$
$$(CHOH)_3$$
$$CH_2OH$$

This is the formula for levulose, another carbohydrate It will be seen therefore that the carbohydrates are the aldehydes (aldoses) or the ketones (ketoses) of hexatomic alcohols.

II. Fats

Composition.—Like the carbohydrates, the fats are composed of the elements, carbon, hydrogen, and oxygen. There is, however, a marked difference in the relative number of the atoms of the elements in the fat molecule compared with that found in the carbohydrate. From the formula for a carbohydrate—$C_6H_{12}O_6$—it is evident that the hydrogen and oxygen atoms are in the proportion to form water. In the fat this is not the case. For example, the composition of a very common fat, stearin, is expressed by the formula $C_{57}H_{110}O_6$. It will be noticed that only 12 of the 110 hydrogen atoms can be united with the oxygen atoms present in the molecule. When the glucose molecule undergoes oxidation, the number of oxygen atoms uniting with the whole molecule is the same as the number of oxygen atoms required to transform the carbon of the glucose into carbon dioxide:

$$C_6H_{12}O_6 + 6\ O_2 = 6\ CO_2 + 6\ H_2O.$$

On the other hand, when stearin is oxidized not only must oxygen be added to form carbon dioxide from the carbon, but a large amount is consumed in transforming the hydrogen of the fat into water:

$$2\ C_{57}H_{110}O_6 + 163\ O_2 = 114\ CO_2 + 110\ H_2O.$$

Of the 326 atoms of oxygen, 98 are used to oxidize the 196 atoms of hydrogen not already provided with oxygen. This causes the oxidation of the fat to give rise to a great deal more heat than is evolved by the burning of a carbohydrate; in fact, the potential energy (heat value) of a pound of fat is equal to that of $2\frac{1}{4}$ pounds of sugar or starch.

A molecule of a fat is formed by the union of one molecule of glycerol (glycerin) and three molecules of what are known as fatty acids. There are a large number of fatty acids; acetic acid (in vinegar) is a very simple example. The fats found in our food and in our body are nearly all formed from three kinds of fatty acid— oleic, palmitic, and stearic acid. By the union of these acids with glycerol we obtain the three most common fats: olein, palmitin, and stearin.

It will be recalled that alcohols contain one or more OH groups, giving rise to monatomic, diatomic, or triatomic, alcohols. Glycerin, or glycerol, is a triatomic alcohol of the following composition:

$$\begin{array}{c} CH_2OH \\ | \\ CHOH \\ | \\ CH_2OH \end{array}$$

We have also learned that the oxidation of a primary alcohol gives rise to an aldehyde. Let us introduce another atom of oxygen in the same group; the aldehyde is now transformed into an organic acid. Thus:

$$\begin{array}{ccc} \text{CH}_3 & & \text{CH}_3 \\ | & + \text{ O } = & | \\ \text{HC}{=}\text{O} & & \text{HOC}{=}\text{O} \\ \text{ethyl aldehyde} & & \text{ethyl acid or acetic acid} \end{array}$$

We may present the gradual oxidation of the hydrocarbon, ethane, into alcohol, aldehyde, and acid in this manner:

$$\begin{array}{cccc} \text{CH}_3 & \text{CH}_3 & \text{CH}_3 & \text{CH}_3 \\ | & | & | & | \\ \text{CH}_3 & \text{H}_2\text{COH} & \text{COH} & \text{COOH} \end{array}$$

The organic acid is characterized by the *carboxyl group*, COOH, the hydrogen of which is replaceable.

The acids derived from the first four hydrocarbons are:

$$\text{CH}_4 \text{ -------------------------------- H.COOH formic acid.}$$
$$\text{CH}_3.\text{CH}_3 \text{ --------------------------- CH}_3.\text{COOH acetic acid.}$$
$$\text{CH}_3.\text{CH}_2.\text{CH}_3 \text{ ----------------- CH}_3.\text{CH}_2.\text{COOH propionic acid.}$$
$$\text{CH}_3(\text{CH}_2)_2\text{CH}_3 \text{ --------------- CH}_3(\text{CH}_2)_2.\text{COOH butyric acid.}$$

The sixteenth and eighteenth members of the paraffin series are:

$$\begin{array}{cc} \text{CH}_3 & \text{CH}_3 \\ | & | \\ (\text{CH}_2)_{14} & (\text{CH}_2)_{16} \\ | & | \\ \text{CH}_3 & \text{CH}_3 \end{array}$$

The fatty acids formed from them are $\text{CH}_3(\text{CH}_2)_{14}.\text{COOH}$, palmitic acid, and $\text{CH}_3(\text{CH}_2)_{16}.\text{COOH}$, stearic acid.

From organic chemistry it will be recalled that the alcohols act as organic bases, having the power to unite with acids to form water and compounds corresponding to the salts. For example:

$$\text{Na } \boxed{\begin{array}{c} \text{OH} \\ + \\ \text{H} \end{array}} \text{Cl} \rightarrow \text{HOH} + \text{NaCl.}$$

$$\text{CH}_3\text{CH}_2 \boxed{\begin{array}{c} \text{OH} \\ + \\ \text{H} \end{array}} \text{Cl} \rightarrow \text{HOH} + \text{CH}_3\text{CH}_2\text{Cl.}$$

ethyl chloride.

$$\begin{array}{c} \text{ethyl alcohol} \\ + \\ \text{acetic acid} \end{array} \quad \begin{array}{c} \text{CH}_3\text{CH}_2 \\ + \\ \text{CH}_3\text{COO} \end{array} \boxed{\begin{array}{c} \text{OH} \\ \text{H} \end{array}} \rightarrow$$

$$\text{HOH} + \begin{array}{c} \text{CH}_3\text{CH}_2 \\ | \\ \text{CH}_3\text{COO} \end{array} \quad \text{or} \quad \text{CH}_3\text{CH}_2.\text{CH}_3\text{COO.}$$

ethyl acetate

The ethyl acetate is called an ester just as the NaCl is called a salt. Stearin and palmitin are the esters formed by the interaction of the triatomic alcohol (glycerol) and the fatty acids, stearic and palmitic acids, respectively. As glycerol is a triatomic alcohol, i.e., has three alcohol groups, it can unite with three fatty acid radicals, as illustrated:

$$CH_2\boxed{OH \qquad H}OOC.(CH_2)_{14}CH_3$$
$$|$$
$$CH\boxed{OH \qquad H}OOC.(CH_2)_{14}CH_3 \rightarrow 3H_2O +$$
$$|$$
$$CH_2\boxed{OH \qquad H}OOC.(CH_2)_{14}CH_3$$

glycerol   +   3 palmitic acid molecules.

$$CH_2.OOC \ (CH_2)_{14}CH_3$$
$$|$$
$$CH.OOC \ (CH_2)_{14}CH_3 \quad \text{or} \quad C_3H_5[OOC \ (CH_2)_{14}CH_3]_3$$
$$|$$
$$CH_2.OOC \ (CH_2)_{14}CH_3 \qquad \qquad \text{Tripalmitin or palmitin.}$$

In the same manner tristearin, or stearin, is formed, having the composition $C_3H_5[OOC(CH_2)_{16}CH_3]_3$. Olein, or triolein, is the triglyceride of an unsaturated fatty acid, called oleic acid. In an unsaturated fatty acid two or more of the carbons in the chain are linked by two bonds; for example, the formula of oleic acid is:

$$CH_3(CH_2)_7—CH=CH—(CH_2)_7COOH.$$

Unsaturated fatty acids are especially found in the inedible cottonseed oil and linseed oil. By treating these fats with hydrogen at a high temperature and pressure and in the presence of a catalyst the unsaturated fatty acids take up hydrogen at the double bond and thereby become saturated (hydrogenated). Lard substitutes thus formed are fully utilized by the body. The fats in the animal body are generally mixed triglycerides, i.e., to the glycerol are attached one each of the three fatty acid radicals above discussed. Other fatty acids may be present; thus, milk is said to contain all the even numbered fatty acids from butyric to stearic acid.

SOAP.—A fat may be decomposed into glycerol and fatty acids in many ways, among which we may mention the action of certain enzymes, bacteria, and strong alkalies. A fat heated with potassium hydroxide—KOH—or sodium hydroxide—NaOH—is, first of all, decomposed into the fatty acid and glycerol and then the Na or K of the alkali unites with the fatty acid to form soap.

$$\text{Fat} + \text{NaOH} + H_2O = \text{fatty acid} + \text{glycerol} + \text{NaOH}$$
$$\text{NaOH} + \text{fatty acid} = \text{sodium soap} + H_2O$$

This splitting up of the fat into its two component parts is called *saponification*. Fats may also be decomposed by the action of bacteria. The fatty acids thereby set free are most likely split to lower fatty acids (that is, to fatty acids having fewer carbon atoms in the molecule). These lower fatty acids have very penetrating and offensive odors, and give the offensive taste and smell to rancid fats (e.g., "strong" butter).

Properties.—The three common fats, olein, palmitin, and stearin, differ from each other in their melting points, olein melting at about 0° C., while the melting point of palmitin and of stearin is variously given from 45° to 60° and from 55° to 70° C., respectively. Most of the fats we eat (butter, lard, etc.) and also the body fat of an animal are mixtures of the three fats we have been studying. These fats differ from each other in the relative amounts of olein, palmitin, and stearin they contain. The more olein and the less of the other two fats, the lower the melting point of a fat; we may give the melting points of a few common fats (Table XIV).

TABLE XIV

Butterine	31° C.
Butter	36° C.
Lard	44° C.
Mutton fat	51° C.
Tallow	53° C.

When a fat has such a low melting point that at the ordinary room temperature it is melted, it is called an oil; for example, olive oil, cottonseed oil, cod liver oil, etc. The lower its melting point, the more readily a fat is digested and the greater the ability of the body to use it. The human body fat containing from 67 to 80 per cent olein has a melting point below the body temperature (37° C.) and therefore is found in the form of droplets in the cells.

SOLUBILITY.—Fats are insoluble in cold or hot water; they dissolve in hot alcohol and in chloroform, ether, and benzol. When a drop of olive oil is shaken up with a small quantity of water, the two mix as long as the process of shaking continues, but immediately after the test tube is set down, the oil, separating from the water, rises to the top. If the oil is agitated with a water solution of soap, a milky fluid is obtained from which the oil separates very slowly. The fat in this condition is broken up into a countless number of microscopic droplets, each surrounded by a pellicle of soap; by this means the fat can be kept in suspension for a long time. Such a mixture is called an *emulsion* and has a milky appearance; in fact, the white color of milk is to a large extent due to the emulsified fat. If, instead of shaking up a pure fat with a soap solution, we use a rancid fat and a solution of sodium carbonate, the same phenomenon occurs, for the sodium carbonate reacting with the free fatty acid of the rancid fat forms soap. We shall see later on that this plays an important part in the digestion of fats.

Pure fats are odorless and tasteless; the odor of most of the fats we are acquainted with is due to the presence of free fatty acid.

Occurrence.—Fats occur in many of our foods, and they are found in nearly all the tissues of our bodies, of which we may give a few examples in Table XV.

TABLE XV

Bone marrow	96%	Milk	4.0%
Adipose tissue	83%	Liver	2.5%
Nerves	22%	Blood	0.5%
Eggs	12%		

III. PROTEINS

The third group of organic foodstuffs, the proteins, differ from the carbohydrates and fats in many respects, especially in regard to composition. The protein molecule contains at least five elements, present in approximately the following proportion, by weight:

Carbon	50 to 55%
Oxygen	21 to 24%
Nitrogen	15 to 17%
Hydrogen	about 7%
Sulfur	0.2 to 7%

Some proteins contain phosphorus; others contain iron, iodine, etc. Proteins constitute the largest part of the dry material of the cells and are indispensable for life. Egg albumin (white of egg) may be regarded as a type of protein.

Classification of Proteins.—Of the large number of proteins found in food and in plants and animals we shall mention only those more commonly met with in physiology.

I. SIMPLE PROTEINS. These on cleavage yield amino acids only (see infra):

1. *Albumins.*—Egg albumin, lactalbumin, and serum albumin of animal origin; legumelin (peas) and leucosin (wheat) are vegetable albumins. They are soluble in pure water, precipitated by saturating their solution with ammonium sulfate but not by magnesium sulfate or sodium chloride. They are coagulated by heat.

2. *Globulins.*—Egg globulin, lactoglobulin, and serum globulin; fibrinogen of the blood; myosin of the muscle; vegetable globulins, such as legumin (peas), tuberin (potatoes), edestin (wheat). They are insoluble in pure water but are soluble in dilute salt solutions; they are coagulated by heat and precipitated by saturation with magnesium sulfate or by half saturation with ammonium sulfate.

3. *Albuminoids, or Scleroproteins.*—These are among the least soluble of the proteins and are the most difficult of digestion. In the body they are found in the insoluble state, being highly resistant, yet

plastic. Being found in all connective tissue structures, they confer upon the organs and the body as a whole form, strength, rigidity, and elasticity. Among the albuminoids are:

(a) *Collagen* forms the ground substance of bone and cartilage and is found in the white fibrous, or inelastic, connective tissue (tendons, aponeuroses, ligaments, dura mater, pericardium, fascia). By boiling, especially with acidulated water, it is transformed into the well-known *gelatin;* this renders meat tender by boiling. Collagen is digestible, but gelatin more so.

(b) *Elastin* is found in the yellow (elastic) connective tissue in the walls of the blood vessels (especially arteries) and of the air tubes and in the lungs. It is very insoluble and hard to digest.

(c) *Keratin* is found in the outer layer of the skin, in hair, nails, feathers, hoofs, etc. It is indigestible.

4. *Glutelins.*—Glutenin (wheat). Not soluble in water or neutral salt solution; soluble in dilute alkalies and acids.

5. *Prolamines.*—Gliadin (wheat), zein (corn), hordein (barley). Not soluble in water or neutral solvents; soluble in 80 per cent alcohol.

II. Compound, Complex, or Conjugated Proteins.

These are composed of a simple protein united with some other substance and, according to the nature of this second component, we have the following groups of compound proteins:

1. *Chromoproteins.*—In these the simple protein is united with a pigment; e.g., hemoglobin (see Chap. VIII).

2. *Nucleoproteins* are extensively found in the nuclei of the cells (Chap. on Protein Metabolism).

3. *Glycoproteins* are formed by the union of a carbohydrate with the protein; the most important glycoprotein is mucin. The mucin is found, e.g., in the saliva and gives a high viscosity (ropiness) to fluids. It is also found in the secretions of the mucous membranes.

4. *Phosphoproteins.*—Vitellin of the egg yolk and casein of milk. As the name indicates, these proteins contain phosphorus. They are soluble in dilute alkalies; hence the addition of acid causes them to be precipitated (as in souring of milk).

5. *Lecithoproteins, or lecithans,* in which the protein is united with lecithin, a compound of fat containing phosphorus and nitrogen (Chap. XIX).

III. Derived Proteins. These are produced from the above-named proteins in various ways.

(a) Those derived by hydrolysis, e.g., by the action of the digestive enzymes, acids, or alkalies (see infra).

1. *Acid metaproteins,* 2. *Alkali metaproteins,* 3. *Proteoses or albumoses,* 4. *Peptones,* 5. *Peptids;* these will be spoken of in connection with digestion.

(*b*) *Coagulated proteins* formed by heat, etc.

Composition of Proteins.—The most complex chemical compounds in the world are proteins. Their chemical composition and structure are very much involved, but the subject of digestion of proteins and their function and fate in our body is unintelligible unless the student has at least a rudimentary knowledge of the subject. We shall present here the barest outline; for those desiring it, a somewhat more detailed account has been added at the end of this section. When protein, say, egg albumin, is boiled with acid or undergoes digestion or putrefaction, the large protein molecule breaks up into a number of simpler molecules, known as amino acids. In somewhat the same manner as a polysaccharide molecule is formed by the union of a large number of monosaccharide molecules, so the protein is constructed of amino acids. Nearly all organic acids have attached to the main part of the molecule a group —COOH— known as the carboxyl. This group gives the compound its acid properties and therefore enables it to unite with basic substances to form organic salts. To illustrate: let the "body," or nucleus, of the acid be represented by X or Y.

$$
\begin{array}{ccccc}
\text{X} & & \text{Na} & & \text{X} \\
| & + & | & \longrightarrow & | & + \ H_2O \\
\text{COO}\,\underline{\text{H}} & & \underline{\text{H O}} & & \text{COO . Na} \\
\text{Organic acid} & \text{Sodium hydroxide} & & & \text{Organic salt}
\end{array}
$$

The amino acid is an organic acid but there is added to the "nucleus" another group, the amino group, $—NH_2$. The amino group gives the molecule the properties of a base (like NaOH or NH_4OH). Due to the presence of an acid —COOH— group and a basic group $—NH_2—$, two molecules of amino acid can readily unite with each other to form a larger molecule. We may picture this:

$$
\begin{array}{ccc}
\text{COOH} & & \text{COOH} \\
| & & | \\
\text{X} & \longrightarrow & \text{X} & + \ H_2O \\
| & & | \\
\text{H N}\,\underline{\text{H}} \quad \underline{\text{HO}}\text{CO} & & \text{HN} - \text{CO} \\
\qquad \text{Y} - NH_2 & & \text{Y} - NH_2
\end{array}
$$

The product formed in the above illustration is called a dipeptide. It will be noticed that the dipeptide has a carboxyl group at one end, and an amino group at the other. Consequently the dipeptide can unite with a third amino acid molecule to form a tripeptide. And thus the linking can go on almost indefinitely; the successive products are called: amino acids, dipeptides, tripeptides, polypeptides, peptones, proteoses, and proteins. There are 22 kinds of amino acid known to exist in our body. They differ from each other physically and chemically mainly because of what we have called the "body" or nucleus; they all possess one or more carboxyl and amino groups. The student should be familiar with the names of at least seven of the most important amino acids: glycine, leucine, lysine, tyrosine, tryptophan, histidine.

Characteristics of Proteins.—The various proteins differ largely from each other so that it is very difficult to make any general statements concerning their properties.

1. Only a few proteins are soluble in water (peptones and albumins), many are soluble in dilute salt solutions (globulins), others in dilute acid (acid metaproteins) and still others in dilute alkalies (casein of milk, alkali metaprotein).

2. Very few proteins dialyze through the ordinary parchment paper; for this reason they are generally classed as colloids, although crystalline proteins (hemoglobin, edestin) are known.

3. They give certain color reactions:

(a) All proteins give the *xanthoproteic test*. The protein is boiled with nitric acid; this gives a yellow coloration which changes to an orange on the addition of ammonium hydroxide. The various color tests for proteins depend on the reaction of the reagent with certain groups existing in the protein molecule. The xanthoproteic test is due to the benzene ring in the protein molecule.

(b) Most proteins give *Millon's test*. In this the protein is colored a dark red on being boiled with Millon's fluid (a solution of mercuric and mercurous nitrate containing free nitrous acid). Here the reaction is due to a benzene ring to which an OH group is attached. Hence, this test is given also by phenol (carbolic acid—C_6H_5OH) and by the amino acid tyrosine.

(c) *Biuret test*. If an excess of NaOH be added to a solution of a protein, the addition of a drop or two of 1 per cent copper sulfate solution causes a rose-red color with peptones and some proteoses and a violet color with the other proteins.

All these tests, but especially the biuret test, are used to establish the presence of proteins.

4. Precipitation reactions of proteins: Inasmuch as proteins are condensation products of amino acids, they contain both free amino (NH_2) and carboxyl (COOH) groups. Hence they are able to react both as bases and as acids and, by chemically uniting with other acids

and bases, to form compounds similar to the salts in inorganic chemistry. Many of the compounds formed in this manner are insoluble and in consequence the protein is precipitated.

Among the reagents which precipitate proteins are the salts of heavy metals (lead, aluminum, zinc, iron, silver, mercury); in this reaction the protein acts as an acid and an insoluble salt, e.g., lead proteinate, is formed. On the other hand, when a protein reacts with such compounds as tannic acid (tannin) or picric acid, it behaves as a base. Tannic acid is found in the leaves and bark of many plants, for example, tea, and in a somewhat concentrated dose causes a dryness and puckering of the mouth. Applied to the mucosa or the exposed animal tissues the above-named substances bring about a hardening and wrinkling because of the precipitation of the proteins, for which reason they are called *astringents* (*ad*, to; *stringo*, to bind fast). The precipitated protein forms a barrier to the deeper penetration of the astringent into the tissue and thereby localizes the action of the drug. However, many of the salts of the heavy metals (notably mercury) also have a very irritating effect which renders them toxic and unsuitable for astringent purposes.

Because of their power to precipitate the proteins of the blood, the astringents are able to stop the oozing of blood from the capillaries and in this capacity are known as *hemostatics* or *styptics* (ferric chloride, burnt alum). Again, this precipitating action enables many of the salts of the heavy metals, e.g., mercuric chloride, to check the action and growth of bacteria (antiseptics) or to destroy them completely (germicides); however, it must be borne in mind that these various salts may have specific toxic actions upon bacteria, aside from the precipitating effect. Among the other uses of these substances we may mention the use of tannin in the making of leather; the antidotal action of white of egg or milk in poisoning by the salts of heavy metals; and the use of picric or tannic acid (water solution) in burns. Another precipitant for proteins is alcohol.

5. Proteins can be "salted" out of solution by neutral salts such as magnesium sulfate, ammonium sulfate, and sodium chloride. The various proteins differ considerably in the ease with which they can thus be precipitated; in fact, upon this difference depends largely the classification of proteins.

6. Albumins and globulins are coagulated by heat; by this process the soluble proteins are transformed into insoluble proteins. This is frequently used as a test for these proteins in urine and other fluids.

7. Strong acids, such as nitric acid, precipitate many proteins. This constitutes *Heller's test for albumin* in the urine.

Amino acids may be conceived of as formed by the interaction of the alcohol group of an oxyacid and ammonia. An oxyacid, or hydroxy acid, is an organic acid in which one of the CH_2 groups or the CH_3 group has been oxidized.

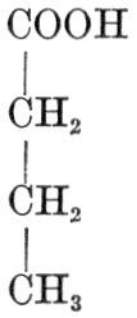

COOH	COOH	COOH
CH_2	CHOH	CH_2
CH_2	CH_2	CHOH
CH_3	CH_3	CH_3
butyric acid	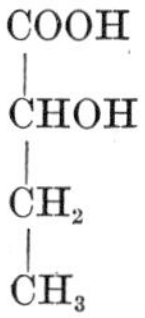 alpha-oxybutyric acid	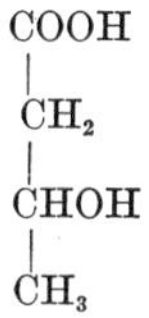 beta-oxybutyric acid

Suppose oxyacetic acid reacts with ammonia; the result may be represented thus:

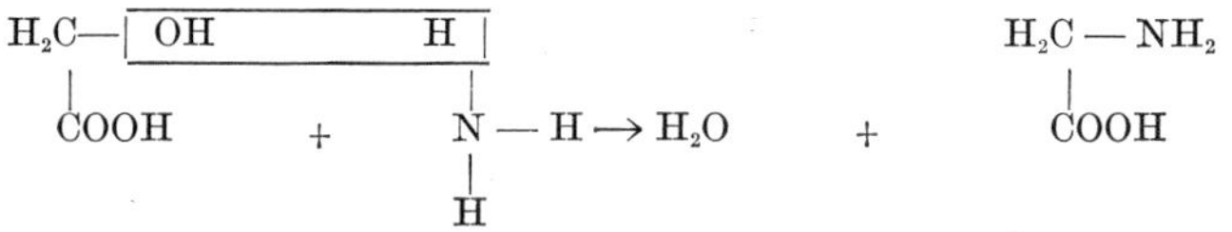

$$H_2C-\boxed{OH \qquad H} \qquad\qquad H_2C-NH_2$$

$$COOH \quad + \quad N-H \rightarrow H_2O \quad + \quad COOH$$

$$H$$

oxyacetic acid   ammonia   amino-acetic acid

Amino-acetic acid is also called glycocoll, or glycine. Another important amino acid is alanine which is the amino-propionic acid:

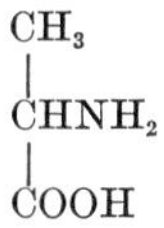

$$CH_3$$
$$CHNH_2$$
$$COOH$$

There are many amino acids formed from the proteins by decomposition but we shall content ourselves with the following:

Leucine, amino-isobutylacetic acid—$CH_3.CH_3.CH.CH_2.CHNH_2.COOH$.
Aspartic acid, amino-succinic acid—$COOH.CH_2.CHNH_2.COOH$.
Tyrosine, para-oxyphenyl-alpha-amino-propionic acid—$C_6H_4.OH.CH_2.CHNH_2.COOH$.
Lysine, alpha-epsilon-diamino-caproic acid—$CH_2NH_2.CH_2.CH_2.CH_2.CHNH_2.COOH$.

Two other complex amino acids of great importance are arginine and histidine. A large number of compounds in the animal body belong to what are known as the cyclic, or aromatic, compounds. The mother substance of these is benzene, C_6H_6, which by oxidation gives rise to oxybenzene, or phenol (carbolic acid).

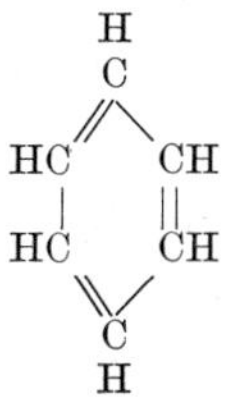

H	OH
C	C
HC⁄⁄ CH	HC⁄⁄ CH
HC CH	HC CH
C	C
H	H
Benzene	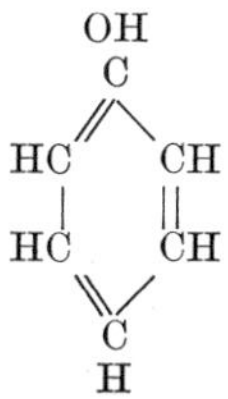 Phenol

These formulas may be simplified by writing them:

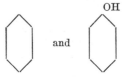

and

In the benzene we may substitute methane and obtain methane benzene, or toluol.

CH₃

Toluol

COOH

Benzoic acid

If now the CH_3 group be oxidized, there is formed benzoic acid, $C_6H_5.COOH$. Or let us suppose that one of the hydrogen atoms of the benzene is replaced by alanine (amino-propionic acid), we obtain phenylalanine:

$CH_2.CHNH_2COOH$ or $C_6H_5.CH_2CHNH_2COOH$.

The alanine can also unite with oxybenzene (phenol), giving rise to:

OH   OH

+ CH₃.CHNH₂COOH =

CH₂.CHNH₂COOH.

This is called para*-oxyphenol-amino-propionic acid, or tyrosine, an exceedingly important amino acid. Still more complicated in structure are the amino acids known as tryptophan and histidine. Cystine is a sulfur amino acid in which two molecules of alanine (amino-propionic acid) are held together by two sulfur atoms:

$$H_2C — S \text{-} S — CH_2$$
$$H_2NCH \qquad HCNH_2$$
$$COOH \qquad COOH$$

Because of their amphoteric reactions the amino acids can unite with each other to form more complex molecules; this we may illustrate by taking the simplest of the amino acids, glycocoll, or glycine.

$$H_2C — NH_2 \qquad\qquad H_2C — NH_2$$
$$OC —\boxed{OH + H}HN\text{-}CH_2 \rightarrow H_2O + OC — NHCH_2 \qquad or$$
$$COOH \qquad\qquad\qquad COOH$$

*The "para" refers to the fact that the OH and the amino-propionic acid are placed at opposite angles of the benzene ring.

$$CH_2NH_2.COOH + CH_2NH_2.COOH = H_2O + CH_2NH_2.CO.CH_2NHCOOH$$

glycine   glycine   glycyl-glycine.

The compound formed when two molecules of glycine unite in the above manner is called glycyl-glycine and belongs to the dipeptides. It will be noticed that the dipeptide molecule still contains the NH$_2$ and COOH groups, hence, like the original simple amino acid, it has acid and basic properties and can therefore unite with still more amino acids; for example:

$$
\begin{array}{llll}
CH_2NH_2 & & CH_2NH_2 & \\
| & & | & \\
OC\text{—}NHCH_2 & CH_3 \rightarrow H_2O + & OC\text{—}NHCH_2 & CH_3 \\
| & | & | & | \\
OC\text{—}\boxed{OH + H}HNCH & & OC\text{—}NHCH & \\
& | & & | \\
& COOH & & COOH
\end{array}
$$

glycyl-glycine   alanine

$$CH_2NH_2.CO.NHCH_2.COOH + CH_3.CHNH_2.COOH \rightarrow$$
$$H_2O + CH_2NH_2.CO.NHCH_2.CO.CH_3.CHNH.COOH.$$

The compound thus formed contains three amino acids and is called a tripeptide. When a still larger number of amino acids unite with each other, polypeptides are formed. Emil Fischer succeeded in synthetically preparing polypeptides that contained eighteen amino-acid molecules. Such polypeptides began to give some of the reactions ordinarily ascribed to the proteins; in fact, we may regard the protein molecule as being formed by the union of many polypeptides of increasing complexity.

Classes of Foods.—We may divide the foods into two great classes:

I. Those rich in proteins:

1. The animal foods which are, generally speaking, poor in carbohydrates. Among these are eggs and meats (including any part of any animal body).

2. Among the vegetables, the legumes contain considerable quantities of carbohydrates in addition to the protein. This class includes beans, peas, peanuts, and lentils.

II. Foods rich in carbohydrates or fats but relatively poor in proteins. Here belong all the vegetable foods except the legumes.

We may give the percentage composition of a few common foods (percentages are of edible portion) in Table XVI.

TABLE XVI*

FOOD	WATER	PROTEIN	FAT	CARBO-HYDRATE	ASH	UNAVAIL-ABLE
Boiled eggs	73.2	12.8	11.4	0.0	0.6	1.2
Potatoes (boiled)	75.5	1.9	0.1	20.0	0.8	1.7
Lean round steak	70.0	20.7	7.5	0.0	1.1	1.0
White bread	35.3	7.1	1.2	52.3	0.8	3.3
Beans (dry)	12.6	15.8	1.6	59.9	2.6	7.5
Lettuce	94.7	0.9	0.3	2.9	0.7	0.5
Milk	87.0	3.2	3.8	5.0	0.5	0.5

*Taken from Farmer's Bulletin, No. 85, U. S. Dept. of Agriculture, 1905.

CHAPTER XV

DIGESTION

I. ANATOMY

Digestion.—Most of the food we eat cannot be used directly by the cells of the body. If egg albumin, starch, or cane sugar were injected into blood vessels, the cells would starve and the food substances would be excreted rapidly by the kidneys; in fact, most foreign proteins injected into the blood stream are toxic. Hence the foods must first be prepared so as to become fit for consumption by the cells; this is accomplished by digestion. Digestion may be defined as the changes that the foods normally undergo preparatory to absorption and assimilation; these changes are physical and chemical and occur in the alimentary canal.

The alimentary canal may be regarded as a winding tube extending the full length of the trunk. It may be divided into five segments: the mouth and pharynx, esophagus, stomach, small intestine, and large intestine. The relation of these various parts can be gathered from Fig. 158.

The small intestine is generally divided into three parts: the duodenum, the jejunum, and the ileum. These three parts form a tube 20 to 25 feet long and about 1.5 inches in diameter. The large intestine is about five or six feet long and one to two and a half inches in diameter. It is composed of five parts: the cecum, the ascending colon, the transverse colon, the descending colon, and the rectum. To the cecum is attached the vermiform appendix.

The structure of the wall of the alimentary canal differs in the various regions of the canal, but, in general, we find it composed of four layers; see Figs. 159 and 170. These coats from without in are: 1, *a serous or fibrous coat,* a thin layer of connective tissue; 2, the *muscular coat* composed of an outer layer of longitudinal fibers and an inner and more highly developed layer of circular fibers; 3, *the submucosa* made up of loose connective tissue elements in which are found numerous blood and lymph vessels and mucous glands; 4, *the mucosa,* or mucous membrane; in this are found the glands peculiar to the alimentary canal.

Sphincters.—At certain places the circular muscles are much enlarged, forming what are known as sphincters; by these the lumen of the tube is held closed until a stimulation for the relaxation of the muscles occurs. Such sphincters are found at the junction of (1) the esophagus and the stomach (the cardia, Fig. 158), (2) the stomach and the small intestine (the pyloric sphincter), (3) the small and large intestine (ileocecal, or ileocolic, sphincter), and (4) the internal and external anal sphincters guarding the anal opening. The function of a sphincter is twofold: to restrain the food in its passage from one part of the canal to another, and to a lesser extent to prevent regurgitation (see Chap. XVII).

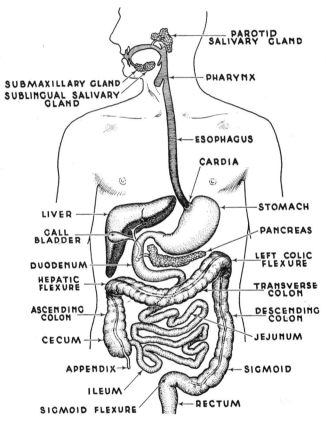

Fig. 158.—The alimentary tube and its appendages.

The Peritoneum.—The interior of the abdominal cavity is lined with a serous membrane, the peritoneum (*peri*, around; *teino*, to stretch). Like the pericardium and the pleura, this is a double membrane; the outer, or parietal, layer is in contact with the body wall; the inner, or visceral, layer envelops the abdominal organs. From the dorsal body wall, a continuation of the peritoneum, known as the *mesentery* (*mesos*, middle, *enteron*, bowel) extends to the small and large intestine. By it these organs are suspended from the body wall, and in it the blood vessels, lymph vessels, and nerves for the intestine are carried. The stomach is attached by a special fold, the *lesser omentum,* to the liver. The *greater omentum* hangs as an apron from the greater curvature of the stomach over the intestine and connects the stomach with the colon. In this fold much fat may accumulate.

The organs of the abdomen are supported also by the abdominal wall in which are found striated muscles. Not infrequently a loop of the intestine protrudes through a weak spot in the muscular abdominal wall—a hernia, or rupture. The blood supply to this part is apt to be cut off (strangulation); this gives rise to great pain and by necrosis may seriously endanger the life of the patient unless speedily relieved.

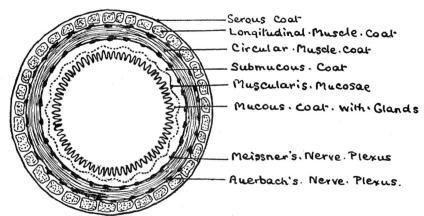

Serous Coat
Longitudinal·Muscle·Coat·
Circular·Muscle·Coat
Submucous·Coat
Muscularis·Mucosae
Mucous·Coat·with·Glands

Meissner's·Nerve·Plexus
Auerbach's·Nerve·Plexus.

Fig. 159.—Diagram of cross section of the alimentary canal. (Hewer: Histology, The C. V. Mosby Co.)

II. GENERAL CONSIDERATIONS

The object of the various processes occurring in the alimentary canal is to change the composition of the ingested food in such a manner as to render it suitable for cell consumption (digestion). The structure of the canal also furnishes means for transferring the digested food into the blood (absorption).

Digestion.—As the ingested food cannot be utilized by the cells mainly because of the large size of the food molecules, digestion is nearly altogether a matter of splitting large molecules into smaller ones. It will be recalled from the study of the alimentary principles, that a disaccharide molecule is made by the union of two molecules of monosaccharides; in a polysaccharide molecule from 25 to 35 monosaccharide molecules are incorporated into one. A fat molecule is made by the union of one glycerol and three fatty acid molecules. A molecule of a native protein, albumin, e.g., is a linkage of a very large number of amino acid molecules. In all of these chemical unions there is an extrusion of one or more water molecules; thus:

$$C_6H_{12}O_6 + C_6H_{12}O_6 \text{ minus } H_2O \rightarrow C_{12}H_{22}O_{11}$$
$$\text{glucose} + \text{glucose} \qquad \text{water} \quad \text{maltose}$$

The same holds true for fats and proteins. During digestion this process is reversed; that is, one or more molecules of water are added to the large molecule and separation, or cleavage, occurs; thus:

$$C_{12}H_{22}O_{11} + H_2O \rightarrow C_6H_{12}O_6 + C_6H_{12}O_6.$$

This process is called hydrolytic cleavage, or hydrolysis, and the above serves as an illustration of the digestion of all carbohydrates, fats, and proteins. In the laboratory hydrolysis of foodstuff can be brought about in various ways; e.g., by the action of relatively strong acids or alkalies, or by a great degree of heat (superheated steam). In our body this is accomplished at a relatively low temperature (37° C.) and without strong chemical agents; the agencies employed are enzymes (see Chap. II). Since enzymes are extremely specific in their activity, a large number of enzymes is required. To supply these enzymes and also the large amount of water needed during digestion is the function of the digestive glands.

Secretion.—In the walls of the stomach and small intestine there are glands which secrete the gastric and intestinal juices, respectively. Near the canal lie the three pairs of salivary glands, the liver, and the pancreas; all of these glands are connected by means of ducts with the lumen of the digestive tube, Fig. 158. While the activities of these various glands differ, they have certain fundamental processes in common; these we shall now consider, using the activity of the salivary glands as an illustration. A gland may be looked upon as a tube composed of highly specialized epithelial cells (gland cells). Some glands are very simple in construction, others are exceedingly complex, Fig. 160, but the following description applies to all types. At one end the tube is closed, at the other the lumen or duct opens up onto a free surface, such as the skin, interior of the mouth, the lumen of the intestine, etc. The tube is surrounded by a dense network of capillaries. Two rather distinct processes may take place in a gland: the gland cell may serve only as a transfer agency, or as a manufacturing plant. Certain materials, water and NaCl, e.g., are taken out of the blood stream (*a*, in Fig. 161) by the gland cell, *b*, transferred through the cell, and passed into the duct or lumen, *c*, to be thrown upon a free surface, *d*. All types of glands, to a greater or lesser extent, transfer water in this manner. Some glands, notably the sweat glands, practically limit their activity to this.

Other glands, however, also manufacture new materials, for their secretions contain substances not found in the blood. To illustrate: the saliva contains a sticky, viscous protein, known as mucin, and an enzyme called ptyalin. Since neither of these substances are found in the blood, they must have been made by the gland cells from materials supplied by the blood. All the various digestive enzymes are thus formed by the digestive glands.

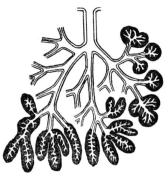

Fig. 160.—Diagram of an external secreting gland. Secretory portions black; ducts double contoured. (Maximow and Bloom, Histology, W. B. Saunders Co.)

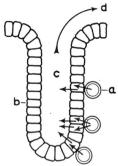

Fig. 161.—Diagram illustrating secretion. *a*, capillary; *b*, gland cell; *c*, duct.

Secretion is therefore not merely a process of diffusion through a membrane. Neither is the blood pressure in the capillaries the driving force which causes the movement of the secretion, for while the blood pressure may be but 125 mm. Hg, the pressure of the saliva in the duct may rise as high as 240 mm. Hg. While it is true that glandular activity is normally accompanied by a great dilation of the blood vessels of the gland, the flow of the blood is not in itself a direct cause of secretion, for it is possible, by atropine, to stop the secretion completely while the flow of blood through the blood vessels of the gland continues.

Secretion must be regarded as an active phenomenon on the part of the gland cells. This view is supported by the following facts:

1. The secretion contains substances not found in the blood; these are made by the gland cells.

2. The salts in a secretion may have a lower concentration than the salts of the blood. To separate from the blood a fluid having a lower molecular concentration (fewer molecules per unit of volume) than the blood, requires an expenditure of energy. This energy is obtained from the potential energy of the foods and the gland cells are the machines which utilize the liberated energy for the transporting of fluids and solids in solution through the membrane.

3. During activity the glands consume more oxygen and produce more carbon dioxide than when they are at rest.

4. Electrical changes are manifested during activity.

5. During the different phases of their activity there are histologic changes in the gland cells. This will be discussed under the subject of saliva.

The Digestive Juices.—During the process of digestion foods undergo numerous physical and chemical changes. These are brought about by the following five juices poured into the alimentary canal: (1) saliva, (2) gastric juice, (3) bile, (4) pancreatic juice, (5) intestinal juice. The glands manufacturing the digestive juices either lie in the walls of the alimentary canal (the gastric and intestinal glands) or form separate organs near the canal and are connected by means of ducts with the lumen of the canal, e.g., the salivary glands, the liver, and the pancreas. The above-named juices bring about the chemical changes in the foods almost exclusively by means of enzymes or ferments. The most important changes are as follows:

Juice	Enzyme	Changes
1. Saliva	Ptyalin	Boiled starch to maltose.
"	Maltase?	Maltose to glucose.
2. Gastric	Pepsin	Ordinary proteins to peptones.
"	Rennin	Curdles milk.
"	Gastric lipase	Fats to fatty acids and glycerol.
3. Bile	None	Emulsification of fats; solution of fatty acids.
4. Pancreatic	Amylopsin	Starch to maltose.
"	Maltase	Maltose to glucose.
"	Steapsin	Fats to fatty acids and glycerol.
"	Trypsin	Proteins to amino acids.
5. Intestinal	Erepsin	Peptones to amino acids.
"	Enterokinase	Trypsinogen to trypsin.
"	Maltase	Maltose to glucose.
"	Invertase	Cane sugar to monosaccharides.
"	Lactase	Lactose to monosaccharides.

III. TEETH AND MASTICATION

Mastication.—The most important physical change that the foods undergo is that of mastication (see p. 377). Among the benefits derived from thorough mastication we may mention the following:

1. By mastication the food is broken up into small particles; this enables the digestive juices to work more quickly and thoroughly upon the food. Many cases of chronic indigestion have been traced to faulty mastication due to bad teeth.

2. Proper insalivation of solid food.

3. The person appreciates better the taste of the food and thus obtains more pleasure from eating. As we shall see subsequently, the greater pleasure causes a greater flow of saliva and gastric juice and thus favors digestion.

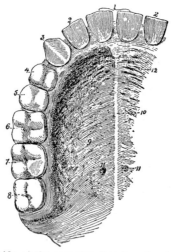

Fig. 162.—The right side of the superior dental arch. *1* and *2*, the median and lateral incisors; *3*, canine; *4* and *5*, the first and second bicuspids; *6, 7* and *8*, the first, second and third molars; *9, 10, 11* and *12*, the hard palate. (After Testut.)

4. Thorough mastication increases very largely the blood flow to all the structures of the mouth; in this the teeth share. In the child it strengthens and increases the size of the jaw bones and thereby gives sufficient room for the proper placement of the teeth.

5. Above all, it brings about a moderation in eating.

Teeth.—Man and certain animals have two dentitions: the temporary and the permanent. The temporary, deciduous, or milk, teeth number for each lateral half of each jaw: two incisors, one canine, and two molars. They erupt from about the sixth or eighth month (lower central incisors) to the twenty-fourth month (second molars).

The eruption of the permanent teeth, which gradually replace and supplement the temporary, begins during the fifth or sixth year (first molars) and continues until the seventeenth or even the twenty-fifth year (third molars, wisdom teeth). This dentition, Fig. 162, comprises two incisors, one canine or cuspid, two bicuspids or premolars, and three molars for each lateral half of the jaw.

A tooth is composed of an inner structure known as dentin, Fig. 163. The part of the dentin (crown) projecting beyond the jaw bone is covered with an exceedingly hard material, the enamel; the part embedded in the bone is surrounded by a layer of cementum. Inside of the dentin is a cavity containing the tooth pulp consisting of a form of connective tissue, and the blood vessels and nerves which enter the tooth by the foramen at the apex. The cement and dentin are almost identical with bone in composition.

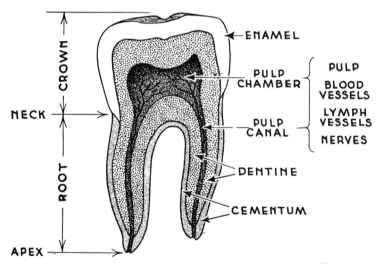

Fig. 163.—Longitudinal section of a human molar tooth.

Bone structure is formed of two distinct substances: an organic basis, or matrix, composed of proteins, and, deposited in this base, a large amount of inorganic, or mineral, matter consisting of calcium phosphate, calcium carbonate, and a small amount of magnesium phosphate. In the enamel we find 5 per cent water; the dry enamel contains 4 per cent organic and 94 per cent of the above-mentioned salts. As the chemistry of teeth is largely a matter of the depositing of insoluble salts of phosphorus and calcium, we shall postpone this discussion until we deal with the subject of bone formation (page 434).

Caries is one of the most prevalent diseases. In caries (Ka'-re-ēz) the insoluble calcium salts of the hard structures of the teeth are by chemical action transformed into soluble salts; these are washed away, and thus a cavity is formed. This destruction of the teeth not only interferes with proper mastication and the subsequent digestion of food, thereby engendering malnutrition, but the infection or the toxins may spread to distant parts of the body and set up secondary infections involving heart, kidneys, or nervous system; very frequently it gives rise to the so-called rheumatic pains ("growing pains" of children), and it may be a cause of anemia.

It is generally conceded that the immediate cause of this chemical change is brought about by acids formed by bacteria from the food lodged upon and between the teeth. But as to the conditions making this action possible, two widely divergent opinions are entertained: (*a*) caries is a local phenomenon depending upon local conditions only; (*b*) the local action is determined by systemic conditions. The scope of this book allows us merely to touch upon two or three points in this most important controversy.

Some investigators lay all the stress upon local factors, such as the presence in the mouth of the proper bacteria (lactobacillus) and of the material from which the acids can be formed. In support of this view one may advance the following: Those places most suitable for the retention of food are also most suceptible to caries. Bunting claims that caries may largely be prevented by the elimination of sugar from the diet; and it is an established fact that diabetic children who eat very little carbohydrate food are not afflicted with caries to any great extent. Candies are generally regarded as favoring tooth decay. Friesell found that a reduction in the number of acid-forming bacteria greatly decreased the amount of tooth decay. The carbohydrates, especially starch, form plaques upon the teeth; this fosters the growth and action of the bacteria. The mucin of the saliva (p. 342) is a predisposing factor, for the more mucin the saliva contains, the less the food is washed away. The chemical state of the saliva, apart from its mucin content, may influence the decay.

It is needless to say that those authorities who lay most stress upon the local factors in tooth decay emphasize the importance of the cleanliness of the mouth from the standpoint of bacteria and food debris. The lodging of food upon and between the teeth is influenced by:

1. The Nature of the Food.—Soft, boiled cereals (mushes) and candies and pastries are of a more sticky nature.

2. Cleansing by Saliva.—By saliva, tongue, and lips the teeth are somewhat cleansed. This partly explains why the decay seldom starts on the inner surface of the teeth.

3. The Detergent Action of Foods.—Raw fruits and vegetables, the coarser breads, toast, and nuts not only demand more mastication but also mechanically scour the teeth and thereby prevent the depositing of tartar.

4. The Nature and Arrangement of the Teeth.—First the surfaces of the individual tooth (pits and crevices in the enamel) and, second, their placement with respect to each other; irregularly placed teeth are kept clean with greater difficulty. Irregularities and lack of alignment may be due to many causes. Mouth breathing, thumb-sucking, an inherited small jaw, or the lack of its proper growth after birth, and the premature loss of the temporary teeth are contributing factors.

5. Oral Hygiene.—The proper use of the toothbrush, dental floss, and cleansing agents as well as periodic examination and prophylactic treatment are important.

Fluorine.—The more recent discoveries as to the rôle of fluorine in drinking water will be discussed on page 431.

In contrast to the above is the view that although caries is a local action and always begins at the exterior of the teeth, the perfection of the chemical and physical structure of the teeth largely determines whether or not decay can occur; i.e., the resistance offered by the teeth is the deciding factor. This resistance is the outcome of many influences most of which are operative during the development and growth of the teeth. Among these is the nature of the diet of the mother during gestation and lactation and that of the infant. It is generally held that an increase in calcium and phosphorus in the maternal diet, above that present in a well-balanced diet, has little or no beneficial influence on the development of the teeth in the fetus; much more important is a liberal supply of vitamin D. Although the calcification begins during the fourth month of fetal life, the amount of calcium salts present in the teeth at birth is but 0.5 gram, an amount equivalent to that found in one pint of cow's milk. As stated by Hess, calcification of the teeth must be regarded as a postnatal phenomenon. It is, therefore, during infancy and childhood that the diet should be well fortified by foods rich in calcium, phosphorus, and vitamins C and D; these materials can best be obtained from milk, egg yolk, cod-liver oil, and citrous fruit juices (see Chap. XX and XXII).

Drain and Boyd, in the history of 500 dental patients, found that caries could be arrested by an abundance of the "protective foods" such as cod-liver oil, milk, fruit, and vegetables; these foods are rich in the above-mentioned salts and vitamins. Agnew was able to cause tooth decay in practically all of his experimental animals by feeding them a diet deficient in calcium, phosphorus, and vitamin D. McCollum fed a number of rats 0.23 gram of phosphorus (in the form of salts) per 100 grams of food; this caused 83 per cent of the animals to develop caries at the end of a 140-day feeding period. When the phosphorus in the diet was increased to 0.41 gram, only 5 per cent acquired tooth decay. Mellanby found that the administration of cod-liver oil decreased the incidence of caries in children.

When all the dietetic demands have been satisfied, the development of the teeth, barring certain infectious diseases, is largely determined by the activity of certain internal secreting glands, such as the thyroid, thymus, parathyroids, gonads, and, especially, the pituitary gland. This will be discussed in Chap. XXIII. It is claimed that the usual diseases of childhood, scarlet fever and measles, may play no small part in the lack of proper tooth development; this is assuredly true for congenital syphilis.

IV. SALIVARY DIGESTION

A. Saliva and Its Functions

The first digestive juice, the saliva, is made by the three pairs of salivary glands: the submaxillary, the sublingual, and the parotid, Fig. 164.

Composition.—Among the ingredients of the saliva we may mention the following:

1. Water, 97 to 99.5 per cent.

2. Mucin, a glycoprotein which gives the high viscosity to saliva. It is formed by the small mucous glands lying in the mucosa of the mouth and by the sublingual gland. The mucin, acting as a lubricant, is of value in the swallowing of food.

3. Salts: disodium phosphate, calcium bicarbonate, calcium phosphate, some potassium salts and chlorides. When the saliva is exposed to the air, the carbon dioxide leaves the saliva and the calcium bicarbonate is transformed into the insoluble carbonate. The precipitation of the calcium salt carries with it the phosphates, epithelial cells, mucin, and the organic debris of the food. Thus is formed the tartar on the teeth.

4. Salivary corpuscles: these are spherical cells which are regarded as modified leucocytes.

5. Epithelial cells from the mouth.

6. Two enzymes: ptyalin and, perhaps, maltase.

7. Gases, chiefly carbon dioxide.

8. In the mouth the saliva generally contains many bacteria and sometimes also molds.

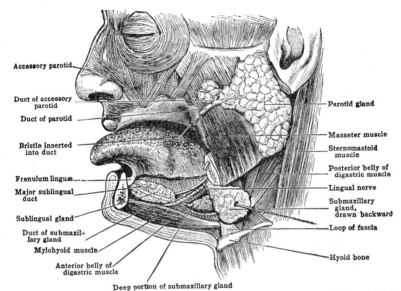

Fig. 164.—The salivary glands. (Morris: Anatomy, P. Blakiston's Son & Co.)

The reaction of saliva is generally stated to be alkaline, owing to disodium phosphate, Na_2HPO_4. The saliva from the submaxillary and sublingual glands is said by some to be more alkaline than that from the parotid gland. Other authors state that saliva is practically neutral; in some instances it may even be acid, as for example, in febrile conditions, digestive disturbances, and diabetes. Whatever its reaction may be, the buffer substances (p. 146) in the saliva enable it to neutralize a considerable amount of either alkali or acid without its reaction undergoing any noticeable change.

Functions.—Saliva performs many functions:

1. By moistening and holding the particles of food together it aids in the mastication and deglutition (swallowing) of the food.

2. It enables us to taste dry foods. A dry substance, like a lump of sugar, placed on the tongue after it has been wiped dry, causes no sensation of taste until some saliva has dissolved some of the sugar.

3. By moistening the mouth it makes speech possible.

4. By washing away the food, it cleanses the teeth and thus aids in preserving them. It is frequently stated that its alkalinity neutralizes the acids which tend to cause tooth decay.

5. Saliva has no digestive action upon fats or proteins. The enzyme, ptyalin (also called salivary diastase), transforms starch into maltose, a disaccharide. The maltose, in turn, is split into glucose by means of a second enzyme, maltase. As in all digestive processes, these changes are hydrolytic cleavages. In these successive cleavages several intermediate products are formed which are more and more soluble as the molecules become smaller; among them we may mention the various dextrins. It is held that about 24 molecules are formed from one molecule of starch.

Many conditions influence the digestion of starch by saliva; we may call attention to the following:

1. The amount of starch we ordinarily digest in the mouth is very limited, but the longer the food is retained in the mouth the more thorough will be the digestion; for this reason we digest the starch of bread and toast better than that of soft mush and porridge.

2. The enzymes of the saliva work best in a neutral or very feebly alkaline medium; acids, even to the extent of 0.003 per cent hydrochloric acid, quickly destroy the enzymes. Hence, in the stomach, where hydrochloric acid is normally present, salivary digestion comes to a standstill.

3. Boiled starch is readily attacked by the ptyalin, but raw starch is very slowly acted upon. This is attributed to the bursting of the cellulose envelope surrounding the starch grains by the boiling or baking process (see Fig. 157). In the raw starch this envelope delays the action of the saliva, so that a large portion of the raw starchy foods is lost by not being digested; hence the importance of preparing starchy foods (bread, potatoes, rice, etc.) properly.

4. Artificially changing starch into dextrins, as occurs in the crust of bread during baking and in the toasting of bread, predigests the food. For this reason toast is more rapidly digested; besides, toast needs more mastication and has a more agreeable taste; all this aids in digestion.

B. The Secretion of Saliva

Saliva is secreted by three pairs of salivary glands, Fig. 164, the submaxillary, the sublingual, and the parotid. When the glands have been resting for some time (i.e., have not poured out their secretion), the cells are loaded with granules; as a result the cells are swollen, and their boundary lines and their nuclei are not very conspicuous, Figs. 165 and 166, *A*. But when the glands have recently secreted (poured out their secretion), the number of granules is greatly lessened, those present being situated near the lumen of the gland, Fig. 166, *B;* it seems that during the act of secretion the granules are dissolved or swept out of the cells into the ducts. There is evidence that certain of these granules are the antecedents of some of the constituents of the secretion. The salivary glands, it is held, do not contain the active enzyme, ptyalin, but the antecedent of the ptyalin to which the name ptyalinogen has been given. This *proferment* ptyalinogen is present and stored up in the cells in the form of granules, and, when the cells begin to secrete, these ptyalinogen granules are transformed into ptyalin. Some of the granules of certain of the salivary gland cells are transformed into mucin; these are termed *mucinogen granules.** In many other glands we find granules; for example, the gastric gland cells contain pepsinogen granules which are, at the proper time, transformed into the enzyme pepsin. These proferment granules are called *zymogen granules.*

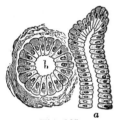

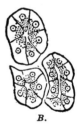

Fig. 165.   A.   Fig. 166.   B.

Fig. 165. — Longitudinal section, *a*, and cross-section, *b*, through a salivary gland. (Klein and Smith.)

Fig. 166.—Cells of the parotid gland showing zymogen granules: *A*, after prolonged rest; *B*, after prolonged secretion. (Macleod, after Langley.)

While the salivary glands are in the so-called resting stage, the cells receive from the blood the various kinds of food and from these foods build up the various constituents peculiar to the saliva, such as mucin, ptyalin, maltase, etc. When the glands become active, there is a great transfer of water from the dilated blood vessels through the gland cell, which leaches out the materials previously constructed by the cells. The formation of the secretion and the flow of the water are to be regarded as two processes for which most likely distinct mechanisms are necessary. How these things happen, how this transfer of water, separated from many of the salts it previously held in solution, is brought about are questions we cannot answer satisfactorily at present.

*The saliva from the parotid gland is a watery fluid; the other salivary glands form a more viscid saliva.

C. Nervous Control of Salivary Secretion

The salivary glands are supplied with nerves of two kinds: sympathetic and parasympathetic. The latter fibers run in the cranial nerves. The sublingual and the submaxillary glands receive fibers from the chorda tympani (a branch of the seventh cranial); the parotid receives fibers from the glossopharyngeal (ninth cranial); all three glands receive fibers from the cervical sympathetic. The stimulation of the chorda tympani has a twofold result: the dilation of the blood vessels of the gland, and a copious flow of thin, watery saliva; in contrast with this, the stimulation of the sympathetic nerve causes vasoconstriction and a scanty flow of thick, viscid saliva. According to Heidenhain, the sympathetic nerve is concerned with the formation of the protoplasm and the peculiar constituents of the saliva and may, therefore, be said to be the trophic-secretory nerve (*trophe,* nourishment). The cranial nerve governs the passage of water and salts from the blood through the gland and is, therefore, spoken of as the motor-secretory nerve.

The salivary glands are not equally active at all times. We speak of the sight or the smell of good food causing our mouth to water, from which it is evident that the salivary glands can be reflexly influenced. The center (salivary center) for this reflex action is located in the medulla, and can be influenced in two ways:

1. **Reflexly by Stimulation of Afferent, or Sensory, Nerves.**—As we just stated, the sight or smell of food may send an impulse up the afferent nerve, the optic or the olfactory nerve in these instances, to the center; the stimulation of the center sends an impulse over the proper efferent nerve to the glands which then become more active. An afferent nerve that is still more frequently stimulated for this purpose is the gustatory (taste) nerve. The nerve of touch (the lingual fibers of the fifth cranial nerve) can also serve as an afferent nerve, as is seen in the flow of saliva on placing a dry, insoluble substance (powder) in the mouth. In this instance the saliva is of a serous (watery) nature and serves to wash away the material. A piece of meat, on the other hand, evokes a flow of mucous saliva which serves as a lubricant. Irritation of the gums acts as a stimulus in the driveling of a teething child.

2. **By the Higher Centers.**—No doubt we have also observed that, when we are hungry, hearing somebody talk about a good dinner may start the flow of saliva. Indeed, in this condition, the mere thought of food is sufficient to bring about this result. The activity of the cells of the cerebral hemispheres, upon which the mental faculties depend, evidently influences the salivary center so as to in-

crease the flow of saliva. Other mental states often have the opposite influence. We may have sat down to dinner with a good appetite, in fact, we may have begun the meal with zest, but the hearing of bad news instantly deprived us of all appetite; the cerebral activity in this instance inhibited the salivary center, and the flow of saliva ceased. There was a cessation not only of the flow of saliva, but, as we shall see presently, the activity of the gastric glands also ceased, and for these reasons appetite failed. To have an appetite means that the proper amount of saliva and gastric juice is secreted; as Pavlov says, "appetite is juice." Depressing states of mind, such as anxiety, worry, and grief, dampen the activity of the digestive glands, thereby depriving us of the digestive juices and of appetite; the result may be poor digestion and laying the foundation for ill health. On the other hand, whatever makes for freedom of mind and gladness of heart, or increases the pleasure in the partaking of food, stimulates the flow of the juices and thereby makes for health. A laugh is the best sauce. By far the most effective method of putting the salivary center in its best condition for secreting abundant saliva is by a fair amount of muscular work, that is, we "work up" an appetite. Many people suffer because they imagine that the spice box can take the place of a legitimately earned appetite.

V. GASTRIC DIGESTION

A. Stomach and Gastric Juice

When the food has been masticated and mixed with saliva, we gather it together as a bolus and by the contraction of the proper muscles it is swallowed, passing through the pharynx and esophagus and into the stomach (see Chap. XVII). This division of the alimentary canal is a greatly dilated portion of the otherwise narrow digestive tube.

The shape and position of the stomach vary considerably in different normal individuals. The opening of the esophagus into the stomach is guarded by a sphincter, the cardia; see Fig. 167. The upper part of the stomach is known as the *fundus;* the lower portion, as the *antrum* or *pyloric part*. The opening into the duodenum of the intestine is called the *pylorus* and is closed by the pyloric sphincter. The musculature of the stomach is arranged, as shown in Fig. 175, not only in the usual circular and longitudinal fashion, but some of the fibers take on an oblique course.

Functions of the Stomach.—The most important function of this part of the alimentary canal is *the storing of food*. In the adult the

capacity of the stomach is from three to five pints; this enables us
to take enough food in two or three meals for the twenty-four hours.
The stomach passes the food on to the intestines in such quantities
as the intestines are able to handle; consequently when the stomach
has been removed, meals must be small and frequent. In addition
to this function, a certain amount of digestion and a very limited
amount of absorption take place in the stomach. Here also, the food
is more or less disinfected (see infra).

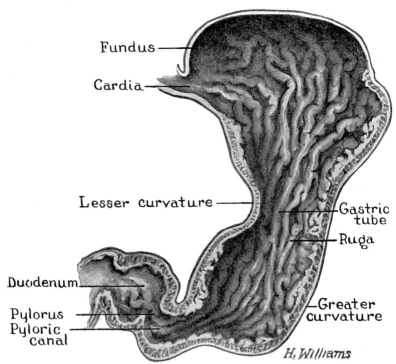

Fundus

Cardia

Lesser curvature

Gastric tube

Ruga

Duodenum

Pylorus
Pyloric canal

Greater curvature

H. Williams

Fig. 167.—Interior of the stomach. (Francis: Fundamentals of Anatomy, The
C. V. Mosby Co.)

The gastric juice is secreted by the glands lying in the walls of
the stomach (see p. 350). It is composed of water (97 to 99.5 per
cent), salts, hydrochloric acid, and three enzymes: pepsin, rennin,
and gastric lipase.

The hydrochloric acid. With the exception of but two or three
fluids, all the fluids in our body have a neutral or an alkaline reaction; the two most important exceptions are gastric juice and urine.
The gastric juice is unique in that it contains about 0.5 per cent of
the strong mineral acid, hydrochloric acid. Concerning its functions
we may note:

1. The hydrochloric acid has a disinfecting action. While most of the countless number of bacteria which we swallow with our food and drink are not pathogenic, yet it is perhaps for the best of the animal economy that almost at the very beginning of the alimentary canal we have a fluid that is inimical to the life, growth, and activity of these germs. Sieber found that 0.25 per cent HCl prevented the putrefaction of meat; even 0.07 per cent prevents the formation of lactic acid by bacteria. However, not all the bacteria ingested are killed by the gastric juice, for we find large numbers of them in the intestines. The germs of tuberculosis, dysentery, and typhoid can thus pass through the stomach, especially when the activity of the stomach is below normal.

2. The HCl splits the proteins of the food, such as albumins and globulins, forming the acid metaproteins (acid albuminate); this constitutes the first step in their digestion.

3. It splits disaccharides into monosaccharides.

4. It furnishes the acid medium necessary for the action of pepsin.

5. It stimulates the flow of bile and pancreatic juice (see infra).

B. Gastric Digestion

The digestion by the gastric juice is brought about by enzymes.

Pepsin.—In the presence of an acid, such as hydrochloric acid, pepsin splits the food proteins (albumins, globulins, etc.) into simpler proteins by hydrolytic cleavage according to the following scheme:

Albumin
↓
Acid metaproteins
↓
Primary proteoses
↓
Secondary proteoses
↓
Peptones

In this gradual cleavage of the food proteins, each succeeding product has, in general, a greater range of solubility and a smaller sized molecule than the preceding. The peptones are generally said to be dialyzable. The primary proteoses are precipitated from solution by half saturating the solution with ammonium sulfate; the secondary proteoses are precipitated by complete saturation; peptones cannot be precipitated in this manner.

In the stomach the action of the pepto-hydrochloric acid, in all probability, does not go farther than the production of peptones; neither are all the native proteins ingested reduced to the peptone stage, as a considerable part leaves the stomach in the form of acid metaprotein or proteoses.

Rennin is a coagulative enzyme which brings about the clotting of milk. Casein, a protein of milk, is changed by rennin to paracasein which unites with calcium salt to form insoluble calcium paracasein-ate. This last, with a quantity of entangled fat, forms the curd (clot, or coagulum). The liquid residue, known as whey, contains the albumin and most of the water, sugar, salts, and some fat.

Gastric lipase is a fat-splitting enzyme, converting the fat into fatty acid and glycerol. Its action is feeble and most likely limited to emulsified fats, such as those found in milk.

Taking the gastric activity as a whole we may say that three events are taking place in the stomach:

1. THE CONTINUATION OF SALIVARY DIGESTION.—As food enters the stomach, it is arranged in an orderly manner; that which is eaten last occupies a central position, away from the gastric walls, Fig. 176. As the walls secrete the gastric juice, the HCl gradually penetrates the food mass, but a great deal of acid is held by the proteins; hence the reaction of the central mass remains neutral or feebly alkaline for a considerable length of time (from fifteen to sixty minutes) and allows the salivary digestion to continue.

2. BACTERIAL ACTION.—As long as the food in the stomach remains alkaline, the microorganisms are at work, mainly in splitting the carbohydrates of the food into gases and organic acids, among which lactic acid may be mentioned in particular. As the concentration of the HCl increases, the action of the bacteria is checked.

3. PROTEIN DIGESTION by the pepsin in conjunction with the HCl. While it is well known that the gastric digestion is not absolutely re-quired, yet it is claimed that in the absence of gastric digestion the pancreatic digestion in the intestines is not so brisk nor complete as under normal conditions.

As a result of these various processes, the food is broken up, a large amount of water (found in the gastric juice) is added to it, and by the activity of the muscular wall the whole semifluid mass acquires a creamy or gruel-like consistency; this acid mixture, ready for further treatment in the intestines, is called *chyme*.

C. The Secretion of Gastric Juice

The gastric glands found in the walls of the stomach are of two kinds: the chief (central, or peptic) cells, and the parietal (border, or oxyntic) cells, Fig. 168. The chief cells are concerned with the production of pepsinogen, which is transformed into pepsin by the action of HCl. The HCl is made in the oxyntic cells. The pyloric end contains chief cells only. For this reason juice collected from this end is neutral.

How the stomach produces such a strong acid is not known, but the sodium chloride of the blood, no doubt, furnishes the necessary chlorine. It has been suggested that by mass action the weaker acids,

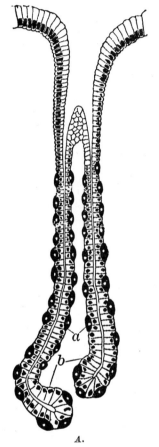

Fig. 168.—*A*, Glands from the fundus of the stomach. *a*, ovoid and *b*, chief cells. *B* shows cross section of a gland. The ovoid are the darker cells. (After Heidenhain.)

such as carbonic acid, liberate the strong HCl; thus, $2NaCl + H_2CO_3 = 2HCl + Na_2CO_3$. Even though we grant this view to be correct, still the questions remain why this process occurs only in these particular cells of the body, and why the acid is thrown into the stomach while the sodium carbonate is absorbed by the blood.

Our knowledge of the secretion of gastric juice was placed on a firm basis by the work of Pavlov. Long before Pavlov investigated gastric secretion, a Canadian hunter, Alexis St. Martin, was accidentally wounded by a gunshot in the region of the stomach. Beaumont treated the patient. The wound healed but left an opening (fistula) through the abdominal wall into the stomach; through this the interior of the stomach could be observed, the juice collected, and the influence of the food and other agencies studied. Since that time, artificial fistulas have been made in lower animals for experimental purposes, and it has sometimes been necessary to make gastric fistulas in human beings in whom the esophagus had become permanently closed, due to the swallowing of caustic substances.

Pavlov not only made gastric fistulas, but also divided the stomach of a dog into two parts so that, after sewing the walls together, the dog had two stomachs: a large stomach connected with the esophagus and intestine and a small (artificial) stomach having no connections with the other parts of the alimentary canal but provided with a fistula, so that its juice could be collected in a beaker suspended below the fistula. By letting the animal eat and swallow food into the large (normal) stomach or by putting food directly into this stomach through a fistula with which it was provided, the secretory apparatus of both stomachs was thrown into operation. The secretion of the large stomach did its normal work of digesting the food so that the alimentation and nutrition of the animal were not disturbed; the secretion of the small (artificial) stomach could be obtained in the pure condition, uncontaminated by food and digestion products. By such experiments Pavlov determined that the gastric secretory apparatus can be set into action in two distinct ways.

1. **Reflex, or Remote, Stimulation.**—Showing a piece of meat to a hungry dog stirs up not only the salivary glands, but from the gastric fistula there soon begin to issue drops of gastric juice. In whatever manner the appetite is aroused, by tasting, smelling, or seeing the meat, the result is always the same, namely, increased activity of the gastric glands. Whether the animal swallowed the food into its stomach or not made no difference, for even in sham-feeding (the esophagus having been cut) the small stomach secreted gastric juice as long as the animal kept on chewing and swallowing the food (in one case for six hours) although the food instead of proceeding to the stomach fell out of the cut end of the esophagus. This method of exciting the gastric glands is a reflex action, for on cutting the vagi, it ceases; on the other hand, proper stimulation of the peripheral end of the cut vagus nerve causes a flow of the juice. It is, therefore,

very likely that there lies in the medulla a center for the secretion of gastric juice, comparable to the salivary center.

In human beings also it has been found possible to demonstrate that the gastric glands can be excited in the above manner. In a young man, in whom the esophagus was completely closed and who had a gastric fistula, the chewing of food caused an increase in the flow of gastric juice and the rate of secretion was in direct proportion to the palatability of the food. Bloomfield found that discussing their favored foods caused the fasting gastric juice secretion to be increased in 12 out of 14 cases. Umber relates a case of a man with a closed esophagus in whom the chewing of meat caused a secretion within three minutes; the secretion continued for forty-five minutes after the cessation of mastication.

The gastric juice, formed in response to the stimulation of the sensory nerves during the process of eating, Pavlov called appetite juice, or psychic juice, for when there is no desire for food or no enjoyment in the eating, there is no reflex secretion of gastric juice. In the same manner as fear inhibits the salivary center and a cheerful frame of mind favors its activity, so the gastric center is also influenced.

2. Chemical, or Local, Stimulation.—Pavlov observed that certain substances introduced through a gastric fistula into the stomach of a dog, even though the dog is unaware of it, set up a flow of gastric juice. This is not a nervous phenomenon, for severing the nerves going to the stomach (vagus and sympathetic) does not change the results. Hence, the action may be said to be local and independent of the gastric center or of the stimulation of any nerves. However, not all substances have this effect. Raw meat placed in the stomach excites the gastric glands, but if a piece of meat is boiled in several changes of water, the solid residue (which to us is a dry, tasteless mass) has not this effect; on the other hand, if the meat broth obtained from the meat is used, the glands begin to secrete in a few moments.

Similar observations have been made in man. Bread placed through a gastric fistula directly into the stomach causes no flow of gastric juice. When a hungry individual chews a tasty piece of bread, there is formed the psychic juice. If the chewed mass is not swallowed (or cannot be swallowed because of esophageal obstruction), the flow of the appetite juice gradually diminishes and generally ceases altogether in fifteen to thirty minutes. But if the chewed bread is swallowed or placed in the stomach, the flow of the gastric juice is more abundant and continues for a greater length of time. We may explain this as follows: The appetite juice, secreted in response to the gustatory stimulation and the enjoyment of eating, begins the digestion of the proteins in the bread; the proteoses and peptones thereby formed have a local stimulating effect, similar to beef broth and extract. Therefore, when a person eats a piece of meat without appetite, even in the absence of the appetite juice, the extractives of the meat act as secretogogs (*ago*, to lead) and a flow of gastric juice is produced. If bread is eaten with little or no appetite, there is little or no psychic juice to start the digestion; and no peptones are formed for the chemical stimulation. Hence the value, in case of a poor appetite, of beginning the meal with those foods, such as meat soups beef teas, etc., that contain secretogogs.

In addition to meat extracts, the products of protein digestion (e.g., proteoses and peptones) and dextrins exert a stimulating influence. But dry bread, starch, cane sugar, native proteins, and alkalies do not function in this manner.

Gastrin.—According to Edkins, the substances which we have called secretogogs liberate in the gastric mucosa a substance, *gastrin* which on being absorbed by the blood stream is carried to the gastric glands and stimulates these structures. Such substances, made in one part of the body and carried to other organs and there exercising an influence upon the activity of these organs, are called *hormones* (*hormao*, to stir up), internal secretions, or chemical messengers.

The facts upon which this theory is based we may briefly relate. When the mucosa of the pyloric end of an excised stomach is heated with beef extract dextrin, acid, or peptone solution, and the extract thus obtained is injected into the blood stream, there is produced a flow of gastric juice containing hydrochloric acid and pepsin. The injection of dextrin, peptone, or beef extracts, or the extracts made from the mucosa of the fundus are without effect. Ivy and Farrell transplanted into the subcutaneous tissue a small gastric pouch which secreted acid gastric juice when the animal ate food or received an injection of gastrin The local application of histamine (of which we spoke in connection with shock and lymph formation) calls forth great secretory activity of the gastric glands This compound, according to Ivy, is identical with the gastric hormone.

A third method of stimulating the gastric glands is by distention of the stomach; this may account for the excitant action of water.

The amount of gastric juice secreted per day varies with the amount and nature of the food; it is estimated at 2 to 3 liters. The so-called empty stomach contains about 20 c.c. of fluid. Concerning the influence of the different kinds of food upon the activity of the gastric glands, we may also call attention to fats. Pavlov fed a dog on 600 c.c. of milk and collected the gastric juice from the little stomach and determined its proteolytic power. The next day the dog was fed upon 600 c.c. of cream and the amount and strength of the juice compared with that secreted the previous day. The results are given in Table XVII.

TABLE XVII

HOUR	600 C.C. MILK		600 C.C. CREAM	
	C.C. OF JUICE	DIGESTIVE POWER	C.C. OF JUICE	DIGESTIVE POWER
1	4.2	3.57	2.4	2.1
2	12.4	2.63	3.4	2.0
3	13.2	3.06	3.1	2.0
5	1.5	7.37	2.2	2.0
8	0.0	0.0	1.5	1.62
Total for 8 hr.	37.7	Mean 3.86	Total 18.9	Mean 1.63

It will be seen that the cream evoked only about one-half the quantity of juice that was poured upon the milk and that the digestive strength of the juice was also much inferior. The same results were obtained when olive oil or any other fat was mixed with meat.

Pavlov also holds that the foods affect the gastric glands in various ways, that is, the gastric juice secreted upon the different foodstuffs differs in quantity and quality. While a meal of bread calls forth a lesser volume of gastric juice, the proteolytic digestive power of this juice is greater than that evoked by meat. Under normal conditions, however, one does not need to trouble oneself about this or that food not calling forth a strong juice, for it was found that 1 c.c. of human gastric juice is able to digest 10 gm. of boiled egg white (or about 1 gram of protein) in three hours. As the stomach secretes about 2,000 c.c. a day, this juice is able to digest 2,000 grams of protein in three hours; but as the diet seldom contains more than 150 grams of proteins, it can readily be seen that abundant provision has been made to insure proper digestion. Glandular fatigue of the human stomach has never been demonstrated.

D. Conditions Influencing Gastric Digestion

Of the many conditions that influence gastric digestion we may mention the following:

1. As the zest with which food is taken largely influences the activity of the glands, the mental and physical condition of the individual plays no small part. Nervous indigestion, associated with the feeling of distention and the eructing of gas (heartburn) may be due to excitement, too close mental application, or worry.

2. Whether cooking food increases or decreases its digestibility depends upon conditions, for by cooking (including any process commonly used) several changes are produced:

(a) The collagen of the connective tissue is transformed into gelatin; this loosens the muscle fibers and renders the meat tender and easy of mastication.

(b) By heating the meat, the red hemoglobin of the meat is decomposed and the meat loses its raw appearance which is repugnant to some persons.

(c) In roasting, highly sapid substances are formed which stimulate the olfactory and gustatory nerves agreeably. For this reason meats should be so prepared as to lose as little of their salts and extractives as possible, for upon them depends the taste of the meat. Hence, the value of sealing up the outside of the meat by coagulating the proteins, as is done by plunging the meat into boiling water, or by exposing it suddenly to intense heat for a short length of time.

(d) A high temperature kills bacteria or parasites (e.g., trichina).

(e) High temperatures are destructive to some vitamins, especially if the food has a neutral or alkaline reaction.

(f) We have already indicated the necessity of properly preparing the vegetable foods by boiling or baking; this renders these foods more appetizing and better digested by breaking up the cellulose cell wall; this enables us to utilize more of the food.

(g) Contrary to the commonly accepted view, raw egg white is not so readily digested as the cooked. It seems that raw egg albumin contains anti-enzymic substances which delay digestion and are destroyed by heat. Clifford showed that meat is least digestible when raw. McCollum states that cooking with water has scarcely any effect on the nutritional value of proteins.

(h) Fats, heated to a high temperature, form compounds which are highly irritating to the alimentary canal.

3. The digestibility of a food is also affected by its physical state for example:

(a) Fresh bread and hot biscuits are not so readily digested as older bread. The mastication of a hot roll ordinarily results in a doughy lump which the juices penetrate and digest with difficulty. The staler bread crumbles between the teeth and can be thoroughly mixed with saliva.

(b) When rennin is added to a beaker of cow's milk, the whole bulk of the milk is transformed into a jellylike substance. By the shrinkage of this jelly a fluid, known as whey, is pressed out and the clot becomes a firm, dense mass which may be more or less diffi cult to digest. The density of the clot can be decreased by diluting the milk with an equal volume of water, or with barley or lime water. Hawk, in experimenting on a person able voluntarily to re-gurgitate his food, found that boiled milk yielded a finer and softer curd than raw milk, and that the addition of cream caused a softer curd to be formed although this remained in the stomach for a greater length of time. He also found, contrary to the frequently expressed belief, that milk drunk rapidly left the stomach sooner and formed a smaller curd than milk sipped slowly. Because of the smaller per-centage of casein, human milk forms a more flaky coagulum when clotted by rennin, and for this reason is more readily digested than untreated cow's milk.

4. The presence of a large amount of salts interferes with diges-tion, for which reason salted meats are generally not so readily digested as fresh meats.

5. Fat also hinders gastric digestion in that:

(a) Fat lessens the amount of gastric juice secreted.

(b) Fat by incasing the food particles (meat fibers, starch grains, lumps of casein, etc.) keeps the enzymes from attacking the food. For these reasons fatty foods, such as pork and goose, are not so well digested as foods containing less fats, such as beef and chicken. It is because of the large amount of fat (30 to 43 per cent) that cer-tain cheeses are digested with great difficulty by some people. Such cheese should be well chewed or, better still, grated. Above all, this applies to the preparation of foods by which the fat is allowed to penetrate the food particle or mass.

6. The mixing of carbohydrates and proteins in a test-meal showed no interference with the secretion or action of gastric juice. The notion of the undesirability of including these two foodstuffs in the same meal is on a par with that of not eating cream or milk with sour fruits.

7. Foods, too hot, cold, or coarse, and corrosive substances and spices, may irritate the mucosa and cause gastritis.

8. Whether it is good to drink much water with a meal is a much discussed question. Some advance the argument that it dilutes the digestive juices. However, the recent experiments by Hawk seem to indicate that drinking water, even in extremely large quantities, is not detrimental.

9. Concerning the influence of sleep, Pavlov says: "Sleep does not exercise the least influence on the secretory work of the gastric glands." Contrary to this, Chaffen found that in nine patients gas-

tric secretion ceased completely, or almost completely, during sleep; Henning and Norpoth reported similar results in 91 sleeping persons.

10. Should food be taken at stated and regular times or should one eat when one feels hungry, irrespective of the time of day? Generally it is for the best of the animal economy that all things be done orderly and according to a system. Definite times and periods of rising and retiring, of work and relaxation, of filling and of emptying the alimentary canal, are best. The various parts of the body become conditioned to doing certain things at regular intervals. Babkin showed that the flow of gastric juice in animals fed at stated times was markedly increased at these times even though no food was given. The advantage of this regularity is greatly enhanced by the fact that the activity of the gastric apparatus arouses other parts of the alimentary canal to action (pp. 362 and 389).

As to whether in human beings these stated times should occur two, three, or more times per day is perhaps a matter for each individual to decide for himself; most of us follow custom rather than physiologic needs.

11. The time-honored advice not to eat when one is much fatigued nor to exercise violently after a hearty meal, finds support in the fact that, according to Campbell, strenuous exercise delays both the secretion of the gastric juice and the emptying of the stomach. A hot bath had the same result. It is possible that this is due to a redistribution of the flow of blood by the vasomotor system. These ill effects did not follow more gentle physical work.

12. The smoking of from 4 to 7 cigarettes during a period of about two hours caused, according to Ivy and Schnedorf, a decrease in the volume and the acidity of the gastric juice in 22 out of 40 normal subjects.

13. To relieve acidity of the stomach by habitually taking sodium bicarbonate may lead to hyperacidity; the stomach increases its secretion of HCl to adjust itself to the alkali.

VI. DIGESTION IN THE SMALL INTESTINES

A. Pancreatic Digestion

The pancreas is a long, narrow (6 by $1\frac{1}{2}$ inches), and thin gland lying back of, and below, the stomach, Fig. 158. In the wall of the duodenum, about three inches below the pylorus, the pancreatic and the common bile ducts open by a common orifice into the intestine (see Figs. 158 and 169). When the food in the stomach has been lique ied to a certain extent and becomes permeated with acid, the stomch gradually expels its contents (called chyme) into the intestine Iere two fluids are speedily poured upon it, namely, the pancreatic uice and the bile.

The pancreatic juice has a strong alkaline reaction (pH = 8.7), wing to its sodium bicarbonate. The amount of pancreatic juice ecreted is stated at 500 to 800 c.c. per day. By its enzymes the pancreatic juice acts upon all the various foods and may, therefore, e regarded as the most important of the digestive juices.

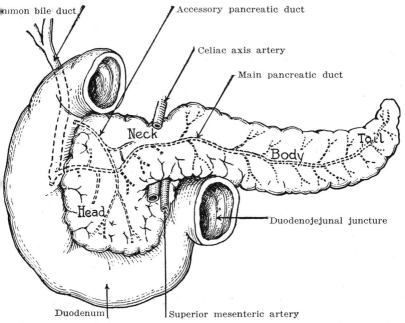

Fig. 169.—Pancreas and duodenum. (Pitzman: Fundamentals of Human Anatomy.)

Proteolytic Enzymes.—From recent work it seems that several enzymes are concerned in the cleavage of proteins into the final digestive products. One of these is known as trypsin. In the pancreatic uice it exists in the zymogen form, trypsinogen. By an enzyme found n the intestinal juice (see infra) the trypsinogen is converted into its ctive form: it is then able to split the proteins into proteoses and polypeptides. Another series of enzymes breaks these last-named substances into simpler peptides and into amino acids.

Pancreatic lipase, or **steapsin,** splits the fat into its two component parts, fatty acid and glycerin. The action of the steapsin is largely aided by the bile salts. If the intestinal contents are alkaline in reaction, the sodium bicarbonate of the pancreatic juice and bile may unite with the fatty acids to form soap which, in turn, emulsifies the fat not yet digested. In an emulsion the fat is divided physically into microscopic droplets; in this condition it is more quickly digested because the droplets present an immense amount of surface for the action of the enzyme. Recent observations seem to indicate that the contents of the canal, at least in the higher levels, are rarely, if ever, alkaline and that soap and emulsion formation cannot take place. It is very likely that, in order to be absorbed, all the fat must be split up into fatty acid and glycerin.

Amylopsin, like the ptyalin of the saliva, transforms the starch into maltose. It acts more energetically upon raw starch than the ptyalin does.

By the **maltase** the maltose which has been formed by the action of amylopsin or ptyalin is split into glucose.

B. Bile

The liver is the largest gland in the body. It lies, as shown in Fig. 158, about on the level with, and to the right of, the upper part, of the stomach. The secretion of bile is only one of the many functions performed by this organ. By means of the hepatic duct the bile is carried from the liver on its way to the intestine. This duct gives off a branch, the cystic duct, by which the bile can pass into and out of the gall bladder (Fig. 158). From its junction with the cystic duct to the intestine, the duct is known as the common bile duct, which empties into the duodenum (Figs. 169 and 212).

The bile, secreted by the liver, is a yellow fluid and has a high viscosity, an intensely bitter taste, and an alkaline reaction. How much bile is secreted during the course of a day is not known. Bile is an exceedingly complex fluid; in addition to water and inorganic salts (chiefly sodium bicarbonate) and a nucleoprotein which gives the bile its great viscosity, it contains two peculiar constituents: bile pigments and bile salts.

Bile Pigments.—Some biles are yellow, others are green; the yellow bile contains the pigment called *bilirubin;* the greenish bile contains *biliverdin.* Both these pigments are made from the old red blood corpuscles which on breaking down liberate the hemoglobin. This last named substance undergoes further decomposition, giving rise, among other products, to heme (see pp. 148 and 150). From the heme the iron is removed and the remainder of the molecule is known as bilirubin. The greater the destruction of red blood cells the more bilirubin is excreted.

Being of no value to us, the bile pigments must be regarded as excretions. Failure on the part of the liver to remove them, either because of their too rapid production or the inability on the part of the liver to excrete what is normally formed (as in the occlusion of the bile ducts by inflammation or gall stones), causes them to accumulate in the blood and tissues and gives rise to the yellow discoloration of *jaundice*. Bile is toxic to the tissues of our body.

It was formerly held that hemolysis took place chiefly, if not altogether, in the liver, but more recent work has shown that the part played by the liver in the formation of bile pigments is very limited; its main function in this matter is the excretion of the pigments. It is in the red bone marrow, and to a much lesser extent in the spleen, that the pigments are made. The extrahepatic origin is shown by the fact that the removal of the liver (in dogs) is followed in a few hours by the presence of the pigments in the blood (jaundice) and in the urine. Mann, in 1927, concluded that most of the bile pigments are made in the bone marrow, and some in the spleen. The part taken by the latter organ is proved by the fact that the blood in the splenic vein may contain three times as much bile pigment as that in the splenic artery. The pigment made in these locations is carried to, and excreted by, the liver.

The bile pigments can be oxidized readily. When bilirubin unites with oxygen, it gives rise to biliverdin which is colored green. Further oxidation produces a substance having a different color. The play of colors formed by the successive oxidations of the bile pigments is the basis of Gmelin's test which may be performed in the following way: In a test tube place a small amount of strong, fuming nitric acid (an oxidizing agent), and carefully float onto it the solution to be tested. If bile is present a play of colors—green, blue, red, and yellow—will be seen.

Bile Salts.—These are very complex salts of two organic acids; they are known as sodium taurocholate and sodium glycocholate. The bile salts are chiefly responsible for the part which bile plays in the digestion and absorption of fats. Their chief functions are as follows:

1. IN THE DIGESTION OF FAT.—Although the lipase in the intestinal juice is capable of digesting as much as 80 per cent of the fats, its action is facilitated by the presence of bile salts. This is due to the bile salts emulsifing the fats, thus providing a greater surface for the action of the enzyme.

2. ABSORPTION OF FAT.—Bile salts unite with the fatty acid of the digested fat to form complex compounds which are absorbed from

the intestines. When the bile does not flow into the intestines, from ⅓ to ⅔ of the ingested fat is lost, appearing in the feces.

3. ABSORPTION OF VITAMINS.—Certain vitamins (e.g., D and K) are not soluble in water. The bile salts make the absorption of these vitamins possible.

4. REABSORPTION OF CALCIUM.—In the absence of bile salts, the calcium excreted in the intestinal juice is not adequately reabsorbed

5. HOLDING CHOLESTEROL IN SOLUTION.—Cholesterol is a fatlike compound and insoluble in water. One of the functions of bile salts is to hold this material in solution. When thrown out of solution, as may occur in injury to the gallbladder, cholesterol gives rise to gall stones.

6. STIMULATE SECRETION OF BILE.—The bile salts are to a certain extent absorbed from the intestines. On reaching the liver, they powerfully stimulate the biliary secretion.

7. LESSEN PUTREFACTION.—It is held that bile lessens the putrefaction in the intestines. By putrefaction we mean the action of bacteria upon proteins (p. 366). Because of this action, bile was formerly regarded as a disinfectant; this, however, is not the case, for bile itself spoils when exposed to the air in a warm room. It will be recalled that the presence of fat is apt to delay the digestion of meat fibers, lumps of cheese, or clotted milk, by coating these substances and thus preventing the digestive juices from attacking them. If bile so largely aids in the digestion and absorption of the fat, the proteins found in the meat or cheese will also be better digested and hence their decomposition by bacteria will be lessened.

C. The Secretion of Pancreatic Juice and Bile

Although the pancreatic secretion can be induced psychically in a manner similar to that of the gastric secretion, this initial flow is very limited. Stimulation of the vagus increases pancreatic secretion, whereas cutting it abolishes this activity; hence this nerve must be regarded as the secretory nerve.

Secretin.—The maximum flow of pancreatic juice takes place from two to four hours after eating and is, according to Bayliss and Starling, brought about by a hormone. These investigators found that the entrance of the acid chyme into the duodenum evoked the secretion of the pancreatic juice; and as this takes place when all the nerve supply to the pancreas is destroyed, the stimulation is in all probability due to chemical excitants. To demonstrate this, they ground up some of the mucosa of the duodenum with sand and boiled it with 0.2 per cent HCl. After neutralizing and filtering the extract thus obtained, they injected it into the blood vessels of an animal and obtained a flow of pancreatic juice. In the mucosa of the duodenum there is present a compound, prosecretin. By the HCl of the chyme this is transformed into secretin. On being absorbed, it is carried to the pancreas and stimulates it to greater activity.

The correctness of this humoral theory is shown by the fact that if the duodenum is tied off and a quantity of 0.4 per cent HCl is injected into it, a copious flow of pancreatic juice results. Ivy and Farrell transplanted the pancreas of a dog into the mammary gland; during intestinal digestion the transplanted pancreas became more active. Certain other substances, when placed in the duodenum, evoke a flow of pancreatic juice; among these are soap, fat, fatty acids, digested proteins, and, especially, bile. According to Mellanby the presence of bile in the intestines renders the absorption of secretin possible; this accounts for the secretion of pancreatic juice in those cases in which the stomach secretes no acid.

The liver, unlike the digestive glands thus far considered, is not supplied with secretory nerves. Similar to the pancreas, its activity is increased by secretin from the intestinal wall. The eating of meat or liver stimulates the secretion of bile, but the ingestion of carbohydrates has no effect, and the effect of fat is doubtful. Being to a certain extent an excretion, the bile is formed continually (from 500 to 1000 cc. per day) but between the periods of intestinal digestion the amount secreted is stored up in the gallbladder which has a capacity of about 50 cc. Here a large amount of water is absorbed from the bile. By the contraction of the muscles in the walls of the bladder and by the relaxation of the sphincter of Oddi at the mouth of the common bile duct in the duodenal wall, the accumulated bile is driven into the intestines. For this, fatty foods, especially egg yolk and cream, and proteins are very effective stimuli; carbohydrates have practically no effect. The expulsion of the acid chyme from the stomach is followed by a discharge of bile into the intestines. Ivy has prepared from the mucosa of the duodenum a motor hormone—cholecystokinin—which acts specifically upon the muscle of the gallbladder.

D. The Intestinal Juice

The intestinal juice, or succus entericus, is secreted by the glands (crypts of Lieberkuehn) found in the walls of the intestine, Fig. 170. It has an alkaline reaction, due to sodium bicarbonate. As to the enzymes found in it, there is much uncertainty; we shall mention the following:

1. Proteolytic Enzymes.—What we said concerning this class of ferments in the pancreatic juice also holds for those of the intestinal juice. Perhaps a number of proteolytic enzymes are present, but it seems that their action is largely confined to the splitting of peptides (chiefly dipeptides) into amino acids.

2. Three Inverting Ferments by which the disaccharides are split into monosaccharides: (a) *maltase*, splitting maltose into glucose. (b) *lactase*, splitting lactose into glucose and galactose. (c) *invertase,* or *sucrase*, splitting cane sugar into glucose and fructose.

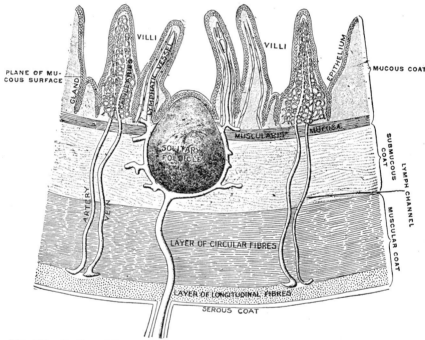

Fig. 170.—Section of the wall of small intestine showing the coats and villi. (Rosewarme: The Science of Nutrition Simplified, The C. V. Mosby Co.)

3. Enterokinase.—We stated that the pancreatic juice contains a proteolytic ferment, known as trypsin. This, however, is not strictly correct, for it has been found that pure pancreatic juice has no digestive action upon proteins. However, if to inert pancreatic juice there be added a few drops of intestinal juice, the pancreatic juice acquires proteolytic action. Intestinal juice, as we have seen, has no ferment that splits the ordinary proteins. This action of the intestinal juice is explained in the following manner: In pancreatic juice there is found the antecedent (trypsinogen) which is transformed into trypsin

by intestinal juice; the active agent in intestinal juice which brings this about is known as enterokinase (*enteron,* intestine).

VII. Digestion in the Large Intestine

In herbivorous animals and in man, when the diet contains a large amount of raw or partially cooked vegetable food, a considerable amount of it may find its way into the colon. This is not true in carnivorous animals and in man, when the vegetable foods have been well prepared and masticated so as to break up the cellulose. In most cases the food has been quite well digested and nearly all of it absorbed in the small intestine. For example, London found that 94.5 per cent of the food in 200 grams of bread fed to a dog had been absorbed when the food mass reached the cecum.

VIII. AUTODIGESTION: AUTOLYSIS

Why are the stomach and the intestines not digested by their own juices? A perfectly satisfactory answer is difficult to find. To say that the mucosa of the alimentary canal is alive and thereby shielded against the digestive enzymes does not answer the question, for we frequently swallow living things which, notwithstanding their being alive, are digested.

Some investigators seek the explanation of this immunity by the presence of anti-enzymes. In the intestines we sometimes find living animals, such as worms. Wienland studied the question of how it is possible for these worms to exist in a fluid having great power to digest animal tissue. On placing some pancreatic juice having strong proteolytic action and a piece of fibrin (a protein) in a test tube, the fibrin was digested and dissolved; but when Wienland added an extract made from the intestinal worms, the fibrin was not digested. These worms contain antitrypsin and antipepsin which antagonize the action of the proteolytic enzymes. Many tissues of the body contain anti-enzymes. A living spleen or kidney sewed into an opening into a stomach remains undigested as long as its circulation is maintained. When the circulation ceases, the formation of anti-enzymes also comes to an end, and the tissue becomes a prey to the proteolytic ferments. It is possible that the mucosa of the alimentary canal contains antipepsin or antitrypsin so that, if the pepsin and trypsin should penetrate into the cells, their action is prevented by these antibodies. Antipepsin is known to exist in the blood.

Another possible explanation for this phenomenon lies in the specificity of ferments (p. 48). An ameba, as we have seen, engulfs the protoplasm of a plant or of another animal and digests this protoplasm in the very midst of its own protoplasm. Why do not the enzymes also digest the protoplasm of the ameba itself? The proteins found in the ameba are not identical with those of its food and a proteolytic enzyme capable of digesting the latter would be incapable of digesting the former. Such a distinction exists between the pepsin of the calf's and that of the pig's stomach; the former digests casein readily but splits coagulated egg albumin with difficulty; the latter digests both proteins with rapidity.

A third explanation for the absence of autolysis is found in the reversible action of the proteolytic enzymes. It is best, however, to defer this matter until we have discussed protein anabolism (p. 397).

IX. BACTERIAL ACTION IN THE INTESTINE

With our food and drink we ingest a large number of bacteria, many of which are killed in the stomach by the hydrochloric acid. Some succeed in passing through the stomach and find in the intestine a medium facilitating their growth and allowing them to act upon the foods. This bacterial action we divide into two kinds:

1. FERMENTATION, the action of bacteria on carbohydrates, by which are produced the gases, CH_4 (methane), H, CO_2, and organic acids, such as acetic, lactic, butyric, etc.

2. PUTREFACTION, the bacterial disintegration of proteins by which there are formed in addition to the above-named product, the gases H_2S, NH_3, and a number of aromatic substances: indol, skatol, phenol, and cresol.

Bacterial action may be useful so far as the bacteria split the foods into the same products as those formed by the digestive enzymes. They disintegrate the cellulose and thus liberate the enclosed food for proper digestion. For this reason a meal rich in cellulose may cause flatulence. By the bacteria the native proteins are transformed into peptones; fats, into fatty acid and glycerol; disaccharides are inverted. If, however, these products are still further decomposed, the action becomes wasteful and, according to some authorities, the products on being absorbed by the blood are poisonous to the body (intestinal intoxication). This was held to be especially true for the putrefactive products, such as indol and skatol. Some of these compounds are thrown out with the feces, but the remainder is absorbed.

The Detoxicating Function of the Liver.—All material absorbed from the intestine by the mesenteric veins is carried to the liver by the portal vein (see Figs. 78 and 219). *The liver is the great gateway* *into our body* and this organ exercises a certain selective action upon the material seeking entrance. When the putrefactive compounds arrive at the liver, they are, to a certain extent, taken out of the circulation and transformed, by uniting with acid potassium sulfate and in other ways, so as to lose their toxicity. They are then put back into the circulation and excreted by the kidneys. In this manner the indol, formed in the intestines, is changed by the liver into a compound called indican, and as such it is found in the urine. Sometimes a large amount of indican is excreted, a condition known as indicanuria. This is an illustration of another of the many functions of the liver—its detoxicating function. When strychnine is absorbed from the intestine, a part of it is rendered harmless by the liver, for the dose of strychnine necessary to throw the animal into convulsions is less when the liver has been removed.

Intestinal Intoxication.—Although extensively held, the theory of intestinal intoxication rests on no very secure scientific basis. Not denying that intoxication due to the absorption of toxins from the alimentary canal may and sometimes does take place, it is held by many that the symptoms of so-called ''biliousness'' and those frequently attributed to excessive putrefaction and the lack of proper peristalsis are not caused in this manner. Some of the facts substantiating this view we may briefly state as follows:

Notwithstanding much search, no substance having toxic influence when injected into the blood vessels has ever been shown to be absorbed in quantities sufficiently large to account for the symptoms of intestinal intoxication. Indol and indican are generally looked upon as representatives of these toxins. But frequently the urine is free from indican while indol is found in large quantities in the feces. The colon is not an organ for absorption (except for water). In constipation the stasis of the feces is nearly always in the colon, the ileum being generally empty; hence the stasis occurs in that part of the alimentary canal which has the least power and opportunity for absorption. During constipation there may be no increase in the urinary indican. On the other hand, people have been known to excrete large amounts of indican without any auto-intoxication. Moreover, some people, without experiencing any ill effects, go through life with only one bowel movement in several weeks or months.

As most of us know, the symptoms of ''auto-intoxication'' pass away almost immediately after the impacted fecal matter has been discharged. This was brought out by experiments conducted by Donaldson in which a number of young men voluntarily refrained from defecation for ninety hours. All developed the ordinary and well-known symptoms, such as headache, mental depression, etc., and others not so apparent (increased sugar in the blood, increased basal metabolism). The evacuation of the bowels at the expiration of the ninety hours very promptly dispelled all the symptoms. Such speedy relief can hardly be due to ridding the system of poisons.

Alvarez explains these effects of constipation as being brought about by the distention and irritation of the rectum—a nervous and not a chemical matter. The coating of the tongue and the bad breath may be due, according to this investigator, to "ripples of reverse peristalsis" by which gastric and perhaps even intestinal contents are brought in small quantities to the mouth.

As to lessening the amount of putrefaction the following may be noted. Sterilization of the food and the use of intestinal antiseptics have been found to be of no avail; neither is aid derived from purgations. Attempts have been made to displace the putrefactive bacteria by administering by mouth a certain acidophilic (acid producing) type, such as B. acidophilus (of sour milk). This method was highly recommended by Metchnikoff and his followers. It seems that a better way of changing the intestinal flora is changing the nature of the diet. Weinstein placed rats on a meat diet. When the acidophilic bacteria had disappeared from the feces, the addition of banana, apple, cranberry, or raisin powder soon restored the acidophilic organism. Tomatoes or prunes did not have this effect. The addition of lactose, or of trilactic acid, was very effective. In general, an increase in the carbohydrate and a decrease in protein foods may bring about beneficial results.

Whether animal life is possible without the intestinal bacteria was definitely decided by the observation of Levin, who found that in many instances the intestinal contents of bears, seals, and ducks living in the Arctic regions are completely sterile.

X. FECES

The amount of feces formed in a day varies largely with the amount and the nature of the food. From 150 to 200 grams is the usual amount voided per day. On a vegetable diet more feces and more watery feces are formed. The amount of water ingested has practically no influence on the consistency.

The feces contain undigested food (muscle fibers, casein, starch, fat droplets, etc.), indigestible material (especially cellulose), mucin, putrefactive products, bacteria and sometimes parasites, certain salts, such as phosphates of calcium and magnesium, and a coloring matter called stercobilin which is derived from the bile pigments.

The alimentary canal must also be regarded as an excretory organ by which certain mineral constituents, such as the calcium, iron and magnesium salts, are eliminated.

CHAPTER XVI

ABSORPTION

Two Channels for Absorption.—In order that the digested food shall reach the cells where it is needed, it must be transferred from the lumen of the alimentary canal into the blood stream; this process is called absorption. For this there are two channels:

1. *The direct,* by which the food passes through the mucosa of the alimentary canal and through the wall of the capillaries into the blood. In general we may say that all foods, except fats, pass this way. All the blood from the small and large intestines is collected by the superior and inferior mesenteric veins which empty into the portal vein; by this the blood is carried to the liver.

2. *The indirect channel.* The mucosa of the small intestine is thrown into many transverse folds, known as the *valvulae conniventes,* Fig. 171. These folds are studded with millions of minute (1 mm.) tonguelike elevations, the villi, Fig. 170. In the center of the villus we find a little blind duct, Fig. 172, which communicates at the proximal end with a larger duct; this in turn connects with other ducts to form still larger ducts until finally there is formed the thoracic duct, Figs. 78 and 173. These small vessels in the intestine are lymph vessels and are filled during absorption with a milky fluid, for which reason they are called *lacteals* (*lac,* milk). This fluid is composed chiefly of the absorbed fat, in the emulsified form, which is carried forward by the larger vessels to the thoracic duct which discharges its contents into the left subclavian vein near the heart, Fig. 78.

I. MATERIALS ABSORBED

a. **Water and Salts.**—Water is absorbed mainly from the small and large intestine by the direct channel; that absorbed from the stomach is very limited. The amount taken up by the blood depends upon the amount ingested, for the feces are not rendered more watery by an increase in the water drunk. Salts also are absorbed chiefly by the blood capillaries. The sodium salts of monobasic acids, such as NaCl, NaBr, Na acetate, are readily absorbed, but sodium sulfate (Glauber's salt) and phosphate, and magnesium sulfate (Epsom salt) are less easily taken up; for this reason the last-named salts are used as cathartics. Isotonic, hypotonic, and hypertonic solutions are finally all absorbed.

b. Carbohydrate Absorption.—The end products of carbohydrate digestion are the monosaccharides, chiefly glucose. It is only in the form of monosaccharides that the body can use carbohydrates, and in this form they are absorbed into the blood stream.

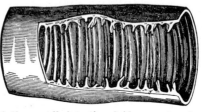

Fig. 171.—A piece of the small intestine laid open to show the valvulae conniventes.   (Brinton.)

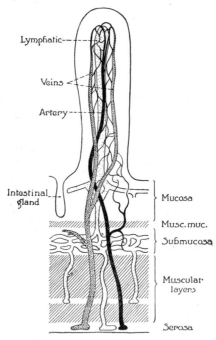

Fig. 172.—Diagram of a villus.   The artery is black; the vein is heavily stippled; the lymph vessel, or lacteal, is lightly stippled.   (Pettibone's Physiological Chemistry, The C. V. Mosby Co.)

c. Proteins.—These are absorbed by the direct channel in the form of amino acids or the simpler peptids. The blood of a fasting animal contains about 4 milligrams of amino acid nitrogen per 100 c.c.; during absorption this may be increased to 9 mg. The amount of the food protein absorbed depends largely upon the kind of food. From 97.5 to 99 per cent of the proteins of meat, milk, and eggs are absorbed; from wheat, about 90 per cent; from potatoes, it is stated, only 75 per cent. This difference is due to the cellulose of the vegetables inclosing the protein material making it difficult for the juices to digest the proteins; hence, the great necessity of cooking the vegetable foods.

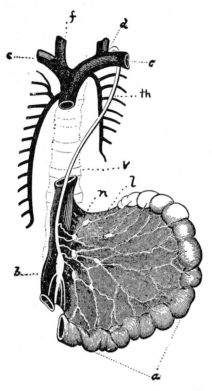

Fig. 173.—Diagram showing the lymphatics of the intestine. *a*, intestine held in place by the mesentery in which are seen the lacteals, *l*, and lymph nodes, *n*, which empty into the thoracic duct, *th*, at the lower end of which is seen a dilated portion known as the receptaculum chyli; *b*, inferior vena cava; *d*, junction of the thoracic duct with the left subclavian vein, *c*; *f*, right internal jugular vein; *v*, vertebral column. (Dalton.)

d. Fat.—Fat absorption takes place, as we have stated, by means of the lacteals, at least to a very large extent. It was formerly taught that fats could be absorbed as an emulsion, but it is now held that all fat must be split up into its two component parts—fatty acid and glycerol—before absorption can take place. The fatty acids are highly insoluble in water, but the presence of the bile salts renders them soluble in the fluid of the intestines. It is, therefore, as glycerol and fatty acids that the fats leave the alimentary canal. Yet it is generally stated that in the thoracic duct and in the blood we find not the fatty acid and glycerin, but very finely emulsified fat. This finds its explanation in that in the epithelial cells of the villi fatty acid and glycerol are reunited into fat. The microscopic fat globules, visible in the epithelial cells, in some manner or other pass through the body of the villus and into the lacteals. Some hold that this is brought about by the leucocytes. The villi are supplied with delicate muscle fibers which by their contraction materially shorten them; by alternate shortening and lengthening of the villi the chyle is pumped out of the lacteals into the network of lymph vessels found in the submucosa, Fig. 172. From these vessels, well supplied with valves, the chyle is driven onward to the thoracic duct which, in turn, carries the fat to the blood where it is found as particles of about 0.001 mm. diameter. Gradually the fat leaves the blood to enter the tissue cells. During the height of fat absorption the plasma may have a milky appearance.

Because of the great solvent action of the bile salts, the absence of bile in the intestines causes a loss of fat of from 30 to 60 per cent. When the fat is not properly removed, it hinders the digestion of the other foodstuffs by coating them with an oily layer. In view of the great importance of the bile salts, it is small wonder that they are absorbed from the lower part of the intestines and taken out of the blood stream by the liver to be again thrown with the bile into the upper intestines.

The percentage of fat absorbed depends upon its melting point, as shown by the following three fats: olive oil with melting point at 0° C. = 97.7 per cent; mutton tallow, m.p. at 49° C. = 92.6 per cent; pure stearin, m.p. at 60° C. = 10 per cent.

II. THE SEAT OF ABSORPTION

As to the part of the canal where the absorption of the various products takes place we may briefly state the following:

a. In the Stomach.—Very little absorption takes place in the stomach; water and water solutions are said not to be absorbed at all. A dog was given 500 c.c. of water by mouth; 25 minutes later 495 c.c. were found in the duodenum.

b. In the small intestine nearly all absorption (except that of water) takes place. This part of the alimentary canal is admirably adapted for this function. First of all, it is a long and rather narrow tube, being about 25 feet long and averaging one and one-half inches in diameter; this creates a considerable amount of surface in contact with the food mass. Next, the 800 or 900 valvulae conniventes serve to restrain the passage of the food through the canal and afford more surface for absorption. This surface is still further increased by the four or five million villi, so that the total absorbing surface is estimated at about 10 square meters. The motility of the villi is very largely increased by a material, called *villikinin,* formed by the action of the HCl discharged from the stomach into the intestine. The stimulation by villikinin increases the absorption of glucose by 12 to 30 per cent.

Heile found that 98 per cent of the protein of ingested meat (from 250 to 500 gm.) and all of 75 gm. of cane sugar were absorbed in the small intestine. In a human being it was found that only 560 c.c. of water reached the large intestine when the diet had contained 1,300 c.c. and the digestive juices furnished at least 3,000 c.c. more. Of the 150 gm. of fat eaten Honigman found only 3 per cent at the ileocecal fistula.

c. In the Large Intestine.—While it may be possible for some absorption to take place in the large intestine, normally the quantity is very limited because most food has been quite well absorbed before it reaches this organ. As the chyme entering the colon contains a fairly large quantity of water and as ordinarily the feces do not, absorption of water must occur in this region. As to the extent of absorption in the large intestine when the food is directly placed in the colon (nutritive enema) opinions differ greatly. Most observers agree that glucose cannot be absorbed.

III. THE MECHANISM OF ABSORPTION

In regard to the mechanism by which digested food leaves the lumen of the alimentary canal and enters the blood there is a great diversity of opinion. Some maintain that the physical or physicochemical forces of diffusion and osmosis are sufficient to explain the facts of absorption; especially has stress been laid on the osmotic pressure of the blood proteins to which the capillary wall is almost impermeable.

But many difficulties are encountered as may be gathered from the following facts: From a certain quantity of distilled water placed in a loop of the intestines only 59 per cent was absorbed; the absorption from a 0.4 per cent NaCl solution amounted to as much as 95 per cent. The absorption of the water and the NaCl from a 1.2 per cent NaCl solution took place at an equal pace. Most difficult of explanation is the fact that absorption may occur when the fluids on the two sides of the membrane are identical, as, for example, when the serum obtained from the animal's own blood is rapidly and completely ab-sorbed from the intestines.   Again, the rapidity with which a sub-stance diffuses plays but a small part in its absorption, as is shown by the fact that glucose with a lower diffusibility is absorbed almost as rapidly as sodium chloride.   Disaccharides are freely soluble and diffuse fairly rapidly, yet without previous conversion into mono-saccharides they are never absorbed.   From isotonic solutions of glucose and Na_2SO_4 placed in the intact intestines, the glucose was absorbed much more rapidly than the salt; this difference did not exist when a piece of isolated gut was used.   These and similar facts have led many investigators to maintain that purely physical forces are not adequate and that forces intimately associated with the life of the intestinal wall are brought into play.

Rapidity of Absorption.—Absorption may take place with great rapidity.   Radioactive mineral elements emit radiation and thereby can be detected in the body.   Radioactive sodium could be detected in the hand 3 to 6 minutes after being introduced into the intestines.

CHAPTER XVII

THE MOVEMENTS OF THE ALIMENTARY CANAL

I. INTRODUCTION

To be properly digested, the food must be constantly moved forward in order to be brought within the sphere of activity of the digestive juices secreted by the various glands placed along the alimentary canal. And to bring the enzymes of these juices into intimate contact with all food particles, the contents of the canal must be constantly churned. Furthermore, the absorption spoken of in the previous chapter cannot be complete unless the digested food, more or less fluid in nature, is brought into contact with the walls of the intestine. Finally, a certain amount of the ingested matter is indigestible and therefore must be expelled; for this the proper movements of the canal are necessary. These movements are brought about by the musculature of the alimentary canal.

Excepting those found at the two ends of the digestive canal, the muscles are visceral, or smooth, muscles. They are arranged in a longitudinal and a circular manner. The far more abundant circular muscle fibers border upon the submucosa, Figs. 159 and 170. The longitudinal muscle layer is found just beneath the outer, serous, coat. At certain points the circular layer is much increased in size and forms what are called sphincters; of these the most important are: the cardia and the pylorus at the entrance and exit, respectively, of the stomach Fig. 167; the ileocolic (or ileocecal) sphincter between the small and the large intestine; the internal and the external anal sphincters (the latter formed of skeletal muscle fibers).

The muscles of the alimentary canal, being visceral muscles, are supplied by nerves from the autonomic nervous system and are involuntary. The control exercised by the autonomic system over the musculature of the various parts of the canal is in some points not very clear, and most likely is not the same in all animals. Before we enter upon this, it may be helpful to compare the neuromuscular system of the digestive canal with that of the heart.

The cardiac muscle may be regarded, for the present, as a visceral muscle; it is involuntary and its automatic action is governed by both divisions of the autonomic nervous system: the sympathetic and parasympathetic. The postganglionic fibers of the former reach the heart by way of the cervical sympathetic nerve and are excitatory in nature. Those of the parasympathetic are found in the vagus and end at ganglia in the heart itself. In addition to this extrinsic nerve supply, it will be recalled that there is an intrinsic supply in the heart, which we called ganglia or nodes and bundles, e.g., the sino-auricular node. The heart activity is not determined by the extrinsic nerve supply, but is closely governed by it. In a similar manner, the musculature of the alimentary canal is supplied with an intrinsic nervous system. Between the longitudinal and circular muscle layers is found a network of nerve tissue known as Auerbach's nerve plexus (Fig. 159) and between the circular muscle layer and the submucosa, the plexus of Meissner.

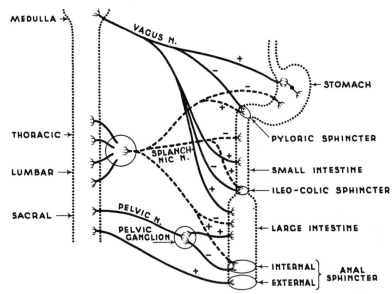

Fig. 174.—The innervation of the alimentary canal. All nerves are efferent. The postganglionic neurons of the vagus, lying in the walls, are not indicated, except in the stomach. Plus signs indicate excitation; minus signs, inhibition. The external anal sphincter is innervated by a somatic nerve.

The fibers of the sympathetic nervous system reach the alimentary canal by way of the splanchnic nerve. The preganglionic fibers of the parasympathetic are derived from two very distinct regions of the central nervous system, namely, from the medulla oblongata in the brain and from the sacral portion of the spinal cord. The fibers from the medulla travel by way of the vagus nerve and supply the muscles of the stomach, small intestine, and the upper half of the large intestine. As in the case of the heart, the vagal fibers make synaptic connections with neurons lying in the organ itself, i.e., in Auerbach's plexus. The preganglionic fibers from the sacral cord reach the pelvic ganglia by way of the pelvic nerve; the postganglionic fibers govern the lower half of the large intestine and rectum. The results of the stimulation of these two nerve supplies cannot be stated categorically; it seems that the results are not identical in all animals, and even in the same animal the result depends upon the condition of the particular part of the digestive canal under consideration. But in general it may be stated that (follow Fig. 174) the parasympathetic (full lines) is excitatory (indicated by plus signs) for all the musculature except the sphincters; for these it is generally inhibitory (indicated by minus signs). The sympathetic (broken lines) is excitatory for the sphincters and inhibitory for the remaining muscles. Similar to the heart, it will be noticed that the two nerve supplies are antagonistic as far as any one part of the digestive tube is concerned; but in our study of the various parts we shall discover that, as far as the proper propulsion of the food and chyme is concerned, they are complemental.

II. MASTICATION

The first muscular activity of the canal is that of mastication, the great value of which we considered in our study of digestion.

Mastication of the food is brought about by the motion of the lower jaw. The various movements and the muscles producing them may be tabulated as follows:

1. Raising:—masseter, temporal, and internal pterygoids.
2. Lowering:—digastric, mylohyoid, and geniohyoid.
3. Projection:—both external pterygoids when they act at the same time.
4. Retraction:—lower fibers of temporal.
5. Lateral movements:—external pterygoids acting first on one side and then on the other.

The grinding action produced by the raising, projection, retraction, and lateral movements of the jaw grinds the food very efficiently. To crush a piece of meat required a pressure of from 30 to 300 kilograms; the same meat was torn by grinding by a pressure of from 2 to 5 kg.

III. DEGLUTITION

By deglutition the food is propelled from the mouth into the stomach. This is an exceedingly complex process in which a large number of muscles play a part and may conveniently be divided into three stages. During the first stage the food is placed upon the back of the tongue, E, Fig. 175, and the tip of the tongue pressed against the hard palate, A; this elevation of the tongue against the palate travels

back to the root of the tongue, and by it the food is propelled from
the mouth toward the isthmus of the fauces, *2.* This is generally said
to be a voluntary process.

The second stage is the pharyngeal stage. The pharynx is a funnel-shaped tube (from *2* to *4*); above it opens into the mouth and
nose, *H*, below into the esophagus, *4*, and the larynx, *D*. The *larynx,*
it will be recalled, is the voice box, which forms the uppermost portion
of the trachea, or windpipe. The pharynx is, therefore, a common
passageway for both the food, which is to pass down the esophagus,
and the air which passes through the larynx and trachea. The passage of the food through the pharynx, from the isthmus, *2,* to the

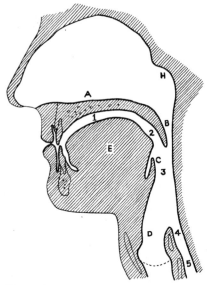

Fig. 175.—Diagram illustrating the pharynx. *A,* hard palate; *B,* uvula; *C,*
epiglottis; *D,* trachea; *E,* tongue; *H,* nasal cavities; *4* and *5,* esophagus.

esophagus, *4,* is involuntary and takes place very quickly. In order
to prevent the food from entering the larynx, *D,* and choking the individual, this structure is drawn up close to the root of the tongue,
E, the tongue moves backward and meets the larynx, and the vocal
cords in the larynx approach each other, thereby closing the glottis.
The epiglottis, *C,* does not fold over the larynx like the hinged lid
on a box, as was formerly held, for removal of this structure has not
been found to disturb swallowing. The upward movement of the
larynx during the act of swallowing can be felt or seen very readily,
and if, by grasping this structure (the Adam's apple) between thumb
and finger, its elevation be prevented, the act of swallowing cannot

take place. To prevent still further the food from entering the trachea and the lungs, the act of swallowing is preceded by a short inspiration and during the first and second stages of deglutition all inspiratory and expiratory movements are inhibited. The opening of the pharynx into the nasal cavity, *H,* is closed by the elevation of the soft palate and of the uvula, *B,* and by the contraction of the muscles found in the posterior pillars of the fauces. The transit of the food through this dangerous area is very fast.

The third stage consists in the food passing through the esophagus into the stomach. Liquids are squirted, by the contraction of the muscles of the mouth and pharynx, to the very lowest part of the esophagus without any further muscular action on the part of the esophagus. But the solid and semisolid food passes more slowly and is pushed downward by the contraction of the circular muscle fibers found in the walls of the esophagus. When the food reaches a certain part of the esophagus, the ring muscles behind the food contract, thereby narrowing the tube and exerting pressure upon the food. As the food is pushed downward, the next part of the esophagus con-stricts, and in this manner the movement of the food is continued until it reaches the stomach. This wavelike constriction of a tube by its circular muscles is called *peristalsis.*

At the lower end of the esophagus the circular muscle fibers are highly developed, forming what is known as the cardiac sphincter, or cardia (Fig. 167). Generally relaxed when the stomach is empty, this sphincter contracts and thereby closes the entrance of the stomach when this organ contains food. During the passage of food through the esophagus, the circular fibers immediately in front of the food mass dilate; this also applies to the cardia.

The passage of the food along the various parts of the alimentary canal can be studied best by means of x-rays. The food is mixed with a small quantity of bismuth subnitrate or barium sulfate; as these salts are opaque to the rays, the food impregnated with them will cast a shadow upon the fluoroscope and the rate of travel can thereby be ascertained. The entrance of food into the stomach can also be ascer-tained by placing a stethoscope over the area of the cardiac sphincter and noting the sounds as the food enters the stomach. Deglutition time varies considerably. Fluids reach the end of the esophagus in about one second but remain above the closed sphincter for four or five seconds, waiting for a peristaltic wave to open the sphincter. For semisolids the time may be from six to twenty seconds, depending up-on the degree of fluidity of the material. Under certain conditions the material escapes from the stomach into the esophagus and the stimulation of the mucosa by the acids of the regurgitated fluid gives rise to "heartburn."

Deglutition is a reflex action, the center for which is located in the medulla; when the sensory surfaces of the mouth are not stimulated (as when the mouth is empty of saliva or food, or when the sensory nerve endings are paralyzed by cocaine) swallowing is impossible. Only when this stimulation is present can we voluntarily start the act. The second and third steps are entirely beyond our control.

IV. THE STOMACH

In the wall of the stomach are found three layers of smooth muscles: the external or longitudinal, the middle or circular, and the internal or oblique, Fig. 176. At the pyloric end the circular fibers form the pyloric sphincter. The external fibers are continuous with the longitudinal fibers of the esophagus and duodenum. The shape and position of the stomach vary in different individuals and with various conditions.

When empty, the walls of the stomach are practically in contact with each other, so that the cavity is almost obliterated. As food enters, the walls yield and are pushed outward; hence filling the stomach does not increase the intragastric pressure. Neither is the pressure in the abdomen (outside of the stomach) increased by eating; the muscular wall of the abdomen accommodates itself, by relaxing more or less, to the amount of the gastric contents. Were it not for this arrangement, the circulation through the organs of the abdomen would be seriously menaced by the ingestion of food.

The first food swallowed is placed in contact with the walls of the stomach, especially in the pyloric end. The next quantity is placed nearer to the center of the stomach and is surrounded by the food previously swallowed and, therefore, not in contact with the walls of the stomach. The last food ingested has a central position and lies next to the cardiac orifice (Fig. 177).

The fundus and the upper half of the body of the stomach differ in function from the remainder. The muscles of the fundus exercise a constant gentle pressure upon the food which is thereby gradually squeezed into the antrum. Because of the orderly arrangement of the semisolid food and because of the absence of any churning action the food is not mixed with HCl, and salivary digestion can continue for a considerable length of time. The function of this part of the stomach is, therefore, mainly that of storing the food.

In the remainder of the stomach active peristaltic action occurs. A constriction appears about midway in the body of the stomach, brought about by the contraction of the circular muscle fibers. This constriction travels downward toward the pylorus. After it has traveled a short distance a new constriction begins and follows the first; a third and a fourth may be started before the first wave has reached the pylorus; as a result the antrum assumes a beaded form, as shown in Fig. 178. These waves may follow each other at the rate of three per minute and have been observed, in cats, to continue for seven hours. By the peristaltic action the food is macerated and thoroughly mixed with the gastric juice, fresh food being constantly brought into contact with the walls of the stomach.

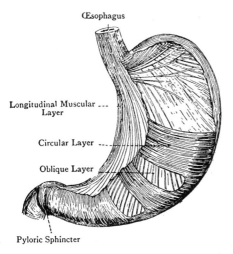

Fig. 176.—External view of the stomach after removal of the serous coat. Most of the longitudinal and much of the circular layer have been removed to show the oblique layer. (Buchanan.)

Fig. 177.—Section of a frozen stomach (rat) some time after feeding with food given in three differently colored portions. (Howell: *Textbook of Physiology*, W. B. Saunders Co.)

Innervational Control of Gastric Movements.—The parasympathetic nerve supply reaches the stomach by way of the vagus nerve (see Fig. 174). The sympathetic is by way of the splanchnic nerves. Very little can be said with any degree of certainty concerning the part played by the extrinsic nerves in regulating the motility of the gastric apparatus.

It is generally held that the vagus is the excitatory and the splanchnic the inhibitory nerve; however, the result of the stimulation of these nerves depends upon the degree of tonicity exhibited by the muscles. In a state of low muscle tonus, stimulation of the vagus brings about increased activity, but in a high degree of tonicity the same stimulation may produce an inhibition of already existing peristalsis. Severing all the extrinsic nerves to the stomach leads only to a temporary paralysis; normal motility is restored in a few days. The extrinsic nerves, therefore, do not initiate but only regulate the gastric movements. In its automaticity, the gastrointestinal canal resembles the heart; some authors favor the theory that this automaticity is due to the intrinsic nerve structures (plexuses).

It is supposed by some that a center for the gastric movements is situated in the medulla oblongata; others place such a center in the midbrain.

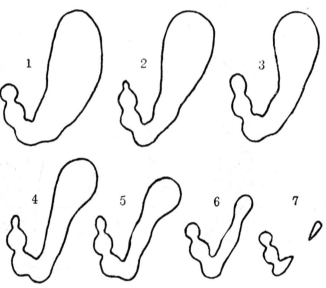

Fig. 178.—Tracing of the shadow cast by the stomach (cat) showing changes in the shape of the organ at intervals of an hour during the digestion of a meal. (W. B. Cannon: The Mechanical Factors of Digestion, Copyright, Longmans, Green & Co.)

From our study of the heart it will be recalled that the transmission of impulses from the vagus nerve ending to the cardiac muscle fiber is mediated by means of a chemical compound known as acetylcholine and that adrenalin is formed at the ending of the sympathetic nerve fiber. This also holds true for the vagal excitatory and the sympathetic inhibitory impulses for the gastric muscle. This view finds support in that the effects of acetylcholine and adrenalin upon this musculature are similar to those generally associated with vagal and sympathetic stimulation, respectively. The normal gastrointestinal motility depends upon nicotinic acid vitamin.

Evacuation of the Stomach.—Some investigators hold that during gastric activity the pylorus is open for about nine-tenths of the time and that every peristaltic wave reaching the pyloric canal succeeds in expelling some chyme. According to this view, it is by increasing or decreasing the peristalsis rather than by altering the tonus of the sphincter that the evacuation of the stomach is controlled. The gastric peristalsis is influenced by the nature of the contents of both the stomach and the intestines. It has been fairly well established that the relative amount of acid in the stomach or in the duodenum plays little or no part; but the consistency of the material is of importance. Fluids, for example, leave the stomach soon after being swallowed, semifluids perhaps not quite as rapidly, and solid particles are held back for a long time; it seems as if the pylorus acts as a strainer for the ejaculated material. Fats slow the gastric peristalsis and thereby increase the emptying time; but it is on reaching the intestines that this power of delaying gastric evacuation becomes very prominent. As shown by fluoroscopic examination, peristalsis and the evacuation of food from the stomach are delayed by fat placed through a fistula into the jejunum. The mere fullness of the duodenum has the same influence. We may therefore conclude that stimulation of the upper intestines, by decreasing gastric peristalsis, delays gastric evacuation; it is in this manner, and not by governing the tone of the sphincter, that the rate of discharging the food from the stomach is adapted to the secretory and motor capacity of the intestines. Recently it was shown that the injection of an extract prepared from the upper part of the intestines was able to inhibit gastric peritsalsis; the humoral agent responsible for this has been designated as *enterogastrone.* It is possible that the inhibition, caused by fat spoken of above, is mediated by means of this humoral mechanism.

That certain mental states can influence the activity of the stomach and intestines is common knowledge. Cannon found that the active peristalsis in the cat ceased immediately when the animal became enraged or exhibited signs of fear or anxiety. ''Whenever the animals (cats, dogs, rabbits, guinea pigs) showed any indications of being uncomfortable or distressed, the movements were inhibited and the discharge from the stomach checked.'' Even a strange surrounding may so affect the stomach of a dog as to stop all action for two or three hours. The importance of this phase of the subject is apparent. In the same manner as the disagreeable and violent emotions of grief, worry, anger, and fear in general, have an injurious influence upon the secretions of the alimentary canal, so they also affect its motor activity.

Length of time the food remains in the stomach. Food begins to leave the stomach a few minutes after eating and an ordinary meal passes through the stomach in two to four hours. It seems that the physical nature of the food has some influence on the rapidity of its discharge. Water, for example, leaves the stomach very rapidly. Hawk found that 500 c.c. of water left the human stomach in ten to twenty minutes after ingestion; 100 grams of beef left the faster type of stomach in about 2½ hours while it remained one hour longer in the slower type. In this respect very little, if any difference exists between rare, medium or well-done beef; pork leaves the stomach at a little slower rate. A meal composed largely of

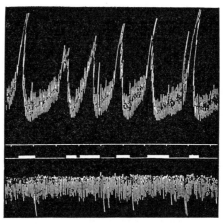

Fig. 179.—The top record represents intragastric pressure (the small oscillations due to respiration, the large to contractions of the stomach); the second record is time in minutes (ten minutes); the third record is the report of hunger pangs; the lowest record is respiration registered by means of a pneumograph about the abdomen. (W. B. Cannon: Bodily Changes in Pain, Hunger, Fear and Rage.)

carbohydrates, such as bread, dates, and porridge, leaves the stomach before meats; this is perhaps due to their more speedy maceration and physical disintegration. Fats and fatty foods are the last to be ejected.

Hunger.—In this connection we may say a few words about the sensation of hunger. Many theories have been advanced as to the causes of this sensation, none of which proved very satisfactory until the work done by Cannon and others showed that hunger is due to the rhythmical contraction of the musculature of the stomach. The experiments showing this may be briefly discussed. The individual under observation swallowed one end of a rubber tube; the end in the stomach was provided with a small soft rubber balloon, while the other end was attached to a water manometer. Contraction of the muscles of the stomach compressed the air in the rubber balloon; this increase of air pressure was communicated to the manometer, causing the water in the distal end to rise. When the sensation of hunger was felt, the individual pressed an electric key which by means of an electric signal caused a heavy straight line to be written below the manometer curve on the kymograph. In this manner Fig. 179 was produced. It will be noticed that whenever the individual experienced the sensation of hunger (shown by the short solid lines on the third record from the top) the manometer pen (top record) rises, indicating more powerful contractions of the stomach muscles. The contractions last about thirty seconds and occur in periods of thirty to forty-five minutes; these periods are separated by periods of repose lasting from one-half to two and one-half hours. The contractions are inhibited by emotions, such as fear, anger, joy, and by fatigue; intellectual work seems not to affect them and they continue during sleep. Tobacco smoking stops them and this inhibition may continue from five to fifteen minutes after the cessation of smoking.

The cause of the hunger contractions has been referred to two sources: (a) to local changes in the stomach itself and (b) to systemic changes involving the blood and nervous system. Hunger pangs are not determined by a need of more food, for these pangs are experienced when there may be much food in the intestines, and, on the other hand, they disappear largely after two or three days of starvation. That the condition of the stomach plays a part is seen in that filling it with some indigestible material (cellulose) inhibits the pangs for some time. The usual hunger pangs are not due to a decrease of sugar in the blood, for the percentage of sugar is the same before, during, and after the hunger period. But the lowering of the glucose content which follows the administration of insulin (p. 415) initiates or increases the hunger contractions; the injection of sugar causes them to cease. This fact has been utilized to increase the hunger pangs in undernourished people with poor appetites.

Appetite.—Although generally thought of as closely related, hunger differs from appetite. The former is a sharply localized and disagreeable sensation; generally it is a signal that food is needed. The term appetite is more closely associated with the ability to eat and to enjoy one's food. Hunger and appetite may exist independently of each other. Some authors associate a good appetite with a high degree of tonus of the gastric musculature. It is certainly true that the mental conditions which decrease the tonicity also inhibit the appetite. And, as we shall learn in our study of the vitamins, the lack of vitamin B_1 greatly reduces the appetite.

The Act of Vomiting (emesis) is preceded and accompanied by a feeling of nausea and a great flow of saliva. The mechanical process of vomiting may be described as follows: The individual makes a deep inspiration and suddenly closes his glottis; retching results in a great pressure applied to the contents of the abdomen by the descending diaphragm, the imprisoned air in the thorax preventing the diaphragm from being forced upward by any pressure applied to the undersurface of this structure. Next, there is a strong contraction of the muscles of the abdominal wall which causes the stomach to be squeezed between the diaphragm and the abdominal wall. In addition, the antrum of the stomach contracts while the fundus and the cardiac sphincter dilate. The great pressure externally applied to the stomach and the contraction of the antrum, together with the lessened resistance in the fundus and esophagus, cause the food to be thrown into the pharynx and the mouth. The glottis and usually also the nasal passages are closed. It is generally held that the contraction of the musculature of the stomach is not necessary for emesis. Magendie replaced a dog's stomach by a rubber balloon, connecting it with the esophagus and intestines, and showed that vomiting could take place. On the other hand, as a result of overdistention of the stomach, vomiting may take place in young children without the abdominal muscles playing any part.

Nervous Mechanism.—Vomiting is a reflex action, the center for which is situated near the respiratory center in the medulla oblongata. From the above description it will be noticed that the muscles concerned in emesis are largely those producing inspiration and expiration. The reflex can frequently be caused by stimulation of the mucosa of the pharynx (tickling with a feather, or by sticking a finger down one's throat). The mucosa of the stomach may be affected chemically, e.g., by zinc sulfate, mustard, or by the products of fermentation (vomiting resulting from the ingestion of spoiled foods). Vomiting may also be set up by gallstones, renal calculi, or by strangulated hernia. Again, the center may be directly stimulated by drugs (emetics) such as apomorphine. Disagreeable emotions also have the power to stimulate the center, hence we speak of nauseating sights.

V. MOVEMENTS OF THE SMALL INTESTINE

In the intestines we may observe two distinct sorts of movement: peristalsis and rhythmic segmentation.

Rhythmic segmentation is best described by reference to the accompanying diagram, Fig. 180. A quiescent loop of the intestine, *1*, suddenly divides itself by the contraction of its circular muscle fibers into a number of segments, *2*. After two or three seconds each of these segments divides into two parts and the halves of the two neighboring segments unite to form a segment of the same size as the original, *3*. The dividing and reuniting may go on for half an hour or more in a single loop or stretch of the intestine; by it the food mass is not moved downward but is thoroughly mixed with the digestive juices. The circulation of both blood and lymph through the wall of the intestine is also aided by this activity.

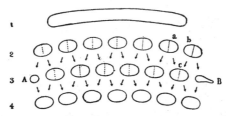

Fig. 180.—Diagram representing the process of rhythmic segmentation. Lines *1, 2, 3, 4,* indicate the sequence of appearances in a single loop. The dot lines represent the regions of division. The arrows show the relation of the particles to the segments they subsequently form. (W. B. Cannon: The Mechanical Factors of Digestion, Longmans, Green & Co.)

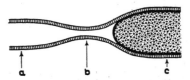

Fig. 181.—Peristalsis; illustrating Starling's law of the intestine. For explanation of lettering, see text.

Peristalsis.—When the mucosa of the small intestine is mechanically stimulated at a certain point, *a*, in Fig. 181, as by a mass of food, the circular fibers just above this point contract, *b*, while those below the point of stimulation, for a distance of one or two feet, relax, *c*. Pressure is thereby applied from behind the food, the resistance ahead is lessened, and the food mass pushed downward. This coordination of the circular muscle fibers above and below the point of stimulation is called Starling's *law of the intestines*. The contraction and the relaxation travel for a short distance down the tube, at the rate of from one-half to one inch per minute. It is generally held that this wave always travels in the direction of the large intestine. In addition to these slow waves, there is also what is known as the *peristaltic rush* in which the constriction travels at a much faster rate (2 to 25 cm. per second) and may sweep over long stretches of the small intestine.

NERVOUS REGULATION.—The increased muscular activity following vagus stimulation is well shown in Fig. 182 and the inhibitory effect of the splanchnic, in Fig. 183. This last is in line with the inhibitory

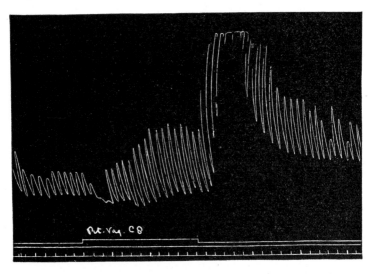

Fig. 182.—Curve showing the effect of stimulation of the right vagus on the intestinal contraction. (Starling.)

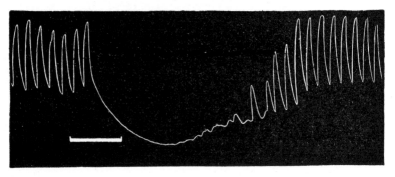

Fig. 183.—Curve of intestinal contraction. During the duration of the heavy white line the splanchnic nerves were stimulated. (Starling.)

effect of adrenalin upon the intestine, for the results produced by this hormone are always similar to those of sympathetic nerve stimulation. The cutting of the extrinsic nerve supply does not permanently paralyze the peristalsis but, when the intrinsic neural mechanism is destroyed by poisoning with cocaine or nicotin, all peristaltic action ceases; it is therefore concluded that this activity is dependent upon the intrinsic nerve supply (plexuses). As this last procedure does not abolish the rhythmical segmentations, these actions are of myogenic origin.

The ileocolic sphincter follows the law of the intestines in that stimulation of the intestines just above the sphincter, as by the pressure of food at this part, causes its relaxation. On the other hand, pressure of food in the cecum increases its contraction. According to Alvarez, the function of this sphincter is to prevent a too rapid emptying of the small intestines by the peristaltic rushes.

VI. THE LARGE INTESTINE

The chief function of this part of the alimentary tract is not digestive, for the digestion has been almost completed before the food reaches the colon; nor does it normally absorb food to any great extent excepting water, for about 90 per cent of the digested material has been taken out by the small intestine. The absence of the valvulae conniventes and the villi, so abundant in the small intestine, indicates the lack of any large amount of absorbing power.

The movements of the large intestine differ somewhat in various animals and there is considerable uncertainty as to their nature in man. Cannon showed by x-ray examination that in cats the ejection of the digested food mass from the small intestine (especially by the peristaltic rush) is followed by peristalsis of the cecum and ascending colon; this is soon followed by a marked constriction near the end of the ascending colon, which travels backward—*antiperistalsis*—and presses the fecal mass firmly into the cecum and proximal part of the ascending colon, the ileocolic sphincter meanwhile being closed. The object of this antiperistalsis is, no doubt, to prevent a too hurried passage of the fecal matter through the colon and thus to allow sufficient time for the absorption of a large portion of the water from the fecal matter. In this manner the ascending and transverse colon become filled and finally the antiperistalsis gives place to a peristaltic wave which sends the mass into the descending colon and rectum.

Among the conditions affecting the colon we may especially mention the entrance of food into the stomach and duodenum. By this reflex—*the gastrocolic reflex*—powerful waves of peristalsis pass from the cecum over the entire length of the colon. *This mass peristalsis* is comparable to the peristaltic rush of the small intestine and explains the usual desire to defecate soon after breakfast. Such mass peristalsis may occur two or three times a day. That the activity of the colon is subject to certain mental conditions is a well-known fact. Sleep has an inhibiting influence.

Defecation.—The rectum comprises the lowest four or five inches of the large intestine and leads to the exterior by way of the anus. The anus is guarded by an internal sphincter, composed of smooth muscle fibers, and an external sphincter which is a striated, or skeletal, muscle. When a certain amount of fecal matter has arrived at the lower part of the descending colon and the sigmoid flexure (see Fig. 158), the sensory nerve endings are mechanically stimulated by the distention of the canal, and a desire for emptying the bowels arises. The rectum is normally empty until the moment of defecation.

In a young child and in adults suffering from injury to the spinal cord, defecation is a reflex action. The sensory impulses above spoken of are carried to the lumbosacral portion of the cord and reflexly the musculature of the colon and rectum is thrown into action and the sphincters are inhibited; the pressure thus generated forces the fecal matter through the anal canal. In the normal adult this reflex may be volitionally assisted or suppressed. By the voluntary contraction of the muscles in the abdominal wall a large amount of pressure is exerted upon the descending colon, the sigmoid flexure, and the rectum; this aids in the expulsion of the feces. In order to prevent the upward movement of the abdominal contents and thereby annul the beneficial results, the contraction of these muscles is preceded by a deep inspiration and closure of the glottis. The descending diaphragm causes pressure upon the contents of the abdomen. Next the internal sphincter is inhibited reflexly; the relaxation of the external sphincter is usually under voluntary control.

The length of time consumed by a certain quantity of food and its residue in passing through the whole alimentary canal varies so largely in different individuals and with the changing conditions in each person that no definite figures can be given. It is generally held that from 16 to 24 hours are required for this passage, although others have stated the time in days. The frequency of evacuation of the bowels depends largely upon the nature of the food and other conditions, some of which we may here note.

1. THE NATURE OF THE FOOD.—On a heavy meat or milk diet the movements will be few, even as few as one in two or three days. When the meal includes a large amount of vegetable food rich in cellulose, there may be two or more movements a day. Cellulose has this effect because it not only furnishes much bulk to the feces, but because it also mechanically stimulates the motor activity of the alimentary tract to more hurried peristalsis. A small part of the

cellulose may undergo fermentation thereby producing gases and acids, both of which increase the peristalsis. Cellulose is found extensively in all fresh vegetables, especially the bulky ones such as lettuce and cabbage, nearly all fruits (except bananas), and the coarser grain products (bran, graham flour, whole wheat flour). Agar-agar, a seaweed product, behaves in the alimentary canal much like cellulose. The best regulators of the bowels are foods. The quickened peristalsis leaves the fecal matter more watery and thereby makes the emptying of the bowels easier. The mere drinking of water may excite the gastrocolic reflex but ordinarily does not cause a more watery feces.

Two types of constipation are the spastic and the atonic. The former, said to be far more common than the latter, may be the result of fear, worry, shock, or mental overwork and causes too great activity of the intestinal musculature (spasm); to stimulate the muscles still more by a large amount of roughage is contraindicated. The atonic type, due to depressed activity of the intestinal musculature, is more frequently found in obese or elderly people and in those with a deficiency of vitamin A in the diet; here there is lack of muscle tonus, hence the stimulating action of cellulose may be beneficial. In case of poor digestion and flatulence (gas in stomach and intestine) harm may result from the ingestion of much indigestible material; the irritation by bran may lead to colitis.

Present-day foods are perhaps overrefined and overcondensed. The following are generally regarded as constipating: Liquid foods, such as gruels, boiled milk and soups; starchy foods devoid or nearly devoid of cellulose, such as rice, fine wheat bread, tapioca, and cornstarch; foods composed almost entirely of proteins, for example, lean meat, egg white, and gelatin.

2. LUBRICATION of the alimentary canal with oils. Any food fat or oil would serve this purpose, but being highly condensed food it may lead to fattening or the omission of coarse foods from the diet. Hence paraffin oil (or liquid petrolatum) which is not absorbed and has no food value is sometimes useful.

3. CATHARTICS.—The use of cathartics is to be discouraged, for their continued use renders the intestines insensitive toward the normal stimulations and thus aggravates the constipation. In certain forms of constipation in which the intestines are already too active, cathartics are contraindicated.

4. PROPER EXERCISE by which the contents of the abdomen are massaged and the circulation in the digestive organs increased. Especially would be recommended those exercises which strengthen the

muscles in the walls of the abdomen, for frequently constipation is due to a lack of tonus of these muscles.

5. HEMORRHOIDS are not infrequently the cause of constipation. The hemorrhoidal veins which drain the blood from the rectum and adjacent parts are not supplied with valves and are therefore very susceptible to enlargement and varicosity (p. 248), a condition known as a hemorrhoid. From what we said in general of varicose veins it will be recalled that an obstruction to the flow of the blood in a vein may lead to this condition; hence, congestion of the portal vein may be the cause of hemorrhoids. Any condition that causes congestion of the rectum, such as the strong contraction of the muscles of the rectum, may also be followed by a varicosity of these veins; this is frequently seen in prolonged straining efforts. For this reason constipation may develop hemorrhoids, and the hemorrhoids aggravate the constipation; in other words, a vicious circle has been established. As constipation favors the development of hemorrhoids, people of sedentary occupations are frequently troubled with this affliction. Exercise by which the blood vessels of the abdomen are massaged, a diet that will cause freer bowel movements, and, above all, regularity in the use of the toilet are the means of alleviating this trouble; heavy lifting over a period of time should be avoided, as also excessive straining at stool.

6. HABIT.—Of utmost importance is heeding the call for evacuation. Neglect of this causes the rectum to adjust itself by the relaxation of its muscles; this abolishes the mechanical stimulation of the sensory nerve endings by the fecal mass, allows the feces to be excessively condensed (impacted), and thereby makes subsequent defecation more difficult. When this overloading of the lower colon is continued over a long period of time, the muscles gradually lose their tonus and the wall becomes very thin. The great value of training the lower part of the alimentary canal for stated periodic evacuation is apparent.

7. In DIARRHEA the contents of the small intestine are forced with abnormal rapidity into the colon; as this seriously curtails the digestion and absorption of the food, persistent diarrhea leads to malnutrition. Excessive peristalsis may be induced by emotional disturbances, by the fermentation or putrefaction products in spoiled food, by unripe fruits, or by bacterial infections, such as typhoid.

CHAPTER XVIII

PROTEIN METABOLISM

We have studied in a previous chapter the changes the foods undergo in the alimentary canal and in what form and by what channel the digested products are brought to the blood. We must now study the fate of these foods in the body proper. The sum total of all the chemical changes taking place in the body is called metabolism. These changes concern either the building up of material, anabolism, or its destruction, catabolism. In the normal adult body these two processes balance each other; the individual is then said to be in physiologic equilibrium and his body weight is constant. It must be evident that in this condition the ingesta (food, drink, oxygen) must equal the egesta (excretions by lungs, alimentary canal, skin, and kidneys). For purpose of discussion, it is convenient to consider separately the metabolism of the various foodstuffs. Among the ingredients of the cell, the protein material is the most abundant (excepting water) and plays an indispensable rôle in the life processes. In the growing animal this material must be laid down anew; in all animals the already existing proteins suffer a certain amount of wear and tear and must be renewed. This construction of proteins we may now consider.

I. AMINO ACIDS AS BUILDING STONES OF PROTEINS

From our introductory study (review p. 33) it will be recalled that the number of different kinds of protoplasm is exceedingly large. This assertion flows from the accepted statement that differences in function of various protoplasms result from differences in their construction. The protoplasmic activities are very largely determined by the protein constituents of the protoplasm; this acquires broader significance in view of the modern concept that enzymes are proteins. How is it possible to have thousands of differently constructed compounds which, notwithstanding their individual differences, resemble each other closely enough to enable us to group them into one class of compounds, the proteins? It will be recalled from our discussion of foods, that, because of the carboxyl group—COOH—and the amino group—NH_2—the amino acids are able to unite with each other in large numbers to form ever larger molecules. Successively, as these molecules become larger, the products formed are called peptids, dipeptids, tripeptids, polypeptids, peptones, proteoses, and, finally, proteins.

In this building up of proteins, four factors must be kept in mind: (1) there are 22 varieties of amino acids entering into the composition of different proteins; (2) the arrangement of the amino acids with respect to each other in the make-up of proteins; (3) the number of molecules of each one of the 22 amino acids in the protein molecule; (4) the exceedingly large size (molecular weight) of the protein molecule.

The building of protein molecules from amino acids is much like word-building from the 26 letters of the alphabet. To illustrate: from the Scotch word "ain" by the addition of only one letter we may obtain gain, lain, main, pain, rain, or vain; by the expansion of "rain" we have train, entrain, entrainment. Very slight changes in orthography may result in wide differences of meaning. In this manner the thousands of words in the English and other European languages are built up from but 26 constituents. Now let us imagine a theoretical protein molecule composed of only four different amino acid units, each of which is used but once. These four molecules could be arranged in 24 ways; e.g., glycocoll-alanine-leucine-lysine, or glycocoll-leucine-alanine-lysine, or alanine-glycocoll-leucine-lysine, etc. In each case a different compound with its peculiar chemical and physical properties would be obtained. If only one single molecule of each of the 22 known amino acids combined with each other to form a protein molecule, the number of possible combinations amounts to 39×10^{25} (i.e., 39 followed by 25 zeros).

Let us suppose that the number of the amino acid molecules in the protein remains 22 but that two or more of the 22 kinds are replaced by increasing the number of the others. The number of possible combinations is increased enormously. The size of a molecule is expressed by its molecular weight, and the molecular weight of any substance is estimated by comparing it with that of the hydrogen molecule, which is 2. The molecular weights of the various proteins range between extremely wide limits; e.g., that of egg albumin is placed at about 35,000 and that of certain viruses* at 7,600,000 or more. The molecular weights of amino acid molecules also vary; we may place the average at 150. These values would put the number of amino acid units in the albumin molecule at approximately 240. Combining all these facts we may conclude that the number of various proteins possible is ample to account for the endless number of plant and animal protoplasms.

*A virus is a living, virulent, nonbacterial cause of disease; e.g., the virus of the common cold or infantile paralysis.

How largely proteins differ from each other in the number and in the kind of amino acid units entering into their composition may be shown by two such closely allied proteins as egg albumin and lactalbumin. The lactalbumin contains 4.9 per cent tyrosine and 14 per cent leucine, while the egg albumin contains 1.77 per cent tyrosine and 10.7 per cent leucine. In Table XVIII is given, in percentage, the amount of eight of the amino acids found in five well-known proteins.

TABLE XVIII

	LACTALBUMIN	OVALBUMIN	CASEIN	GELATIN	ZEIN
Glycine	0.4	0.0	0.0	25.5	0.0
Alanine	2.4	8.4	1.8	8.7	9.8
Leucine	14.0	15.2	9.7	7.1	25.0
Aspartic acid	9.3	6.2	4.1	3.4	1.8
Tyrosine	1.9	4.2	4.5	0.0	3.6
Lysine	9.2	5.0	6.0	5.9	0.0
Tryptophan	2.7	1.3	1.5	0.0	0.1
Cystine	3.4	2.0	?	0.0	1.0

The difference in the composition is very striking when two such diverse proteins as casein and gelatin are compared. We would especially call attention to the fact that tyrosine is practically missing in the gelatin (other proteins contain from 1 to 5 per cent) and that it lacks tryptophan and cystine.

II. SYNTHESIS OF PROTEINS IN THE BODY

Note. Nearly all the matter discussed in this chapter is graphically presented in Fig. 186.

We have seen that the ingested protein is digested into amino acids and as such absorbed into the blood stream. The nitrogen of these absorbed amino acids reappears in the urine as urea, uric acid, creatinin, etc. What happens to the amino acids during their sojourn in the body?

The amino acids formed in the alimentary canal are carried by the blood stream to the various parts of the body. The cells take those amino acids they are in need of for reconstructing the tissue proteins which may have undergone a certain amount of wear and tear. At first it looks as if the digestion of the protein into amino acids and the building up of the amino acids into proteins is a very roundabout way of doing things, if not an altogether unnecessary process. But the object of this disintegration and reintegration of the protein becomes intelligible when we recall what we repeatedly stressed on former occasions, namely, **the function of an organ is de-**

termined by its chemical composition. Muscle tissue has the property of contractility because of its peculiar chemical composition; the function of a nerve differs from that of a gland because the proteins and other constituents of the protoplasm of these two tissues differ chemically.

All the various proteins of the tissues must be repaired by means of the food proteins. Both food proteins and tissue proteins have exceedingly large molecules which differ, as we have seen, in the number and kind of amino acid molecules and in their arrangement in the protein molecules. To transform food protein into tissue protein, it is necessary to cut the food protein molecule into its *building stones*, that is, into amino acids. From the separated amino acids each particular tissue can take the number and kind it needs for restoring the loss it has sustained. Thus it is possible for an animal to eat but one or two kinds of protein (as on a milk diet) and yet each cell is able to construct its own specific proteins from these two food proteins; this ''is one of the most astounding attributes of living things.'' The evidences upon which this is based are many; a few must suffice.

a. Absorption and Resynthesis of Amino Acids.—The ingested protein material does not appear in the blood stream as protein but as amino acids. During absorption the amino acids in the blood increase from the starvation level of about 6.5 mg. per 100 c.c. to 8.5 mg. This appears to be the only nitrogenous material (except perhaps a small amount of very simple peptids) normally furnished to the cells of the body.

A food protein entering the blood is treated and behaves as a foreign protein. If the molecule of the injected protein is small enough to pass through the excreting cells of the kidney (as in case of egg albumin and gelatin), it is excreted in the urine. The injection of a certain protein may cause the formation of antibodies (p. 164) by which the animal is immunized against this particular protein. If a second injection takes place, allergic symptoms appear and death may result. If the same kind of protein is eaten and digested the absorption of the digestion products or their injection into the blood is not followed by the above results. We may therefore conclude that digestion of the proteins safeguards the animal; this is well shown by the impunity with which snake venom (a protein) may be swallowed.

b. Feeding Amino Acids.—Abderhalden and Rona fed a dog not on protein but on the digestion products obtained by submitting the protein to tryptic digestion until it had completely disappeared and only amino acids were present. The dog was able to utilize these amino acids for repairing its waste; this was true even when these products were injected into the blood vessels of the animal.

c. **Incomplete Proteins.**—It will be recalled that the protein gelatin is derived from collagen which is classed with the albuminoids, or scleroproteins. For some time it has been known that while gelatin can be used by the body, it differs from the albumins and globulins in that, while the latter are able to sustain the life of an animal, gelatin cannot do this. In other words, if an animal should eat no other protein than gelatin, it would die of protein starvation. The reason for this difference between these various proteins is now clear.

From Table XVIII it appears that gelatin is deficient in the amino acids, glycine, lysine, tryptophan, and cystine. In addition to these, other amino acids are lacking. If gelatin is the only protein fed, the animal obtains no tyrosine, cystine, lysine, or tryptophan, amino acids found in nearly all the proteins of its body; hence the repair of the body protein is impossible and the animal dies in consequence. That this is the true explanation was proved by Kaufmann who found that, if in addition to the gelatin the animal be fed with the amino acids lacking in the gelatin, life can be sustained. From the foregoing it can be seen that the various amino acids are, in general, not interconvertible in the animal body. Further evidence of this will be given in Chapter XXII.

How Is Anabolism Brought About? How the protoplasm takes the necessary amino acids out of the tissue fluid and synthesizes them into its own specific proteins is difficult to state. Perhaps the plasma membrane by its selective permeability permits the entrance of only definite quantities of certain amino acids. Perhaps specific intracellular enzymes are responsible.

According to the last theory the building of amino acids into proteins is a function of certain enzymes always found in the cells of our body. But an enzyme capable of synthesizing must also be able to split up the compounds they form—reversible action of enzymes (Chap. II). Whether these cellular enzymes accelerate the building up of tissue proteins or their tearing down depends upon the point of equilibrium of the substrate. When the supply of amino acid is adequate, the enzymes build up tissue proteins; when this supply dwindles, the proteins are decomposed. This will be considered in a following section.

As stated on a preceding page, the power of a cell to manufacture from "common" materials found in the blood its own specific proteins is an astounding phenomenon. But even more wonderful is the power of the protoplasmic mechanism to construct exceedingly specific materials previously not found in the body. As an example of this we may mention the formation of antibodies, such as bacteriolysins.

III. PROTEIN CATABOLISM

The destruction of proteins in the body gives rise to two classes of waste products, the nitrogenous and the non-nitrogenous, the latter including carbon dioxide and water which are also produced by the catabolism of the fats and carbohydrates. The nitrogenous products are peculiar to protein catabolism, since the proteins are the only foods that contain nitrogen. The most important of these products are urea, uric acid, creatinin, and ammonia salts. In addition to these, the proteins give rise to waste materials containing sulfur and phosphorus. The waste products containing nitrogen, sulfur, or phosphorus are excreted almost exclusively by the kidneys. Before discussing the manner in which the nitrogenous waste products are formed from the proteins during catabolism, it may be well to study their physical and chemical properties.

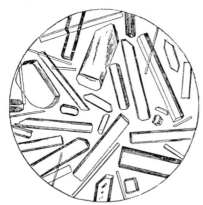

Fig. 184.—Urea crystals. (Lehmann.)

Fig. 185.—Uric acid crystals.

A. Nitrogenous Waste Products

Urea.—Urea is a white, crystalline substance, Fig. 184, easily soluble in water; the solution has a neutral reaction. It is excreted to the extent of 20 or 30 grams a day; this quantity depends very largely upon the nature of the food eaten, for the more protein one consumes, the more urea is excreted. Its great solubility and relative nontoxicity render urea a very admirable means of transporting and eliminating the larger part of nitrogenous waste material. The urea usually contains from 85 to 90 per cent of all the nitrogen found in the waste products in the urine.

That urea contains nitrogen can be proved by placing a small amount of it in a dry test tube and gently heating it. When the urea has melted, a little further heating will drive off ammonia, as can be detected by the odor and by letting the fumes come in contact with moist red litmus paper.

The composition of urea is expressed by the formula $(NH_2)_2CO$, or

$$\begin{array}{c} NH_2 \\ / \\ C = O \\ \backslash \\ NH_2 \end{array}$$

At this time we may call attention to the close relationship between ammonia—NH_3—, ammonium carbonate—$(NH_4)_2CO_3$—, and urea. The ammonium carbonate has the graphic formula:

$$\begin{array}{c} O - NH_4 \\ / \\ C = O \\ \backslash \\ O - NH_4 \end{array}$$

It can readily be seen that by taking one molecule of water from each of the O—NH_4 groups the ammonium carbonate is transformed into urea. This close relationship is also seen in the fact that the above-described transformation of ammonium carbonate into urea has been accomplished in the laboratory.* On the other hand, urea can be transformed into ammonium carbonate by heating it with alkalies. This is also brought about by the action of certain microorganisms which readily develop in voided urine and thereby cause the ammoniacal odor of putrid urine:

$$CO(NH_2)_2 + 2H_2O = (NH_4)_2CO_3$$

Urea is also decomposed by treating it with nitrous acid:

$$CO(NH_2)_2 + 2HNO_2 \rightarrow CO_2 + 3H_2O + 2N_2$$

The decomposition of urea can also be brought about by bromine water to which excess of NaOH has been added (this forms sodium hypobromite—$NaBrO$). This reaction gives us a means of determining the amount of urea present in the urine. The gas, CO_2, evolved in the above chemical action is absorbed by the alkaline fluid (sodium hydroxide) ; the other gas, nitrogen, is then collected and measured.

*Urea was the first organic substance artificially made in the laboratory. Wöhler, in 1828, produced it from ammonium cyanate. $CO.N.NH_4$.
According to Werner urea is formed by the union of NH_3 with the cyanic acid, $H-N=C=O$, which is derived by oxidation of proteins. Its formula should be written:

$$H - N = C - O \atop \backslash \, / \atop NH_3$$

From the formula of urea—$(NH_2)_2CO$—it can be seen that the molecular weight of urea is $(14 + 2) \times 2 + 12 + 16 = 60$. Of this the nitrogen contributes 28 parts, or approximately one-half. From the amount (by weight) of the nitrogen collected from a sample of urine, the amount of urea in the urine can be readily calculated. A very simple manner of doing this is by means of a ureometer.

Uric acid, $C_5H_4N_4O_3$, is excreted to the extent of 0.25 to 1 gram a day. It is a white crystalline solid, Fig. 185, sparingly soluble in water. Being an acid, it unites with alkalies to form salts such as sodium urate and ammonium urate, which are slightly more soluble than the acid itself. The feeble solubility may cause urates to be deposited in the joints (gout).

Creatinine, $C_4H_7N_3O$, is excreted from one to two grams per day. For the chemistry of creatinine and creatine the reader must consult some advanced work on Physiological Chemistry.

Hippuric acid (*hippos,* horse) is a nitrogenous product formed synthetically by the kidneys. Benzoic acid, C_6H_5COOH, derived exclusively from the products found in the vegetables and fruits eaten, is poisonous and cannot be oxidized by the body. To prevent its deleterious action, the kidneys cause it to unite with glycine (amino acetic acid), forming benzoyl-glycine, or hippuric acid. This synthetic reaction is another illustration of the detoxication by which the body protects itself.

Ammonium salts are excreted to the extent of about 0.7 gram per day (reckoned as NH_3). These salts are chiefly those of the inorganic acids, for the organic ammonium salts are largely transformed into urea (see infra).

B. Formation of Waste Products

Destruction of Amino Acids.—Not all of the amino acids absorbed by the blood from the alimentary canal are used for the repair of the cells. There may be a surplus of certain of the amino acids derived from the food proteins; being of no use in this form, the body changes them in the following manner: From our discussion of amino acid in the chapter on foods, the reader will, no doubt, remember that the amino acid molecule may be considered as made up of a "central body" and two molecular processes, namely, the carboxyl group —COOH—and the amino group—NH_2. The former group renders the molecule an acid; the latter, in conjunction with the carboxyl, makes it an organic amino acid. Certain tissues have the power to split the NH_2 group from the rest of the molecule. The split off part takes the form of ammonia, NH_3; this process is called **deamination.** However, by far the larger part of the original amino acid molecule still remains as an organic acid which retains about 95 per cent of the original energy. We shall deal with this carbon moiety in our study of carbohydrate metabolism.

The Formation of Urea.—One of two things may happen to the ammonia set free by deamination of amino acids:

(*a*) It may unite with sulfuric acid—H_2SO_4—or phosphoric acid —H_3PO_4—(formed during the oxidation of certain proteins) and thereby form ammonium sulfate or phosphate. These salts are excreted by the kidneys.

(*b*) It may unite with water and form ammonium hydroxide —NH_4OH. This reacts with the carbonic acid—H_2CO_3—(formed by the union of H_2O and CO_2) to form ammonium carbonate— $(NH_4)_2CO_3$—thus $2NH_4 \boxed{OH + H_2} CO_3 \rightarrow (NH_4)_2CO_3 + 2H_2O$. By the removal of water the ammonium carbonate is transformed into urea. The object of this chemical change must be sought, no doubt, in the detoxication of the injurious ammonium carbonate into the less toxic urea.

In the formation of urea the liver plays an important part, as can be learned from the following facts:

1. Amino acids added to liver pulp are decomposed, ammonia being liberated. This action is due to a deaminizing ferment, which has been found in many organs besides the liver, such as the lungs, pancreas, kidneys, etc.

2. When certain amino acids are circulated through the liver, the blood becomes richer in urea, while the acids disappear. Administering amino acid by mouth also increases the urea output.

3. Ammonium carbonate circulated through the liver is also transformed into urea.

4. After removal of the liver, there is, according to Mann, no urea found in the animal body.

From these facts we may conclude that a certain amount of the amino acids carried by the portal vein from the intestines to the liver is deaminized and the nitrogenous moiety transformed into urea by the liver. In the wear and tear which the proteins sustain during cellular activity, the amino acids are also deaminized; the resulting ammonium carbonate is carried to the liver to be transformed into urea.

Nucleoproteins and Uric Acid.—Forming the essential material of the nucleus, the nucleoproteins and nucleins play a very important part in the functions of the cell. During the process of digestion the ingested nucleoprotein is first split up into a simple protein and nuclein; this nuclein is still further broken up into a simple protein and a substance called nucleic acid. According to some investigators the nucleic acid is decomposed by an intestinal enzyme, known as nuclease. Or it may be absorbed and decomposed in the body, giving rise to a large number of products which we may tabulate in the following manner:

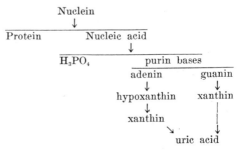

Each step is the result of the action of a special enzyme.

The uric acid directly formed from the food is called *exogenous uric acid.* The amount of uric acid excreted varies from ¼ to one gram per day, depending upon the nature of the food eaten. When a person lives on such foods as potatoes, milk, eggs, rice, white bread, sugars, and fats, the amount of uric acid is markedly decreased. Such foods are known as *purin-free foods.* On the other hand, most animal foods, especially glandular organs, like the sweetbreads (thymus and pancreas), kidney, and liver, and such vegetables as peas, beans, oatmeal, and asparagus, contain nucleins and therefore give rise to an increased formation and elimination of this waste product. Or the purin bases may be ingested, as, e.g., the hypoxanthin found in meat extracts. Siven found that feeding an animal with meat extracts caused a greater excretion of uric acid, but, when meat from which the extracts had been removed was fed, the uric acid was not increased beyond the normal.

When an individual lives on a purin-free diet, the uric acid excreted is derived from his own tissues and is called *endogenous uric acid.* The amount varies with different people from 0.3 to 0.5 gram per day, but for the same individual it is very constant. As to the origin of this uric acid, we may say that it is formed from nucleoproteins and purin bodies of the tissues. Increased activity of leucocytes has by some been regarded as giving rise to much endogenous uric acid. This occurs, e.g., after recovery from pneumonia and after extensive burns in which much tissue has been destroyed. In fevers, and in severe muscular work in which the wear and tear of the tissues is increased, it is claimed the endogenous uric acid excretion is augmented. Some believe that the disintegration of the nucleus extruded from the red blood cell is also concerned. As to where uric acid is made, we are still in the dark.

Synthesis of Nucleoproteins.—The animal body possesses the power to synthesize the purins and nucleins, for on a purin-free diet the amount of endogenous uric acid excreted is constant. To do so, the diet must contain the amino acids, arginine and histidine. The chick embryo also is able to form nucleoproteins, seeing that the amount of these proteins in its body is greater than that present in the egg; the phosphoprotein, vitellin, of the yolk is used no doubt for this purpose.

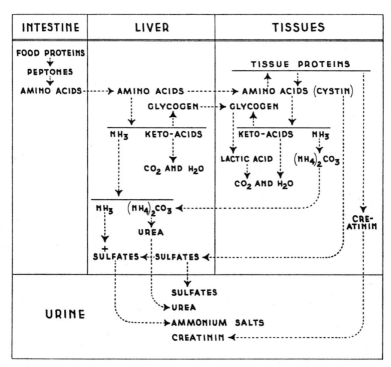

Fig. 186.—Diagram to illustrate protein metabolism.

Creatinine Formation.—This nitrogenous waste product—$C_4H_7N_3O$—is, like uric acid, of both exogenous and endogenous origin. To go into the chemistry of its formation would take us beyond the scope of this book. Only one feature needs to detain us. While on a diet fairly rich in proteins the urea excreted contains from 85 to 90 per cent of all the nitrogen lost by the body and the creatinine only 3.5 per cent, on a diet poor in proteins these values are changed to 60 and 17.2 per cent, respectively. From this it is concluded that creatinine is an index of the real tissue wear and tear. It is stated that increased tissue destruction, as during severe muscle work and fever, increases the production of creatinine.

Ammonium salts are excreted to the extent of about 0.7 gram per day (reckoned as NH_3). These are chiefly salts of inorganic acids It is usually found that as the excretion of ammonium salts increases, the urea excretion decreases. This relationship is due to the fact that when there is an excess of acid salts to be excreted, ammonia derived from urea, is used to neutralize these acid radicals (see p 401). Thus the fixed bases of the body (Na, K, Ca, etc.) are preserved.

Sulfur and Phosphorus Compounds.—By the oxidation of the sulfur of the protein molecule sulfuric acid is formed. As the nucleo proteins also contain phosphorus, on oxidation they give rise to phosphoric acid. The ammonia formed as indicated above unites with some of these acids, thereby neutralizing them; the resulting ammonium sulfate and phosphate are excreted by the kidneys. The more acids formed, the greater is the quantity of the ammonium salts in the urine.

IV. METABOLISM DURING STARVATION

It can be readily understood that as long as the animal lives it expends energy, and therefore the destruction of material must go on All the secretions and the excretions, although lessened, continue to be formed; even the alimentary canal discharges a small amount of material composed of the residue of secretions, epithelial cells, and mucous. After the first two or three days of starvation, no pain is experienced. As the body wastes away, the individual becomes weaker and spends a great deal of time in sleep. A day or two before death the rate of pulse and respiration is lessened and the body temperature drops.

To supply the necessary energy for running the body machinery the stored-up energy in carbohydrates, fats (adipose tissue), and proteins is drawn upon. During the first day or two carbohydrates furnish the larger part of the energy, for they form the most readily available reserve material. This supply, however, is soon exhausted and then the fats to a very large extent (80 to 90 per cent) and the proteins of the body to a lesser extent (10 to 20 per cent) are utilized In the last stage of starvation nearly all the energy is derived from the proteins. The weight loss sustained during starvation is not the same for all organs: the skeletal muscles lose 31 per cent; the liver 55; the pancreas and lungs, 18; the heart and brain, 3 per cent. That the skeletal muscles, which are used but little during inanition, lose 31 per cent while the constantly active heart suffers a loss of only 3 per cent is, at first, somewhat puzzling, but may find its explanation in autolysis.

Autolysis.—All organs contain within themselves the agencies for their own destruction. For example, an excised liver, obtained aseptically and placed in chloroform water to exclude the proteolytic action of bacteria, undergoes autolysis, or self-destruction, brought about by the unrestrained activity of the proteases, lipases, and carbohydrases normally present in the organ. By these enzymes the proteins, fats, and carbohydrates are decomposed. While during normal life such destruction is largely prevented, we frequently see evidence of a carefully controlled autolysis; for example, the atrophy of the mammary glands at the close of lactation and of the uterus after parturition, the general atrophy of old age, and the resolution (dissolving) of the exudate formed in the lungs during pneumonia.

During starvation some organs (heart and brain) are absolutely necessary and their activity cannot be dispensed with; hence they must be supplied with proteins. These proteins are obtained from the skeletal muscles, which must be looked upon not only as organs of contraction but also as storehouses for proteins. The proteins of the muscles and other organs are digested, perhaps, by the proteolytic enzymes present in the tissues into soluble products, amino acids, which are then carried by the blood stream to the vital organs. Another striking illustration of the transfer of proteins from one organ to another is seen in the tremendous development, in the spawning and fasting salmon, of the ovaries at the expense of the muscles, which lose as much as 30 per cent of their weight.

V. NITROGENOUS EQUILIBRIUM

In a protein fast, during which an individual takes an adequate amount of energy-yielding food (carbohydrates and fats) but no protein, the nitrogen excretion, chiefly in the form of urea, gradually diminishes until a fixed level of nitrogen loss (much below the normal level) is reached. This is called the *irreducible nitrogen excretion* and is thought to represent the amount of body protein lost by unavoidable wear and tear. Suppose that such an individual excretes 15 grams of urea; as 1 gram of urea represents approximately 3 grams of protein,* there is a loss of 45 grams of body proteins. If now he eats 45 grams of proteins, one would think that this ought to cover the loss sustained and that the ingested and egested nitrogen should be equal. However, such is not the case, for the excretion of urea

---

*The following is a useful table:

1 gram nitrogen = 2+ grams urea
1 gram urea = 3 grams protein
1 gram N = 6.25 grams protein
1 gram protein = 5 grams muscle tissue

is now considerably more than 15 grams, and the individual is still in a negative nitrogen balance. The reason for this lies in the fact that the ratio of the various amino acids in the food protein is not the same as that of the amino acids in the body protein which the food protein must replace (see p. 395). Therefore, a certain amount of these food amino acids must be discarded. The more closely the protein of the diet approximates in exact composition the body proteins, the less protein will have to be fed in order to balance the irreducible nitrogen loss.

Levels of Nitrogenous Equilibrium.—Let us suppose that a person is in nitrogenous equilibrium on a diet composed of 200 gm. protein and 350 gm. carbohydrate; decreasing the amount of proteins below 200 grams causes a loss of body proteins. But, if the amount of carbohydrate be increased to, say, 400 grams, it is possible to maintain nitrogenous equilibrium with 150 gm. proteins. On the other hand, if the amount of carbohydrate be reduced to 300 gm., it is necessary to raise the amount of proteins. We therefore learn that:

(*a*) Nitrogenous equilibrium can be established at various levels; i.e., with a large or with a small amount of protein in the diet.

(*b*) When the equilibrium is at a high level, some of the protein can be replaced by carbohydrate, or fat. In a high level of equilibrium, a certain amount of protein was used for fuel purposes; this function can be taken over very advantageously by the other organic foodstuffs. Hence carbohydrates and fats are called the *protein sparers;* in this the carbohydrate is of far more value than the fat. The great economic importance of this is seen readily when we stop to consider that a pound of food protein costs from 15 to 30 times as much as a pound of carbohydrate. But this replacement has its limits, for no matter how large an amount of carbohydrate or fat the diet may contain, a certain irreducible minimum of tissue wear and tear takes place; this can be restored only by the eating of proteins. What constitutes the minimum amount of protein necessary to establish nitrogenous equilibrium, and whether a high level of nitrogenous equilibrium is better than a low level, are points we shall discuss in Chapter XXII.

Storage of Proteins.—Let us suppose that to a diet of 150 gm. proteins and 400 gm. carbohydrates (which maintains an adult man in nitrogenous equilibrium and furnishes a sufficient amount of energy) there be added 50 grams of protein. The result is that all of the protein is destroyed in the body; none is saved. We may conclude:

(*a*) The amount of protein destroyed in the body is determined by the amount eaten.

(*b*) The power of the adult human body to save and store proteins from an excessive amount of proteins fed is practically nil.

(*c*) In these two respects proteins differ radically from carbohydrates and fats. The latter are not destroyed in proportion to the amount eaten but may be stored in the body chiefly in the form of fats.

Increasing the amount of protein in the food beyond that necessary for repairing the wear and tear of the body may cause the carbohydrates and fats, otherwise necessary for fuel purposes, to be spared and stored. Consequently, it is possible for an animal to be in nitrogenous equilibrium with a large amount of protein, and actually to store up some carbohydrate or fat; in this condition the body weight increases. On the other hand, on a low level of nitrogenous equilibrium the amount of nitrogen in the food may be sufficient to cover all the protein catabolized, but the animal needs more energy than can be obtained from its food, and to obtain it the stored-up carbohydrates and fats are attacked; hence, in this condition the body, although in nitrogenous equilibrium, loses weight.

To the above statement of the inability of the body to store proteins three exceptions must be made:

(*a*) When new tissues are being constructed, as in the growing child and in pregnancy.

(*b*) When the body has previously lost a large amount of its proteins, as after wasting diseases and starvation.

(*c*) Also protein is stored during a period of muscle hypertrophy, e.g., as a result of muscular exercise.

VI. FUNCTIONS OF THE PROTEINS

The food proteins, after their digestion into amino acids, serve several functions, of which we may mention the following:

1. The amino acids carried by the blood to the cells are synthesized into the proteins characteristic of the cells. As we have seen, each cell selects a certain number of amino acids of the types necessary for the reconstruction of its proteins and protoplasm.

2. They are used by the cells in the manufacture of enzymes, genes, hormones, and other nitrogenous cellular products.

3. From them are made the blood proteins which are indispensable, among other reasons, because of their colloidal osmotic pressure.

4. Used as a source of energy, the nitrogen of the amino acid is of little value. However, when the amino group—NH_2—has been split off from the amino acid, there remains the larger part of the molecule which is devoid of nitrogen but contains nearly all the carbon of the original amino acid. This residue can be utilized, like the carbohydrates and fats, for the production of energy. If not immediately needed, certain of the amino acids, such as glycine, alanine, cystine, and arginine, are transformed into carbohydrate such as glucose or glycogen. The evidence for this will be given when we discuss the subject of glycosuria (Chap. XIX). In their function of supplying energy the proteins are greatly inferior to the fats and carbohydrates, being financially and physiologically uneconomical.

CHAPTER XIX

CARBOHYDRATE AND FAT METABOLISM

I. CARBOHYDRATE METABOLISM

The importance of carbohydrate metabolism is readily appreciated when we learn that carbohydrates constitute 50 to 60 per cent of our food and that about 60 per cent of the protein, and, according to some investigators, about 10 per cent of the fats (glycerol) are transformed into carbohydrates in the body.

Functions of Carbohydrates.—Our study of muscles has shown us the great part played by carbohydrates in supplying energy for muscle work. As approximately only 20 per cent of the liberated energy is utilized for the mechanical work, the carbohydrate food becomes an important factor in the maintaining of the body temperature; in fact, with the usual diet, from 50 to 60 per cent of the total heat produced in the body is derived from this source (see Chap. XXI). In our study of fat metabolism we shall learn that carbohydrates in excess of what is immediately needed by the body or of what can be stored as glycogen are transformed into fat.

Compared with the other organic foodstuffs—fats and proteins—carbohydrates are peculiar in that they are the most readily available and most easily oxidizable material in the body. Thus, the ingestion of 100 grams of glucose was followed within twenty minutes by an increase in the respiratory quotient (see p. 440), indicating that in this short length of time an extra amount of carbohydrate was being oxidized. Contrasted with the proteins, the waste products of carbohydrate catabolism—water and carbon dioxide—are easy of elimination and, under the usual conditions, have no deleterious effects.

Absorption.—The carbohydrates of the food are split up by digestion into monosaccharides. From the starch is formed glucose; the lactose of milk gives rise to glucose and galactose, while the cane sugar forms glucose and fructose. As the main carbohydrate in our food is starch, glucose is by far the most important monosaccharide, and it is also possible that the other monosaccharides are transformed by the body into glucose; for our purpose therefore we need only speak of glucose. In this form the carbohydrates are absorbed by the direct channel, that is, by the blood capillaries of the intestine.

The venous blood from the small intestine is collected by the superior mesenteric vein which empties into the large portal vein and is thus brought to the liver. In the liver the portal vein splits up into capillaries which again unite to form the hepatic veins which empty into the inferior vena cava, Fig. 78. This blood supply to the liver, it will be noticed, is venous; it may be called the functional circulation. In addition to this, the liver is supplied with arterial blood by means of the hepatic artery (from the abdominal aorta) which finally also discharges its blood into the hepatic veins; this may be spoken of as the nutritive circulation.

A. Storage of Carbohydrates

Since carbohydrates are the materials most directly and most readily utilized by muscles for the production of energy, a supply of glucose ought to be always and readily available. A large amount of sugar poured into the blood during absorption might raise the osmotic pressure to heights detrimental to the tissues. Some mechanism must, therefore, exist to make possible the former and to prevent the latter. Both of these requirements are met. During absorption of an ordinary meal the amount of sugar in the general blood stream rises but little above the usual concentration of 0.07 to 0.1 per cent* and this subsides within an hour or two. Neither is there during the ordinary muscle work any marked decrease of sugar in the blood for any length of time.

Glycogenesis and Glycogenolysis.—The manner in which the sugar content of the blood is regulated was first investigated by Claude Bernard in 1853. He and later investigators found:

1. During the height of absorption, the blood in the portal vein contains more sugar than the hepatic veins or any other blood vessel.

2. If a rabbit be well fed for two or three days on carbohydrate food (carrots, e.g.) and immediately after death the liver be examined for glucose, only a small quantity is found; on the other hand, such a liver contains a large quantity of a polysaccharide known as glycogen, $n(C_6H_{10}O_5)$.

3. When the liver, obtained in this manner, is not examined immediately but is left at the room temperature for several hours, it will be found to contain more glucose and less glycogen than in the previous case.

These various facts are explained in the following manner (Fig. 187): When the blood in the portal vein, during the absorption of carbohydrates from the intestine, contains an excess of glucose (that

---

*It may be of interest to note that at this percentage the amount (5 grams) of sugar in the total blood is about one teaspoonful. This is equivalent to 20 Calories = 8520 Kgm. or 61,720 foot-pounds. This would enable a 150 pound person to climb a stairs about 400 feet in height.

s, above the usual amount of 0.1 per cent), most of this excess is removed by the liver cells, transformed into glycogen, and stored as such. This process is known as glycogenesis. The sugar in the arterial blood is used by the cells of the body, especially the muscle; this decreases the amount of sugar, and the glycogen is now transformed into glucose and thrown into the blood stream. This process is known as glycogenolysis. Glycogenesis and glycogenolysis are, no doubt, enzymatic actions which may be expressed by the following equation:

$$nC_6H_{12}O_6 \rightleftarrows n(C_6H_{10}O_5) + nH_2O.$$

Muscles also possess the power to form glycogen from glucose and to store it to the extent of about 1 per cent. During work the glycogen, as we have seen in a previous chapter, is broken down into lactic

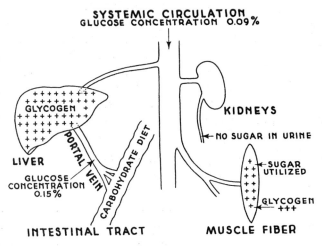

Fig. 187.—Illustrating the history of glucose in the normal body. (After Gradwohl: Blood and Urine Chemistry, The C. V. Mosby Co.)

acid; this loss is replenished by the absorption of glucose from the blood. The amount stored by the liver is generally placed at about 100 grams; that in the muscles at 350 grams. The total amount of carbohydrates is about equivalent to that consumed with the food in the course of two days. It can readily be seen that this amount fluctuates constantly. As the carbohydrates are utilized for the production of energy, any condition calling for an increase in the expenditure of energy, such as muscular exertion and exposure to cold, is accompanied by an increased consumption of glycogen. In starvation also the amount is decreased.

Sources of Glycogen.—Glycogen can be derived from four distinct sources.

1. *The three monosaccharides,* glucose, fructose (from cane sugar), and galactose (from lactose, or milk sugar) are all used in the formation of glycogen. Perhaps the last two must be converted into glucose before they are transformed into glycogen.

2. We have learned that during activity the muscle glycogen is split into *lactic acid.* Some of this acid is reconstructed into glycogen in the muscles themselves; part of it passes into the blood stream and is carried to the liver where the same process takes place.

3. It has been firmly established that the proteins of the food or body may serve as the source of this glucose. Fasting dogs, for example, fed on washed fibrin or casein deposit liver glycogen, and in rats this can be brought about by feeding the amino acid, alanine. In the previous chapter we discussed the deamination of *amino acids.* The residue of the amino acid, after the removal of the NH_2 group, contains all the carbon and constitutes by far the larger part of the original amino acid molecule; it also holds approximately 95 per cent of the energy. This material, an organic acid, is therefore rich in energy. It may be used immediately for the production of kinetic energy, or, similar to the lactic acid, it may be transformed in the liver to glycogen.

4. The *glycerol* formed by the digestion of fat is also used in the formation of liver glycogen. There is no convincing evidence that the fatty acid (palmitic, stearic, etc.) can thus be used.

Glycosuria.—When, for reasons to be discussed presently, the amount of sugar in the general blood stream exceeds a certain limit —about 0.17 per cent—the condition is known as hyperglycemia (*hyper,* above, glyc = glucose, *emia,* blood) ; on reaching the kidneys, this excess of sugar is removed by these organs and thrown into the urine. The presence of sugar in the urine is called glycosuria.

B. Regulation of Carbohydrate Metabolism

Carbohydrate metabolism is closely regulated by both a neural and a humoral mechanism. Probably five hormones, either directly or by influencing each other, play a part; this renders the subject exceedingly complex. At present there is so much conflict in the experimental results and in the opinions as to how the various factors operate, that no satisfactory brief statement is possible. We shall note what is generally accepted as perhaps the most likely exposition of the matter.

By injury to the central nervous system Claude Bernard produced glycosuria in dogs. The presence of sugar in the urine of a diabetic had been recognized for years. In 1899 the memorable observation was made by Minkowski and von Mering that extirpation of the pancreas invariably leads to very severe glycosuria. Death follows in two or three weeks.

It was soon recognized that the glycosuria resulting from removal of the pancreas was due to an unusual amount of sugar in the blood and that the disturbances in digestion, which of necessity follow this operation, have nothing to do with the excretion of glucose. If a small piece of the pancreas, having no duct connection with the intestine, be allowed to remain, no glycosuria sets in. Ivy and Farrell

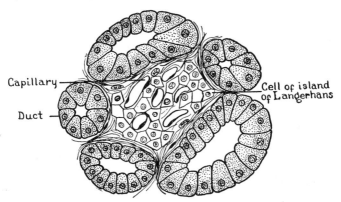

Fig. 188.—Structure of the pancreas showing the islands of Langerhans and the alveoli of the glands forming the pancreatic juice. (Francis: Fundamentals of Anatomy, The C. V. Mosby Co.)

removed the pancreas and transplanted a part of it into the mammary gland; this prevented hyperglycemia and glycosuria. As the nerve supply to this transplant was not necessary for the prevention of glycosuria, it was argued that the pancreas controls the glucose content of the blood by manufacturing a hormone, or internal secretion, which on being thrown into the blood governs some organ or organs concerned with carbohydrate metabolism. This hormone was isolated by Banting and Best in 1922, and is known as insulin (*insula,* island). Abel, in 1926, obtained insulin in a crystalline form.

In the body of the pancreas are situated small masses of cells, *the islands of Langerhans* (Fig. 188) which form no connection with the pancreatic duct and are not concerned in the formation of the pancreatic juice; these cells elaborate the hormone, insulin, which is thrown into the blood stream. By feeding depancreatized dogs with food essential for normal dogs and injecting insulin, they have been kept alive for well over four years.   The hyperglycemia and the resulting glycosuria which follow extirpation of the pancreas are generally attributed to (a) the loss of the power of the tissues to utilize the carbohyrates for energy purposes and (b) the inability of the liver and, perhaps, the muscles to convert glucose into glycogen and to store this product, Fig. 189.   We may present the following evidence for these statements.

1. The value of the respiratory quotient is increased (to unity) by the consumption of carbohydrates; proteins and fats, on the other hand, decrease the quotient (p. 409).   In a normal animal using all

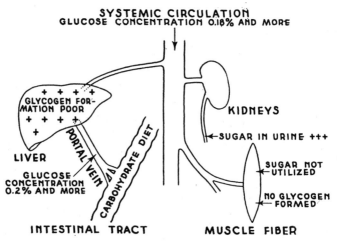

Fig. 189.—Illustrating the history of glucose in pancreatic glycosuria. Compare this with Fig. 187. (After Gradwohl: Blood and Urine Chemistry, The C. V. Mosby Co.)

three foodstuffs the respiratory quotient is about 0.82, but in a diabetic animal it falls to 0.7; this shows that no preformed carbohydrates are used.   The injection of insulin brings the quotient to normal, showing an increase in the consumption of carbohydrates.

2. Normally the venous blood flowing from the active muscles contains less glucose than is found in the arterial blood, an indication of the using of the glucose by the muscle.   In a depancreatized animal this arteriovenous difference is less than normal, proving the inability of the tissues to use the blood glucose; this is restored by the administration of insulin.

3. When a normal excised heart is perfused with blood containing both glucose and insulin, more glucose is retained and, no doubt, used by the cardiac muscle than when the blood contains only glucose.

The above-discussed facts may be explained by assuming that the insulin confers upon the tissues the power to transform blood glucose into muscle glycogen; in this form the carbohydrates can be used by the tissues. This view is supported by the fact that:

4. When a normal animal with 0.1 per cent glucose in its blood receives an injection of insulin, the percentage of glucose falls below the normal (hypoglycemia) without any of it having been excreted by the kidneys. Part of the sugar which disappeared from the blood has been found in the muscles in the form of glycogen.

5. After a muscle in a normal animal had performed a certain amount of work, the glycogen content of the muscle was restored within one hour. In a depancreatized dog, with the same amount of work, more than 24 hours were required.

6. In addition to its influence over the carbohydrate metabolism in the muscles, insulin restores to the depancreatized animal the ability to store liver glycogen by inhibiting the glycogenolysis and perhaps also by favoring the depositing of glycogen (glycogenesis) in this organ.

Before discussing the influence of other hormones on carbohydrate metabolism we must for a moment digress to consider the pathologic condition of diabetes.

Diabetes Mellitus.—The disease generally known as diabetes is closely related to, if not identical with, pancreatic glycosuria, and consequently the modern treatment of this disease is the injection of sufficient insulin so that the carbohydrates absorbed may be properly utilized by the body.

In severe diabetes, sugar is excreted whether the diet contains carbohydrates or not; in fact, even in total starvation the urine contains sugar, sometimes in astonishingly large quantities. In this case the sugar could not have been derived from carbohydrate, for the body contains but a very limited supply of glycogen and glucose; the excreted sugar must therefore have originated from proteins or fats.

As in severe diabetes carbohydrates cannot be utilized for the production of energy, the diabetic uses far more fat and proteins than a normal individual. It is often said that "fats burn in the fire of carbohydrates." In consequence of the lack of this fire, the oxidation of the fats is incomplete and gives rise to highly detrimental compounds, the so-called acetone bodies, which are excreted by the kidneys (acetonuria or ketonuria—see p. 421). Being unable to use the carbohydrates of the food for the production of energy, the diabetic experiences great hunger and fatigue; and, because much water is excreted by the kidneys in order to eliminate the excess sugar of the blood, one of the outstanding symptoms is great thirst. The power of the tissues to resist infections is largely decreased. By restoring the power to transform glucose into muscle glycogen, insulin enables the diabetic to utilize carbohydrates; as a result the excessive destruction of fats and proteins and the resulting ketonuria cease, the body weight is increased, strength is regained, and life prolonged. Although no complete recovery has ever been recorded, yet sugar tolerance and, therefore, sugar utilization by a diabetic are increased by the continual use of insulin. Unfortunately insulin cannot be administered by mouth because it is destroyed by either pepsin or trypsin.

REGULATING THE SUPPLY OF INSULIN.—The administration of too large a dose of insulin causes an abnormal reduction of the glucose in the blood. When the amount drops below 0.07 per cent (hypoglycemia), there are great pallor, dilated pupils, increased heartbeat, sweating, hunger pangs, muscular weakness, mental confusion, and hyperirritability; at 0.045 per cent violent convulsions occur and finally coma; these disturbances are very speedily relieved by the ingestion of a small quantity of glucose.

ADRENALIN.—Before we endeavor to explain the symptoms of severe hypoglycemia, we must speak of another internal secretion, adrenalin, which plays a large part in carbohydrate metabolism. This hormone, also known as adrenin, is made by the adrenals, or suprarenal glands, lying just above the kidneys, Fig. 219. The perfusion of a frog's liver with Ringer's solution containing adrenalin causes an increase of glucose in the solution. From this we may conclude that adrenalin accelerates glycogenolysis and thus renders the blood hyperglycemic and may cause glycosuria. The two hormones, insulin and adrenalin, are therefore antagonistic in that the former causes carbohydrates to be stored as glycogen in the various parts of the body, while the latter mobilizes the sugar for cell consumption. In a normal animal an increase in blood sugar is followed by an increased formation of insulin which insures the storage of the excess sugar; on the other hand, when the blood becomes hypoglycemic the adrenals are stimulated to a greater production of adrenalin, and the resultant mobilization of carbohydrates brings the percentage of sugar up to normal. As soon as the blood glucose has been either decreased or increased sufficiently as the case may demand, the production of these hormones ceases for the time being. But when an excessive amount of insulin has been given to a diabetic, the continual hypoglycemia calls forth a large amount of adrenalin. In our study of the adrenals (Chap. XXIII) we shall learn that adrenalin stimulates those organs that are largely responsible for many of the distressing symptoms mentioned in the previous paragraph. It is therefore important that the dose of insulin bear a correct ratio to the amount of carbohydrates ingested. The important facts of carbohydrate metabolism and the influence of insulin and adrenalin are illustrated in Fig. 190.

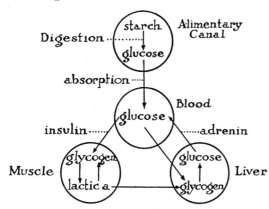

Fig. 190.—Diagram to illustrate carbohydrate metabolism.

The secretion of adrenalin during hypoglycemia was beautifully shown by Cannon and others. A denervated heart is readily accelerated by adrenalin. By the injection of insulin the glucose content of the blood was decreased; when this fell to about 0.07 per cent, the heart beat faster, and, as the blood became more and more hypoglycemic, the cardiac acceleration increased. If the adrenals were removed previously to the injection of insulin, no quickening of the heartbeat occurred, notwithstanding the hypoglycemia. The conclusion that a decrease in blood glucose calls forth an outflow of adrenalin is substantiated by the observation that the injection of glucose into the hypoglycemic blood speedily reduced the greatly accelerated heartbeat to normal.

It will be recalled that a decrease in the sugar content of the blood is held by some to initiate the hunger contractions of the stomach. As insulin causes hypoglycemia, the injection of this hormone has been employed in extremely lean people to create a greater appetite and thereby favor a greater depositing of body fat.

Emotional Glycosuria.—It is well known that severe stimulations of certain sensory nerves may cause glycosuria, as, for example, in neuralgia of the vagus. Perhaps closely allied to this is what Cannon has called emotional glycosuria. Cannon found that out of the 25 men constituting a football squad, 12 had sugar in the urine after the game was finished; this was especially true of the men who had not participated actively in the game. A difficult examination caused glycosuria in four out of the nine people examined; when the examination was easy, only one out of the nine excreted sugar. He also found that when a cat is thrown into great rage or fright the amount of glucose in the blood is increased and glycosuria follows.

As related under the subject of Circulation, Cannon was able to discover an increase of adrenalin in the blood of a cat under the above-mentioned conditions. He therefore concludes that the hyperglycemia and glycosuria accompanying great emotional strains, such as fear, anxiety, and overwhelming grief, are brought about by hormonal influence. Other investigators have sought to locate in the lower portions of the brain a center (diabetic or glycogenolytic center) which by way of the splanchnic (sympathetic) nerves directly influences the liver cells.

The Thyroid Gland.—The thyroid, an endocrine organ (Figs. 209 and 210), will be discussed in Chapter XXIII, but it is necessary to anticipate here one of its functions. The removal of this gland, or its hypofunction in man, leads to a marked decrease in metabolism, as shown by decreased consumption of oxygen and production of CO_2. On the other hand, injection of its active principle (known as thyroxin) or hyperfunction of the gland in man increases metabolism, the absorption of sugar from the intestine is accelerated, the liver loses some of its glycogen, and in severe cases a mild hyperglycemia and glycosuria may occur. In brief, this gland mobilizes the carbohydrates. Whether this is the result of direct action upon the organs involved or accomplished by intervention of pancreatic endocrine activity is still a question.

The Pituitary Body.—This endocrine gland, attached by means of a stalk, or pedicle, to the brain (Figs. 279 and 291), plays a part in regulating carbohydrate metabolism. Our knowledge of this control is very uncertain; the following is perhaps the best exposition of the matter at present. Extirpation of the pituitary, or its hypofunction in a human being, is associated with a reduction in oxidation, amounting to as much as 35 per cent; as a consequence the body temperature is generally subnormal. In this condition the liver glycogen is not as readily mobilized by adrenalin, nor does hyperglycemia set in. On removal of the pituitary body the animal becomes susceptible to insulin so that a smaller dose of insulin is required to induce hypoglycemia.

On the other hand, injection of the pituitary extract increases the blood sugar and leads to glycosuria; and the hypoglycemia brought about by insulin is reduced by the injection of this *diabetogenic hormone*. From these facts we may conclude that *the influence of this blood-sugar-raising hormone of the pituitary is antagonistic to that of insulin;* in other words, it is an inhibitor of the controlling influence exercised by the pancreas over the utilization of carbohydrates. This is attested to by the fact that by the simultaneous removal of the pituitary, the results of the removal of the islands of Langerhans (hyperglycemia, decreased sugar consumption, and glycosuria) are to a large extent averted and the life of the animal prolonged by several months. Whether this influence of the pituitary is exercised directly upon the organs concerned with carbohydrate metabolism (liver, muscle, e.g.) or whether its hormones control the pancreas and other glands (thyroid, adrenals, e.g.) concerned in the regulation of carbohydrate metabolism is not clear.

Influence of Muscle Work.—A study of blood sugar changes has shown that in moderate exercise the level does not change, while in short bouts of very strenuous exercise the blood sugar materially increases. However, in long continued exhaustive exercises, the blood sugar falls to a low level. These changes are explained as follows: In moderate work, the liver is able to supply sugar to the blood as fast as it is used by the muscles. In strenuous work of short duration, the excess adrenalin which appears in the blood stream, causes the liver to produce sugar in excess of the amount used by the muscles; but if severe exercise is performed for a sufficient length of time, the liver glycogen is exhausted, resulting in a fall in the sugar content of the blood.

The Fate of Carbohydrates.—From our study of carbohydrate metabolism we learn that this foodstuff:

1. May be used immediately for energy production.

2. May be stored temporarily as glycogen in the liver and muscles.

3. After the carbohydrate has been transformed into fat, may be stored more permanently in the adipose tissue.

4. It may unite with other substances: for example, with proteins to form glycoproteins, such as mucin; or with fatty materials, giving rise to cerebrosides found in the brain.

5. When in excess in the blood, it is excreted by the kidneys.

II. LIPID OR FAT METABOLISM

Lipids.—Among the important constituents of the body are a number of substances variously known as lipids, or lipoids. These include: (*a*) the neutral, or true, fats, such as olein, palmitin, and stearin, (*b*) sterols, and (*c*) phosphatids, or phospholipids.

THE STEROLS (*stereos,* solid; *ol,* suffix for name of alcohols) are highly complex compounds belonging to the aromatic alcohols. Of these we shall mention only *cholesterol* ($C_{27}H_{45}OH$) which was first discovered, in crystalline form, in gallstones (*chole,* bile). Although found in every living animal structure, not much is definitely known concerning its functions. It is especially abundant in the white matter of the nervous system; the gradually increasing amount from 0.5 per cent in the fetal, to almost 2 per cent in the adult brain may be an index of its importance. It is not improbable that, with lecithin, it serves as the insulator of the nerve fiber. It has also been suggested that it aids in maintaining the semipermeability of plasma membranes so frequently referred to in these pages. Cholesterol constitutes 19 per cent of the sebum secreted by the oil glands (skin fat); because of its great insolubility and its resistance to the action of bacteria and enzymes it does not become rancid, and this may play an important part in preserving the integrity of the skin. This sterol is also found in lanolin (wool fat). Derived from cholesterol or chemically closely related to it are a number of important physiological agents, such as bile acids and salts, sex hormones, and vitamin D.

PHOSPHOLIPIDS.—Of this class the most important is a substance called lecithin. In this one molecule of the fatty acid radicals united with the glycerol in a simple fat is replaced by a very complex nitrogenous substance (choline) and phosphoric acid. Like cholesterol, it is present in all cells and in blood and appears to be essential to life; but its specific rôle is problematic.

Lecithin decreases surface tension and as a result it is largely adsorbed at the surface of protoplasm (see page 72). This renders it very likely that these fatlike substances form important constituents of the plasma membrane and contribute in no small degree to its semipermeability. Some attribute the narcotic (*marke,* numbness) action of ether, chloroform, and similar drugs to their power as fat solvents. While the fatty material in the adipose tissue is present mostly as simple neutral fat, in the cells it exists in the more complex form of phosphatids and the esters of cholesterol; in these esters the cholesterol is united with fatty acids derived from the fats. Because of their limited solubility they "appear to make up the framework which supports the protein constituents of cell protoplasm."

Metabolism of Fats.—The fatty acid and glycerol resulting from the digestion of the food fats are absorbed by the lacteals. The form and manner in which fats are carried by the fluids of the body and how they enter into and are used by the cells are very imperfectly understood. Some hold that the absorbed fatty acid and glycerol are resynthesized into neutral fat which is found in the blood in the form of microscopic droplets. According to Bloor, the fat becomes united with other compounds to form, for example, lecithin, which, as we have seen, is found in the blood stream. Some of the absorbed fat may be used immediately by the cells for the production of energy; some of it is stored up for a longer or shorter length of time in the adipose tissue, the fat depots of our body.

By catabolism the fat gives rise to two final waste products, namely, water and carbon dioxide, but the manner in which the fat molecule is gradually broken down is obscure. According to some observers the fat molecule undergoes a preparatory change in the liver by which some higher compound, such as lecithin, is formed; it is in this form that the fat is used by the cells.

In the decomposition of fat the long chain of 16 or 18 carbons is gradually split up, perhaps by the cutting off of two carbons at a time. Finally a residue containing four carbons is obtained, e.g., aceto-acetic acid ($CH_3.CO.CH_2COOH$) and oxybutyric acid ($CH_3.CHOH.CH_2.COOH$). It seems that these substances can be oxidized only in the presence of carbohydrates undergoing oxidation, for in the absence of carbohydrate catabolism, as in diabetes and starvation, the above-named acids accumulate in the body. Under these circumstances a ketone (p. 319) known as acetone and having the composition, $CH_3.C = O.CH_3$, is also extensively formed; its accumulation in the body is spoken of as ketosis, and its excretion in the urine is called ketonuria, or acetonuria. Inasmuch as the oxidation of carbohydrates prevents this condition, these foods are spoken of as antiketogenic.

Acidemia or Acidosis.—The large amount of acid (oxybutyric acid, e.g.) formed in abnormal carbohydrate metabolism and starvation causes an increase in the H-ion concentration of the blood; by this the respiratory center is powerfully stimulated and the individual gasps (air hunger). As the alkaline reserve of the blood has been largely used up by the above-mentioned acids, the ability of the blood to remove the CO_2 from the tissues is decreased to such an extent as to interfere with the functions of the cerebral hemispheres and unconsciousness (coma) results. This condition is spoken of as *acidosis;* however, this does not mean that the body or blood is acid in reality, but that the pH value of the blood has been decreased.

Functions of Fat.—1. Oxidation for the production of energy is, no doubt, one of the important functions of fats in the cells. We have already dwelt upon this fact in our discussion of the source of muscle energy in the absence of a sufficient amount of carbohydrate. This view gains strength from the fact that the amount of fat in the very active heart or red skeletal muscle is greater than in the less active or paler variety. Whether fat must be transformed into a carbohydrate previous to its being utilized for muscle energy and whether this transformation takes place in muscle cells as well as in the liver are controversial matters. In supplying energy, fats are much superior to carbohydrates or proteins.

2. Fats aid in making certain necessary substances soluble, e.g., vitamins A and D.

3. The more complex lipids form integral constituents of the cells.

4. Stored up as adipose tissue, it performs several functions which we shall discuss in the following section.

Adipose Tissue.—The adipose tissue is a modification of the areolar tissue. From our brief discussion of the histology of the tissues it will be recalled that in the areolar tissue the cellular elements are of two kinds: the migratory, or wandering, cells and the fixed cells of which there are several kinds. In many parts of the body these fixed connective tissue cells become charged with a few microscopic droplets of fat. These droplets run together to form a larger drop and this, by the acquisition of more fat brought to it by the blood stream, grows in size until finally it occupies the whole cell with the exception of a narrow rim of protoplasm in which is lodged the nucleus (Fig. 15). Such tissue, called adipose tissue, is found chiefly beneath the skin, in the intermuscular connective tissue, and in the abdominal cavity (around the kidneys and in the mesentery and omentum).

Function of Adipose Tissue.—Adipose tissue (fat) serves four important functions:

1. RESERVE FOOD MATERIAL.—During starvation when the body is unable to obtain food from the external environment, the fat lodged in the connective tissue cells is reabsorbed by the blood and carried to those organs in need of energy-furnishing material. As much as 97 per cent of all the deposited fat may be withdrawn. With respect to its storage we may call attention to the superiority of fat over carbohydrates. The amount of glycogen that can be stored by the liver is about 100 grams, and that by the rest of the body amounts to 350 grams; this is about equivalent to a two days' intake of carbohydrates in the food. In contrast to this, the power of the body to store fat is enormous. Again the excellence of fat as a stored food can be seen in that the energy content of a fat is $2\frac{1}{4}$ times as great as that of the same amount of either carbohydrate or protein.

The stored fat is of great value in case of the deprivation of food or the inability to digest it, as the following shows. A lean man during starvation obtained 80 per cent of the energy expended from fat and consumed 88 grams of his own body-proteins; a fat man obtained 90 per cent of the energy from his fat and consumed only 50 grams of protein.

2. HEAT INSULATION.—As a poor conductor of heat the subcutaneous fat tissue lessens the radiation of heat from the body, and thus diminishes the amount of food necessary to keep the body warm. This is illustrated in mammals, like seals and walruses, which al-

though living in the Arctic regions in ice-cold water are able to maintain a body temperature as high as our own.

3. MECHANICAL PROTECTION.—By its resilience fat forms for certain organs a protective cushion against excessive pressure and mechanical injuries by jolts. The fat in the soles of the feet may be considered as acting like "rubber heels"; the fat around the eyeball may prevent this delicate organ from being injured by the jars which the body frequently receives.

4. CONTOUR.—Properly distributed it gives a pleasing contour to the body.

The sources of the stored up fat are threefold:

1. FROM THE FOOD FAT.—If a fat having a much lower melting point than the body-fat of an animal is fed in large quantities, the animal may deposit this food fat in its adipose tissue. A dog fed upon linseed oil deposits a fat that has a much lower melting point than the normal fat of the dog. Feeding experiments with cattle have also demonstrated this; cows fed with food containing much linseed oil yield a milk fat with such a low melting point that the butter is not marketable.

2. FROM CARBOHYDRATES.—That carbohydrates (sugars and starches) can be transformed by the animal body into fat is one of the best proved facts in metabolism.

A cow was fed for ninety-five days upon grain and hay. In addition to an increase in the animal's body weight by 47 pounds, some of which must have been fat, the milk contained 62.9 pounds of fat. To furnish this, the food contained only 5.7 pounds of fat, leaving at least 57.2 pounds of butter fat which must have been derived either from the carbohydrates or proteins of the food. The nitrogen excreted during this period, multiplied by 6.25, gives the amount of protein the animal actually consumed; this amounted to 33.3 pounds. It will be recalled that when amino acids are deaminized, the non-nitrogenous part may be stored. Suppose that all of this non-nitrogenous part of the 33.3 pounds of protein consumed was transformed into fat, the amount produced would equal about 17 pounds. The food fat plus the maximum amount obtained from the protein equal 22.7 pounds. The difference between this and that actually produced by the body (62.9 pounds) is 40.2 pounds, which can have been obtained only from the carbohydrates.

Whether the animal uses the fat or the carbohydrates of its food in the formation of adipose tissue depends upon conditions. It is sometimes stated that carnivorous animals by preference use the food fat; in herbivorous animals the carbohydrates seem more suitable for fattening purposes. The fats derived from the carbohydrates are of a firmer nature (higher melting point) than those deposited from the food fat.

3. From Proteins.—The possibility of deriving a small amount of body fat from the proteins of the food is generally granted. Under the subject of glycosuria we have seen evidence that proteins (or the deaminized amino acids) can be transformed in the body into carbohydrates. Since carbohydrates readily serve as a source of fat, it must be possible, in a roundabout way, to obtain fat from proteins.

Some have supposed that the so-called fatty degeneration of such organs as the heart, brain, and kidney, was evidence of the transforming of the proteins of these organs into fat. But this has been quite satisfactorily disproved. The fat in most tissues is present in complex form, such as lecithin, and does not reveal itself by the ordinary test for fat; but when the tissue or organ undergoes degeneration caused, e.g., by diphtheria toxin or phosphorus poisoning, these complex fat compounds are broken up and the fat is unmasked.

Obesity.—The storing of fat in the adipose tissues sometimes becomes excessive, and the body weight and bulk increase beyond what may be regarded as normal. In some instances the obesity is due to constitutional causes, and no limiting of the diet will reduce the amount of fat without endangering the health of the individual. But many cases of "simple obesity" are due to a disproportion between the amount of food eaten and the amount of food used by the body for the production of energy; in other words, most people are fat because the intake is greater than the output; they eat too much and do not exercise enough. Why some people readily lay up fat while others remain lean is difficult to say; it is quite possible, as we shall see in a subsequent chapter, that the glands furnishing the internal secretions have much to do with it. Again, it has been supposed that in some people the body is a more economical machine than in others and can therefore run on less fuel; but this does not seem likely if, as stated by certain investigators, the basal metabolism (p. 441) is no less in obese than in other people. It has also been suggested that in some obese individuals the specific dynamic action of the foodstuffs (p. 447), especially of the proteins, is less than in a normal person; this would enable them to lay up fat on a diet just sufficient to maintain the normal individual in constant body weight. Finally, as in all other physical and mental characteristics, heredity may play an important rôle. But, whatever the ultimate reason may be, a large amount of fat adds an unnecessary burden, and may work great harm, for:

1. In the performance of muscle work an obese person is handicapped. Because of the great body weight, the extra work done in walking, stair-climbing, etc., puts more strain on the heart. Since

the subcutaneous fat is a poor conductor of heat, the heat generated during muscle work is not lost so easily; this results in great discomfort and profuse sweating.

2. The extra work in carrying this useless weight of fat soon causes fatigue and therefore obesity tends to reduce bodily activity. Generally it is the lack of activity that, with too much eating, causes obesity. And the more fat is deposited the less inclined the individual is to bestir himself actively; consequently a vicious circle is established. The lack of body activity ultimately leads to a deterioration of the functions of digestion, respiration, circulation, and elimination. Obese persons are more susceptible to many ills than are those of normal weight. Adams of the Mayo Clinic found that 91 per cent of

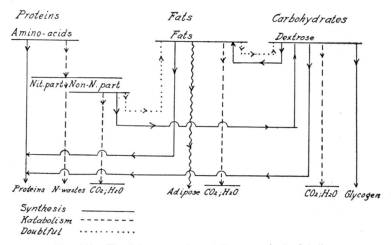

Fig. 191.—The interconversion of the organic foodstuffs.

diabetic patients were overweight and almost 83 per cent were more than 10 per cent overweight before diabetes set in. Headaches, dizziness, and dyspnea are found proportionately more frequently in fat persons; they are more prone to a high blood pressure and cancer; and it is claimed they have a higher mortality in pneumonia and nephritis than individuals of normal body weight. In dogs the normal fat content of the liver (4 or 5 per cent) may be increased to over 30 per cent by excessive fat ingestion; in this condition of a fatty liver the animal tolerates ether anesthesia and surgical operations very poorly.

What constitutes the right amount of fat in an individual is difficult to say. The tablets of age, height and weight issued by life insurance companies may be of value, but, in addition to this, a phys-

ical examination as to the size of the skeleton and the amount of subcutaneous fat should be made.   It is, however, universally agreed
upon that, after the age of 30 or 35, overweight distinctly shortens
life; *leanness and longevity go hand in hand.*   On the other hand,
in the young person underweight is associated with less resistance to
disease and a greater mortality rate; this is especially true in case
of pulmonary tuberculosis.

If it is true that most people are obese because the intake is greater
than the output, the remedy for obesity is clear:

1. Decrease the intake of the fattening foods, that is, fats and
carbohydrates, such as white bread, potatoes, cereals, pastries, sugar,
cream, butter, olive oil, cheese, egg yolk, nuts, and fat meat.   In
reducing the carbohydrates, the ketogenic effects of fats and proteins
should be kept in mind.

2. Attempting to reduce body weight by physical exercise is generally futile.   Calculating the energy value of butter, Benedict found
that the "reducing" accomplished by climbing to the top of Washington Monument is equivalent to eliminating one pat of butter, or
$\frac{1}{3}$ oz., from one's food.

3. Don't count the calories; watch the body weight.

THE INTERRELATIONSHIP OF THE ORGANIC FOODSTUFFS

The interrelationship of the three organic foodstuffs and a brief
summary of what befalls them in the body may be gathered from
the diagram shown in Fig. 191.   In this scheme no account is taken
of the origin of enzymes, hormones, and similar substances.

CHAPTER XX

WATER AND MINERAL METABOLISM

I. WATER METABOLISM

The Importance of Water.—On a number of occasions we have stated that the living material, protoplasm, is an intimate mixture of crystalloids and colloids in which water forms the solvent for the first, and the medium for the dispersion or suspension of the second substances. From this it is evident that water plays a major part, second only to oxygen, in the existence and activity of the living being. This view is substantiated by the fact that while a fasting animal may survive a loss of practically all its fat and of half its proteins, a loss of one-fifth of its water-content is fatal. The amount of water is not the same in all forms of life, varying from such extremes as 8 per cent in dormant seeds to 96 per cent in the jellyfish. For the human body the amount is generally stated at about 63 per cent; it is the lowest in the dentine of the teeth (10 per cent) and highest in the gray matter of the brain (85 per cent). The younger and the more active protoplasm is, the greater is the amount of water it contains. The human embryo at six weeks contains 97 per cent water. Senescence is to a certain extent a matter of dehydration.

Functions of Water.—No other chemical compound has so many distinct and vital functions as water. This is largely due to its great solvent power, to the fact that it is chemically a neutral substance, and that ionization of most materials takes place more freely in water than in any other medium. We may summarize these functions:

1. It furnishes a medium for digestion, absorption, metabolism, secretion, and excretion. All these processes, chemical or physical, can take place only in the presence of water.

2. The water moistens the surfaces of the lungs so that gas diffusion is possible.

3. By absorbing heat from the region of greater heat production (e.g., the active muscle) and transporting it to less active parts, water aids in equalizing the body temperature. Its high specific heat and great thermal conductivity render water admirably adapted to this function. As the blood circulates through the superficial parts of the body, heat is dissipated. This aids in maintaining the body temperature.

4. It furnishes a vehicle for the transportation of food, waste, hormones, gases, etc.

5. It takes a part in hydrolytic cleavage, as during digestion.

6. It serves as a lubricant for moving surfaces, such as joints (synovial fluid), the heart, and intestine.

7. The evaporation of water from the skin is an important method of losing heat from the body.

8. Water plays an indispensable part in sense organs. Taste and smell are the result of stimulation by chemical compounds in solution. Sound is conducted through the inner ear by a liquid, which is chiefly water. The function of the semicircular canals as sense organs of equilibrium depends upon the presence of water in these canals. The transparency of the media of the eye to light is maintained by water.

9. The cerebrospinal fluid serves as a cushion for the brain and spinal cord.

Sources of Water.—The water in our bodies is derived from three main sources:

1. From the water and beverages ingested.

2. From the foods which contain various quantities of water, e.g., green vegetables, 90 to 97 per cent; meat, 50 to 75.

3. From the water formed by the oxidation of the organic foodstuffs in the body. The oxidation of any organic substance containing hydrogen must give rise to water. From their formulas it can readily be calculated that in burning 100 grams of these foodstuffs the following amounts of water are produced: proteins, 40 grams; fats, 105; carbohydrates, 55.

Elimination of Water.—Water leaves the body by four channels: kidneys, lungs, skin, and alimentary canal. How much water is excreted by each of these organs depends upon many external and internal conditions, but under the usual atmospheric conditions, and with the body at rest, the ratio for the organs, in the order given above, is generally placed at 6:2:2:1. Whatever increases the elimination by one organ decreases correspondingly the output by the other organs. In diarrhea the elimination by the alimentary canal is largely increased at the expense of the amount voided by the kidneys. Again, the warmer and drier the air, the more water is lost by the skin and lungs and the less by the other channels. It will be noticed that the large amount of water (at least 4 liters per day) taken into the alimentary canal by drinking and by the secretion of the various digestive juices is almost completely absorbed into the blood.

Water Balance.—The amount of water in the body is carefully regulated. The intake is controlled by the sensation of thirst, and the outgo, by the various excretions. In health it is unnecessary to prescribe any definite amount of water per unit of time. If one depends upon thirst as a guide, he will drink an adequate amount. The consumption, in the course of six hours, of as much as 5.5 liters of water (a quantity more than the entire volume of the blood) failed to dilute appreciably the blood as judged by the percentage of hemoglobin. The extra water is taken from the plasma very largely by the skin; the intercellular spaces of the loose connective tissue serve as reservoirs. When there is a loss of water by the blood either because of increased excretion from the body or because of inability to replenish it, the stored water is surrendered by the connective tissue to the plasma. In this manner are the molecular concentration and the volume of the blood, at least in part, regulated. The importance of this in hemorrhage is apparent. A loss of water equal to 6 per cent of the body weight constitutes a serious dehydration. If the reservoirs are already well filled, an extra intake of fluid leads normally to increased renal excretion.

II. MINERAL METABOLISM

The body contains about 5 per cent of ash, most of which is found in the bones. The inorganic material includes the chlorides, sulfates, and phosphates of potassium, sodium, calcium, and magnesium, and also some copper, iron, and iodine. These minerals must be looked upon as an integral part of the protoplasm just as truly as the proteins, fats, and carbohydrates. Many other elements, such as fluorine, cobalt, manganese, silver, chromium, and tin, have been found in minute amounts in the human body, but whether they are merely contaminants or whether they play a definite part in the activity of the body is not known. Frequently the inorganic is united chemically with the organic material, as, for example, iron in the hemoglobin of the red blood cells, and iodine in the thyroxin of the thyroid gland. Physiologic activity is impossible without the salts normally present in the cell. The chloride, phosphate, and sulfate salts of sodium, potassium, calcium, and magnesium are important in maintaining the correct ion balance and concentration in the fluids of the body. On a diet entirely devoid of salts, the digestion is seriously impaired and soon the animal refuses to eat; weakness and finally paralysis set in, which end in death. The addition of NaCl alleviates these disturbances for a long time, but eventually other salts must also be added in order to maintain life.

Sodium.—The great importance of this element is indicated in the above paragraph. It is a matter of common knowledge that herbivorous animals will travel, at great risk, to very distant salt licks. When the amount of sodium in the diet is decreased, the elimination of sodium (chiefly by the kidneys) diminishes and may cease almost entirely. The sodium salts contribute largely to the osmotic pressure of the body fluids, aid in dissolving certain proteins (e.g., globulins, fibrinogen), and, as bicarbonates, play a leading part in the maintenance of the hydrogen ion concentration of the body. We may also recall the significance of sodium in the origin of the heartbeat. It has been observed that workmen (miners, e.g.), laboring in a hot environment, losing a large amount of NaCl by profuse sweating, and drinking a correspondingly large amount of water, become afflicted with a muscular disability known as miners' cramps. The addition (0.01 to 0.02 per cent) of NaCl to the drinking water prevents these ill effects.

Potassium.—While the chemical resemblance between sodium and potassium is striking, in the body these two elements cannot replace each other to any great extent. Their distribution within the body is noteworthy: potassium predominates in the cells, sodium is chiefly found in the fluids and secretions of the body (blood, lymph, milk, etc.). The specific action of potassium in cardiac activity, in which it antagonizes the action of calcium, will no doubt be recalled. For growth potassium is indispensable; on a diet containing less than 15 mg. of potassium per day young rats failed to grow. Under the subject of the hormone, cortin, we shall speak of the regulation of sodium and potassium metabolism.

Iron.—The iron of the food is absorbed by the duodenum of the small intestine. By the disintegration of the red blood cells in the bone marrow and spleen iron is liberated; most of this is stored in the liver, spleen, and red bone marrow, but some is lost by excretion in the colon and to a very slight extent by the kidneys. To meet this loss, from 10 to 15 milligrams of iron per day must be ingested. Iron is found in the following foods (mentioned in the descending order of iron content): molasses (6.1 parts per 100,000), liver, oatmeal, apricots, eggs, raisins, spinach (0.5). White flour contains a very small amount of iron, for the iron of the wheat is found chiefly in the outer layers of the grain. Milk, according to Bunge, contains only 0.0002 per cent of iron and must, therefore, not be relied upon, in case of anemia, to supply a liberal amount of iron. The mammal before birth is supplied by the mother with a reserve supply of iron for the formation of red blood cells during the suckling period; hence the greater demand for iron in the food during pregnancy.

In a baby this reserve would last, if none were excreted, for six months, during which time no food iron need be supplied. After this, the rapid growth of the infant also calls for a proportionately greater supply of this element.

Function of Iron.—The amount of iron in the body is stated at about 5 or 6 grams (about ⅕ ounce). About one-half of this is lodged in the form of hemoglobin in the red blood cells, but most likely all cells contain a minute amount. In the muscles (especially the red variety) we find an iron-containing protein, myochrome, closely related to hemoglobin. In all these locations it appears to concern itself with the processes of oxidation. The carrying of oxygen by the hemoglobin will be recalled, and also the part played by respiratory ferments.

Magnesium.—McCollum and Orent demonstrated the necessity of this element in the life of rats. Deprived of magnesium for a few days, the animals became highly irritable and were thrown into convulsions by the slightest disturbance; in the majority of cases this proved fatal. McCollum associates this influence of magnesium with the function of the adrenals. The above is in agreement with the fact that magnesium has an anesthetic effect on many animals.

Iodine.—This element, found in the thyroid gland, plays an exceedingly important part in the physiology of this organ. We shall deal with this in Chapter XXIII.

Fluorine.—Recently it has been found that this element plays an important part in the construction and preservation of teeth. In Illinois, for example, some towns obtain their drinking water from artesian wells and this water contains a small amount of fluorine salts: other towns are supplied with lake water which has no fluorine. We may compare Elmhurst and Evanston, towns of about the same social and economic status. In the former town (with 1.8 parts fluorine per million of water) examination of school children (12 to 14 years) showed 25 per cent to be free from caries and revealed 252 caries per hundred mouths. In Evanston (no fluorine in the drinking water) only 3.9 per cent showed no caries and the caries per 100 mouths was 673. In the county of Deaf Smith, Texas, almost no caries exists in the mouths of the native born; this is also attributed to the fluorine in the drinking water. Fluorine in proper concentration seems to render the teeth more caries-resistant, and the number of acidophilus bacteria in the mouth is much decreased. However, it must be stated that an excess of fluorine in the drinking water (more than 2 parts per million) causes mottled teeth; such teeth are claimed to be more resistant to caries.

"**Trace Metals.**"—Copper, cobalt, zinc, manganese, and perhaps other metals are needed in such minute quantities that they are frequently referred to as "trace metals." The function of **copper** was considered in the formation of red blood cells. It appears to be stored in the liver, especially in the young animal. To illustrate the powerful effects of some of these trace metals: one part of copper in 100,000,000 parts of water kills algae. The lack of **manganese** in the diet of rats leads in the male to the degeneration of the epithelium which gives rise to the spermatozoa; in the female it prevents the ripening of the ovum, interferes with lactation, and causes her to lose all interest in her offspring.

Calcium.—The importance of calcium in the body and food can hardly be overstated, especially in the young animal or child. While it is true that 99 per cent of all the calcium (about 3 pounds in the adult body) is found in the skeleton and teeth, the remaining one per cent is vitally needed by every cell.

Calcium salts are absorbed with difficulty from the alimentary canal. The absorption is facilitated by an acid reaction of the intestinal contents; this may explain why the addition of lactose (lactic acid fermentation; see p. 47) to the food is of value in calcium metabolism. Normally calcium is excreted chiefly by the intestine and to a lesser extent by the kidneys.

We have learned in Chapter X that when the calcium in the fluid bathing the heart is decreased, the rhythmical activity of this organ gradually ceases. It is also necessary for the rhythmical action of the intestines. On the other hand, removal of the calcium salts from a skeletal muscle (by precipitation with, e.g., sodium oxalate) throws the muscle into violent rhythmical contractions. And when the calcium content of the plasma is decreased from the normal 10 milligrams per 100 c.c. to 5 mg., the irritability of the neuromuscular system increases to such an extent that twitchings and tetany of the skeletal muscles set in (p. 497). Again, the passage of a nerve impulse across the synapse or the myoneural junction seems to depend upon the proper amount of calcium. If this conduction is determined, as some maintain, by the increase in the permeability of the synaptic membrane, the increase in irritability spoken of above can readily be understood, for it will be recalled (p. 76) that the maintenance of the normal permeability of the plasma membrane depends upon the proper ratio of calcium, sodium, and potassium salts. This supposition is strengthened by the fact that an increase in the blood calcium is associated with hypotonicity and hypo-excitability of the neuromuscular system, this being true for both smooth and striated muscles. In speaking of permeability, we may recall that the permeability of the capillary wall is also increased by a decrease in the blood calcium; thus it has been found that the inflammatory reaction to mustard oil is prevented by previous administration of calcium salts. Calcium metabolism is governed by the hormones of the parathyroid and of the sex glands (pp. 000 and 000).

The beneficial results of a liberal supply of calcium in the food of a young animal is well illustrated by Sherman's experiment with young rats. With the amount of calcium constituting from 0.64 to 0.8 per cent of the total food, the percentage of body calcium in a one- month-old animal was equal to that of a five- or six-month-old rat subsisting on a 0.2 per cent calcium diet. The experiment also showed that the rich calcium diet not only favored growth and development, but also the length of life.

Phosphorus is present in all the cells of the body, but like calcium, the greater part is found in the skeleton (70 per cent, or about 1,400 grams). Its importance is apparent when we recall the part played by the phosphatids (lecithin, e.g.) in the transportation and metabolism of fats (p. 000) and in the permeability of the plasma membrane; we have also noted the rôle of the phosphorus compound, phosphocreatin, in muscle activity, and presently we shall speak of the function of hexose phosphates in bone formation. The nucleoproteins, important constituents of all cell nuclei, contain the phosphorus compound, nucleic acid. It will be recalled that phosphates play a minor part as buffer substances. In blood, phosphorus is present to the extent of 5 mg. per 100 c.c. of plasma. As the amount of calcium is about 10 mg., the product of these two—known as the *calcium-phosphorus product*—is $10 \times 5 = 50$. The great importance of this product will become evident in our study of vitamin D.

Bones

Unlike the soft structures thus far studied, bones contain a comparatively small amount of water (about 25 per cent) but are very rich in mineral matter (45 per cent); the organic materials constitute about 30 per cent. Similar to all connective tissues, bones are composed of a few cells and much intercellular material. The latter is composed of an organic substance in which is deposited a large amount of inorganic matter. The organic framework of a bone is chiefly composed of a protein, collagen, which on boiling with water is transformed into gelatin. It may be freed from the inorganic material by treating bone with hydrochloric acid which dissolves the mineral constituents; the organic matrix which remains is flexible and translucent and gives toughness to bone.

The minerals are composed chiefly of calcium and a small amount of magnesium. In what form these salts are present is not fully understood; generally it is stated that tricalcium phosphate— $Ca_3(PO_4)_2$—forms about 85 per cent and calcium carbonate—$CaCO_3$ —about 10 per cent. These salts give hardness and rigidity to bones. Bones perform three mechanical functions: (a) they furnish protection to the softer tissues as is well illustrated by the cranium which almost entirely encloses the brain; (b) they support various organs, as e.g., the vertebral column to which is affixed, by means of the mesentery, the intestinal canal; (c) they act as levers for the transfer of movements executed by the muscles, as is seen in the bones of the extremities.

In addition to the above functions, the *bones serve as a storehouse for the indispensable calcium and phosphorus.* Bones are living structures and are not to be looked upon as absolutely fixed in their composition; both calcium and phosphorus can be withdrawn and under proper conditions be redeposited. In starvation the excretion of sodium and potassium practically ceases, but that of calcium and phosphorus continues; these latter elements are obtained from the skeleton. Such a withdrawal of calcium may also occur when extra demands are made upon it, as in pregnancy and lactation; this, however, does not apply to the calcium of the teeth. Even when phosphorus only is lacking in the diet, the bones become spongy and may suffer a loss of one-third of their mineral content.

Bone tissue is a very labile tissue and is readily affected by changes in the diet, by exercise, etc. The bone cells control the inorganic part of the bone; an example of this is found in the uniting of a broken bone. By means of radioactive phosphorus it was found that within 50 days one-fourth of the mineral constituents of a normal bone were renewed.

The manner in which the calcium and phosphorus salts are laid down in the growing bone and tooth is obscure. There is much speculation as to the form in which phosphorus is held in the blood. Some investigators suppose that part of it is present in a soluble organic form—in what are called phosphoric esters, such as hexose phosphate and glycero-phosphoric esters, $C_2H_5(OH)_2.O.PO_3H_2$. In their development many bones are laid down in previously constructed hyaline cartilage. In the calcifying areas certain cells, known as osteoblasts, secrete a *bone enzyme,* or *phosphatase,* which hydrolyzes the phosphoric esters, and thereby releases free phosphoric acid and an excess of phosphate ions. These ions, reacting with the calcium salts, form an insoluble calcium-phosphate compound.

The evidence for the existence of a calcifying enzyme is based upon the following facts: Certain bones (those of the limbs, for example) are laid down in previously formed cartilage, in distinction to the membranous bones, such as the parietal and frontal bones of the skull. In those cartilages that are destined to undergo ossification much phosphatase is found, while it is absent, or nearly so, in non-calcifying cartilages, such as the tracheal and costal cartilages. The enzyme makes its appearance at the time when the first evidence of ossification is noticeable and it has been detected in embryonic bone growing in vitro (i.e., artificially; "in glass"). But we must not neglect to state that certain facts speak against the theory here outlined.

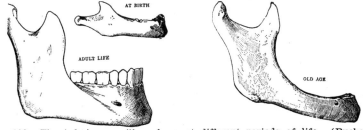

Fig. 192.—The inferior maxillary bone at different periods of life. (Buchanan.)

Many other factors are concerned in bone and tooth formation, among which we may mention the proper intake of calcium, phosphorus, and vitamin D, the calcium-phosphorus product, the pH of the blood, the pH of the intestinal contents, and the hormone of the parathyroid and, perhaps of other endocrine glands (Chaps. XXII and XXIII). We may here call attention to one more factor, namely, that the size, internal structure, and strength of a bone are also determined by the stress or pressure to which it is subjected; that is, structural needs determine bone growth. This is well illustrated in case of the jaw bone (Fig. 192) which, after the loss of the teeth and the consequent partial loss of function, decreases in size by as much as 50 per cent. The removal of the teeth from one lateral half of the jaws of a pup causes a lack of development of the bones of this side of the face. The pressure exerted in chewing by the deciduous teeth of a child no doubt stimulates the growth, in size and strength, of the jaw bones and thereby influences the amount of space available for the permanent teeth. The "place-preserving function" of the deciduous molars is of special importance. The composition of the bones changes with age. There is a decrease in water, an increase in the mineral content, and a decrease in the organic materials which normally give the bone elasticity and toughness; as a consequence, the bones become more brittle and heal more slowly. An increase in calcium content with advancing years is not limited to bones, for we have seen that this element may be deposited in the arterial wall in cases of arteriosclerosis.

CHAPTER XXI

ENERGY METABOLISM

In the chapters immediately preceding we have considered the changes undergone by various foodstuffs in their assimilation and utilization in the body. As a result of some of the changes described, a certain amount of energy is made available to the body. This energy is either dissipated as heat or used in doing work. The work done may be either external or internal. All the external work is done as mechanical work, i.e., walking, etc. The internal work may be chemical, e.g., growth, or mechanical, e.g., the work of the heart. By energy metabolism we mean the sum total of these changes.

I. CALORIMETRY

The Unit of Energy.—The energy unit usually used in physiology is the kilogram calorie, usually written Calorie, with a capital C to distinguish it from the gram calorie. The kilogram calorie, or Calorie, is $\frac{1}{100}$ the amount of heat required to raise the temperature of one kilogram of water from 0° C. to 100° C. The relation of the Calorie to other common units of energy measurement is:

> 1 Calorie = 426.85 kilogram-meters
> 1 Calorie = 3087.4 foot-pounds
> 1 Calorie = 1000 calories

The source of energy in the body is the oxidation of organic foodstuffs. The heat which the foodstuffs generate when they are oxidized is measured by means of a calorimeter. A metal vessel, *A,* in Fig. 193, is surrounded by a layer of water, *B,* which in turn is surrounded by a poor conductor of heat, *E.* The food, placed in the inner vessel, is ignited by an electric spark (the wires shown at *D*). By means of a tube oxygen is supplied; the gaseous products are removed by means of tube *C,* which is coiled through the water. The heat generated by the burning of the food is absorbed by the water. By observing the temperature of the water before and after the experiment, and knowing the quantity of water in the calorimeter and the quantity of material oxidized, it is easy to determine how many Calories one gram of the material produces. For the foodstuffs the following approximate values have been found:

> Carbohydrates—4 Cal.
> Fats—9 Cal.
> Proteins—5.6 Cal. physical heat value.
> Proteins—4 Cal. physiologic heat value.

Fats and carbohydrates are completely oxidized in the body and, therefore, the above amount of heat is set free within the animal body as well as in the calorimeter. But it will be recalled that the proteins give rise to the nitrogenous waste products—urea, uric acid and creatinine. All of these substances can be still further oxidized and heat be thereby liberated; one gram of urea, for example, sets free 2.5 Cal. The energy of the proteins is, therefore, not perfectly utilized in the body; the amount available is generally placed at about 4 Cal.; this is called the physiologic heat value of proteins.

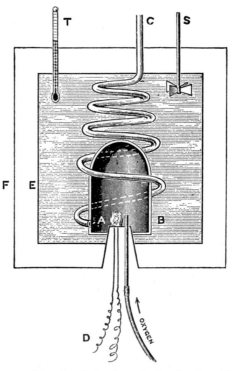

Fig. 193.—Diagram of bomb calorimeter. *A*, chamber in which food is placed; *B*, chamber containing water; *C*, outlet tube for the gases; *D*, electric wires for igniting the food; *E*, outer chamber containing some poor conductor of heat; *F*, outer wall of the calorimeter; *S*, stirrer; *T*, thermometer. (After Thomsen.)

Direct Calorimetry.—The heat generated by an animal or a human being can also be determined by the calorimeter. Some of these calorimeters not only enable us to ascertain the heat set free, but are so constructed that the amount of oxygen consumed and the carbon dioxide and water eliminated by lungs and skin are also measured. Such an apparatus, called a respiration-calorimeter, is sketched in Fig. 194. The individual whose metabolism and heat production are to be studied occupies the calorimeter chamber. The walls of the outer chamber are electrically heated to exactly the same temperature as that of the inner chamber. Along the inside wall runs a system of tubes through which constantly circulates a stream of water. By taking the temperature of the water as it enters and again as it leaves the chamber and by measuring the amount of water passing through the chamber, the amount of heat can be determined. Except for one inlet and one outlet tube, the chamber is hermetically sealed when once the subject is placed inside. Food, etc., are passed into and out of the chamber by means of a double window. By means of an inlet tube fresh air is forced into the chamber and the old air is removed

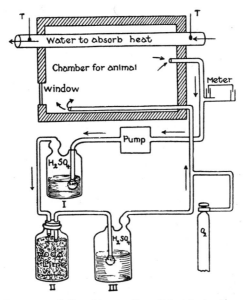

Fig. 194.—Diagram of the Atwater-Benedict calorimeter. (Macleod.)

through an outlet tube. The outlet tube is connected with a vessel containing sulfuric acid for the absorption of water, and with a vessel containing soda-lime for the absorption of the carbon dioxide. The air, deprived of its water and carbon dioxide, is mixed with fresh oxygen and returned by means of an air pump to the chamber. The amount of oxygen passing into the chamber for any unit of time is known. By weighing the soda-lime and the sulfuric acid, the amount of carbon dioxide and water eliminated can be found. As the amount of nitrogen in the food and in the egesta (urine and feces) is also measured, a nitrogen balance, and, therefore, a protein balance, can be struck. In this manner a complete metabolism balance sheet can be drawn up, showing the gain or less of proteins, fats, and carbohydrates in the body.

Indirect Calorimetry.—Since all the energy spent by the body is derived ultimately from the oxidation of organic foodstuffs, a simple and accurate method of determining the total energy expenditure over a short period of time has been developed. It consists of measuring the amount of oxygen used and of carbon dioxide given off. Three materials are oxidized in the body, namely, carbohydrates, fats, and proteins. The nature of the material used can be determined from the ratio of the amount of carbon dioxide produced to that of the oxygen consumed. This ratio, $\dfrac{CO_2}{O_2}$, is known as the *respiratory quotient,* usually abbreviated R.Q. The numerical value of this quotient varies with the different foodstuffs, as the following shows:

Equal volumes of gases (measured under the same pressure and temperature) contain the same number of molecules (Avogadro's law). The oxidation of a molecule of glucose may be expressed:

$$C_6H_{12}O_6 + 6O_2 = 6CO_2 + 6\ H_2O.$$

In this equation the number of molecules of oxygen consumed is the same as that of the CO_2 produced. If, therefore, six volumes of oxygen are used, six volumes of CO_2 are produced and the R.Q. of carbohydrates is 6/6, or 1. When a molecule of fat, let us say palmitin, is oxidized we have:

$$C_{51}H_{98}O_6 + 72\tfrac{1}{2}\ O_2 = 51\ CO_2 + 49\ H_2O.$$

The R.Q. of this fat is 51/72.5, or approximately 0.7. By a similar process we find the R.Q. of proteins to be 0.8. If a person could oxidize nothing but carbohydrates, his R.Q. would be 1. However, this never occurs in the body; all three foodstuffs are simultaneously used, and on a mixed diet, such as most people take, it is customary to evaluate the R.Q. at 0.825.

It will be recalled from page 67 that one mol of any gas* under standard temperature-pressure conditions (i.e., at 0° C. and 760 mm. Hg—S.T.P.) occupies 22.4 liters. In the equation showing the oxidation of glucose, it will be seen that to oxidize one gram-mol (180 grams) of glucose requires 6 gram-mols, or $22.4 \times 6 = 134.4$ liters, of oxygen; in this process 134.4 liters of CO_2 and 18×6, or 108, grams of water are produced. The amount of heat liberated when a liter of

---

*A mol of a gas is the amount of that gas in grams equal to the molecular weight of the gas; thus a mol, or gram-mol, of O_2 represents 32 grams of oxygen.

oxygen unites with glucose has been found by calorimetry to be about 5 Cal; for fats this value is 4.686 and for proteins, about 4.5 Cal. If all three foodstuffs are utilized and the R.Q. may be assumed to be 0.82, the heat liberated by the union of one liter of oxygen with this mixture of carbohydrates, fats, and proteins is placed at 4.825 Cal.

From the foregoing it must be clear that the simplest method of estimating the energy metabolism of an individual is by measuring the volume of oxygen used. This is easily done by having the subject breathe from a spirometer filled with oxygen. The expired air, after being passed over soda-lime to absorb CO_2 is returned to the spirometer. The decrease in the volume of gas in the spirometer is a measure of the volume of O_2 used by the subject. This volume (reduced to S.T.P.) multiplied by 4.825 gives the Calories produced by the subject during the period of measurement.

If we desire to know how much of the total energy was supplied by the catabolism of proteins, we may proceed as follows: We have seen (p. 405) that the amount of protein consumed can be calculated from the amount of nitrogen in the urine. One gram of urine nitrogen represents the oxidation of 6.25 grams of protein; and one gram of protein supplies the body with 4.1 Cal. of heat. As one gram of protein requires for its oxidation 0.95 liters of oxygen, the amount of oxygen utilized by the protein may be subtracted from the total amount of oxygen consumed; the remainder will be that used in the fat and carbohydrate combustion.

II. BASAL METABOLIC RATE

As the extent of metabolism increases with the amount of energy expended by the body in muscle work and in heat, it is evident that the minimum requirement will be found when the body is in a resting condition and surrounded by an atmosphere calling for a minimum heat production. After 2 or 3 hours of complete rest in bed, in a comfortably warm room, and eighteen hours after the last meal, and kept free as much as possible from environmental distractions, the average amount of heat produced by an adult is somewhere between 1,500 and 1,800 Calories per day. This amount of metabolism is known as the *basal metabolism* and represents the minimum expenditure of energy compatible with life; that is, it represents the amount of energy expended for the internal needs of the body, such as the heartbeat, respiratory movements, activity of the alimentary canal, maintenance of body temperature, tonus of skeletal muscles, etc.

Stated in terms of body weight the average basal metabolism (or basal heat production) in an adult male is about one Calorie per kilogram of body weight per hour; hence a person weighing 70 kilograms produces 1,680 Cal. daily. Calculated on the basis of body (skin) surface, it is stated to be approximately 40 Cal. per square meter per hour. Variations of ± 10 per cent are within normal limits.

III. FACTORS INFLUENCING ENERGY METABOLISM

a. **Size of Animal.**—A smaller animal has, in proportion to body weight, a much larger surface exposed to the environment, and, therefore, radiates more heat per unit of body weight; consequently it must consume more food and generate more heat in order to maintain its proper body temperature. This is illustrated in Table XIX.

TABLE XIX

	BODY WEIGHT	CALORIES PRODUCED IN 24 HOURS	
		PER KG. OF BODY WEIGHT	PER SQ. METER OF BODY SURFACE
Man	64.000 Kg.	32.1	1,042
Dog	15.000 Kg.	51.5	1,039
Mouse	0.018 Kg.	212.0	1,188

The heat production in the mouse, per kilogram of body weight, is almost seven times as great as in man. On the other hand, if the heat production is stated in terms of unit (square meter) of body surface, there is very little difference between the man, the dog, and the mouse. This relationship between the extent of the body surface and the basal metabolism is sometimes referred to as Rubner's law.

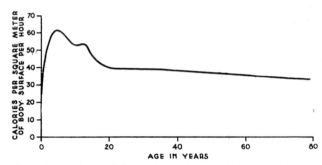

Fig. 195.—Curve to illustrate relation between basal metabolism and age. (DuBois: Am. J. M. Sc., 1916.)

b. **Age.**—Because of the larger body surface of a child in proportion to his weight as compared with that of an adult, we find that a child has a greater metabolism per kilogram of weight than has the adult. From Table XIX we might be led to conclude that per square meter of body surface the basal metabolism is the same in the child as in the adult. This, however, has been found not to be true, as is shown in Fig. 195. From the curve we learn that the basal metabolism as expressed in terms of the body surface is least in the newborn child; it increases rapidly during the first few years, reaching a maximum at from five to ten; it then decreases rapidly until the age of twenty, after which the decline is very gradual for the remainder of life. From this we must conclude that, irrespective of the extent of body surface, the metabolic fires burn brightest during the first few years of life and that the rate of living soon slows down. Moreover, because of growth some of the energy taken in by the child will not be expended but stored; this increases the total amount required. The amount of energy needed at various ages may be gathered from Table XX (from DuBois).

TABLE XX

AGE YEARS	MALES CALORIES PER HOUR	FEMALES CALORIES PER HOUR
10-12	51.5	50.0
12-14	50.0	46.5
14-16	46.0	43.0
16-18	43.0	40.0
18-20	41.0	38.0
20-30	39.5	37.0
30-40	39.5	36.5
40-50	38.5	36.0
50-60	37.5	35.0
60-70	36.5	34.0

As the basal metabolic rate decreases with advancing age, it is well that, for a person past middle life, the amount of food be somewhat reduced. To be sure, this depends largely upon the physical activity of the individual, but in general the assimilative powers of the body are declining and the organs of digestion and elimination should not be overtaxed.

c. Sex.—Per square meter of body surface men have a metabolism rate which is 6 or 7 per cent above that of women; this is also shown in Table XX. As there is a fairly definite ratio between the usual demand of oxygen by the body and the number of red blood corpuscles and the amount of hemoglobin, the above fact may explain the smaller number of red cells in the female.

d. Weight.—In thin people the metabolism per kilogram of body weight is almost 50 per cent higher than in fat people but stated in terms of square meter of surface the rates differ but little.

TABLE XXI

| | CALORIES PER 24 HOURS | |
	PER KILOGRAM	PER SQUARE METER
Normal weight	26.2	926
Underweight	30.4	917
Overweight	15.1	922

e. The Effect of External Temperature.—Next to muscle work no factor has so much influence on metabolism as the temperature of the environment. This can be gathered from Table XXII by Rubner which gives the Calories produced by a dog at various external temperatures:

TABLE XXII

EXTERNAL TEMPERATURE	CALORIES PER KG.
30° C.	56.2
20° C.	55.9
15° C.	63.0
7.6° C.	86.4

It has been shown by Grollman that low temperature (0 to 20° C.) causes an increase in metabolism because of increased muscle tonus and shivering, a form of muscular activity. Between 20° C. and 30° C., there is a gradual decline because of muscular relaxation. Metabolism again increases from 30° C. to 45° C. since there is an increase in sweating, cardiorespiratory and cellular activity.

The greater loss of heat at the lower temperatures must be made good by an increased food consumption. That the cutaneous stimulation by cold sharpens the appetite is a familiar fact. It also increases the rate of oxidation in the cells; in this certain hormones (Chap. XXIII) may play an important part. We may restate in this connection that a slightly greater intake of proteins may be of value because of their high specific dynamic action. By adjusting the amount and nature of the clothing, human beings endeavor to maintain the air in immediate contact with the skin at a temperature as nearly constant as possible. The influence of external temperature will be more fully considered in Chapter XXIV.

f. Body Temperature.—For every degree centigrade increase in body temperature there is an increase in metabolism of 13 per cent.

g. Internal Secretions.—The internal secretions of the adrenals, thyroid, pituitary, and gonads (sex glands) have a profound influence on the metabolic rate. In overproduction by the thyroid, the metabolic rate is from 40 to 75 per cent higher than in normal persons. The lack of this secretion (myxedema) reduces the rate 20 to 30 per cent below normal. In normal rats, exposure to a temperature of 4° C. caused the metabolism to be increased by as much as 170 per cent; on removal of one adrenal the increase was 139 and on removal of both adrenals it was but 81 per cent. The removal of the pituitary was followed by a decrease of 40 per cent in the basal metabolic rate. It is generally also decreased on extirpation of the ovaries or testes. Hypofunction of any of these glands may therefore be a factor in endogenous obesity.

h. Mental Work.—While the basal metabolic rate of the brain is of a very high order, the increase in metabolism during mental work is almost negligible. Benedict found that the extra energy consumed during one hour of intense mental work could be furnished by one-half of a peanut.

i. Muscle Work.—We have learned in our study of muscle physiology that during the production of the energy for muscular activity there is concomitantly a great liberation of heat which can not be utilized for the performance of mechanical work. From this and the fact that the muscles constitute about 45 per cent of the body, it can be readily understood that no other factor so powerfully influences the amount of energy liberated in the body as the activity of the skeletal muscles. This is well illustrated in Table **XXIII** from Lusk:

TABLE XXIII

Man in bed for 24 hours	1,840 Cal.
In bed 8 hours; sedentary occupation for 16 hours	2,168 Cal.
In bed 8 hours; in chair 14 hours, walking 2 hours	2,488 Cal.
Active outdoor life, as that of farmer	3,500 Cal.

We may next inquire as to the particular food, if any, that furnishes the necessary energy. Liebig held that the source of muscle energy is derived from the proteins which he called the plastic foods, in distinction to what he termed the respiratory foods (carbohydrates and fats) which served only for the production of heat in the body, not for the generation of muscle energy. This idea, which still survives in the minds of many people who hold that to do a fair day's physical work a good share of meat or eggs is essential, clashes with three or four well-established facts:

1. Our knowledge of the domestic animals ought to be sufficient to upset this theory, for beasts of burden are not fed on foods rich in protein such as meat, cheese, eggs, peas, or beans.

2. Whether or not proteins supply the energy for physical work can readily be decided by the nature (nitrogenous or non-nitrogenous) of the waste products formed during work as compared with the resting period. Judged by the excretion of urea and other nitrogenous waste products, it has been found that, if the diet contained a sufficient amount of nonprotein food, muscle work severe enough to double the amount of energy liberated did not increase the amount of protein catabolized.

3. It will be recalled (p. 440) that the oxidation of carbohydrates results in the production of a quantity of CO_2 equal to the volume of the oxygen consumed and that therefore the respiratory quotient (CO_2/O_2) is one. Fats, on the other hand, have a quotient of about 0.7. Now it has been found that under normal conditions and when the duration of the work is not too prolonged, the respiratory quotient tends to become one, showing that carbohydrates are utilized as the source of muscle energy. But in longer stretches of work the quotient is likely to fall, indicating that fats are drawn upon.

4. In those cases in which carbohydrates are not available, as in diabetes or in a diet such as that of the Eskimos, the fats furnish the greater part of the energy. But there is little, or no, evidence that the muscles can use fats directly; in all probability they must undergo a preliminary change into carbohydrates. When the carbohydrate and fat in the diet are insufficient to supply all the muscle energy, the protein is called upon. In regard to the muscle efficiency with the various foodstuffs, very little difference exists. The efficiency is said to be 5 per cent greater with carbohyrates than with either fats or proteins. The great importance of carbohydrates can be gathered from the fact that in marathon races the greatest exhaustion is shown by those contestants whose blood sugar level is the lowest. While all three foodstuffs can be used in muscle work, it appears that the carbohydrates are used by preference, are used directly, and with a slightly greater economy.

The amount of energy required for the daily work depends upon the nature and the duration of the work. Assuming a basal metabolic rate of 1,800 Cal. per day, a tailor would produce 2,500 Cal., a carpenter 3,200 Cal., and a stone mason 4,400 Cal.

The stimulating effect which muscular work has on metabolism furnishes a method by which the efficiency of the body as a machine may be determined. In order to make this calculation, the B.M.R., the metabolic rate during work and the amount of work done must be determined. To find the efficiency of the subject, the work done, expressed in Calories (426.85 Kgm. = 1 Cal.), is divided by the increase in metabolism due to the work performed. Investigation has shown that the efficiency of man as a machine is about 21 per cent.

j. The Influence of Food.—The ingestion of food causes a marked increase in the amount of metabolism. A man of 70 kilograms produced the following amount of heat per day:

Absolute rest in bed without food_____1,680 Cal.
Absolute rest in bed with food_____1,840 Cal.

The increase in heat production following the ingestion of food is known as the *specific dynamic action* of the foodstuffs. We may especially call attention to the behavior of proteins in this respect. Soon after the ingestion of proteins there is a large increase in heat set free as the experiment in Table XXIV shows, in which days of starvation alternated with days of protein feeding:

TABLE XXIV

DAY	DIET	HEAT LIBERATED
1	Starvation	718 Calories
2	400 grams of protein	1,046 Calories
3	Starvation	746 Calories
4	400 grams of protein	1,105 Calories

The increase of approximately 300 Cal. on the second and fourth days cannot be ascribed to the increased work on the part of the digestive organs, for the increased movements of the alimentary canal by saline purgatives do not have much effect upon metabolism. Furthermore, the intravenous injection of amino acids, the digestion products of proteins, is also followed by an increase in the heat production. However, if the amino acids are injected into an animal deprived of the liver, this does not take place. Now we have seen (p. 401) that some of the absorbed amino acids on reaching the liver are deaminized; the removal of the nitrogenous part from the remainder of the amino acid molecule is associated with the liberation of heat. Some authors therefore hold that this may account for the heat production following the ingestion of proteins; but it is doubtful whether the matter can be wholly explained in this manner. The specific dynamic action is not the same for all the three organic foodstuffs; that for proteins is generally stated as 30, for carbohydrates, 6, and for fats, 4 per cent of the foodstuff Calories absorbed.

The extra heat that the mere presence of the foods in the blood calls forth cannot be utilized by the organs of the body (muscles, glands) for the performance of their work. If the external temperature is below 30° C. (86° F.), it can be used to warm the body and thereby save other fuel material. But if the external temperature is above 30° C., the extra heat is a pure and simple waste and must be got rid of; it may cause discomfort to the individual. As the specific dynamic action of proteins is about five times as large as that of carbohydrates or fats we can see a reason why it is not desirable to eat large quantities of proteins on a hot day, especially if muscular work is to be done; the vegetables and fruits are the "cooler" foods. On the other hand, people of sedentary occupation and exposed to cold may find a larger share of proteins in the food very advantageous.

CHAPTER XXII

FOOD REQUIREMENTS OF THE BODY

Introduction.—Among the many factors which determine the normal function of an organism and its power to resist the onslaught of pathogenic bacteria, the proper supply of food materials in a sufficient quantity plays no mean part. Not infrequently the diet is deficient in one or more of the ingredients necessary for the growth, maintenance, or function of certain structures; again, it may contain more materials than the body can use and thereby cause dysfunction directly, or indirectly. The nature and the amount of the materials best adapted for the body vary with the changing conditions of the body and of the environment. That the selection of the food materials should not be entrusted to ''instinct'' is evident from the fact that, were this a reliable guide, no one would ever suffer from food-deficiency diseases, such as scurvy, rickets, or pellagra. Hence, the great importance of studying the needs of the body so that an intelligent selection of food materials may be made.

The losses sustained by the organism must be repaired by the taking in of proper materials. We have learned how, by means of the respiration-calorimeter, the amount of oxygen consumed and the amount of water and carbon dioxide produced are determined. Of this carbon dioxide the amount formed by the oxidation of the proteins can be calculated by determining the nitrogen found in the urine ($N \times 6.25 =$ protein); subtracting the CO_2 equivalent of this from the total amount of carbon dioxide gives us the amount formed from the fats and carbohydrates. The amount of water in the food and drink is known; the difference between this amount and that given off by the body is the amount of water formed by the oxidation of the hydrogen of the carbohydrates, fats, and proteins. If we subtract that derived from the proteins, there is left that formed from fats and carbohydrates. From the chemical formulas of fats, carbohydrates and proteins and from the amount of water and carbon dioxide produced from each of them, the amount of the various foodstuffs consumed, stored, or lost by the body can be determined. In our study of diet we shall call attention to only a few fundamental principles based upon physiologic facts already familiar to us.

I. AMOUNT OF PROTEIN REQUIRED

To supply all the energy needed by the body any one of the three organic foodstuffs would suffice. But, as described in foregoing chapters, the individual foodstuffs have distinct functions apart from furnishing energy; this is especially true for proteins. The expenditure of energy is, of course, associated with the use of material by the body. In estimating the amount of material used it is generally sufficient to determine by methods, discussed on p. 440, the amount of carbon and nitrogen excreted. From our study of the various conditions of the body and of the environment which influence the extent of metabolism it is evident that the amount of carbon and nitrogen lost in twenty-four hours may undergo large variations; Table XXV gives the amounts for a person engaged in light work.

TABLE XXV

	CARBON	NITROGEN
In urine	6 grams	15 grams
In feces	11 grams	1 gram
In respiration	208 grams	0

To replace this loss, a certain amount of the three organic foodstuffs must be ingested. The proportion of these foodstuffs can vary considerably; Ranke's diet consists of the following (Table XXVI):

TABLE XXVI

	CARBON	NITROGEN
100 grams Proteins	53 grams	16 grams
100 grams Fat	79 grams	0
250 grams Carbohydrate	93 grams	0
Total	225 grams	16 grams

This diet, with a heat value of 2,300 Cal., is suitable for persons with sedentary occupations. As the call for more heat and muscle energy increases, the amount of food must be augmented. The amount of proteins required per day is a matter concerning which there is considerable difference of opinion. There are those who advocate a relatively large amount, from 100 to 120 grams; others hold that from 60 to 75 grams is quite sufficient.

a. The advocates of a high protein diet claim that a diet poor in proteins reduces the vitality and thus increases the susceptibility to infectious diseases. Especially are comparisons made between the native Bengali and the Europeans living under practically the same conditions in India. The former, consuming a very limited amount of protein, is much inferior to the European and far more susceptible to infectious diseases. The Eskimo, on the other hand, living on a diet exceedingly rich in protein, has (or at least had until he acquired the white man's diseases) remarkable health and strength, and, according to Thomas, is comparatively free of renal, heart, and blood vessel diseases.

b. The proponents of the low protein diet point to the increased intestinal putrefaction following the intake of a large amount of proteins. Whether the putrefactive products have an injurious effect or whether the liver is able sufficiently to detoxify these products after their absorption into the blood stream is perhaps a debatable matter.

A diet rich in proteins yields a large amount of nitrogenous waste products, such as urea, uric acid, creatinine, and ammonia salts. Some of these, as we have learned, are elaborated in the liver and all are excreted by the kidneys. Whether the increased production and excretion of these products is injurious to the liver and kidneys is a question. Newburgh and others claim to have found nephritis (inflammation of the kidney) in rats and rabbits fed upon large amounts of protein. The same uncertainty exists as to whether a high protein diet is a possible factor in arterial hypertension. Wakeham and Hansen showed that the basal metabolism of vegetarians is considerably lower than that of non-vegetarians.

c. We have in a previous chapter, learned that for the production of energy in the body, proteins are not necessary, carbohydrates and fats being sufficient for this purpose. We may, therefore, grant that the food proteins are required for the wear and tear which the body sustains and perhaps for the formation of certain biologic products, such as enzymes, antibodies, and hormones; when these demands are met, the body is in nitrogenous equilibrium. How slight these demands are can be gathered from the fact that Thomas maintained himself in nitrogenous equilibrium with 13.75 grams of protein per day.

d. From the composition of human milk, as given on page 683, it can be calculated that the nursing infant derives a little better than 10 per cent of the daily calories from proteins. On this basis, 240 of the 2,400 Calories necessary for an adult would be obtained from proteins. As each gram represents 4 Calories, a total of 60 grams of proteins ought to suffice, an amount equal to about one-half of that generally advocated.

The distribution of the energy obtained from the three organic foodstuffs in the diet of various nations differs greatly, as shown in

Table XXVII, and depends chiefly upon the ease (cost) with which they can be procured.

TABLE XXVII

| | PERCENTAGE OF TOTAL ENERGY OBTAINED FROM | | |
	PROTEIN	FATS	CARBOHYDRATES
Greenland	44.0	48.0	8.0
Natives of India	9.6	21.8	68.6
Malayas in Java	8.9	8.3	82.8
United States	12.3	34.2	53.5
England	12.5	25.5	62.0

It is self-evident that the growing child in storing proteins needs, weight for weight, more proteins than does the adult. According to Berg, a boy of 16 or 18 years needs 50 per cent more protein than an adult. The largest share of the meat, eggs, etc., should, therefore, fall to the boy and not to his father. When to this is added the extreme muscular activity of children, their ravenous appetites are fully justified.

II. THE NATURE OF FOOD PROTEIN

From our previous studies, the reader will recall that the body needs primarily not protein but amino acids which are the building stones from which the body constructs the nitrogenous constituents of the cells and the indispensable internal secretions. Of these building stones the body requires a fairly large variety; some of these, e.g., glycine, alanine, cystine, and tyrosine, the body is able to construct from other amino acids. But *certain amino acids are essential,* or indispensable, in that the body cannot manufacture them; they must, therefore, be supplied with the food derived from the plant world.

It will be recalled that the proteins differ from each other in the relative amounts of the various amino acids. Certain proteins are capable of sustaining life because they contain all the necessary amino acids; this is true for casein, lactalbumin, glutelin (of maize) and glutenin (of wheat). Other proteins cannot sustain life because they lack certain essential amino acids; thus, gelatin lacks tryptophan; zein (of maize) contains no lysine or tryptophan; these are sometimes spoken of as **incomplete proteins.**

But even when a protein contains all the required amino acids, the amount of one or more of these acids present may be very small and thus reduce its *"physiologic"* or *"biologic value."* In this respect the proteins of the whole egg rank highest of all; in descending order are: milk, liver, kidney, heart, skeletal muscle, whole wheat, potato,

rolled oats, whole corn, white flour, and navy beans. In general, the
more connective tissue in meat (cheaper cuts), the lower the biological
value. There is little or no difference between the skeletal muscles of
ox, hog, or sheep. Vegetable proteins are nearly always inferior to
those of animal origin. Pasteurization of milk has no influence on
the biologic value of its proteins. From the above it is evident that
the question whether the diet should contain 60 or 125 grams of
protein is beside the point unless the kind of protein selected is
known.

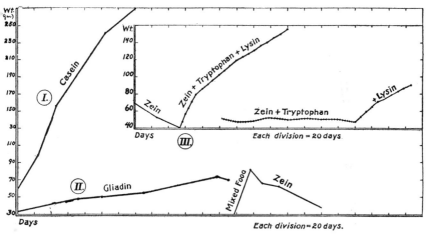

Fig. 196.—Curves illustrating the increase or decrease in body weight (ordinates
in grams) of young rats fed upon the food indicated on the curves. The abscissae represent periods of 20 days. *I* is the curve of growth with casein and is
to be regarded as normal. (Macleod, after Mendel and Osborne.)

Growth.—Among the factors necessary for normal growth may
be mentioned: an adequate supply of necessary amino acid, vitamins,
minerals, and hormones; perhaps a "hereditary" factor should also
be included. The distinctive physiologic value of the various amino
acids is nowhere better illustrated than in their influence on growth.
Young rats fed, in addition to all the other necessary food materials,
upon no other protein than casein grow normally, as shown by Curve
I in Fig. 196. Compare with this the growth Curve II when the
young depends for its amino acids upon gliadin. Gliadin, a protein
abundantly found in wheat and rye, lacks a sufficient amount of lysine
to maintain growth. However, it contains about 42 per cent of the
amino acid known as glutamic acid; as this is far in excess of that
present in any protein in the human body, the ingestion of large
quantities of gliadin gives the body a useless surplus of this amino
acid which must be disposed of.

The history of zein, as shown by the curves in Fig. 196, is most interesting. By consulting the table on page 395, it will be seen that this protein contains no glycocoll, lysine, or tryptophan. With zein as the sole supply of amino acids, growth is impossible; in fact, the animal loses body weight. The addition of tryptophan to the zein prevents the loss in weight but does not promote growth; the addition of both lysine and tryptophan insures a normal growth. From this it is evident that these two amino acids do not play the same rôle in the animal body; tryptophan is necessary to maintain nitrogenous equilibrium and body weight; lysine is required for the building of new tissue, i.e., growth. This experiment also shows that the amino acid, glycocoll (which is lacking in the zein), can be manufactured

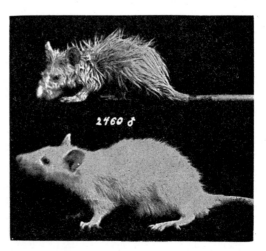

Fig. 197.—The upper photograph shows the effect of a diet deficient in the amino acid, valine. The lower picture shows the same rat after valine had been administered for 25 days. (Rose and Epstein: J. Biol. Chem. 127: 683, 1939.)

by the animal body. Of the 22 amino acids Rose found only 10 as indispensable or essential for growth and maintenance; among these are lysine, tryptophan, histidine, leucine, arginine, and valine. The astonishing effects of the lack of only one amino acid, valine, is shown in Fig. 197.

How far-reaching the results of slight variations in the protein of the diet may be can be learned from experiments conducted by Sherman and Campbell on 400 rats living under similar conditions save that of food. Two hundred rats were fed on an adequate wheat diet plus a small amount of milk; the other 200 received the same food excepting for a larger quantity of milk; the span of life of the latter was 10 per cent greater than that of the former. The addition of one pint of milk to a diet which was considered correct in every respect caused the body weight of boys to increase by almost 7 pounds a year instead of the 3.85 pounds on the same food but without milk. The effect of milk on growth is well shown in Fig. 198.

The selection of the proper protein in the diet is of greatest importance when there is a special demand for the building of tissue, as in growth, convalescence, pregnancy, and lactation. Fortunately, when growth has been stunted because of the lack of a sufficient

Fig. 198.—Two puppies of the same age. The larger one had an abundant supply of milk; the smaller one had little milk but plenty of other food. (Hawley and Carden: The Art and Science of Nutrition. The C. V. Mosby Co. Courtesy of Shattuck Farms, Andover, Mass.)

amount of the essential amino acids, by proper food the loss may be regained, to a certain extent, even in animals normally past the growing age. From our discussion it will be observed that the *vegetable proteins, in contrast to those of animal origin, are more apt to be of low biologic value.* It is therefore well to include several different proteins in the diet, in order that one protein may correct the defects of another. And by not limiting the protein in the diet to the mere minimum amount, as some would advocate, we avoid the possibility of deficiency of one or more essential amino acids, and are thereby better nourished and, according to some investigators, better able to ward off infectious diseases.

Aside from their indispensability in growth, a few specific functions have been attributed to certain amino acids. Thus, a lack of tryptophan in young rats leads to cataract (and, therefore, to blindness) and to poor development of tooth enamel. In old as well as young male rats it causes baldness and impairs the generation of spermatozoa. Tyrosine is claimed to be necessary for the production of the hormones, adrenalin, and thyroxin.

III. CARBOHYDRATES AND FATS

The bulk of the energy requirements of the body is supplied by the fats and carbohydrates. The amounts required per day depend upon the size and activity of the individual; this matter was discussed in Chapter XXI.

Fig. 199.—These rats are litter mates. The one on the left received a diet containing 20 per cent lard; the one on the right received no fat. (Courtesy of Dr. George Burr, from Hawley and Maurer-Mast: The Fundamentals of Nutrition, Charles C Thomas Co.)

Since these two foodstuffs are largely used for the generation of energy, they can replace each other, to a very large extent, in the ratio of their heat value, i.e., $2\frac{1}{4}$ parts of carbohydrate to one part of fat. But neither the one nor the other should be entirely excluded from the diet. A great curtailment of the carbohydrates leads to acidosis. The effect of a diet completely devoid of fat is shown in Fig. 199. Certain of the vitamins (A and D, e.g.) are not soluble in water but are fat-soluble; an inadequate allowance of fat may therefore lead to vitamin deficiency disease (see under vitamin A). It is now claimed by some investigators that in addition to the common fats, olein, stearin, and palmitin which constitute almost the entire bulk of our food-fat, small amounts of other fats are indispensable.

Among these is, for example, the fat formed from linoleic acid (this and other fats belonging to this class are found in linseed and peanut oil) in lard, soybean, olive oil and egg yolk, but only to a very limited extent in butter. The body is unable to make these highly unsaturated fatty acids. They are essential for maintaining a healthy skin.

IV. INORGANIC SALTS

Seldom, if ever, is the diet deficient in sodium, potassium, magnesium, copper, sulfur, phosphorus, or chlorine; but not infrequently there may be an insufficient amount of calcium, iron, fluorine, or iodine. In milling most of the mineral constituents are removed, and as a result the white flour contains but one-third as much calcium and iron as the whole wheat. Again, in certain regions of the globe the drinking water and the food usually consumed are deficient in iodine and thereby may give rise to goiter. We have already dealt with the functions of iron in Chapter XX. Calcium, magnesium, phosphorus, and fluorine enter into the normal composition of the bones and teeth. They can be studied best in connection with the vitamins in a subsequent section. It is important to remember that the growing child needs relatively much larger amounts of minerals in the diet than does the adult; this is particularly true for the bone-forming elements. Fruits and vegetables contain significant amounts of minerals.

V. WATER

Water is one of the most essential items of the diet. An animal succumbs much more rapidly to a complete fast than to a fast which allows an intake of water. The amount of water required per day depends upon the water loss from the body. The average person under basal conditions requires a water intake of 2000 c.c. per day. This may be regarded as a minimum rather than the optimum. (See also p. 429).

VI. THE VITAMINS

Introduction.—On many occasions we have learned that the various activities of the living body are controlled either by neural mechanisms or by chemical compounds. The chemical, or humoral, regulators readily fall into two classes: those produced by the body itself, and those introduced into the body with the ingested food. The former, generally known as hormones, or internal secretions (see Chap. XXIII), we have referred to in our study of the circulation of the blood, the secretion of the digestive juices, the metabolism of carbohydrates, and other topics. Of equal importance with the hormones are the chemical regulators found in our foods.

Although the scientific knowledge of vitamins is very recent, what are now called deficiency diseases were known for centuries. Five hundred years before our era, Hippocrates, the Father of Medicine, used ox liver as a cure for night blindness. The Indians showed Cartier how a tea of spruce tree needles could stay the ravages of scurvy that were decimating his men. Cod-liver oil has been used for hundreds of years to combat certain physical ailments. It is perhaps correct to say that light was first thrown on the cause of these deficiency diseases and their cure by Eijkman who, in 1897, found that pigeons fed no other food than polished rice and water acquired polyneuritis, an inflammation of the peripheral nerves and one of the outstanding symptoms of beriberi. Grave nervous disturbances resulted so that the animal staggered and was finally unable to stand. By feeding the hulls of the rice, or a water extract of them, the symptoms disappeared promptly. The outer covering of the rice contains, evidently, a material indispensable for the life and health of an animal fed on rice. Funk called these substances vitamines (vitamins).

At present many physical and even some mental disturbances which formerly so commonly afflicted mankind can be prevented or cured. Among these we may mention scurvy, rickets, pellagra, beriberi, night blindness, certain forms of eye diseases, and the hemorrhage in newborn children. The pathologic conditions resulting from an insufficient supply of one or more vitamins may be very severe, incapacitating the person from carrying on his daily duties and even resulting in death (avitaminosis) ; or they may exist in a milder form (hypovitaminosis) in which the health and vitality are more or less below par. That hypovitaminosis is, even at present, still quite prevalent is evidenced by the fact that in this country, which is better fed than any other country in the world, 100,000 persons are said to suffer from pellagra. The reason for this dreadful situation, in the face of our extensive knowledge of vitamins, is due very largely to ignorance and/or poverty of the individual. This ignorance reveals itself in a poor selection of the materials making up one's food or in the improper preparing of the food, as in milling and other "refining" processes (e.g., sugar) and in cooking the food. In some instances the person does not partake of a sufficient quantity of properly selected food, or he may not be able to absorb an adequate amount of vitamins.

Characteristics.—Vitamins, of which a score or more are now known, do not constitute a class of chemically related compounds, such as the proteins or carbohydrates do. Indeed, they have, chemically, nothing in common except that they are all organic substances. Their being grouped together as "vitamins" is quite accidental and entirely devoid of meaning. What characterizes vitamins is: (1) they are indispensable for the life or well-being of most higher animals; (2) the amount required per day is very small; in fact, in some instances unbelievably small (see vitamin D); (3) in general, the animal body is unable to produce them. We should add, however, that in some cases the animal body is able to change the immediate precursor (or pro-vitamin) into the vitamin. In all these respects, however, vitamins do not differ materially from some other food ingredients, such as the essential amino acids, the highly unsaturated fatty acids, and minerals.

Sources.*—As implied in the above statement, animals are dependent ultimately for vitamins upon the vegetable world. There is, however, no uniform distribution of the various vitamins in the many different foods we consume; to obtain an adequate supply a somewhat wide selection of foods is necessary. It is for this reason that people living on a restricted and monotonous diet composed of dried, salted, or improperly canned foods, are very likely to show hypovitaminosis. But to select a properly balanced diet, from a vitamin point of view, it is not necessary that the amount of each vitamin in each of the food materials consumed be known; rather, a broad understanding of what constitutes the so-called "protective" foods is all that is needed.

Many (about 12) of the vitamins have been isolated in pure form and some have been produced synthetically. As such they can now be obtained by the public, but their consumption in this form is less desirable than eating the natural foods in which they are found. Nevertheless, if people insist on eating fine white bread, instead of that made from whole wheat flour, the re-enforcing of the white flour with vitamin B_1 and other substances is of decided advantage.

Daily Requirement.—The amount of vitamins required varies from one kind to another. It is sometimes expressed in milligrams or micrograms ($\frac{1}{1000}$ mg.); in other cases it is stated in International Units established by the Committee on Health of the League of

*For a very complete tabulation of the Vitamin Content of Foods, see Miscellaneous Publication No. 275 by the U. S. Dept. of Agriculture, 1937.

Nations. Under special conditions there is an extra demand for vitamins, as during the period of growth, pregnancy, nursing, and convalescence.

How Vitamins Work.—Although it is known quite definitely what changes occur when a certain vitamin is lacking in the diet, yet how they operate to prevent these harmful changes is still unknown. In the very small amount required to maintain life and health and to insure normal growth, vitamins strongly resemble hormones and enzymes. Since some of the vitamins are found in every living cell, plant or animal, thus far investigated, the rôle they play must be very fundamental. We may perhaps quite correctly assume that they constitute part of that grand admixture of a host of ingredients which we call protoplasm. All of life's activities, growth and maintenance of bodily structures and functions, are chemical processes in which catalysts, as we have seen, play an indispensable part. Previously, we have called the cell a "nest of catalysts"; it may, perhaps, be proper to include along with the enzymes, some, if not all, of the vitamins in the "nest."

Regarding Nomenclature.—When the first two or three vitamins were discovered, they were designated by some letter of the alphabet, such as, vitamin A, vitamin B, etc. As the specific action of a vitamin was more completely understood, a more expressive name chosen for this vitamin disclosed its main action; for example, the antirachitic vitamin. Many of the vitamins have now been identified chemically, and where this has been the case, they are called by the chemical name. As all three methods are in use in the literature, we shall give all three designations where possible.

1. Vitamin A: Antikeratinizing Vitamin

Function.—Several diets deficient in this vitamin have been formulated; we may quote that given by Osborne and Mendel.

Purified casein	18%
Corn starch	48%
Lard	30%
Salts	4%
0.3 gram dried yeast (for vitamin B_1)	

Subsistence on this diet for any length of time stops the growth of young animals (see Fig. 200); and for this reason vitamin A was formerly designated as the growth-promoting vitamin. As, however, other dietary deficiencies also stunt the growth, it does not seem proper to name vitamin A in this manner, to the exclusion of its chief function related in the following paragraph.

The primary effect of lack of vitamin A is atrophy of epithelial tissues. In many parts of the body this tissue undergoes keratinization (*keras,* horn), that is, it acquires a horny character similar to that of the outermost layer of the skin, and loses its function. For this reason vitamin A is frequently referred to as the antikeratinizing vitamin.

Epithelial tissue covers the outer surface of the skin, and forms the inner lining of all the tubular structures of the body. Glands also are composed of glandular epithelium. From this it must be apparent that the results of the lack of vitamin A may be widespread; we shall, however, confine our discussion to a few of the more thoroughly established disturbances.

Fig. 200.—Inhibition of growth in the rat produced by restriction of vitamin A in the diet. The animals, litter mates, were 21 days old at the start of the experiment, which was continued for thirty-three days. The animal at left received a diet containing all nutritive substances except vitamin A; the animal at right received an adequate diet. Note the xerophthalmia in vitamin A deprived rat. (Courtesy of the Upjohn Company, Kalamazoo, Mich.)

1. NIGHT BLINDNESS is one of the earliest and most constant indications of a deficiency of vitamin A. A person may show no visual disturbances as long as the intensity of the light is fairly great, such as in diffused daylight, but in dim light (twilight) he is unable, or finds it very difficult, to discern the objects about him. This abnormal condition is similar to what we all experience in going from a bright street into a dimly illuminated moving picture house. The normal

person recovers rather quickly from this blindness by a process known as dark adaptation (see page 560); but in a night-blind individual this process takes place more slowly or is absent altogether. According to Jeans and Zentmire, one-half of the children in the villages of Iowa are thus afflicted to a greater or lesser degree; normal night vision is restored by the administration of a sufficient amount of vitamin A.

2. XEROPHTHALMIA.—The lack of vitamin A causes the eyelids to be swollen and scabby; the conjunctiva (the reddish membrane lining the eyelids) is inflamed with a bloody or purulent (pus) discharge; the cornea is dry and may become involved in the inflammation, Fig. 200. This condition, called xerophthalmia (*xeros,* dry; *ophthalmos,* eye), is due to the keratinization and the drying up of the lacrimal (tear) glands; if not relieved, it results in blindness. Vitamin A is for this reason sometimes referred to as the antixerophthalmic vitamin.

3. TEETH.—The enamel organ, which gives rise to enamel of teeth, is of epithelial origin. It also is affected in A-avitaminosis. Bessey and Wolbach state that "in all probability, vitamin A deficiency during the formative period of teeth outranks in the human being all other vitamin deficiencies in importance." The effect of lack of vitamin A will be discussed under vitamin D.

4. DIGESTIVE TRACT.—The glands of the oral cavity, the salivary glands, and the gastric glands are also involved in the keratinization. To this, perhaps, may be attributed the loss of body weight sustained during A-avitaminosis.

5. RESPIRATORY ORGANS.—Any part of the respiratory tract may undergo keratinization. In infants the trachea and bronchi are readily affected; this may account for the frequent occurrence of pneumonia when there is a lack of this vitamin. (See infra.)

6. UROGENITAL TRACT.—The seminiferous epithelium which produces the spermatozoa and the epithelium giving rise to ova also undergo keratinization. Some are inclined to connect kidney-stone formation with an inadequate supply of this vitamin.

7. RESISTANCE TO INFECTIONS.—It is generally agreed that in vitamin A deficiency there is an increased susceptibility to infections, especially of the respiratory tract. But there is no satisfactory evidence that warrants us in looking upon this vitamin as an antiinfective vitamin. Using night blindness as an indication of an insufficient intake of the vitamin, Jeghers found that the incidence of colds was no greater in persons obtaining a subnormal amount than in those obtaining a normal amount of vitamin A.

We may summarize these functions: **Vitamin A is necessary for the proper functioning of nearly all epithelial structures in the body.**

Sources of Vitamin A.—Hopkins discovered that growth in animals deprived of this vitamin recommenced almost immediately on the addition of 2 cc. of milk to the daily ration. McCollum found that the milk could be replaced by cheese, egg yolk, butter, or the liver oil of cod, salmon, or halibut. Due to the substitution of margarine for butter, Danish children, during World War I, suffered much from xerophthalmia. This was readily relieved by supplying butter in the children's diet. Subsequently it was shown that nearly all yellow fruits and vegetables and many of the green vegetables are able to ameliorate the symptoms of A-avitaminosis. This action is due to a yellow pigment, *carotene;* this must be regarded as the pro-vitamin which is transformed by the liver of the animal into vitamin A. Recently this change has been brought about outside of the animal body. Carotene gives the yellow color to nearly all yellow fruits and vegetables; it is also found, although masked by the chlorophyll, in many green plants; among these the following excel in vitamin A: broccoli (leaf), chard, dandelion, kale, parsley, lettuce, and spinach. The white varieties of corn, potatoes, asparagus, lettuce, carrots, and turnips are devoid, or nearly devoid, of it, as are also vegetable oils, lean meat, white flour, lard, and rice. Butter and egg yolk contain, in addition to vitamin A, some carotene which has escaped conversion into the vitamin. Grass and alfalfa are rich in carotene.

Vitamin A can be stored to a considerable extent by the animal in the liver, fat, and milk. The newborn human infant is very low in reserve vitamin and is, therefore, directly dependent upon an ample daily supply. During the pasturing season a quart of cow's milk contains approximately from one-fourth to one-half of the amount of vitamin A required by a child. In the winter season, unless carotene is fed, the content of A in cow's milk is decreased by almost 50 per cent.

Stability.—Vitamin A is not destroyed by ordinary cooking at 100° C.; canned foods, therefore, rank with the corresponding fresh foods. The vitamin is injured by exposure to light, especially ultra-violet rays. Eggs stored frozen for nine years suffered no loss of this vitamin.

Requirements.—The daily requirement of vitamin A varies with age, and is higher during pregnancy and lactation. The average adult requires daily about 5000 units.*

---

*A crystalline preparation of vitamin A isolated by Holmes and Corbet was found to have a potency of 3 million units per gram. Thus, the daily requirement is probably a little less than 2 milligrams.

2. Vitamin B₁, or Thiamin

Of the large number of vitamins grouped together as the vitamin B complex only two have been definitely shown to be of importance in human beings. One of these is B_1, or thiamin. The chief deficiencies arising from an inadequate supply of this vitamin are:

1. NEURITIS.—In the adult a deficiency of vitamin B_1 leads, in man, to a condition known as beriberi. While many changes occur, the outstanding symptom is an inflammation and degeneration of the peripheral nerves (neuritis), especially of those supplying the lower limbs. The neuritis causes intense pain and results in paralysis and a wasting of the muscles. In animals neuritis is also present. Fig. 201 illustrates the muscular weakness and the loss of the coordinating power of a rat fed upon a diet deficient in vitamin B_1. Other forms of neuritis, such as that of alcoholism or pregnancy, have been found to be greatly benefited by thiamin.

Fig. 201.—Illustrating dietary deficiency in vitamin B₁. The animal on the right received no vitamin B₁; its litter mate on the left did. (Courtesy of Wisconsin Alumni Research Foundation.)

2. APPETITE.—One of the most common characteristics of B_1-avitaminosis is the loss of appetite (anorexia), which leads to great inanition. No satisfactory explanation has been offered for this condition. Babkin claims to have found a marked decrease in the secretion of the digestive juices; he showed that the feeding of yeast and other materials containing thiamin restores the appetite.

3. METABOLISM.—The amount of the vitamin needed by the body increases as the rate of metabolism is accelerated; it was found, for example, that the administration of thyroid hormone (p. 495) increases the amount of B_1 necessary to ward off the effects of B_1-avitaminosis. This seems to be true especially when the increased catabolism concerns the carbohydrates. Peters has advanced the view that a nerve cell, in order to obtain a sufficient amount of energy for its normal activity from the combustion of carbohydrates, must be supplied with vitamin B_1. This may account for the above-de-

scribed nervous disturbances. From its universal distribution in all forms of life, from the lowest organized bacteria and fungi to the highest forms of plant and animal life, we may conclude that thiamin is a normal and constant component of all protoplasm.

4. GROWTH.—The amount of vitamin B_1 necessary for normal growth of animals was found to be from three to five times the amount required to prevent neuritis in the adult. Young pigeons, fed on a diet consisting of polished rice, butter fat (for vitamin A), raw onion (for vitamin C), and water, not only ceased almost immediately to grow but experienced great loss in weight and finally died as the result of the avitaminosis. The addition of a small amount of wheat germ or dried yeast to the diet prevents these results. How emphatically this is true for children appears from the work of Morgan and Barry on underweight children. By feeding two wheat germ rolls at the noon meal, the gain in body weight was from 150 to 170 per cent above the expected gain; the control group of children receiving white flour rolls gained from 50 to 71 per cent of the expected gain.

5. THE ''MORALE VITAMIN.''—It is claimed that an inadequate supply of vitamin B_1 upsets the ''morale'' of the individual. He experiences a loss of power to concentrate and self-confidence; memory is more uncertain and he becomes anxious, depressed, and highly irritable. The vitamin is said to increase alertness and the capacity for physical work.

Sources.—Thiamin is found abundantly in yeast, and, in descending order of concentration, in dried soy beans, lean pork, oatmeal, whole wheat, dried beans and peas, whole rye, egg yolk, skimmed milk, and walnuts. In the grains B_1 is found in the husk and germ, for which reason whole wheat bread contains from 4 to 8 times as much vitamin B_1 as is found in white bread. Cow's milk, it is claimed, contains three times as much B_1 vitamin as is found in human milk. Milk, fruits, oils, and fats are poorly supplied.

Vitamin B_1 has been isolated in crystalline form and also prepared synthetically $(C_{12}H_{16}N_4SO)$. It is frequently added to the table salt for the convenience of the consumers, many of whom, according to Eddy and other authorities, subsist on a suboptimal allowance of vitamin B_1.

Stability.—The vitamin is not destroyed by cooking at $100°$ C. for one hour; but the cooking-water may contain no small amount of the vitamin originally present in the food. The addition of soda increases the destruction.

Daily Requirement.—The amount of thiamin required varies with: (1) the body weight; (2) the number of calories supplied by the food; (3) the extent of carbohydrate metabolism; (4) growth. (5) The amount needed during pregnancy and lactation is from two to three times that usually required. The daily requirement of the average adult is approximately 2 mg. of thiamin hydrochloride. The vitamin can be stored to but a very limited extent in the liver and in a few other organs; we are therefore dependent upon a daily supply of it in the food.

3. Vitamin P-P, Antipellagra Vitamin or Nicotinic Acid

This vitamin, another of the B complex, has been shown to be nicotinic acid—C_5H_4NCOOH—or, popularly called niacin.* It has been isolated and synthesized. It is a specific for the prevention and cure of pellagra. Pellagra, which in 1921 affected 200,000 Americans,

Fig. 202.—The diet of the upper rat was deficient in riboflavin. The lower rat received the same food plus 90 micrograms of riboflavin weekly; it shows no evidence of alopecia (baldness). This picture was taken on the seventy-fifth day of experiment, at which time they weighed 35 and 150 grams, respectively. (Day et al.: J. Nutrition 13: 392, 1937.)

is a poverty disease. It is found in certain parts of the United States during times of financial stress (especially during the winter months), where the individual lives largely on corn, molasses, and bacon; it is characterized by want of strength and vitality, indigestion, diarrhea, skin eruptions, pain, and sometimes great mental disturbances. Goldberg, in 1925, concluded that these disturbances were caused by the lack of a particular food ingredient which is found very abundantly in yeast; it is also found in fresh, dried, or evaporated milk, lean meat, eggs, tomatoes, cabbage, peas, beans, liver, and wheat germ.

The daily requirement of nicotinic acid depends upon the size and activity of the person. A daily allowance of 25 mg. should meet the requirements of the adult.

---

*Niacin, nai'-a-sin; not to be confused with nicotine.

4. Vitamin B₂, or G, or Riboflavin

Riboflavin is probably necessary for the normal carbohydrate metabolism of nerve cells. While no specific deficiency disease due to a lack of riboflavin has been described, it is generally agreed that a deficiency of this vitamin is the cause of a characteristic inflammation of the skin in the corners of the mouth. Fig. 202 shows the results of riboflavin deficiency in the diet of a growing rat. In general it occurs in the same foods as thiamin. The chemical formula for riboflavin is $C_{17}H_{20}N_4O_6$.

The daily requirement is generally regarded as 2 to 3 mg.

5. Vitamin B₆ or Pyridoxine

No specific deficiency disease in human beings has been proved for this vitamin. It appears that some of the symptoms of deficiency are extreme nervousness, abdominal pains, and weakness. Its composition is given as $C_8H_{11}O_3N$. The sources and requirements are similar to those of thiamin.

6. Pantothenic Acid, Biotin, and Para-aminobenzoic Acid

These substances have been shown to belong to the vitamin B complex, but, up to the present time, no deficiency disease due to lack of them has been proved in the case of man.

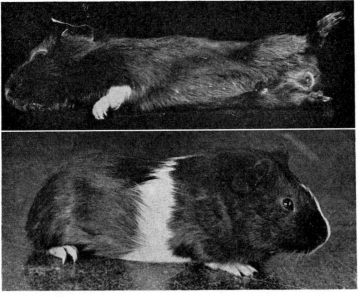

Fig. 203.—Showing dietary deficiency of vitamin C. (Courtesy E. R. Squibb & Son, New York.)

7. Vitamin C, Ascorbic Acid, Antiscorbutic Vitamin

A guinea pig fed upon hay and water develops scurvy, a disease exceedingly common a century or two ago. Scorbutus, or scurvy, is characterized by (a) the destruction of the capillary wall, which leads to hemorrhages beneath the skin and in the mucous membranes (such as the gums and the alimentary canal) and under the periosteum; (b) certain changes occur in the bones which render them more liable to fracture, especially at the epiphyses (head) of the long bones; (c) aching joints; (d) swollen, spongy, and bleeding gums and loose teeth. In severe cases death ensues (Fig. 203). Ascorbic acid prevents or cures scurvy, for which reason it is sometimes spoken of as the antiscorbutic vitamin.

Vitamin C and the Intercellular Substance.—It will be recalled that the various forms of supporting and connective tissues—bone, cartilage, white fibrous tissue, etc.—are characterized by a large amount of intercellular material which is laid down by the widely separated cells found imbedded in this material. In the absence of vitamin C, in the young animal, the formation of the osteoid tissue in which are to be deposited the calcium salts in bone construction does not take place normally. It is probable that degenerative changes in the material binding the endothelial cells of the capillary walls together account for the fragility of these vessels and their rupture. The cells responsible for the depositing of the intercellular materials depend for this function upon the proper amount of vitamin C.

There is conflicting evidence as to the effect of vitamin C deficiency on teeth. Some assert that the dentin undergoes changes quite similar to those in bone tissue. It is generally agreed that for normal tooth growth an adequate amount of vitamin C is necessary.

Sources.—Ascorbic acid has the chemical composition: $C_6H_8O_6$. Dry cereals and legumes are devoid of ascorbic acid, but on sprouting they become rich sources of this vitamin. Indeed, the growing parts of nearly all leafy plants—such as spinach, kale, green or red peppers, cabbage—are well provided with ascorbic acid. To a lesser extent it is present in potatoes, apples, and bananas. Of all sources, citrous fruits and tomatoes excel. It is claimed that fresh juices of rutabaga and raw cabbage are as potent as orange juice. Butter and eggs do not contain ascorbic acid.

Requirements.—A normal adult needs from 75 to 150 mg. of ascorbic acid per day. Children under one year require about 30 mg. During pregnancy and lactation, the supply should be increased. Orange juice contains from 40 to 60 mg. per 100 c.c. Human milk contains from four to five times as much ascorbic acid as cow's milk. As the latter contains approximately 5 mg. per pint, cow's milk, at its best, cannot supply a sufficient amount of vitamin C for the child; hence the great need of supplementing the diet with fruits or the juices of fruits or vegetables.

Stability.—Ascorbic acid is destroyed by heating, salting, drying, contact with air, and aging. The effect of high temperature and especially long boiling is, however, chiefly due to oxidation. For this reason canned fruits and vegetables and those boiled in a pressure cooker (at 248° F.) are superior to those boiled in an open kettle at 212° F. For example: raw cabbage and spinach, which excel all other vegetables in this vitamin, are twenty times as effective as when boiled in the usual manner for one hour; but the loss sustained by canning the cabbage is only one-fourth of this. Milk powders contain vitamin C; pasteurized milk has considerably less. The destruction of this vitamin is also hastened by the presence of alkalies, such as baking soda; these should, therefore, never be added to boiling vegetables. Acid fruits and vegetables may be rich in vitamin C after boiling in the absence of oxygen (e.g., canned tomatoes and grapefruit). As vitamin C is easily soluble in water, the vitamin content of the cooking-water and the water from canned fruits and vegetables may be very high. Heavy metals, especially copper, are very destructive to this vitamin.

8. Vitamin **D**: Antirachitic Vitamin

Rickets.—On certain diets the bones of an infant frequently show lack of proper ossification; in consequence they lack normal rigidity and, because of stresses and strains placed upon them, become misshapen. This condition, known as rickets, or rachitis, exists in all degrees of severity. The most noticeable defects are bowed or knock-kneed legs, a very narrow "pigeon" chest and scoliosis (lateral curvature of the spine). The wrists and ankles are swollen; due to the delayed closing of the fontanelles the head is large and flat; the pelvis is contracted; the eruption of the teeth is delayed, and a line of knobs on each side of the chest where the ribs join the cartilages feels like a string of beads, known as the rachitic rosary (Fig. 204).

The mineral content of the bone falls from the usual 60 to 30 per cent, or even lower. The microscope and x-ray reveal the structural defects of such bones. Rickets rarely sets in after the second year and, with proper diet and hygienic measures, gradually disappears, excepting the bowing of the legs and contraction of the pelvis. This last defect may be of serious consequences in women.

Bone Formation.—Under the influence of certain cells, known as osteoblasts, calcium salts are deposited in the interstitial material found between the widely separated cells of certain cartilage and bone tissues. The composition of this calcium salt is very complex; we may regard it as a large molecule formed by the union of calcium phosphate—$Ca_3(PO_4)_2$—and calcium carbonate—$CaCO_3$; in thi calcium phosphate accounts for about 88 per cent of the molecule For the depositing of this salt to proceed in a normal fashion, severa factors may be concerned; we shall briefly speak of the following:

1. CALCIUM AND PHOSPHORUS.—For the building of bone from the calcium and phosphorus, the diet must contain a sufficient amoun of these materials. Diets, it is stated, are more frequently deficien in calcium than in any other element although many foods are rich

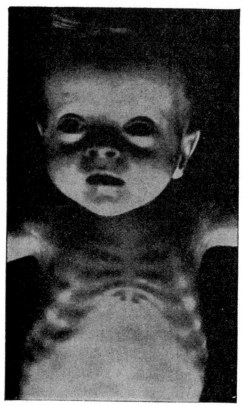

Fig. 204.—Rickets. Note the square head, large frontal bosses, enlarged junctions between the ribs and the costal cardiages, the "rachitis rosary." (Marriott: Infant Nutrition, The C. V. Mosby Co.)

in calcium—cow's milk (1 gram per liter), cheese, green vegetables, egg yolk, bran, molasses, beans, peas, almonds, and peanuts. Cow's milk is three times as rich in calcium as human milk is. Foods poor in calcium are lean meats, white flour, polished rice, potatoes, and bananas. The amount of calcium required is stated at from 1 to 2 grams per day. Foods very rich in phosphorus are liver, lean meats, fish, milk, cheese, and egg yolk. The amount needed per day by an adult is generally placed at about 1.5 grams; women during pregnancy and lactation require a greater amount. Children also need more.

It is self-evident that a diet which contains a calcium or phosphorus allowance far below par must inevitably bring on rickets; but it is equally true that the mere presence of a sufficient amount of these elements does not assure sound bones, for severe rickets frequently develops in children fed on an abundance of cow's milk which is rich in calcium and phosphorus. Even more important than the absolute amount of calcium and phosphorus is the ratio of these two elements. For example, young rats fed upon the following diet, formulated by Sherman, showed rickets within thirty days:

White flour	95.0%
Calcium lactate	2.9%
Sodium chloride	2.0%
Iron citrate	0.1%

In this diet the Ca:P ratio is 65:1. Whenever the Ca:P ratio in the blood is much disturbed, rickets sets in (unless vitamin D is administered). In rickets the blood phosphorus may drop from the normal 5 mg. to 2 or 3 mg. per 100 c.c. of blood serum, while the amount of calcium remains normal (10 mg. per 100 c.c.). McCollum states that no rickets occurs in rats when both the Ca and the P content of the diet is low, if the Ca:P ratio is approximately normal (1:1 or 2:1). We may therefore conclude that in rickets it is not so much the lack of calcium, as is commonly supposed, but rather a want of blood phosphorus—hypophosphatemia.

2. VITAMIN D.—As we stated in a previous paragraph, rickets may exist in children even when the diet contains a sufficient amount of Ca and P in the correct ratio. Long before the word "vitamin" was coined, it was known that cod-liver oil was of great aid in rickets. Mellanby demonstrated that a diet deficient only in the Ca:P ratio is not likely to cause rickets if to such a diet there be added a small amount of cod-liver oil. Another factor, therefore, enters into the proper construction of bone tissue; namely, an ingredient, vitamin D, found in cod-liver oil and in a few other foods.

Not only does this vitamin prevent rickets, but it also is a specific cure; for this reason it is frequently spoken of as the *antirachitic vitamin.*

3. INFLUENCE OF SUNLIGHT.—Rickets has been called the disease of sunless areas and of the winter months. Hess and other investigators observed that the incidence of rickets was higher in winter months than in the summer. These observations led to the study of the influence of light on bone development. Six young rats were placed on

a diet lacking in vitamin D and were kept in complete darkness; in from twenty to thirty days all developed rickets. Seven other rats received the same diet and were also kept in darkness excepting for a fifteen- or twenty-minute period each day during which they were exposed to sunlight; these rats showed perfect growth of bone tissue. Rats kept in complete darkness but receiving a supply of vitamin D were also free from rickets.

Soon after this discovery the relation between the antirachitic power of sunlight and of vitamin D was elucidated by Steenbock and others who found that if certain foods not possessing the antirachitic property, such as commercial (impure) peptones, dried milk, flour, olive oil, and lettuce, were exposed to light (especially ultraviolet light), they acquired the power to cure or prevent rickets. The materials in the foods which by irradiation by sunlight or artificial light

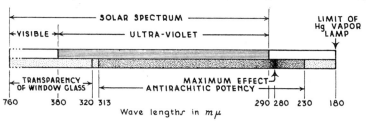

Fig. 205.—Diagram illustrating the extent of the antirachitic potency of ether vibrations.

acquire the antirachitic property are of either animal or vegetable origin. In animal foods there is found a lipoid, known as *cholesterol;* on being activated by irradiation, this acquires the above-discussed property. In plants we find a closely related compound, *ergosterol,* which undergoes a similar change. These two substances may therefore be regarded as D provitamin and in their irradiated form constitute vitamin D. Irradiating ergosterol for 22½ minutes bestows upon this substance antirachitic properties 250,000 times as great as that found in cod-liver oil. The activated ergosterol is sometimes referred to as *calciferol,* or *viosterol.**

Ultraviolet Light.—The visible sunlight (see Fig. 205) extends from the longest ether vibration (red) of 760 millimicrons† to the shortest (violet) of 380 mμ wave length. Beyond the 380μ the invisible solar spectrum extends to the 290 mμ wave length; this portion is spoken of as the ultraviolet. The ether vibrations able to confer antirachitic power upon otherwise inert foods are found between

---

*It should be noted that there are nine sterols of slightly different composition all of which exhibit antirachitic activity in varying degrees when properly irradiated by ultraviolet light.

†A millimicron (mμ) = 1/1,000 micron (μ) = 1/1,000,000 mm.

the 313 and the 265 mμ wave lengths; the maximum effect is at 280. It will, therefore, be seen that only about one-half of the effective rays are found in the ethereal energy derived from the sun and that the most beneficial rays (at 280 mμ) fall outside of the solar spectrum. When we learn that the vibrations of a carbon arc lamp extend to 220 and those of the mercury vapor lamp to 180 mμ, it is easy to understand why these lights possess such marked antirachitic powers. Irradiation of the body by ultraviolet light increases the antirachitic power by activating the sterols always present in the skin. Even the excised human skin gains in antirachitic power when exposed to ultraviolet rays.

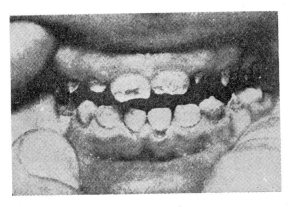

Fig. 206.—Showing the effect of vitamin D deficiency on the teeth. This 11-year-old child had severe rickets when 8 months old. (Courtesy of the Wisconsin Alumni Research Foundation.)

The short ether vibrations are largely shut off from the body by dark and heavy clothing; they are also absorbed to a great extent by dust, smoke, and vapor suspended in the air. As these atmospheric contaminants are more abundant, especially in densely populated districts, during the short winter days, when at the best the ultraviolet rays reaching the earth are markedly less than in summer, it can readily be seen that a growing child, unless plentifully supplied with vitamin D, is in great danger of rickets. In addition to this, it should be borne in mind that ether vibrations of 320 mμ wave length are the shortest waves able to pass through ordinary window glass, Fig. 205. Quartz, vitaglass, and helioglass are transparent to the ultraviolet rays. Hess found, in a large number of infants, the blood phosphorus during the month of March to be about one-half of the normal.

Vitamin D and the Teeth.—In regard to tooth formation McCollum and Klein fed young hogs (having, like man, two dentitions), as well as the sow during the lactation period, on a rachitic diet. As a result, the teeth developed more slowly and were poorly calcified, the size of the jaw bone was inferior, and the percentage of malpositions of the teeth was more than three times as great as in the control animals. In a rachitic child the eruption of the first tooth may be delayed by as much as six to nine months. The effect of a rachitic diet on the formation of the child's teeth is illustrated in Fig. 206. Microscopic examination reveals an inferior structure which renders future decay highly probable. That vitamin D is an important factor in the prevention and cure of caries is confirmed by numerous observations.

The Mode of Action.—The manner in which vitamin D brings about its beneficial results is not very clear. It is generally agreed that it does not act directly upon the osteoblasts. The most outstanding result of the administration of vitamin D or ultraviolet light seems to be a better absorption of Ca from the intestine and an increased excretion of phosphorus by the kidneys. In the rachitic patient the very low phosphorus content of the blood is rapidly brought to normal. Even when the ratio of the Ca and P in the food deviates widely from the specified 2:1 ratio, vitamin D improves the ratio of these elements in the blood. It seems that this renders it possible for the bone cells to utilize these salts for the calcification of bone tissue. We shall speak of this matter again in our study of the parathyroid glands.

Sources of Vitamin D.—Of all vitamins this is the most limited in its distribution. It is never found in natural foods of plant origin. Of the animal foods only milk, egg yolk, and the liver and body oils of certain fishes contain appreciable amounts of vitamin D. The blue tuna fish oil is the richest of all sources, containing from 100 to 400 times as much vitamin D as is found in cod-liver oil.* Salmon, sardines, and herring are also rich in this vitamin. Next in importance are egg yolks but the amount depends upon the amount of vitamin in the food and upon the irradiation of the hen. To a still smaller extent, vitamin D is found in milk fat (butter).

The amount in cow's milk is not increased by pasture feeding, but the addition of irradiated yeast to the feed very largely increases the amount of vitamin to about 430 I.U. per quart (metabolized vitamin D milk). The amount

---

*To appreciate the very small amount of the vitamin necessary for preventing widespread and serious harm, we may state that a barrel of cod-liver oil contains about 0.25 gram (0.008 ounce) of vitamin D.

s also increased (to 135 I.U.) by ultraviolet light irradiating the milk (irradiated milk) or by addition of 400 units of D to one quart of milk (fortified vitamin D milk).

Stability.—Vitamin D is one of the most stable vitamins. It is not readily oxidized and is not destroyed by pasteurization or even boiling.

Requirements.—The amount of vitamin D required varies with the extent of the calcium and phosphorus metabolism; this is, of course, greatest in the young child (from 400 to 800 international units daily). In the adult, under normal conditions, the vitamin is of much less importance; the irradiation of the skin may generate a sufficient amount of the vitamin. During the last two months of pregnancy and still more during lactation great demands are made upon the calcium and phosphorus stores of the maternal body and, in consequence, large supplies of these minerals and vitamin D are needed in the diet (400 to 800 units daily). Without this supply, the calcium and phosphorus are withdrawn from the bones of the mother, and the bones of the infant are poorly formed. Contrary to the popular opinion, this withdrawal of calcium and phosphorus does not apply to the teeth; according to Schour and others, the teeth are not to be regarded as storehouses for calcium. It is stated that breast-fed infants are less liable to rickets than those subsisting on cow's milk.

9. Vitamin E: Antisterility Vitamin: Alpha-tocopherol

In 1920 Mattill and Conklin found that rats fed with a sufficient amount of all the then known vitamins became sterile. In the male the germ cells perish, the whole of the seminiferous tubules which generate the spermatozoa (p. 684) being destroyed. In the female the ovaries remain normal, but the fetus dies a few days after fertilization. These results can be avoided by feeding the rats a small amount of the embryo, or germ, of wheat and the favorable results are attributed to a material which has been called vitamin E, or the *antisterility vitamin*. It is also found in the germs of other cereals, in meat, egg yolk, in green leaves, such as lettuce, and to a lesser extent in vegetable oils and very sparingly in milk and cod-liver oil. This vitamin has now been produced synthetically; it is known as alpha-tocopherol (*tokos*, childbirth; *phero*, to bear)—$C_{29}H_{50}O_2$.

In addition to the effects on the reproductive system, deficiency of vitamin E intake in experimental animals results in dystrophy of the striated muscles and leads to marked weakness. The hindlegs are affected first. By administering alpha-tocopherol this condition can be both prevented and cured. This suggests that certain of the muscular dystrophies of the human being might be due to vitamin E deficiency. To date, vitamin E treatment has led to conflicting results.

10. Vitamin K: Antihemorrhagic Vitamin

The antihemorrhagic vitamin was discussed under the subject of coagulation on page 159.

11. Choline

Choline, Best discovered, is necessary for the proper functioning of the liver It is found in meat, egg yolk, yeast, and sauerkraut.

VII. THE BALANCED DIET

It is very doubtful whether Nature supplies man with a single complete food. Milk, the nearest approach to it, is frequently lacking in certain vitamins, contains practically no iron, and, for the adult, is an altogether too dilute food (86-88 per cent water). If we should limit our quest merely to the obtaining of a sufficient amount of nitrogen (15 grams) and carbon (250 grams), it will be seen from Table XXVIII that no single food supplies these two ele-

TABLE XXVIII

	15 GM. N ARE FOUND IN	250 GM. C ARE FOUND IN
Lean meat	440 gm.	1,860 gm.
Wheat flour	650 gm.	625 gm.
Oatmeal	580 gm.	620 gm.
Potatoes	3,750 gm.	2,380 gm.
Peas	430 gm.	700 gm.
Milk	2,380 gm.	3,540 gm.

ments in the balanced (15:250) ratio. And when we consider the distribution of the various and indispensable salts and vitamins, we see abundant justification for a mixed and varied diet. In a temperate climate a diet composed of 10 to 15 per cent protein, 20 to 35, fat, and 50 to 70, carbohydrate, is the most suitable.

Inasmuch as fats and carbohydrates are almost entirely used for the production of energy, they are largely interchangeable in the ratio of their potential energy content, namely, $2\frac{1}{4}$ parts of carbohydrate to one part of fat; however, it is for the best of the animal economy that the intake of neither the one nor the other should fall below a certain minimal value. Thus, we have seen that an insufficient amount of carbohydrate metabolized gives rise to an incomplete oxidation of the fat with its resultant acidosis and ketosis (p. 421). On the other hand, it is very undesirable to reduce the fat beyond a certain point, no matter how much carbohydrate is substituted, see Fig. 199. The food fats are valuable:

a. They are obtained by us (as butter, olive oil) in far less bulky state than are the carbohydrates.

b. While carbohydrates are completely digested in about 3 hours, from 5 to 6 hours are required for fats; this causes them to ''stick'' better and delay the onset of hunger.

c. Fats undergo less fermentation in the intestines.

d. Many of the food fats and oils are associated with vitamins.

e. We have seen that they are necessary in the manufacture of lecithin and other highly complex substances in the body.

As the nature and amount of food required varies with the changing conditions of the body and environment, we can, in treating of a balanced diet, do no better than to state in general terms the outstanding features of the main divisions of our foods: flesh food, dairy products, cereals, green vegetables, fruits, tubers, legumes, and nuts. Many of these characteristics we have spoken of in previous pages and a mere mention here will suffice.

(*a*) The *flesh foods* (including any food product, excepting eggs and milk, derived from any animal—poultry, fish, "meat," etc.) are condensed protein foods of high biologic value, containing, in fact, all the necessary amino acids. Excepting that the red meat contains a little higher percentage of iron, there is no nutritive difference between the meats of various sources.

Among the objections to the inclusion of too much flesh foods in the diet we have noted: the lack of intestinal ballast, calcium, and vitamins (except in the fat and internal organs); they bring about more intestinal putrefaction, favor the formation of acids in the body, and throw more work upon the liver and kidneys. They are expensive foods. Beef extracts and juices are not to be seriously considered as foods.

(*b*) Among the *dairy products* milk takes first place. The high biologic value of its proteins (the casein contains, according to Sherman, not less than 17 distinct amino acids) and its high content of minerals, especially calcium and phosphorus, render it "an almost perfect nutrient fluid for the young of the same species." It should, however, be borne in mind that milk, especially human milk, may be poor in vitamins B, C, and D. *Milk, eggs, and green vegetables* McCollum regards as the **protective foods.** As milk offsets the dietary shortcomings of cereals, a combination of the two makes an adequate diet at low cost. Cheese is a highly condensed food, high in proteins and calories.

(*c*) Egg yolk is rich in essential proteins, vitamins, and salts.

(*d*) The *cereals* (wheat, rye, corn, rice, etc.) supply most of the energy for the average man, and are the most economical foods. Whole wheat may furnish vitamins B_1, P-P, and E. The fine milled flour is deficient in these as well as in salts, essential amino acids, and roughage.

(*e*) The *green vegetables and fruits* are exceedingly valuable for their salts and vitamins, and for their laxative and base-forming properties.

Containing very small amounts of proteins and fats and but little carbohydrate (vegetables seldom more than 5 per cent), their energy value is very low.

(*f*) The *legumes* (beans, peas, etc.) may be considered as condensed protein and carbohydrate foods and, therefore, high in energy; they also furnish a large supply of calcium, iron, and vitamin B. Excepting the soy-bean, the proteins are of low biologic value.

(*g*) The *tubers* are very poorly supplied with proteins and fats but are fairly rich in salts. Potatoes contain 18 per cent carbohydrates.

(*h*) *Nuts* are highly condensed foods—12 to 25 per cent protein and 40 to 65 per cent fat. They are rich in salts.

VIII. ACID-FORMING AND BASE-FORMING FOODS

By their oxidation in the body certain foods give rise to acids; from other foods basic salts are obtained. This matter will be spoken of in greater detail under the subject, Renal Secretion (Chap. XXV). While the hydrogen-ion concentration of the blood cannot be increased or decreased to any appreciable extent, the introduction of bases into the system results in a lessening of the acidity of the urine; this may be of great importance in certain instances. Fruits and vegetables are base-forming foods rich in protein and the cereals form acids.

IX. ECONOMIC CONSIDERATIONS

With most people the cost plays an important part in the selection of a diet. So far as the obtaining of energy is concerned, some of the least expensive foods are rich in energy. But we have learned that in addition to this, a diet must supply a sufficient amount of proteins of high biologic value, salts, and vitamins; this is especially true for the food of children. As these food substances are found in dairy products, eggs, meats, and fresh vegetables and fruits, rather than in cereals (bread), dried legumes, and tubers, they are frequently lacking in the diet of the poorer classes. In their food the carbohydrates to a very large extent replace the proteins and, more especially, the fats found abundantly in the diet of the more prosperous families.

X. FACTORS INFLUENCING DIGESTION AND ABSORPTION

In addition to the vitally important characteristics mentioned in the foregoing pages, there are other features that merit attention. Among these we may mention:

a. **Digestibility and Absorbability.**—It is not sufficient to furnish with the food the amount of carbon and nitrogen lost by the body in its catabolism, but the digestibility and absorbability of the food must also be taken into account. Some foods are more completely digested and absorbed than others; this is especially true when we compare animal and vegetable foods, as Table XXIX illustrates.

TABLE XXIX

FOOD	FOOD ABSORBED IN PER CENT OF THAT EATEN		
	NITROGENOUS MATERIAL	FAT	CARBOHYDRATE
Milk	93.5	95	99
Meat	97.5	94	—
Eggs	97	95	—
Cheese	95	90	98
Fine wheat flour	81	75	92.5
Coarse wheat flour	72	55	98.5
Carrots	61	—	81.5
Potatoes	70	—	93
Peas	83	—	97
Green vegetables	72	93	83.5

If the diet is a mixed diet, including meats, cereals, vegetables, and fruits, the absorption of these ingredients is about as shown in Table XXX.

TABLE XXX

	PROTEIN	FAT	CARBOHYDRATE
Animal foods	98%	97%	100%
Cereals and sugar	85%	90%	98%
Vegetables and fruits	80%	90%	95%

The greater loss sustained by the vegetable foods does not lie in the nature of the protein or carbohydrate but merely in the lesser accessibility of these materials and in the hurried peristalsis caused by the vegetable foods. By thorough cooking and mastication the loss may be materially reduced. It must be remembered that a person with an active digestion is more capable of fully utilizing his food, for it is not what one eats, but what one absorbs from the alimentary canal, that nourishes the tissues.

b. **The Psychology of Eating.**—The psychologic aspect of eating is important since the emotional state of the individual is an influencing factor in digestion, absorption, and elimination. The artistic appearance of food, good fellowship, and an environment of happiness while eating make for good health. Tasty foods, emitting their characteristic odor, are important as stimuli for a copious flow of digestive juices. Many instances of indigestion and constipation can be traced to a hurried gulping of food while family differences are being settled.

In this connection we may mention *condiments*. Because of their agreeable effect upon the sense of smell and taste, the condiments, such as pepper, mustard, salt, cloves, etc., are of value in stimulating the flow of the digestive juices. By means of them we can impart to food otherwise devoid of taste a pleasing taste or flavor. The excessive and constant use of them is not advisable, for it leads to overeating. The use of much of the hot condiments, like pepper and mustard, blunts the taste for the simpler foods, and thereby limits the number of tastes and flavors we otherwise experience. Many of the more commonly used spices when used in excess have an irritating effect on the alimentary mucosa, the liver, and the urogenital tract. Hence they should be avoided by those having gastric or intestinal catarrh or congestion of the urinary system.

c. Peristalsis.—Attention must also be paid to the bulk and other characteristics of the food in their influence on peristalsis. Although roughage is a requirement in the diet, there is no virtue in overindulgence in this type of food. In fact, too much roughage leads to digestive disturbances, such as colitis and excessive gas.

CHAPTER XXIII

HORMONES OR INTERNAL SECRETIONS

I. INTRODUCTION

To insure the harmonious interaction of the various organs of the complex animal body and thereby make possible the wonderful adjustment of the organism to its environment, communications between the organs must be established. How this is brought about by the central nervous system and the network of nerves which bring all parts of the body into intimate relation with each other, we have had many occasions to illustrate. We have also seen evidence of the humoral, or hormonic, influence which the secretions, or hormones, of certain ductless glands exercise upon the heart, blood vessels, alimentary canal, etc. The most important ductless glands are the adrenals, thyroid, parathyroids, pituitary, and certain parts of the pancreas, ovaries, and testes. Perhaps to this list should be added the thymus, pineal gland, kidneys, and duodenal mucosa. Their location is shown in Fig. 207.

External Versus Internal Secretion.—Similar to the glands of external secretion, found, e.g., in the digestive organs, kidneys, and skin, the ductless glands are composed of epithelial cells. In some the epithelial cells are arranged in the shape of a sac which incloses a vesicle; the whole structure is supported by connective tissue and surrounded by a network of capillaries, Fig. 208, *a*. In other glands the epithelial cells are in small solid masses, without any vesicles, as shown in Fig. 208, *b*. In the glands of external secretion the matter secreted is ultimately poured upon a free surface, Figs. 164 and 165. But in the ductless glands the secretion manufactured by the epithelial cells is poured directly into the blood or lymph; for this reason these glands are called glands of internal secretion, or endocrine glands (*endo,* within; *crino,* to separate). The secretion is variously known as an internal, or endocrine, secretion, a chemical messenger, or, more commonly, a hormone (*hormanein,* to excite).

Now, it must be evident that all the cells of the body produce compounds that are poured into the blood; namely, the waste products. Some of these materials may have an influence on certain structures, as, e.g., the stimulating action of carbon dioxide upon the respiratory center. But the term internal secretion is limited so as to exclude the ordinary waste products formed by the organs and tissues in general and to include only those substances which are produced by the ductless glands and which (1) increase or decrease the activities of other organs, (2) stimulate or retard the metabolism in general, or (3) influence the growth or development of the whole body or some particular part of the body.

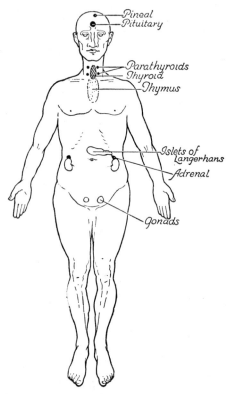

Fig. 207.—Location of the endocrine glands (Williams: Personal Hygiene Applied, W. B. Saunders Co.)

Neural Versus Hormonal Control.—The two systems of intercommunication between the various parts of the body, namely, the neural and the hormonic, differ in two or three important respects: the action mediated by the nervous system is generally localized, specific, and speedily executed; that following the production of a hormone is vastly slower, frequently more widespread throughout the body and, because of the continued presence of the hormone, of a more lasting nature. To illustrate: the result of the stimulation of a certain vasoconstrictor nerve may affect the blood vessels in a very circumscribed area and may disappear the moment the stimulation ceases. But in a vasoconstriction brought about by a hormone, e.g., adrenalin or pituitrin, there occurs a relatively long latent period in the formation of the hormone and its absorption into, and distribution by, the blood stream; its wide and indiscriminate distribution causes a multitude of vessels to constrict and to remain constricted until the hormone is either removed or destroyed. The humoral regulation is, therefore, crude, more primitive, and confined to such activities as may or must be continued for a considerable length of time, as, for example, the flow of pancreatic juice brought about by secretin, or the growth of the skeleton. The neural control is of later development, more highly specialized, and concerns itself with processes that should take place very quickly, last for a rather brief time, and cease as soon as the need for them has ended, as, for example, salivary secretion.

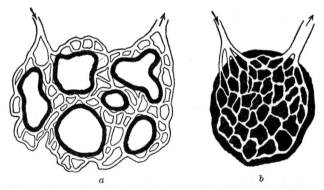

Fig. 208.—Diagrams of endocrine glands. *a*, gland composed of irregular sacs (heavy black lines) surrounded by connective tissue and blood vessels; this type includes thyroid and ovaries. *b*, represents most endocrine glands in which the epithelium (black) has no lumen and is penetrated by dense networks of blood vessels (white). (Maximow and Bloom: Histology, W. B. Saunders Co.)

The number of hormones known at present is fairly large. Many of the endocrine glands secrete two or more hormones; the pituitary, for example, is credited with from ten to twelve. In not a few instances the hormones secreted by one gland affect the activity of another gland by either stimulating or inhibiting its production of hormones. Because of the large number of hormones and their complicated interrelationship, the study of hormones is a bewildering subject. In this short chapter only a brief survey is possible.

Chemists have been able to obtain several of these hormones in a pure crystalline form and have succeeded in producing some of them, e.g., thyroxin and epinephrine, synthetically. In a few instances, the presence of the hormone can be demonstrated only by its specific effects.

Methods of Investigation.—The functions of an endocrine gland are studied by the following methods: (*a*) extirpation of the organ; (*b*) feeding the gland tissue obtained from other animals to, or injecting the glandular extract into, either a normal animal or one deprived of this gland; (*c*) examination and treatment of human beings suffering from disturbance in the activity of any endocrine gland.

Importance of Hormones.—Very few disturbances in our body are followed by such grave results as the hypo- and hyper-activity of the endocrine organs. Not only physical life but in some instances mental and emotional life also may be disastrously affected. Whatever may be the ultimate nature of thought, emotion, or "instinct," that they are dependent ultimately upon the proper chemical constitution of the body is beyond dispute. We have already seen that in rats "maternal love" flies out the window unless manganese enters by the door. Without iodine, as we shall learn presently, there is no growth or development of mind. To all intents and purposes, the mating "instincts" in animals and the love between the sexes in man blossoms forth as certain chemical compounds make their appearance.

And the possibility of an endocrine disturbance is not small. It has been calculated that, if the various endocrine organs secrete, collectively, 15 distinct hormones and the secretory activity of each gland can be normal, above normal, or below normal, there are 14,348,907 combinations of gland activities possible. Fortunately for suffering humanity, the hormones are, as a rule, interchangeable from one animal to another. Thus, the horrible effects of deficiency of thyroid secretion in man can, to a certain extent, be abolished by the administration of the thyroid gland or its extract taken from other animals (sheep, cow).

II. THE ADRENALS OR SUPRARENALS

The adrenals (*ad*, near; *ren*, kidney) are two small yellowish masses of tissue lying above or near the kidneys, Fig. 219. Histologically the adrenal gland is composed of two distinct parts, a cortical, or outer, layer, and the medullary portion. The latter is developed from the same kind of embryonic tissue that gives rise to the sympathetic nervous system; the cortex, on the other hand, is formed from tissue from which the reproductive organs are developed. These two parts have also very distinct physiologic functions. The adrenals are said to receive, per gram of weight, the richest supply of blood of any organ in the body, excepting the thyroid. Each adrenal weighs from 4 to 7 grams.

As long ago as 1855 Addison described the symptoms of a disease which he associated with the adrenals (Addison's disease). This disease, which is always fatal although its course may run through a number of years, is characterized by vomiting, a peculiar pigmentation of the skin—a bronzing—and by a great weakness of all the muscles, both skeletal and visceral.

When in a dog or cat these glands are extirpated, death results generally in about ten days. The disturbances are much the same as in Addison's disease; the muscles of the blood vessels lose their tonus and hence the blood pressure is low; there is great prostration, muscular weakness, and loss of appetite.

A. The Medullary Adrenals

Removal of the medullary portion of this gland is not fatal, neither does the administration of its active principle, known as adrenalin, adrenin, or epinephrine (*epi*, upon; *nephros*, kidney), save the life of an animal from which the entire glands have been removed. Adrenalin has been obtained from the medullary portion in a pure crystalline form and, more recently, it has been produced synthetically.

Adrenalin.—Notwithstanding that much is known concerning the physiologic action of this hormone, its rôle in the animal economy is but little understood. The injecting of adrenalin produces many changes:

1. THE CARDIOVASCULAR SYSTEM.—(*a*) The heart is accelerated, especially if the inhibitory nerves (vagi) are previously cut. The ventricles empty themselves more completely and the output is largely increased.

(*b*) In our study of the vasomotor control (Chap. XI) we have learned that the muscles of the arterioles, especially of the splanchnic area, are powerfully stimulated, resulting in a marked increase in blood pressure (Fig. 118); but, as seen from the tracing, this high blood pressure passes off very speedily. The vessels of the skeletal muscles, the coronary system and, perhaps, the lungs do not share in this constriction but undergo a dilation.

2. BLOOD.—The blood undergoes many changes: adrenalin causes contraction of the muscles of the spleen and thereby augments the number of the circulating red blood cells (pp. 151 and 308). In studying carbohydrate metabolism, we have seen that the liver glycogen is mobilized and the blood sugar increased. The coagulation time of the blood is decreased.

3. METABOLISM.—The oxygen consumption is increased and the heat production may be raised as much as 17 per cent above the basal level. It is said this calorigenic action takes place in the muscles without any augmentation in their contractile activity; this falls in line with the observation of Cannon that external cold causes a greater secretion of adrenalin. We have already spoken of the influence of this hormone on carbohydrate metabolism.

4. VISCERAL MUSCLES.—Practically all the visceral muscles of the body are affected, some being stimulated and others inhibited. Those stimulated are the muscles of the blood vessels (except as noted above) and the spleen; the radial muscle of the iris (dilators of the pupil, p. 554); the pyloric, ileocolic, internal anal, and bladder sphincters; and the pilomotor muscles of the hair follicles. The muscles of the stomach (Fig. 53), intestine, bronchioles, and urinary bladder are inhibited.

5. SKELETAL MUSCLES.—Another effect of the injection of adrenalin to which we must refer is the increased power it bestows upon the skeletal muscles. Schaefer and Oliver found that when the extract of the adrenals was injected into a frog, the contractions of the excised gastrocnemius muscle were 33 per cent higher and continued 66 per cent longer than in a normal muscle. This, it will be seen, is in harmony with the fact that in Addison's disease and in the extirpation of the glands in animals, there is great muscular weakness. Moreover, it was found by Gruber that while under usual conditions the irritability of a fatigued muscle is restored in from fifteen minutes to two hours, if a small dose of adrenalin is given, the normal threshold may be restored in three to five minutes. Since the effect has been observed in the excised muscle also, adrenalin must act, at least in part, directly upon muscle tissue.

The Sympathico-adrenal System.—From our study of the innervation of the heart, blood vessels, alimentary canal, and liver, it will be evident that all the above-mentioned results produced by adrenalin are similar to those obtained by the stimulation of the sympathetic nerves supplying the organs enumerated, except the sweat glands (see Chap. XXX). The sympathetic nervous system and the adrenals are referred to as the sympathico-adrenal system. Our study of the inhibition of the heart showed us that stimulation of the vagus nerve generates in the heart a material—*acetylcholine*—which must be regarded as the direct agent bringing about the cessation of cardiac muscle activity. It is generally held that the neurohumoral transmission of impulses from a nerve fiber to the next histologic structure also holds for the sympathetic nerves. When a nerve belonging to the sympathetic nervous system is stimulated, there is formed at the endings of the nerve in the smooth muscle or gland a compound known as *sympathin*. Because sympathin and adrenalin produce similar physiologic effects, the former substance is claimed by some to be adrenalin, but others regard it as an adrenalin-like compound.

Tonic Influence Versus the Emergency Theory.—It is generally conceded that the amount of adrenalin ordinarily secreted is below that necessary to exert a tonic influence upon the muscles supplied by the sympathetic nerves. Thus, the constant constriction of the blood vessels, by which a fairly definite amount of blood pressure is maintained, does not depend upon the continuous production of adrenalin. This is shown by the fact that no fall in blood pressure is experienced when, for several hours, the adrenals are cut off from the circulation.

The results of many experiments conducted by Cannon led him to formulate the "emergency theory" of adrenal activity. We may briefly relate this. Cannon found that certain mental conditions, such as rage, fright, and anxiety, cause the amount of adrenalin in the blood stream to be increased. To determine this, the action of adrenalin upon the intestinal muscle was used. A strip or segment of the intestines was fixed in a holder, into which could be poured a physiologic salt solution or the blood to be tested for its adrenalin. In order to keep the tissue alive, a current of oxygen was passed through the solution, which was kept at body temperature. The contractions of the intestinal muscle were recorded. Blood from a quiet animal had no effect on the contractions, but the blood drawn from an animal in fear or rage always showed an inhibiting action. So delicate was this reaction that one part of adrenalin in 200,000,000 parts of the solvent showed an effect.* More recently Cannon was able to demonstrate, by the increased activity of a denervated heart, its presence in a dilution of 1 part in 1,400,000,000. The increase in blood sugar during great fright or anger is mediated by the adrenals, as the observation by Britton demonstrates. This investigator removed the adrenals from a cat; on now frightening the animal with a barking dog, no increase in the glucose content of the blood was discovered.

The adjustment to those conditions of the environment which arouse emotions of fear and anger calls for a large expenditure of energy by the skeletal muscles, for the preservation of life may depend upon fight or flight. To supply this extra demand of energy and to make

---

*We may translate the above ratio into the following terms: One drop of blood in 110 barrels of water has the ratio 1:200,000,000.

its utilization possible is, according to Cannon, the function of the sympathico-adrenal system, which governs the vegetative functions (p. 139). The increased secretion by the medullary adrenals stimulates those structures that cause vascular constriction in the skin (as shown by the pallor of the face) and in the abdomen, while the vessels of the skeletal muscles, the heart, and perhaps the lungs are dilated. The redistribution of the blood flow thus brought about supplies a large amount of blood to the organs concerned in the energetic adjustment of the animal. This is aided by the higher blood pressure and the more abundant systolic output due to the increased rate and force of the heart. The larger supply of oxygen needed for the continued liberation of energy is made possible by the dilation of the bronchi, bronchioles, and pulmonary blood vessels and by the increased rate and depth of the respiratory movements. To provide a greater amount of energy-furnishing food to the muscles, the increased production of adrenalin hastens the conversion of liver glycogen into blood glucose. The advantages of a decreased susceptibility to fatigue and of a more rapid coagulation of the blood are readily perceived. Perhaps of lesser importance in this adjustment are the dilation of the pupils and the erection of the hair, seen in many animals.

Nervous Control of Adrenals.—The stimulation of the splanchnic nerve results in an increased output of adrenalin. There is some evidence for the existence of a center in the medulla oblongata. The various conditions mentioned above may stimulate either this medullary center or the adrenal glands themselves.

Medicinal Uses.—Because of its pronounced action upon blood vessels, adrenalin is often used locally to stop small hemorrhages, as in nosebleed and in minor operations; but not in pulmonary bleeding. For the same reason it has been employed to counteract the histamin-like compound which causes the great vascular dilation in hives. By constricting the blood vessels adrenalin* shrinks the mucous membrane and thereby clears the nasal passages which were "blocked by a cold." It is also used in conjunction with procaine, or similar drugs, to produce local anesthesia; by its powerful vasoconstriction the adrenalin lessens the removal of the anesthetic from the injected area and thus prolongs and intensifies the anesthesia. And due to its inhibiting influence on the bronchial muscles, adrenalin is frequently used in asthma, a condition in which the excessive contraction of these muscles makes breathing difficult.

---

*The chemically related ephedrine and benzedrine also have this effect.

B. The Cortical Adrenals

While removal of the medullary portion is not incompatible with life, the extirpation of the cortex is fatal. From this portion of the gland a hormone, *cortin,* has been isolated, which prolongs the life of a suprarenalectomized animal almost indefinitely and has proved of great value to human beings suffering from Addison's disease. From the diversity of its action, it is probable that two or more individual hormones are formed by the cortex.

As to the cause of death on removal of the adrenals and as to the function or functions of the cortex, matters are very unsettled. Some investigators stress the power of cortin to regulate carbohydrate metabolism, basing this on the observation that in suprarenalectomy the amount of glycogen in the muscles and liver is greatly reduced, the blood is hypoglycemic, and the animal is thrown into convulsions; and in the fatigued muscles the synthesis of glycogen is retarded. This disturbance in carbohydrate metabolism may, at least in part, be the cause of the outstanding characteristic symptom of cortico-adrenal insufficiency in man, namely, *great muscular weakness.* These symptoms disappear on the injection of cortin.

The adrenal cortex plays a part in the potassium, sodium, and water metabolism. In addition to a lowered sugar content, the blood in adrenalectomy suffers a marked reduction in sodium salts because of their increased excretion by the kidneys. As this reduces the osmotic pressure of the plasma, there follows a greater excretion of water, and the volume of the blood is decreased. Some authors attribute the cause of death to a *derangement of the sodium-potassium balance.* Much evidence has been set forth in favor of this view. In the crisis of Addison's disease the potassium content of the blood is increased; this is brought down to the normal amount by the administration of cortin. Addison's disease has been treated, without cortin, by supplying a diet very low in K but containing a sufficient amount of Na salts. On the other hand, feeding an animal a large amount of K salts induces symptoms greatly simulating those of adrenal insufficiency.

The Suprarenal Cortex and the Sex Organs.—The close relation between these organs is seen clearly from the following:

(*a*) Increased activity of the cortex in children causes precocious maturing of the secondary sex characteristics. A boy of four years may have the matured sex organs and the growth of pubic and facial hair of an adult; in the young female the mammary glands are hypertrophied and menstruation sets in. (*b*) During pregnancy the cortex is enlarged. (*c*) This also occurs in animals during the mating season. (*d*) Castration in the male causes hypertrophy of the cortex. (*e*) Tumors of the cortex in the adult female lead to masculinization; the bearded ladies of the circus offer an extreme example.

III. THE THYROID GLAND

The thyroid gland, weighing about 25 grams (Figs. 209 and 210), is composed of two lobes, one placed on each side of the upper part of the trachea just below the larynx, or voice box, and a connecting

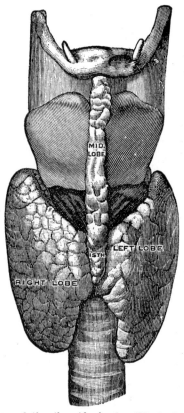

Fig. 209.—Anterior view of the thyroid gland. (Macleod and Seymour: Physiology, The C. V. Mosby Co.)

part called the isthmus. The thyroid is an extremely vascular organ; in proportion to weight it receives, in a unit of time, three and one-half times as much blood as the brain. Owing to its anatomical relation to the trachea, it can readily be seen that a greatly hypertrophied thyroid may interfere seriously with breathing.

Histologically the gland is composed of a large number of very small closed vesicles (*vesica*, bladder) the walls of which are formed, as shown in Fig. 211, of a single layer of columnar or cuboidal epithelium. These vesicles, held together by areolar tissue, are surrounded by a rich network of capillaries. The lumen of the vesicle is filled, to a greater or lesser extent, with a colloidal material made by the epithelial cells. This is generally regarded as the hormone or as its immediate antecedent. As occasion demands, the colloid passes back into the cells and is passed directly or after undergoing the final change into the capillary blood stream.

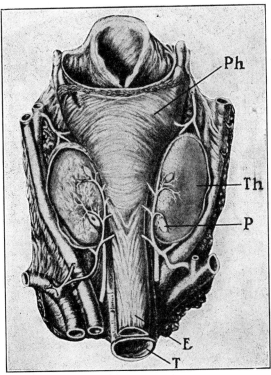

Fig. 210.—Posterior view of thyroid gland showing four parathyroid glands. *E*, esophagus; *P*, parathyroid gland; *Ph*, pharynx; *T*, trachea; *Th*, thyroid gland. (Halstead: The Operative Story of Goiter, Johns Hopkins Press.)

The functions of the thyroid are twofold:

1. Morphogenic, in that it controls, in conjunction with other endocrine organs, the growth and development of the body.

2. Metabolic; it exerts a stimulating influence upon catabolism.

The Thyroid Hormone, Thyroxin.—From thyroid tissue Baumann obtained a nitrogenous compound containing a considerable amount of iodine; this he called iodothyrin. Kendall succeeded in breaking up this compound still further, obtaining a substance—*thyroxin*—

containing 65 per cent iodine. This hormone produces in normal animals and in those with deficient thyroids the same effects as the thyroid extracts. Harington has prepared synthetically a substance having the same physiologic properties as thyroxin. All tissues contain iodine. A little less than one-half of the total amount (about 25 mg.) in the body is found in the thyroid.

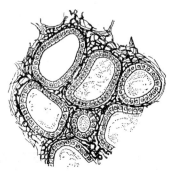

Fig. 211.—Section of the thyroid, showing vesicles and the network of blood vessels surrounding them. (Buchanan: Human Anatomy, The C. V. Mosby Co.)

A. Effects of Extirpation or Hypofunction

a. Extirpation in Animals.—Extirpation, if the parathyroids are not disturbed, is not fatal, but most profound changes occur. In the young animal growth is delayed or arrested. Von Eiselberg removed the thyroid from two eight-day-old lambs and kept a third lamb as a control. After seven months, the control animal weighed 77 pounds, while the animals which had been operated upon weighed only 24 and 30 pounds, respectively. In tadpoles thyroidectomy delays or arrests their metamorphosis into frogs, but they continue to grow far beyond the usual tadpole size (giant tadpoles); feeding thyroid gland tissue caused a loss in weight but accelerated the metamorphosis (pigmy frogs).

b. Arrested Development in a Child.—In a child the lack of function of the thyroid results in a condition known as *cretinism*. The bones cease to grow in length, the body retaining, therefore, the size of a child (Fig. 212, *C*); there is a lack of development of the sexual organs; the texture of the skin is abnormal, and the hair is scant. There is an abnormal development of connective tissue, and as a result, the face is puffy, the tongue protrudes, and the hands and feet are thick and short. The teeth are generally late in erupting and are of poor quality. Mental development is also arrested; the child is idiotic, as its very face indicates. When such a young child is fed upon thyroid gland or its extract, or if the extract is injected hypodermically, there is in all cases some improvement (see Fig. 212). But of 29 patients reported by Brown, only two reached an intelligence quotient of 100; in about 75 per cent the quotient remained below 80, and in 25 per cent, below 45 (imbecile level). The treatment must be continued as long as the individual's own thyroid gland does not function.

c. Hypofunction in the Adult.—As already remarked in an earlier chapter (p. 444), extirpation of the thyroid in an adult animal or the lack of proper secretion in man—*hypothyroidism*—leads to a marked reduction in the basal metabolism, as shown by the decreased CO_2

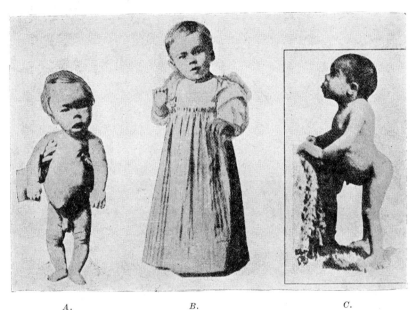

A.   *B.*   *C.*

[Fig. 212.—Illustrating cretinism. *A*, a cretin, 23 months old and *B*, the same child after having received thyroid treatment for eleven months. *C*, an untreated cretin 15 years old. (Osler.)

production and oxygen consumption. In consequence, the heat production is correspondingly lessened, the body temperature is lowered, and the individual always feels cold (especially his hands and feet) even in a warm room. Because of the reduced consumption of food and oxygen in the tissues of the body, there is less call for an active circulation; hence, the heartbeat is slowed, and its stroke volume falls below the normal. For the same reason there are reduction in muscle tonus, pronounced asthenia (*a*, not; *sthenia*, strength), and great susceptibility to fatigue. The nervous system is also much affected; the individual shows a lack of interest and becomes drowsy and phlegmatic. The mental faculties gradually become dulled (e.g., great forgetfulness); this may finally result in imbecility. A condition known as *myxedema* develops in which there is a great accumulation of water in the subcutaneous connective tissue. This causes the skin to become thick, swollen, and wrinkled and the eyelids and lips puffy; the face is bloated and has a stupid expression (Fig. 213). All the above-discussed symptoms disappear on the administration of thyroxin which acts as the draft to life's fire.

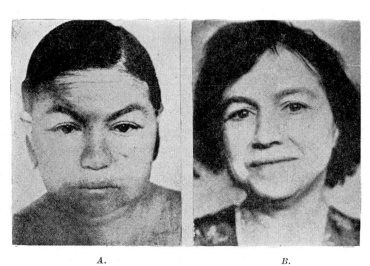

A.   *B.*

Fig. 213.—*A*, myxedema in a woman of 34 years; *B*, same woman after 10 months' treatment with thyroid substance. (By permission from Endocrinology; C. K. Canelo and H. Lisser.)

B. Simple Goiter

We are all familiar with the fact that in some persons the thyroid becomes more or less enlarged and forms what is commonly known as a goiter. This increase in size constitutes a compensatory enlargement by which the gland strives to make up for the thyroxin insufficiency by forming more gland cells. The deficiency in thyroxin is generally attributed to a lack of sufficient iodine in the food and drink or to a greater demand for thyroxin than usual. Among the conditions which seem to call for a greater supply of the hormone are exposure to cold, the ingestion of much fat or protein food, and, more especially, puberty, menstruation, pregnancy, lactation, and menopause (p. 670). While the amount of iodine ingested under the ordinary conditions of life may be sufficient for the production of the required amount of thyroxin, this may fall short in times of greater demand for the hormone; as a result the gland undergoes hypertrophy.

In many countries, e.g., Switzerland, it is, or was until recently, an endemic disease. In our country there are also regions, such as the Great Lakes region, the Rocky Mountain states, the Cascade Mountains of Oregon and Washington, etc., where it is quite prevalent.

That an insufficient supply of iodine may bring about simple goiter was convincingly demonstrated by giving, over a period of three years, 2 grams of sodium iodide in ten daily doses twice a year to each of 2,190 schoolgirls in Akron, Ohio. Of these girls only five developed goiter. Of 2,305 girls not receiving this treatment 495 developed goiter during the three years.

The amount of iodine required for the maintenance of proper thyroid activity almost belongs to the realm of the incredible. The administration of 1 milligram of thyroxin increases the basal metabolism by 3 per cent and its effect persists for as long as six weeks. One milligram per week prevents thyroid enlargement in dogs, and a little more than one part of iodine in 1,000,000,000 parts* of the drinking water is sufficient to ward off goiter in man. A very small amount of iodine (1:5000) is frequently added to table salt by the manufacturer.

As the thyroid of a young infant contains very little, if any, iodine, the infant must obtain this element from milk. In this respect human milk is said to be superior to cow's milk. Davenport found that in mice a thyroid deficiency in the mother caused stunted growth of the young.

C. Hyperthyroidism

Too great a secretion of the thyroid hormone causes an increase in the basal metabolic rate (usually from 50 to 75 per cent above normal). As a consequence, more food is consumed, but notwithstanding this there is a loss of body fat and weight. The increased demands by the body cause an augmentation in the work done by the heart; this results in palpitation and a rise in the systolic blood pressure. Because of increased heat production the individual feels unduly warm at all times. The high rate of metabolism also leads to a rapid mobilization of the liver glycogen, to an increase in the sugar content of the blood, and to mild glycosuria; some hold that these effects may arise from the influence exerted by the thyroid secretion upon the islands of Langerhans. The nervous system is hyperirritable so that the patient "overacts toward all emergency situations or to nocuous stimuli"; there is great mental excitement and sleeplessness. In some instances a very characteristic symptom is the widely

---

*This oligodynamic action may be expressed as one ounce of iodine in 7,500,000 gallons of water.

dilated pupil and the great prominence of the eyeball—*exophthalmic goiter*. This condition is four or five times as prevalent in women as in men. To alleviate the above-mentioned distressing symptoms, the amount of active thyroid tissue is lessened by surgery. Strange as it may seem, the administration of iodine to patients with hyperthyroidism has proved of great benefit, at least temporarily.

Because of its great influence on catabolism it has been suggested that the difference between an active, lean person and a sluggish, obese person is the difference between a more active and a less active thyroid gland. It is conceivable that the normally diminished activity of the glands after the age of forty-five or fifty is responsible for many of the changes coming on with advancing years, such as the drying and wrinkling of the skin, the tendency to deposit fat, the gradual development of connective tissue in many of the organs of the body, and the accompanying lessened regenerative powers.

Control of the Thyroid.—The thyroid receives a nerve supply from the sympathetic system, but it is doubtful whether these nerves govern the activity of the gland. In our study of the pituitary body we shall learn that this organ exerts a great influence upon the activity of the thyroid. In fact, in the simple goiter discussed above, the hypertrophy is directly induced by the increased stimulation of the thyroid by the pituitary hormone.

The interrelationship of the thyroid and sex organs is shown by enlargement of the thyroid during menstruation and gestation. On the other hand, lack of proper thyroid secretion, as in myxedema, is frequently associated with disturbances in the sexual life of both male and female. Reference was made previously to the infantile state of the sex organs in a cretin.

IV. THE PARATHYROIDS

Closely connected with, and sometimes embedded in, the dorsal surface of the thyroid are four small glandular bodies, about 8 mm. long, known as the parathyroids, Fig. 210.

Extirpation or Hypofunction.—In many animals extirpation of the parathyroid glands is fatal in a few days. Before death, and more especially in young rats which frequently survive the operation, two marked disturbances appear: (*a*) a change in the calcium and phosphorus metabolism, and (*b*) tetany. The former of these is shown by:

1. Defective calcium depositing in the bones, causing subnormal bone growth. The healing of a fractured bone is delayed.

2. The defective formation of dentin and enamel causes brittleness of the teeth and greater susceptibility to caries.

3. The calcium in the blood falls from the normal 10 mg. per 100 c.c. of blood plasma to 7 mg.

These disturbances, which have also been observed in human beings suffering from hypoparathyroidism, cease upon the implanting of a normal parathyroid into the body or the injection of the parathyroid hormone, *parathormone* or *parathyrin*.

It will be recalled from our study of calcium metabolism (p. 432) that a diminution in the calcium content of the blood increases greatly the irritability of the neuromuscular system. This condition of the blood in parathyroidectomy is responsible for the tremors and convulsions, or tetany. The injection of either calcium or parathormone abolishes them promptly.

Injection of the Hormone, or Hyperfunction.—The injection of parathormone into a normal animal leads to an increase of calcium and a decrease of phosphorus in the blood although the amount excreted is above normal. This excess of calcium is derived from the bones (not from the teeth) which undergo decalcification. It is asserted by many authorities that these disturbances in calcium metabolism are secondary to the influence which the hormone exerts on phosphorus metabolism. According to this view, *parathormone causes an increased excretion of phosphorus* by the kidneys, which leads to hypophosphatemia; this mobilizes the calcium from the bones and as a result there is an increase of calcium in both blood and urine.

Function of Parathyroids.—The above facts render it very probable that *the parathyroids aid in maintaining the normal level of calcium and phosphorus in the blood* and their proper ratio to each other. As a result of this calcium regulation, the parathyroids aid in maintaining the proper excitability of the nervous system. When a great drain is made upon these elements in the body, as during pregnancy and lactation, or when the intake of calcium or vitamin D is curtailed, the parathyroid glands undergo hypertrophy. The relationship between vitamin D and parathormone in bone formation is very obscure, as is also the action of parathormone on phosphatase (bone enzyme).

V. THE PITUITARY BODY

The pituitary body, or the hypophysis cerebri, Fig. 279, is a small body at the base of the brain and lodges in a deep depression of the sphenoid bone (sella turcica), just back of the optic chiasma. It is connected with the brain by means of a short stalk, the infundibulum,

Fig. 283. The pituitary, weighing about ½ gram, is composed of three parts: the anterior lobe (*c* in Fig. 214), which is glandular; the posterior lobe, *h;* and the pars intermedia, *c* and *g*. The infundibulum, in Fig. 214, lies between *c* and *d*.

It is generally stated that extirpation of this gland is fatal, but in carefully conducted operations on young animals some survive for a considerable length of time.

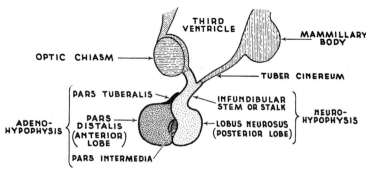

Fig. 214.—Diagram to illustrate the pituitary body. (W. R. Ingram.)

A. The Anterior Lobe

The anterior lobe exerts a powerful influence (*a*) on the growth and development of the body in general, (*b*) on the development of the sex organs in particular, (*c*) on metabolism, and (*d*) on other endocrine organs. These controlling influences are exercised through many hormones, some of which have been fairly well isolated.

a. Influence on Growth.—*Extirpation of the pituitary in young animals markedly retards the growth of the body* (Fig. 215), especially of the skeleton. In tadpoles it prevents the metamorphosis into frogs. In a child hypofunction causes infantilism, which may be accompanied by a lack of mental development. There is also delayed eruption of the second set of teeth, the milk teeth being retained. The injection of extracts of the anterior pituitary into animals deprived of this gland restores growth, and in a few cases the growth in human dwarfs recommenced. It should be borne in mind that dwarfism may be due to other disturbances. In contrast with the greatly deformed cretin, the pituitary midget may exhibit normal intelligence, and in some cases the sex organs function properly. The powerful influence of the pituitary gland on bodily growth is attributed to a specific hormone known as the *growth,* or *somatotropic, hormone* (*soma,* body; *trope,* turning).

On the other hand, *hyperactivity of the anterior part* induced, e.g., by the stimulating effect of a tumor, *in a young person, leads to a marked increase in the growth of the bones (giants).* A boy of 13 thus afflicted measured 6 feet and 1 inch, weighed 178 pounds "and was able to pick his father up and carry him about," Fig. 216. His mental condition was normal. Another individual at the age of 23 measured 7 feet and 8 inches and weighed 312 pounds. In the adult, hyperactivity of the anterior pituitary causes the bones to become more or less misshapen, especially those of the face (beetling brows and protruding jaw with widely spaced teeth), hands, and feet (acromegaly). Due to the excessive growth of fibrous tissue, the eyelids, nose, tongue, and lips become thick and swollen (Fig. 217); there is also an increase in the growth of hair over the body. From the above facts it has been concluded that *the anterior pituitary controls the growth of bones and fibrous tissue.*

Fig. 215.—These three pups, 4 months old, are litter mates. The two small dogs had the pituitary removed when 5 days old. (Riddle: Scientific Monthly, vol. 47, p. 97.)

b. Influence on the Sex Organs.—Distinct from the growth-promoting hormone is a gonadotropic hormone which stimulates the growth and activity of the gonads, i.e., the sex glands—the testes and the ovaries. Removal of the pituitary causes an underdevelopment of the gonads, and, indirectly, of the secondary genital organs (p. 664) and sex characteristics; the subsequent administration of its gonad-stimulating hormone restores the normal sexual state. Its injection into an immature rat causes precocious development of

Fig. 216.—Giantism of a boy of thirteen years; with him are shown his father and brother, aged 9. (Courtesy of Dr. L. H. Behrens, Endocrinology **16:** 120, 1930.)

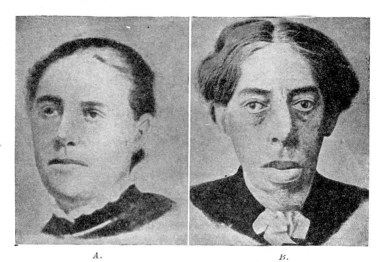

A.   *B.*

Fig. 217.—*A*, the appearance before the onset of acromegaly. *B*, after 17 years of the disease. (After Campbell Geddes.)

the reproductive system. The pituitary gland is, for these reasons, referred to as *the motor of the ovary.*

Another hormone, *prolactin,* has been found which stimulates the secretion of milk by the fully developed mammary glands. Removal of the pituitary from a nursing rat causes a cessation of milk secretion; on the other hand, a virgin rat having received an injection of prolactin retrieves baby rats and cares for them as if they were her own offspring; even squabs, instead of being devoured, are tenderly taken care of. These subjects will be more fully gone into in the chapter on Reproduction (Chap. XXXI).

c. The Influence on Metabolism.—The influence of the anterior pituitary on carbohydrate metabolism was discussed in a previous chapter. The great decrease in carbohydrate metabolism may lead to a depositing of fat. Thus, an eleven-year-old boy weighed 363 pounds; in this case the basal metabolic rate was reduced by 23 per cent. But whether this adiposity is a pure pituitary deficiency or whether brain lesions are involved is a question.

d. Influence on Other Endocrine Organs.—(*a*) *On the Thyroid.*— The marked influence of the pituitary upon the development and activity of the thyroid is seen in the degeneration of this gland when the pituitary is extirpated and in the hypertrophy resulting from injection of pituitary extract. In addition, this injection is followed by all the symptoms of hyperactivity of the thyroid, such as increased basal metabolism and heart action. As all these results fail to appear if the thyroid has previously been removed, it is concluded that the pituitary extract contains a hormone, designated as the *thyrotropic* hormone, which stimulates the thyroid to greater activity. On the other hand, the thyroid seems to influence the pituitary, for in cretinism, myxedema, and in extirpation of the thyroid the pituitary undergoes hypertrophy.

(*b*) *On the Adrenal Cortex and Islands of Langerhans.*—Extirpation of the anterior pituitary lobe leads to lack of proper development of these two endocrine organs. The gland is said to form an adrenotropic hormone which stimulates the adrenals (cortex?).

B. The Posterior Lobe

a. Influence on Visceral Muscles.—From the posterior lobe extract, known as pituitrin, Kamm isolated two distinct hormones. The first of these, called pitressin, or vasopressin, powerfully stimulates the muscle of the arterial system and thereby increases greatly the blood pressure. According to Krogh, this hormone is necessary for the maintenance of the tonus of the capillary wall.

The second active principle, oxytocin, or pitocin, has a pronounced stimulating effect on the musculature of the uterus. So powerful is the action of *oxytocin** that one part in 20,000,000,000 parts of physiologic salt solution still shows its effects. This drug is therefore used to augment the contractions of the uterine muscles during childbirth, although it is claimed that parturition (the expulsion of the fetus from the uterus) is not dependent upon the posterior lobe of the pituitary.

Because of its powerful stimulating action on the intestinal muscles, the extract (pituitrin) of the posterior lobe is used in paralysis of the intestinal canal.

b. Anti-diuretic Effect.—Another function ascribed to the posterior pituitary is the regulation of the renal secretion. It is a well-known fact that copious drinking is soon followed by a corresponding increase in the output of urine. If after a large intake of water the individual receives an injection of postpituitary extract, this increased renal output is delayed for several hours. Certain lesions to the base of the brain result in a pathologic condition in which the patient voids exceedingly large quantities of urine (polyuria), a condition known as diabetes insipidus; this is alleviated by the injection of an extract of the posterior lobe of the pituitary gland. This action is generally ascribed to the reabsorption of water by the renal tubules of the kidneys (see p. 524).

SUMMARY

From the foregoing the widespread influence of the pituitary hormones is apparent: (1) general development and growth of the body; (2) development and function of the sex glands; (3) the development and function of many endocrine organs, such as the adrenal cortex, the islands of Langerhans, the thyroid, and probably the thymus; (4) the metabolism of proteins, carbohydrates, fats, and water; (5) the secretion of milk; (6) the activity of the muscles of the organs of reproduction, alimentary canal, and blood vessels. *The pituitary may fittingly be called the master of all the endocrines.* No doubt many of the effects accompanying hypo- or hyperactivity of the pituitary are brought about indirectly by its controls over the activity of many other endocrines that directly influence the various parts of the body.

---

*ok-se-to'-sin; pit-o'-sin.

VI. THE THYMUS GLAND

The thymus (popularly known as the neck sweetbread) is a glandular structure situated between the upper part of the sternum and the pericardium. It is a temporary organ, reaching its greatest development at the age of fourteen to sixteen years, after which it gradually atrophies because of the activity of the sex glands.

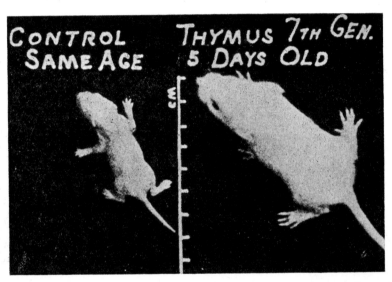

Fig. 218.—These two animals are of the same age. The one on the right is a five-day-old thymus-treated rat of the seventh generation. (Rowntree et al.: Ann. Int. Med. 9: 359, 1935.)

The recent work by Hanson, Rowntree, and others has demonstrated the influence of the thymus upon the early development and growth of animals. The injection of thymus extract into a white rat has little or no effect upon the animal itself, but the development of its offspring is greatly accelerated, and when the injections are continued through several generations of rats, the result "is almost beyond belief," Fig. 218. We may tabulate a few of these:

TABLE XXXI

	CONTROL ANIMAL	THE FIFTH GENERATION OF THYMUS-TREATED RATS
Weight at birth	4.6 grams	5.7 grams
Teeth erupted	9-10 days	1 day
Eyes opened	14-17 days	3 days
Testes descended into scrotum	35-40 days	4- 5 days
Vagina opened	60-70 days	18-19 days

But it should be noted that thymus treatment becomes less and less effective in speeding up growth, hence this treatment does not create giants.

To what extent the sex life of the animal is speeded up can be gathered from the fact that while a normal rat does not reproduce until the age of from 50 to 70 days, a male rat of the fourth generation of thymus-treated animals is capable of reproducing at 29 days. The number of litters borne by a rat and the number of young in each litter are greater in treated than in untreated animals, and mortality of the young is less. The reciprocal relationship between the thymus and the sex glands is demonstrated in that castration retards; on the other hand, sexual activity (mating, pregnancy) hastens the involution (retrogressive changes) of the thymus.

VII. THE PINEAL GLAND

The pineal gland is a little cone-shaped body lying between the anterior corpora quadrigemina on the dorsal aspect of the brain, Fig. 282, *33*. At the age of seven it undergoes degenerative changes and in the adult it consists of fibrous tissue. Rowntree and his associates injected the young of four successive generations of rats with extracts of this gland. There was a marked accruing retardation of general body growth (dwarfism) but the development of the organs, especially those of reproduction, was greatly accelerated. We may call attention to the similarity between the thymus and the pineal gland in their influence on the development of the body, and to their dissimilarity with respect to growth. It should, however, be noted that the removal of the pineal gland neither retards development nor hastens or enhances growth.

VIII. OTHER HORMONES

Certain agencies other than those formed by the ductless glands are sometimes classed with the hormones. We have in our study of the secretion of the digestive juices become acquainted with the chemical messengers formed in the mucosa of the alimentary canal which stimulate the gastric and intestinal glands; indeed, it was the discovery of secretin by Bayliss and Starling in 1903 that initiated the modern concept of hormones. Among the hormones are also sometimes included the neurohumoral substances formed at the distal end of a nerve pathway. These compounds differ from the hormones made by the ductless glands in that they exert their physiologic action at the point of formation, instead of being carried to some remote portion of the body.

Lipocaic is said to be formed in the pancreas. Its absence is purported to result in a disturbance in the utilization of fat and to lead to an accumulation of fat in the liver and perhaps to arteriosclerosis.

IX. THE INTERRELATIONSHIP OF HORMONES; ANTIHORMONES

The interrelationship of the various endocrine organs is most involved and bewildering. The reader will, no doubt, recall several instances of such relations, especially as concerns the pituitary gland. In the chapter on Reproduction we shall meet with other examples.

In our study of autolysis and autodigestion (p. 365) we found that the activities of enzymes are frequently controlled by antibodies, known as antiferments. Hormones, judged by the quantity needed to produce their stimulating or inhibitory effects, are exceedingly powerful agents. And we have also learned that pathologic conditions may arise from hyperactivity of the glands (e.g., exophthalmic goiter). The question therefore presents itself, how are the hormones normally controlled? In the last few years Collip and other workers have demonstrated that the animal body is able to produce compounds—antihormones—which neutralize the action of hormones.

Antihormones for several hormones have been discovered, but we shall mention only one example. It will be recalled that an animal receiving injections of the thyrotropic hormone of the anterior pituitary body shows an increase in the size of the thyroid gland and all the symptoms of increased thyroxin stimulation, e.g., increased basal metabolic rate. But it was found that when these injections were continued from 30 to 40 days, the animal no longer responded to even very large doses of the hormone; the metabolic rate dropped down to the normal level. When the serum of an animal which had become resistant to the thyrotropic hormone was injected into a normal animal, this animal also became refractory to the subsequent administration of the thyrotropic hormone in that there was no increase in metabolism. The resistance thus gradually acquired Collip attributes to a substance antagonistic to the injected hormone—an antihormone. What part, if any, antihormones normally play in the body is an unsolved problem; there is evidence that exophthalmic goiter (due, in all probability, to excessive formation of thyroxin under the influence of the thyrotropic hormone) is brought about by the inability of the body to form the antithyrotropic principle.

CHAPTER XXIV

REGULATION OF BODY TEMPERATURE

It is common knowledge that the temperature of the human body is almost constant. Yet there are several factors that tend to upset this constancy. From our study of muscles we learned that when a muscle becomes active there is, in addition to the activity characteristic for this tissue, a liberation of heat; in fact, about 80 per cent of the energy consumed during the work is transformed into heat. Again, the body is generally warmer than the environment and hence there is a continual loss of heat. On the other hand, on certain occasions the temperature of the environment is higher than that of the body and under these conditions the body tends to gain in heat. But, notwithstanding all this, the body temperature varies little, if any; evidently the body is equipped with a heat-regulating mechanism.

Cold-Blooded and Warm-Blooded Animals.—It is customary to classify animals as warm-blooded and cold-blooded. The body of a warm-blooded animal (mammals and birds) is not only warm but has practically the same temperature day in, day out, in winter and in summer. Cold-blooded animals, on the other hand, are cold when they are subjected to external cold, but when placed in a warm environment, their temperature rises. Hence, it is better to classify them as animals with a constant body temperature (homoiothermic) and as those with a varying body temperature (poikilothermic—*poikilos,* varied). The hibernating mammals during their waking state are homoiothermic, but during their winter sleep the body temperature falls.

I. BODY TEMPERATURE

The body temperature of man, generally stated at about 37° C., or 98° F., varies in the different parts of the body. The mouth temperature is a little lower than the rectal temperature; the liver is the warmest, and the skin, the coldest part. It also varies slightly with conditions of the body and the environment, among which we may enumerate the following:

a. **Muscle Work.**—As we have seen, muscle work influences the heat production in our bodies very pronouncedly, but ordinarily it has but a slight effect upon the temperature of the body, the increase being from 0.1 to 1 degree. Soon after the cessation of the work, this rise subsides. When, however, large groups of muscles are simultaneously thrown into severe and rather prolonged contractions, as in tetany and during a rapid series of epileptic attacks, the body temperature may rise considerably; in marathon races, temperatures of 104° F. have been recorded. The rise in body temperature increases the rate of respiration and heartbeat and aids in the liberation of oxygen from the oxyhemoglobin; in so far it may be of benefit to the animal organism.

b. Sleep, because of the muscular inactivity, causes a slight fall.

c. Diurnal Variation.—In the morning, between 2 and 5 A.M., the body temperature is at its lowest; it is highest between 5 and 8 P.M. These variations extend through about 1° F.

d. Age.—A newborn child has a slightly higher temperature than an adult. It is, however, more important to remember that the body temperature of the young child is more variable because of the lack of control exercised by the nervous system over the blood vessels and other organs operative in temperature regulation; indeed, the young of some warm-blooded animals must be regarded as poikilothermic.

e. External Temperature.—The ordinary changes in the atmospheric temperature, such as we experience in winter and summer, have very little effect on body temperature.

f. Cold and warm baths have a far greater influence than air at the same temperature, but the ordinary exposure to these baths is so short that they have little effect on the normal body temperature. Lefevre stayed in a bath at 15° C. (59° F.) for three hours during which his temperature fell but one degree, although a very large amount of heat was lost from the body. But it can readily be seen that the condition of the individual (size and fat) is an important factor. When the body temperature is abnormally high (fever), the cold bath is able to cause a fall. When the body is immersed in water above the body temperature, the body temperature tends to become equal to that of the water. This is due to the fact that the chief mechanism for losing heat cannot operate under this condition (see infra).

II. THE PRODUCTION OF HEAT

Sources.—The chief source of heat in the human body is the oxidation of the organic foods. We take in a small amount of heat with hot foods and drinks, but this is almost negligible. The amount of heat produced in a day by an individual depends upon many conditions. As most of this subject has been discussed under the heading of Metabolism, brief mention of the most important facts will suffice.

An individual of sedentary occupation expends between 2,000 and 2,500 Calories per day (p. 445). From the heat value of the three organic foodstuffs, it can be seen that Ranke's diet furnishes this amount of heat:

100 grams of fat	× 9 =	900 Calories
100 grams of protein	× 4 =	400 Calories
250 grams of carbohydrate	× 4 =	1,000 Calories
Total		2,300 Calories

The necessary energy could be obtained from many other combinations of these three foodstuffs; this was discussed under Diet. The more muscle work performed the more food is consumed and the more heat is liberated. It will also be recalled that a small animal produces more heat, in proportion to its body weight, than a large animal. The lower the external temperature becomes, the greater will be the heat produced by the body; but as the temperature of the body falls, the oxidations and heat production become less.

Seat of Heat Production.—Oxidations take place, as we have learned, in the tissues themselves, and these oxidations are associated with the production of heat. It is estimated that the skeletal muscles constitute about one-half of the active (soft) tissues of the body, and as they are by far the most active of all our tissues, the largest amount of the heat must be furnished by them. The glands are also of importance in this respect; especially is this true of the liver.

III. LOSS OF HEAT

Channels.—Heat is lost from the body by three channels: the skin, lungs, and excretions. Of these the most important is the skin, the relative amount lost by this organ being placed at about 85 per cent, although this depends somewhat upon external and internal conditions. Heat is lost from the skin (a) by radiation when the temperature of the surrounding objects (walls, furniture, etc.) is lower than that of the body; (b) by convection when the temperature of the air is below the body temperature; (c) by conduction and (d) by the evaporation of perspiration from the skin, for the evaporation of any fluid absorbs heat from the surrounding objects and air. The proportion of heat lost in these different ways varies largely with the condition of the body and of the environment. In a properly heated room during the winter approximately 50 per cent is lost by radiation, 25 per cent by convection, and 25 per cent by evaporation.

Conditions of the Air.—The external factors which determine the amount of heat lost are the temperature and humidity of the air, the velocity of air currents, and the amount of heat radiation. How largely the loss of heat is influenced by the humidity of the air is readily seen in the fact that although only 100 Calories are required to raise the temperature of one liter of water from 0° to 100° C., to evaporate this quantity of water 536 Calories must be applied. The more rapid the evaporation, the greater is the cooling effect; this varies directly as the temperature of the air and inversely as the relative amount of moisture already present in the air; when the latter reaches the saturation point, all evaporation ceases.

In addition to influencing the amount and rapidity of evaporation from the skin, the air humidity also affects the loss of heat by convection and conduction; the greater the amount of moisture in the air, the greater will be the loss by these methods. At 65° F., or below, when very little sweating occurs, the body is excessively chilled when the humidity is high; dry cold air is more easily borne and we say it has a bracing effect. Above 70° F. sweating sets in and now high humidity by lessening the evaporation of sweat, prevents the cooling of the body. Therefore, between 65° and 70° F. the humidity has little effect on the loss of heat by the body.

The variations in humidity experienced in our living rooms during the winter months are said to be relatively unimportant; the necessity for artificial humidification has never been established by properly conducted tests. In fact, most normal persons prefer a rather low humidity (15 per cent) to that of 40 or 50 per cent. It is true that a humidity of 15 per cent may cause drying of the respiratory mucosa, but this low humidity is nearly always due to overheating (beyond 70° or 72° F.). As such hot dry air favors a rapid evaporation of water from the skin, it may actually feel colder than the same air reduced to a temperature of 65° or 70° F. and having, therefore, a higher relative water content. In air conditioning our living rooms during cold weather, the chief difficulty lies in maintaining a comfortable air whose cooling effect (determined by its temperature and the velocity of air currents—drafts) around the feet (the most sensitive parts of the body) is properly regulated without raising the temperature of the air in the "breathing zone" above the optimum.

The Influence of Bodily Conditions.—The rapidity of heat radiation from the body is modified by the amount of subcutaneous fat. Fat people may complain of feeling chilly just as soon as lean people, for the sensation of cold or heat is determined largely by the amount of blood flowing through the cutaneous blood vessels. But on exposure to cold a fat person loses heat less rapidly than a lean one, and, therefore, needs to produce less. A child having proportionally a larger body surface exposed to the air loses heat faster than the adult.

Light-colored clothing is a better reflector and poorer absorber of heat than dark clothes, hence dark clothing should not be worn in hot weather. Clothing containing much air space is a poor conductor of heat; hence feathers, furs, and wool are warmer than cotton, linen, or leather. In the matter of clothing, especially in colder weather, it is, however, not only a question of heat conductivity, but also of the power of a garment to absorb and retain sweat. Because of its great power to absorb moisture and to part with it slowly, wool prevents a too rapid chilling by evaporation, after one has worked himself into a sweat.

IV. THERMOTAXIS, THE REGULATION OF BODY TEMPERATURE

To maintain the life of a warm-blooded animal, it is necessary to keep the body temperature constant notwithstanding the external and internal conditions which tend to raise or lower it. When the human body temperature falls to about 24° C. (77° F.) and this temperature is maintained for several hours, death usually occurs. On the other hand a temperature higher than 44° or 45° C. (111° to 113° F.) maintained for more than a brief length of time is also fatal. The regulation of the body temperature is brought about in two ways:

1. Regulating, that is, increasing or decreasing, the loss of heat (*thermolysis*) ; this is called the physical heat regulation.

2. Regulating the production of heat (*thermogenesis*) ; this is the chemical heat regulation.

a. Thermolysis.—The regulation of the loss of heat is, to a certain extent, voluntary, for by artificially sheltering the body (clothing, housing, etc.), by warming the food and drink taken into the body, and by warming the air with which the body comes in contact we protect the body against a too great loss. Without such voluntary regulation human life in our climate would be an impossibility.

The involuntary regulation is brought about by:

1. THE VASOMOTOR MECHANISM.—When the external temperature is high or when the production of heat in the body is great, as in muscular work, the cutaneous blood vessels dilate and those in the abdomen constrict, thereby sending a larger volume of warm blood to the surface to be cooled. The blood thus cooled is returned to the inner parts of the body where it acquires more heat, which is then carried to the skin. On a cold day, the reverse takes place, so that the warm blood is restrained from circulating too freely through the skin where much heat would be lost (see p. 245).

2. PERSPIRATION.—When the external temperature rises above 29° C. (85° F.) or when the heat production in the body is increased beyond a certain point, it becomes difficult to lose by conduction, convection, and radiation an amount of heat sufficient to maintain the body temperature; it is then that the sweat glands of the skin (see Chap. XXVI) are stimulated. The evaporation of the sweat is associated, as we have already learned, with the absorption of a large quantity of heat from the skin and from the air in immediate contact with the skin. The higher the air temperature or the greater the heat production by muscular work, the more dependent the body is upon this mechanism for regulating its temperature. This is well illustrated by the following: in a person having no sweat glands the body temperature rose to 102° F. when he stayed for 30 minutes in a room having a temperature of 109° F.; a normal person experienced no rise in temperature.

When the humidity of the air is sufficiently low, surprisingly high temperature (200° to 250° F.) can be borne with impunity for a considerable length of time; but a high degree of saturation coupled with a high temperature (sultry weather) may very largely prevent the evaporation of the perspiration and thus interfere with thermolysis. This results in *heat stroke,* or *heat exhaustion* in which the skin is hot and dry, the pulse rapid, the face flushed and the body temperature high—temperatures of 110° F. have been recorded. At this temperature the brain cells are quickly affected and irreparably destroyed, unless the body temperature is speedily reduced by ice packs and cold baths. Death frequently occurs as a result of heat stroke. Alcohol, in amounts sufficient to paralyze the nervous mechanism of temperature regulation, renders an individual more susceptible to sunstroke.

In young children the mechanism for the control of the loss of heat is poorly developed and hence the body temperature is more likely to undergo variations. While in an adult muscular work affects the body temperature but little, a child may develop a fever by a fit of crying. A pathologic condition which causes a very slight fever in an adult produces a much more pronounced rise in the temperature of a child. For this reason young children should be more closely guarded against too rapid a loss of heat. In old people, in whom the blood vessels are hardened and the skin is more or less atrophied, sweating and peripheral vasodilation are impaired; as a result the death rate from heat stroke is greater. On the other hand, in them the rate of heat production is much lower than in young adults, for which reasons they should be protected against extreme cold.

b. Thermogenesis.—*Regulation of Heat Production.*—When a cold-blooded animal, a frog, e.g., is subjected to cold, the amount of metabolism, as measured by the amount of carbon dioxide exhaled, gradually decreases. This is what we should expect, for all chemical actions are lessened when the temperature is lowered. But with a warm-blooded animal the reverse seems to be true. In Table XXXII are indicated the Calories of heat produced by a short-haired

TABLE XXXII

TEMPERATURE	CAL. PER KG.	
7.6	86.4	chemical regulation
15.0	63.0	
20.0	55.9	
25.0	54.2	physical regulation
30.0	56.2	
35.0	68.5	rise in body temperature

dog at various external temperatures. As the temperature fell from 30° to 20° C., there was no increase in the amount of food oxidized; a drop in body temperature was prevented by the physical regulation, i.e., by decreasing the amount of heat lost by the body. But when the external temperature fell below 20° C., the physical regulation was insufficient to maintain the body temperature; this caused the speeding up of the catabolism so that more heat was produced—chemical heat regulation. The increase in oxidation takes place chiefly in the muscles and finds expression in shivering and the chattering of the teeth. When the external temperature rises to a point where physical regulation is unable to eliminate a sufficient amount of heat, the body temperature rises. This always causes an increase in metabolic rate and, therefore, in heat production. There is a certain range of external temperature within which the oxidation of food is at a minimum;

by means of clothing and the artificial heating or cooling of rooms we try to maintain the temperature of the air in contact with the skin at this point.

Heat-Regulating Center.—How does the lowering of the external temperature cause the oxidations in the body to be increased? And how, in general, is the balance between heat production and heat loss maintained? In a region of the brain known as the hypothalamus lies the chief thermo-regulating center. It coordinates the activities of many centers concerned with the production and the loss of heat, such as vasoconstriction, vasodilation, sweating, shivering, panting, etc. The evidence for the existence of this chief center is as follows:

1. In a warm-blooded animal, a section made just caudalward of the hypothalamus separates the chief center from the subcenters which regulate the above-mentioned processes; as a result the animal is unable to regulate its body temperature.

2. In man pathologic conditions in this region of the brain are often associated with a disturbance in heat regulation and the patient behaves to a certain extent as a cold-blooded animal.

3. The heating of this center by electric means sets the mechanism for thermolysis into action; the animal pants, sweating on the pads of the feet and vasodilation occur, and the body temperature falls several degrees.

4. Cooling this area of the brain has the opposite effect.

How does the heat-regulating mechanism, composed of the chief center in the hypothalamus and the subsidiary centers in other parts of the central nervous system (especially the medulla oblongata) operate? In three distinct ways:

1. Temperature of the Blood.—Warming the blood in the carotid artery (which supplies the brain) causes sweat to appear on the paw-pads of a cat; this does not occur if the nerves to the leg are cut. It is highly likely that in man the physical heat regulation, both by perspiration and vasomotor activity, is a function of a heat-regulating center which is stimulated by changes in the temperature of the blood.

2. Reflexly.—The shivering caused by cold stimulation of the skin depends upon the activity of the chief center in the hypothalamus. As muscles are by far the most important heat-producing organs, they most likely are called upon in a greater demand for heat production. Whether there is a special mechanism for this purpose, apart from increased muscle activity as shown by tonicity or visible contraction, is a much disputed point. Some maintain that increased muscle tonus, without any outward manifestation of activity, can increase heat

production. In some persons able voluntarily to resist, up to a certain extent, the shivering induced by exposure to cold, there is an actual drop in body temperature. When muscle contractions and tonus are abolished by general anesthesia, the heat production is very largely reduced; a warm-blooded animal under the influence of curare behaves as a cold-blooded animal.

3. HORMONAL CONTROL.—A third factor enters into the heat-regulating mechanism, namely, the hormones. It will be recalled (p. 444) that the thyroid hormone controls basal metabolism and therefore basal heat production to no small extent. It is said that thyroid secretion is increased by cold; this, however, depends upon neural connections between the hypothalamus and the thyroid and pituitary body.

Cannon suggests that when the fall in body temperature cannot be prevented by the constriction of the cutaneous blood vessels (physical regulation), there is an increased discharge of adrenalin into the blood stream. Boothby and others have shown that the injection of one milligram of adrenalin causes the catabolism in man to be increased by 50 Cal. If the increased output of adrenalin is also inadequate, the body seeks to augment the heat production by shivering. This theory of the part played by the adrenal glands is strengthened by the observation of von Euler that fever cannot be caused in an animal deprived of these organs, neither does exposure to cold increase the heat production in such animals.

Fever.—A most striking phenomenon of many pathologic disturbances is a rise in the body temperature, a condition known as fever. Such a rise in temperature may be due to a disturbance in the regulation of heat production (more heat being formed than can be lost by the normal channels) or the regulation of the loss of heat is upset. Most investigators hold that while in fever there may be a slight increase in the production of heat, this is too small to account for a rise of several degrees in body temperature. For example, Krauss found that the greatest increase in heat production during fever was only 20 per cent above normal. Now we have learned that by muscle work there may be an increase of 100 or 300 per cent in heat production with only a very slight rise in body temperature; it is, therefore, more than likely that fever is generally not due to a disturbance in the production of heat. That there is a disturbance in the heat dissipation is seen in the paleness of the skin and the absence of sweating. The paleness is due to the constriction of the peripheral blood vessels which results, as Hewlett has shown, in a diminished blood flow through these parts of the body. At the "crisis" of the fever the drop in body temperature is associated with increased heat dissipation brought about by the dilation of the cutaneous blood vessels and by sweating, and with decreased heat production due to the muscles becoming flaccid.

The cause of the rise of body temperature has been illustrated in the following way: The temperature of an incubator must remain constant; this is effected by a piece of apparatus called a thermostat. The thermostat may be set, once for all, for a certain temperature and the temperature of the incubator will be maintained at this point. Suppose we change the thermostat, the regulation of heat production and of heat loss is not disturbed, but the temperature at which the incubator is now kept has either been raised or lowered. The sweat glands and the vasomotor and neuromuscular systems, under the coordinating control of the thermo-regulating center, form the thermostat of our body. This thermostat is, we may say, set so that the relation between heat production and heat loss is such that a body temperature of about 37° C. is maintained. In certain abnormal states the thermostat is set higher, and, while there is a relation between the loss and the production of heat, the body temperature rises. This change in the heat-regulating mechanism is frequently due to bacterial toxins or foreign proteins.

The rise in body temperature is claimed by some to be beneficial in that it aids in the destruction of the invading organism. Paresis, or general paralysis, a nervous malady not associated with fever, is successfully treated by producing in the patient a fever either by short radio waves or by infection with malaria. The spirochetes, responsible for the paresis, are unable to withstand a temperature over 104° F.

CHAPTER XXV

RENAL SECRETION

I. RENAL FUNCTIONS

To maintain as nearly constant as possible—homeostasis—the osmotic pressure, the pH value, the molecular concentration of the crystalloids and colloids, the supply of food, the temperature, and the total volume of the internal medium (blood and lymph) and its freedom from nocuous substances is the purpose of all the vegetative organs of the body. Any but the slightest variation in these characteristics is followed by harmful results. The part played in this by the respiratory, digestive, and circulatory systems, and by the cellular elements of the blood, the skin, and the organs for food storage has been dealt with in previous chapters. We shall now study the manner in which the kidneys aid in homeostasis.

a. The Excretion of Deleterious Substances.—Useless or harmful materials, no matter what their concentration in the plasma may be, are removed by the kidneys. Some foreign proteins entering the blood and certain catabolic products, such as urea, uric acid, creatinine, and various salts (see Table XXVIII) are thus eliminated.

b. The Removal of Excess Materials.— The kidneys excrete substances normally present in the blood, when their concentration is above a certain point, e.g., when the glucose is present to an extent not above 0.17 per cent, the kidneys do not excrete it, but any excess above this is promptly removed.

c. Osmotic Pressure.—The kidneys aid in maintaining the proper osmotic pressure of the internal medium by eliminating water when its excessive concentration in the blood tends to lower the *osmotic pressure*. To the same end an excess of salt, which tends to raise the osmotic pressure and draw water from the tissues, is promptly excreted. Because of this renal activity, the drinking of large quantities of water does not decrease, and the ingestion of much salt does not increase, the osmotic pressure of the blood for any great length of time.

d. Acid-Base Balance.—In our study of protein catabolism we have learned that the breaking up and oxidation of proteins give rise to sulfuric acid, and, in the case of nucleoproteins, also to phosphoric acid. The oxidation of all organic foodstuffs gives rise to carbon dioxide which in the presence of water forms carbonic acid. By muscle work lactic acid also is produced. The production of acids is therefore a constant phenomenon in the body, and by the dissociation of these acids H ions of the blood are produced. As a small increase of H ions in the blood or tissues above the normal is inimical to life, the body is provided with a mechanism for regulating the acid-base balance. As has been indicated earlier (p. 401), the ammonia liberated from amino acids takes a part in neutralizing acids. When there is a great increase in the production of acids in the body, as during severe muscle work, more of the ammonia unites with these acids to form salts that are excreted by the kidneys and a correspondingly smaller amount of the ammonia, after uniting with carbonic acid, is transformed by the liver into urea.

The greater part of the neutralization, however, is brought about by the so-called "buffer substances" of the blood and tissues, namely, the carbonates and phosphates of sodium and potassium and the alkaline protein salts (see pp. 146 and 301). The sulfuric acid acting upon the bicarbonate gives rise to acid sodium sulfate and carbonic acid.

$$NaHCO_3 + H_2SO_4 = NaHSO_4 + H_2CO_3$$

The acid salt is excreted by the kidneys. The carbonic acid breaks up into CO_2 and H_2O, and the carbon dioxide is expelled by the lungs. By the combined action of the buffer substances and the organs of excretion (lungs and kidneys) the proper hydrogen-ion concentration in the body is maintained. The part played by the lungs in maintaining the acid-base balance is of great importance, for the quantity of acid expelled by the lungs (in the form of CO_2 and H_2O) is far greater than that of any other acid; and in ridding the body of carbonic acid the alkali reserve ($NaHCO_3$, etc.) of the body is not lessened, as always occurs when the kidneys excrete acid sulfates or phosphates.

To replenish the basic materials lost in the effort to maintain the acid-base balance is one of the functions of the ingested organic acids and the salts of these acids. In the intestines the organic acids (for example, citric acid of citrous fruits) unite with the alkalies to form salts (sodium citrate, in our example). Sodium lactate (from sour milk) and sodium malate (from apples) may also be mentioned as examples of organic salts. By means of sodium acetate we may illustrate how the organic salts help to maintain the acid-base balance. The composition of this salt is $CH_3COO.Na$. In the body the acid radical, i.e., the CH_3COO group, unites with oxygen and forms CO_2

and H_2O which give rise to carbonic acid, H_2CO_3. This acid, uniting with the sodium of the original organic salt, forms sodium bicarbonate —$NaHCO_3$. So well adjusted are the various factors in the maintenance of the acid-base balance that the concentration of the hydrogen ions in the blood is one of the most constant factors in the body. According to McCollum, the acids found in 2400 c.c. (about 2½ quarts) of orange juice taken in one day are almost completely oxidized as above described. Certain fruits, such as cherries, plums and prunes, contain acids (e.g., benzoic acid) that cannot be oxidized in the body; this also holds for the oxalic acid of spinach and sorrel.

The protein foods with their acid-forming sulfur and phosphorus, render the urine more acid; the vegetables and fruits, on the other hand, reduce this acidity and, indeed, may render the urine alkaline. This fact is taken advantage of in those cases where the acidity of the urine must be decreased as much as possible because of some irritated condition of the urinary apparatus.

e. Detoxication.—Bunge demonstrated that the kidneys have synthetic powers. On perfusing a kidney with a solution containing benzoic acid—$C_6H_5.COOH$—and glycocoll (amino-acetic acid) he found that by their union hippuric acid is formed. The benzoic acid may be produced in the body or may be eaten with certain canned foods in which it is used as a preservative. As benzoic acid is more or less poisonous, this action may be regarded as a detoxifying function.

II. THE URINE

The Amount.—The quantity of urine excreted varies considerably because of marked variations in the amount of water taken into the body and the amount eliminated by the lungs and the skin. The average amount ingested may be stated at 1,000 to 1,500 c.c. per day. The amount lost by the lungs does not vary much, but that lost by the skin depends largely upon the temperature and humidity of the air and the amount of heat we generate by muscular activity. As regards the excretion of water, the skin and the kidneys are complemental; the more we excrete by the one, the less work there is for the other.

Composition of Urine.—The urine excreted during twenty-four hours, if 100 grams of proteins are eaten, has about the composition shown in Table XXXIII.

The Specific Gravity.—The total amount of solids per day is about 60 or 70 grams but this varies chiefly with the amount of proteins eaten (because this determines the amount of urea excreted) and with the amount of sodium chloride ingested. As both the solid and the water contents of the urine are subject to variations, it is not

TABLE XXXIII

Water	1,200.0 cc.
Urea	30.0 grams
Uric acid (as salts)	0.5 gram
Creatinine	1.0 gram
Hippuric acid (as salts)	1.0 gram
Ammonia (as salts)	0.7 gram
Sodium chloride	15.0 grams
Other salts	10.0 grams
Other organic material	3.0 grams

surprising to learn that the specific gravity shows marked fluctuations, even during normal conditions. The specific gravity is obtained by a urinometer. A cylinder is filled about two-thirds with urine, cooled to the room temperature; a hydrometer is floated in the urine and the mark on the stem of the hydrometer level with the top of the urine is noted, this expressing the specific gravity. The normal variations are stated from 1.015 to 1.020. In fevers and diabetes the specific gravity may be 1.030 and over. After much sweating the specific gravity may be above, and after much drinking below, the normal limits here given.

Reaction.—Twenty-four-hour urine is usually acid in reaction toward such indicators as litmus; this acidity (pH = about 6) is due chiefly to the monosodium phosphate, NaH_2PO_4. During starvation the increased protein metabolism increases the urinary acidity; the same result obtains in severe diabetes because of the large amounts of organic acids formed from the fats (p. 421). About an hour after a meal, it is claimed, the urine becomes less acid and may even be alkaline in reaction; by some this has been attributed to the production of the hydrochloric acid of the gastric juice.

III. ANATOMY OF THE KIDNEY

The kidneys are bean-shaped organs, about four inches in length. They are situated in the lumbar region, one on each side of the vertebral column, Fig. 219. Each kidney is composed of thousands of small tubules known as the uriniferous tubules, or nephrons, which constitute the physiologic units of the kidney. Their number in the two kidneys is estimated at 2,000,000 and their total length at approximately 75 miles. From each kidney springs a tube, the ureter (Figs. 219, 220, and 221), which carries the urine to the urinary bladder; from the bladder arises another tube, the urethra, by which the urine is voided (see also Figs. 297 and 300). At its origin the ureter is much dilated and thereby forms the pelvis of the kidney, Fig. 219. The fleshy mass of the kidney is divided into what are termed the pyramids, Fig. 220, the pointed ends of which dip into the pelvis. Each of these pyramids is a collection of tubules which, after uniting with each other, empty by a duct at the apex of the pyramid into the pelvis of the kidney.

The uriniferous tubule, or nephron, is an exceedingly complex tube of which the various parts differ greatly from each other. It begins as a blind tube in the outer portion, or cortex, of the kidney, Fig. 220.

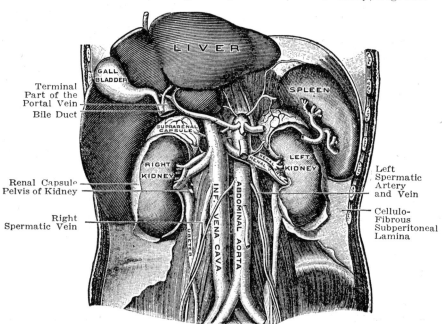

Fig. 219.—Organs of the abdomen; the stomach and intestines have been removed and the liver raised. (Gray's Anatomy, after Sappey.)

The blind end is modified in a peculiar manner so as to give rise to the Malpighian corpuscle, or body, Figs. 222 and 223. We may describe this corpuscle as being formed by the invagination of the blind end of the tubule (much like a pocket formed when a lead pencil is pushed down upon the closed end of the finger of a glove); the little sac thus formed is called Bowman's capsule. From this capsule springs the tubule which, as shown in Fig. 223, describes a very devious course; part of it is known as the convoluted tubule. After many changes in its course and structure and after joining many other similar tubes, it finally forms the collecting tubule which empties, as before stated, into the pelvis of the kidney. In the capsule the walls are composed of broad, thin epithelial cells, Fig. 222; the cells forming the convoluted tubule are much thicker and more cuboidal.

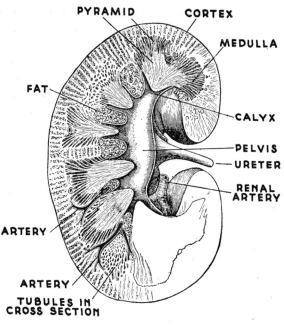

PYRAMID CORTEX

MEDULLA

FAT

CALYX

PELVIS

URETER

RENAL ARTERY

ARTERY

ARTERY

TUBULES IN CROSS SECTION

Fig. 220.—Section through a kidney. (After Tyson.)

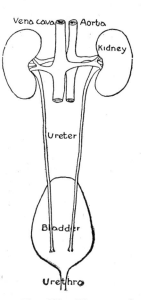

Vena cava Aorta

Kidney

Ureter

Bladder

Urethra

Fig. 221.—Diagram of the urinary system. (Pearce and Macleod.)

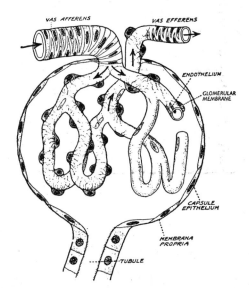

VAS AFFERENS VAS EFFERENS

ENDOTHELIUM

GLOMERULAR MEMBRANE

CAPSULE EPITHELIUM

MEMBRANA PROPRIA

TUBULE

Fig. 222.—Diagram of a Malpighian body. The capsule epithelium is reflected over the outside of the capillaries of the glomerular tuft. Only a few of the capillaries of this tuft are shown. (After v. Möllendorff.) (Winton and Bayliss: Human Physiology, J. and A. Churchill, Ltd.)

The blood vessels of these structures are peculiar in several respects. From a small branch of the renal artery in the body of the kidney springs an afferent vessel (vas afferens) which, as shown in Figs. 222 and 223, enters Bowman's capsule and there breaks up into a large number of capillaries; to this tuft of capillaries, known as the glomerulus (*glomus*, a ball), the inner wall, *b*, Fig. 224, of the capsule of Bowman is closely applied. By uniting with each other

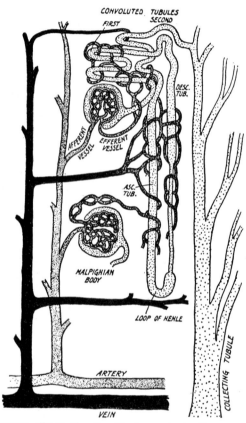

Fig. 223.—Diagram illustrating the blood supply to the renal tubule. (After Mottram.) (Winton and Bayliss: Human Physiology, J. and A. Churchill, Ltd.)

the capillaries give rise to an efferent vessel which leaves the capsule. This vas efferens, it will be noticed from the illustrations, is considerably narrower than the vas afferens which brings the blood to the glomerulus. Soon after leaving the Malpighian body the vas efferens breaks up into a second lot of capillaries which surround the convoluted tubule; these capillaries discharge their blood into a small vein which is drained by the renal vein.

IV. THEORIES OF RENAL ACTIVITY

From what we have already stated concerning the work of the kidneys, we are astonished at the "fine selective discrimination" exercised by these organs. It is difficult, if at present not impossible, to understand how the kidneys excrete no glucose except that above the normal blood limit of 0.17 per cent; how they excrete practically all the urea and only as much NaCl as is necessary to maintain the correct osmotic pressure of the blood, although both substances are highly soluble, diffusible, and dialyzable; how they differentiate between dissolved hemoglobin or egg albumin which are excreted and the plasma proteins which are normally not found in the urine. Of the many explanations offered, we shall content ourselves with briefly reviewing Cushny's filtration-reabsorption theory. According to this investigator, the two structurally very

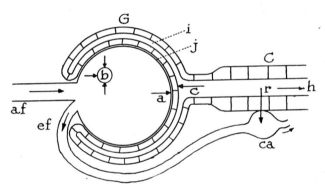

Fig. 224.—Diagram to illustrate renal secretion. *G,* Malpighian corpuscle with the two layers of Bowman's capsule and the space, *i,* between these layers; *af,* vas afferens supplying the glomerular capillaries which fill the capsule and are collectively indicated by the line, *j,* to which the inner wall of the capsule is closely applied; *ef,* vas efferens which drains the glomerular capillaries and supplies the capillaries, *ca,* surrounding the convoluted tubule, *C; a,* the blood pressure in the glomerular capillaries; *c,* the urine (filtrate) pressure in the tubule; *r,* the reabsorption from the tubule into the capillaries, *ca; h,* the urine on its way to the collecting tubule; *b,* the restraining osmotic pressure of the protein molecule.

diverse parts of the uriniferous tubule, namely, the Malpighian body and the convoluted tubule, must also differ in function. The former of these structures, he maintains, acts merely as a filtration mechanism; the function of the convoluted tubule is one of selective absorption, somewhat similar to that of the lacteals of the intestines.

Malpighian Body.—This structure is well adapted for filtration in two important respects. First, the tufts of capillaries forming the glomeruli (*G,* Fig. 224) are very numerous (in the two kidneys estimated at about 2 million); in consequence, the surface for filtration is enormous. Second, it will be recalled that the vas efferens, *ef,* taking the blood from the glomerulus is smaller than the vas afferens, *af,* and breaks up into a second set of capillaries, *ca,* around the convoluted tubule, *C.* This introduces a large amount of resistance to the outflow of the blood from the glomerulus and therefore constitutes another factor favorable for filtration.

The glomerulus is permeable to all the materials (water, glucose, salts, nitrogenous waste products, etc.) of the plasma except the colloidal blood proteins. Therefore, all the ingredients of the urine leave the blood stream by ultrafiltration in the glomerulus and the glomerular fluid thus formed has, according to Cushny's theory, the same composition as the plasma, excepting that it contains no proteins. This has been substantiated in lower animals. By a micropipette (about 10μ in diameter) the filtrate has been obtained in frogs directly from Bowman's capsule and, excepting for the absence of proteins, has been found to have about the same osmotic pressure, urea concentration, and electrical conductivity as the protein-free plasma. That the separation of the glomerular fluid from the blood is a matter of filtration is rendered very likely by the fact that whatever increases or decreases the blood pressure affects the flow of urine in the same sense. Richards and Plant found that if the rate of blood flow through the kidney remains constant, the amount of urine secreted varies directly as the blood pressure.

The capillary blood pressure, stated at 70 mm. Hg, is higher in the glomerulus than in any other capillaries. When the arterial pressure falls to about 50 mm. Hg, all renal secretion stops. The reason for this lies in the fact that the colloidal osmotic pressure of the blood proteins is sufficient to prevent the loss of fluid (see page 256). From this it is evident that the effective filtration pressure is the blood pressure in the glomerulus, *a* in Fig. 224, minus the osmotic pressure, *b,* of the blood proteins which tends to retain the water in the blood and the hydrostatic pressure of the urine present in the tubule, *c.* This readily explains why a physiologic salt solution injected after a hemorrhage soon leaves the body by way of the kidneys. The injected salt solution lessens the concentration of the blood proteins and, therefore, their colloidal osmotic pressure; this increases the effective filtration pressure.

The Convoluted Tubule.—The large amount of filtrate (estimated from 60 to 150 liters per day) is very dilute as compared to the urine. As it passes through the convoluted tubules, the cells of the tubules, *C,* Fig. 224, absorb, *r,* some of its constituents and return them to the blood, *ca;* this causes the 60 liters to be condensed to approximately one or one and one-half liters, the usual amount of urine voided per day. The ingredients reabsorbed by the tubule are:

1. From 97 to 98 per cent of the water of the glomerular filtrate is reabsorbed into the blood. This is rendered possible, in part, by the great decrease in the blood pressure in the capillaries of the convoluted tubule and by the increase in the concentration of the proteins in the blood (because of the loss of much water in the glomerulus) which increases the colloidal osmotic pressure.

2. Some substances, e.g., glucose, are normally entirely reabsorbed into the blood and are, therefore, not found in the urine. That glucose is excreted by the glomerulus has been verified in two ways. The glomerular filtrate of a frog's kidney contains glucose, but the urine in the bladder is devoid of it. In some of the bony fishes, the Malpighian body is lacking and all the elimination is done by the convoluted tubule; in these animals glucose is never present in the urine even though by injection the amount of sugar in the blood is raised to 0.5 per cent. When the amount of glucose in the glomerular filtrate is high (as in diabetes), the absorbing mechanism of the tubule is overtaxed and some of the sugar escapes into the urine. The glycosuria accompanying hyperglycemia is therefore the result of lack of reabsorption.

3. Of other ingredients there is a partial absorption by which the proper amount of these substances is kept in the blood and any excess previously present excreted. This is true for certain of the salts and, in diabetes, also for glucose.

4. Of other constituents, such as urea and uric acid, less absorption takes place; hence their concentration in the urine is very much greater than in the blood.

While the work by the glomerulus can be quite satisfactorily explained by the simple laws of ultrafiltration, in the reabsorption by the tubule we meet with the same difficulties we encountered in our study of absorption by the alimentary canal. For example: glucose is always reabsorbed, but cane sugar injected into the blood vessels always passes into the urine.

Abuminuria.—In about 4 or 5 per cent of healthy individuals a very small amount (0.2 per cent) of the albumin of the blood may find its way into the urine. After severe muscular exertion or after a cold bath this condition is quite general in most subjects. But when the permeability of the glomerular wall is increased by the toxins of various diseases (scarlet fever, typhoid, diphtheria, tonsillitis) or of decaying teeth the amount of albumin in the urine is much augmented. This albuminuria depletes the proteins of the blood and, as we learned in our study of lymph formation, the resultant decrease in the colloidal osmotic pressure of the plasma leads to edema (see p. 263).

V. WORK DONE BY THE KIDNEYS

While the function of the glomerulus, according to the filtration theory, may be a passive affair and not associated with the expenditure of energy on the part of the kidney, this cannot be said of the activity of the convoluted tubule. Here an expenditure of energy takes place, as is evidenced by the fact that under certain conditions its production of carbon dioxide and consumption of oxygen are increased. This greater gas exchange indicates an increased catabolism necessitated by the work to be accomplished. That the kidney does work can best be learned by comparing the urine and the plasma, for all the materials (excepting hippuric acid) excreted by the kidneys are directly obtained from the plasma. It will be noticed from Table XXXIV that the concentration of the urea in the urine is a little more

TABLE XXXIV

PERCENTAGE COMPOSITION OF PLASMA AND URINE

	PLASMA	URINE
Water	90.0	95.0
Protein	8.0	—
Glucose	0.1	—
Urea	0.03	2.0
Sodium	0.32	0.35
Chlorine	0.37	0.6

than sixty times as great as that of the urea in the plasma. If we wish to transform a 0.03 per cent solution of urea, or any salt, into a 2 per cent solution, we may heat the solution until, by the evaporation of the water, the concentration of the solute reaches 2 per cent. Hence, energy must be expended. It has been calculated that the energy required to produce 1,000 c.c. of fluid having the same molecular concentration as urine from blood plasma by evaporation is the equivalent of 300 kilogrammeters of work. The kidney obtains this energy from the food, but how it utilizes this energy in transforming the dilute into a concentrated solution is not known.

VI. CONDITIONS INFLUENCING RENAL ACTIVITY

a. **Nervous Control.**—Like most glands, the kidneys are supplied with nerves; from the great sympathetic nerve, the splanchnic, branches proceed to the kidneys. While stimulation of these renal nerves may affect the secretion of urine, they have no direct influence on the kidney cells. The changes in renal secretion are chiefly brought about by an alteration in the blood pressure. That renal secretion can go on independently of the nerve supply is evident from experiments on lower animals from which both kidneys have been experimentally removed; one kidney was transplanted into some other part of the body and proper vascular connections established. In one instance the animal lived for six years. The renal nerves contain both vasoconstrictors and vasodilators, but chiefly the former; consequently the stimulation of these nerves causes constriction of the renal blood vessels.

b. Blood Pressure.—From our study of circulation it can be readily understood that the blood pressure in the kidney may be altered by:

1. A general constriction of the blood vessels excepting those of the kidneys; this can be brought about by stimulation of the spinal cord after the renal nerves have been severed. This procedure increases the general blood pressure, but as the pathway into and through the kidneys has not been narrowed, the pressure in the renal vessels is increased without any interference with the blood flow, and the urinary output is increased. On the other hand, a great vascular dilation or a diminution of the circulating blood, as by hemorrhage, leads to a fall in glomerular blood pressure and, therefore, to a lessened flow of urine.

2. Stimulation of the renal vessels constricts the afferent vessels to the glomeruli, and thereby decreases the pressure and also the volume flow per unit of time in the capillaries; this lessens renal secretion. This takes place whether there is a general vasoconstriction or dilation.

In our study of muscles we learned from the experiments by Krogh that in the resting muscle not more than one-tenth of the capillaries are patent. It is highly probable that under the usual condition of the blood and blood pressure a large number of the glomeruli are not functioning; this view is substantiated by the fact that one kidney can be removed without seriously influencing the amount of urine formed. But with an increase in general pressure, not associated with renal constriction, more blood is sent into previously closed glomeruli and thereby the available extent of filtration surface is increased.

c. Molecular Concentration of the Blood.—One of the functions of the kidneys is to regulate the osmotic pressure of the blood. The osmotic pressure is increased when the amount of salts and other crystalline substances in the blood is increased; increasing the water decreases the osmotic pressure; both of these alterations cause the kidneys to become active.

d. Hormonal Control.—In our study of the posterior pituitary we learned that an anti-diuretic hormone lessens the flow of urine.

e. Diuretics are chemical compounds that increase renal activity. Among them we may mention the well-known action of caffeine (found in tea and coffee), urea, and water; in fact, the latter is to be looked upon as the great diuretic. How some diuretics work is very obscure; some may increase the general blood pressure, others may dilate the afferent glomerular vessels, or they may bring about the opening of more glomerular capillaries.

VII. MICTURITION

The ureter (see Figs. 219 and 221) is a muscular tube and by its peristaltic contraction the urine is forced in gushes from the kidney to the bladder. Peristaltic contractions, beginning at the kidney, take place at intervals of about ten or twenty seconds. In the wall of the bladder is found a muscular layer composed of longitudinal and circular fibers; collectively these are known as the detrusor muscle. By the contraction of its musculature the bladder is emptied. The outlet of the bladder into the urethra is guarded by a strong circular muscle, the sphincter vesicae, the contraction of which keeps the urethra closed constantly except during the act of urination.

The muscles of the bladder possess a certain amount of tonus so that, even when empty, the pressure in the bladder is about 150 mm. of water. As the bladder fills, the pressure may rise a little but the muscles soon yield and a constant pressure is maintained. However, at a certain point of filling, the pressure increases and the sensory nerves in the wall of the bladder (going to the sacral portion of the cord) are stimulated and thus bring about a desire to urinate.

The detrusor muscle receives excitatory nerve fibers from the parasympathetic and inhibitory from the sympathetic nervous system. The preganglionic fibers of the parasympathetic originate in the second and third sacral segments of the cord and reach the ganglion (at the base of the bladder) by the pelvic nerve, or the nervi erigentes; from there the postganglionic fibers proceed to the detrusor muscle and the sphincter. The preganglionic fibers of the sympathetic nerve originate in the lumbar region of the cord; they are relayed in the hypogastric ganglion from where the postganglionic fibers proceed to the bladder and sphincter. The pelvic nerve is excitatory for the detrusor and inhibitory for the sphincter; the sympathetic is inhibitory for the detrusor and excitatory for the sphincter. It will be noticed that these two nerves are reciprocal in their action. The centers from which excitatory and inhibitory impulses are sent to these two muscles lie in the midbrain, hind-brain, and in the spinal cord.

The innervations for emptying the bladder are exceedingly complex; we have space for only a meager description. In a very young child the vesical center in the sacral cord receives afferent impulses from the distended bladder and sends out impulses for excitation to the detrusor and inhibitory to the sphincter muscle; the bladder is emptied reflexly.

In the adult the sensory impulses ascend from the cord to the brain and the individual becomes conscious of the filled condition of the bladder; he can, then, to a certain extent voluntarily either aid or inhibit the action. By contraction of the abdominal muscles (the glottis being closed so as to fix the diaphragm) the external pressure applied to the bladder is increased, and the expulsion of the urine faciliated. We may call attention to the peculiar situation of voluntary control being exercised over processes governed by the autonomic nervous system. When in an adult the spinal cord is broken somewhere above the sacral region, the emptying of the bladder becomes an unconscious reflex act, as it is normally in the infant. Certain psychic states greatly increase the tonicity of the muscles of the bladder, whereby the internal pressure and the desire for urination are augmented.

CHAPTER XXVI

THE SKIN

The Epidermis.—The skin is composed of two layers: the cuticle, or epidermis, and the dermis, or true skin. The epidermis, as shown in Fig. 225, is a thin outer layer composed of stratified epithelium. The cells in the Malpighian layer of the epidermis multiply and in growing push the older cells upward toward the surface, and, as these move upward, they not only become flattened in shape, but also undergo an important chemical change in that their proteins are transformed into a peculiar form known as keratin. Keratin is the most insoluble of all proteins and gives the cells of the most superficial layer, the stratum corneum, a hornlike consistency. The outermost cells of this layer are dead and are gradually shed. Keratin is also found in the appendages of the skin, that is, the nails and hair. In the lower animals it is found in horns, hoofs, and claws, which are modifications of the horny epidermis. In the palms and soles the epidermis is much thicker than elsewhere. By intermittent pressure the horny layer of the epidermis may be caused to hypertrophy and produce a swelling not only outward but also downward into the next layer of the skin, the dermis, giving rise to a callus, or corn.

The Derma.—The true skin, or derma, lies below the Malpighian layer as shown in Fig. 225; it is formed of loose connective tissue which sends into the cuticle little elevations, known as papillae. At its deeper layer it gradually passes into the areolar subcutaneous tissue. In both the derma and the subcutaneous tissue there is found a variable amount of fat or adipose tissue. Many of the papillae are furnished with modified nerve endings or tactile corpuscles; these are most abundant in the palm of the hand and in the fingers. In a wart the papillae are much enlarged and the epidermis overlying the papilla is thickened.

Glands.—The skin is supplied with two sets of glands, the sebaceous, or oil glands, and the sudoriferous, or sweat glands. The oil glands open into follicles, or depressions, from which the hairs spring. Among the oil glands are also to be reckoned the Meibomian glands of the eyelids. An acute inflammation of a hair follicle and its sebaceous gland, brought about by the entrance of staphylococci through the follicle, gives rise to a boil, or furuncle. A carbuncle may be said to be a number of boils closely set together and involving more or less the subcutaneous tissue. Such eruptions generally indicate a lowered vitality; a diet rich in carbohydrates is said to predispose to boils. We have already seen that the nutrition of the skin and hair depends upon the proper activity of the thyroid gland.

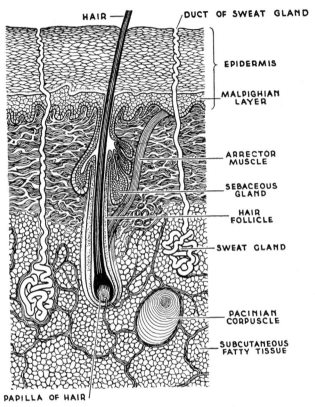

Fig. 225.—Vertical section of the skin (schematic). (Modified from Cunningham.)

The secreting part of a sweat gland lies deep in the true skin and consists of a tube coiled up into the form of a little ball; the discharging duct passes through the upper layers of the skin in the form of a corkscrew. These glands are found in almost every part of the skin, but are most abundant in the skin of the palms and soles. The glands of the ear which secrete the ear wax, or cerumen, are generally regarded as modified sweat glands.

While the epidermis is not supplied with blood vessels, the dermis is very vascular; the sweat glands are surrounded by a cluster of capillaries. In the skin are also found small bundles of plain muscle fibers; most of these are supplied to the hair follicles and by their contraction they elevate the hairs (goose-skin).

The functions of the skin are many and some of them exceedingly important:

1. PROTECTION.—The cuticle of the skin, being composed of hard, resistant cells, forms the body's first line of defense against mechanical and chemical injuries and, above all, against bacterial invasion, for the unbroken skin is almost germ proof. How truly the skin protects us in this last respect is seen in the frequent infections taking place when the skin is injured so as to expose the underlying tissues. Recently Kahn has demonstrated that the skin not only serves as a mechanical barrier, but that it also possesses immunizing powers superior to those of the blood.

In the deeper layer of the epidermis there is found a greater or lesser quantity of a pigment giving color to the skin. This pigment is increased as tan and freckles under the influence of intense sunlight, and is held by some to be of value in protecting the individual against the actinic rays of the hot sun. The absence of all pigment in the skin and hair is known as albinism.

2. SENSE ORGANS.—In the skin are found the sense organs for heat, cold, touch, and pain—Chapter XXVII.

3. BODY TEMPERATURE.—A most important function of the skin is the regulation of the body temperature. This is accomplished by the vasomotor reactions of its blood vessels and by the evaporation of the perspiration—Chapter XXIV.

4. WATER RESERVOIR.—It is held by some that the skin serves as a reservoir of water. Excessive water in the blood is to a certain extent taken up by the skin, to be released in case of need, as in hemorrhage.

5. CALCIUM METABOLISM.—We have already spoken of its antirachitic function when the skin is irradiated with ultraviolet light (p. 472).

6. EXCRETION.—The skin is frequently said to have excretory functions, but this may be safely ignored. From four to eight grams of carbon dioxide are excreted per day by this organ; compared with the 700 or 800 grams exhaled by the lungs, we can hardly call the skin an excretory organ for this waste product. The same holds true for the small quantities of other wastes, such as urea and the various salts.

7. ABSORPTION.—Also as an organ of absorption the skin plays an insignificant part. It is generally held that water and water solutions (of salts, sugars, drugs, etc.) are not absorbed; oils and ointments are to a certain extent taken up by the skin.

The Sebaceous Secretions.—The oil glands are distributed to all parts of the skin, excepting the soles and the palms. The secretion, known as *sebum,* contains fats, proteins, water, salts, and remnants of epithelial cells. Oiling the skin and the hair prevents these structures from drying unduly and breaking, thus preserving the physical integrity of the skin. It also prevents too great imbibition or loss of water by the skin. No secretory nerves governing the activity of the sebaceous glands are known.

The perspiration, or sweat, is composed of 99 per cent water, salts, especially sodium chloride, and traces of urea. The amount of the solids is very small, in consequence of which the specific gravity is low (1.004). In abnormal conditions the sweat may contain many compounds usually not present, such as bile-pigments, albumin, sugar, and blood. The sweat sometimes has an acid, sometimes an alkaline reaction; the odor may be very marked and differs with the various regions of the body.

The amount of water lost through the skin may be placed at from 500 to 2,000 c.c. per day. A considerable amount of this passes through the skin by osmosis (insensible perspiration) without the aid of the sweat glands. A boy destitute of sweat glands evaporated, at an external temperature of 25° C., about the same amount of water as a normal subject does. With his body (not his head) inclosed in a bag through which air at 48° C. was circulated, he lost only 33 grams of water per hour; a normal person lost 336 grams.

Regulation of Perspiration.—The work of the sweat glands is governed by secretory nerves of the sympathetic nervous system. Stimulation of the sciatic nerve may cause drops of sweat to appear on the foot of a cat. It is generally held that a sweat center exists somewhere in the brain; it is stimulated when the temperature of the blood going to the brain is increased by from 0.2 to 0.5° C. This rise in the temperature of the blood is largely determined by the external temperature and by the amount of muscular activity. Nausea, asphyxiation, and psychic conditions, such as great fear, also influence the sweat center.

Bathing.—The value of a bath may be twofold; it cleanses the skin, and it has an influence upon the vasomotor system.

The usual tepid bath (80° to 90° F.) is taken for its cleansing action. By this the excretions of the sweat and oil glands that may have lodged on the skin, and the bacterial products formed from these secretions, are removed; in order to dissolve the excess of oil and fatty acids, soap is used. The accumulation of the bacterial products may irritate the skin and thereby lead to an unhealthy condition. As the excretion by the skin is almost nil, baths are not necessary to aid in the elimination of waste products.

The value of a cold bath (below 65° F.) lies in the stimulating effect it reflexly exerts upon the cutaneous blood vessels; but this beneficial effect is obtained only if the bath is followed by the proper reaction, that is, by the dilation of the skin vessels; to obtain this reaction, friction with a rough towel is useful. Delicate people, and nearly all people not accustomed to cold baths, find these baths a severe shock; one should gradually adapt his system to them. The bracing effect upon the neuromuscular system, and the exercising of the blood vessels are some of the advantages accruing from cold baths, not to speak of the psychic influences. From our study of circulation, it must follow that bathing immediately after a meal, or when one is tired or overwarm, is inadvisable.

Injury to the Skin.—The loss of a certain amount of the skin may cause grave disturbances and even death. The fatal results following the burning of one-fourth or more of the total skin area have been attributed to many causes. It is now generally held that the shock from burns is due to the great dilation of capillaries caused by the absorption of protein decomposition products. The first aid treatment of burns is either to dust the surface with dry starch, flour, or baking soda, or to apply dressings wetted with strong infusion of tea.

CHAPTER XXVII

THE RECEPTORS, OR SENSE ORGANS

General Features

Spencer has defined life as the continuous adjustment of internal to external relations. As the conditions of our environment change, it becomes necessary for us to adjust ourselves to these changes. In order that the body may do so, it must be informed of the external changes; this is the function of the receptor, or sense organ. In the sensory surface the afferent nerve fiber loses its myelin sheath and either ends as a free naked fiber or the ending comes into close contact with a specialized structure, known as sensory- or *neuro-epithelium*, which is physiologically highly differentiated for the reception of a certain form of stimulus.

The nerve impulse generated by stimulation of a sense organ may evoke a reflex action which may or may not be accompanied by a sensation. As the impulse may be inhibited in some parts of the nervous system, it is possible that the stimulation of the sense organ may elicit neither a sensation nor an overt response.

It is customary to say that our sensations are generated by the activity of the cortical cells of the cerebral hemispheres. As we shall learn later on, certain areas of the cerebral cortex are closely associated with definite sense organs and with the sensations resulting from their stimulation (see Localization of Cerebral Functions). Whatever the relation between the brain and the mind may be, it is safe to say that without a corresponding activity on the part of certain brain cells, no sensation ever originates. In fact, when under pathologic conditions these brain areas are excited without the stimulation of the sense organ, a hallucination is experienced.

Their Importance.—On a previous occasion we have called the sense organs the alpha of all our physical, intellectual, and emotional life. The perceptible world is a mental world based upon information given us by the sense organs. Whether there is an external world over and above this perceptual world, and, if so, what its nature and properties are, is an insoluble problem.

High Degree of Irritability.—The sense organ possesses a high degree of irritability so that its threshold stimulus is much below that of the nerve fiber itself. To what almost unbelievable extent this development has taken place may be illustrated by the following examples: A ray of green light stimulating the eye, under the proper conditions, for but 1/8,000,000 second is perceptible. The amount of energy in this quantity of light is equal to that liberated by a weight of 1/300,000,000,000 ounce falling the distance of 1/25 inch. The irritability of the olfactory nerve is so keen that 1/13,000,000,000,000 ounce of mercaptan in a noseful of air can be detected—an amount far too small to be found by any chemical means. Male moths are attracted by compounds emanating from a single female at a distance of three miles.

Adequate Stimulus.—But this high degree of sensitivity of a sense organ is limited to only one kind of stimulus; as the organ gained in sensitivity to one form, it lost in power to respond to other forms of stimuli. For example, the eye is capable of being stimulated by mechanical or electrical stimulation, but the threshold for these is very high compared to that of light. Therefore, we may appropriately call light the adequate stimulus for the eye. The reason for this differentiation must be sought in the physical and chemical structure of the sensory epithelium. Depending upon their selectivity we may speak of the sense organs as chemoreceptors (chemical stimulation, e.g., taste, smell) photoreceptors (light), phonoreceptors (sound), tangoreceptors (pressure—touch).

Classification of Sense Organs.—It is convenient to group the sense organs into three classes:

1. The *exteroceptors* are stimulated by changes occurring outside of the body. In some of these, called the contact receptors (skin, tongue), the source of the stimulation is in direct contact with the sense organ; in others, the distance receptors (eyes, ears), the source is situated at some more remote point.

2. The *proprioceptors* (*proprio*, oneself). Most authors include here (a) the *kinesthetic* impressions derived from muscles, tendons, and joints and (b) the *labyrinthine* impressions from the semicircular canals of the inner ear. By these we become aware of the position and changes in the position of the body or some part of the body. The exteroceptors and proprioceptors enable us to adjust the body to the external environment.

3. The *interoceptors, or visceroceptors,* are found in the viscera (e.g., in the walls of the respiratory and digestive organs) and are stimulated by chemical and mechanical changes occurring in the viscera. By their aid the activities of the various internal organs are regulated to the needs of the body. The sensations obtained from their stimulations include: hunger, thirst, flushing, suffocation, nausea, sexual and distention sensation (stomach, urinary bladder).

Projection of Sensations.—As explained above, we generally consider sensations as more intimately connected with the brain than with any other part of the body. Yet when a sensation is experienced we are never conscious of our brain; indeed, subjectively we are ignorant of its existence. *The sensations are invariably projected, or referred, to one of two distinct locations: either to some part of our own body or to some part of the external world.* A visual sensation is projected, in a definite manner (see p. 564), to a luminous body in space from which the stimulus for the eyes proceeds. Even when the source of the stimulation lies within the eye itself (as, e.g., the floating specks frequently seen because of imperfections in the transparent media of the eye), we refer the resultant sensation to the outer world. In a similar manner we project the sensations of hearing, touch, smell, and taste.

On the other hand, the sensation of hunger is thought of as situated in a certain region of our own body, and is never projected externally. We associate the sensation of heat with the hot object, but the pain on touching this object is always referred to that part of the body affected by the heat. Other sensations are projected either to a definite part of, or diffusely to the whole, body; among these are thirst, nausea, sex, equilibrium, muscle sense (kinesthetic impressions from muscles and joints), fatigue, tickling, itching, and the sense of well-being or its reverse. The sensations of heat and cold are in this respect on the borderline. On touching a warm or cold object, we project the sensations externally; but if the air around us cools our feet, or if the face burns as in a fever, we think of our feet, or face, and not of the outer world.

A moment's reflection shows us the vital importance of properly projecting our sensations; indeed, most of our sensations, particularly those which are sometimes designated as the "special sensations," would be of no value to us unless proper projection accompanied them. In some instances, however, the projection is erroneous, in that the sensation is not properly referred to the source of the stimulation. This is especially true for the sensation of pain originating in the viscera; for example, the pain caused by occlusion of coronary vessels of the heart is "felt" by the patient as a radiating pain in the left arm and neck. These are spoken of as "referred" pains.

The Attributes of Sensations.—Sensations differ from each other in many respects which we may briefly describe:

1. MODALITY.—Sensations aroused by the stimulation of the various sense organs, such as the eye or ear, bear no resemblance to each

other; to most people it is inconceivable that the stimulation of the eyes could evoke the sensation, let us say, of taste or hearing. This characteristic of a sensation by which we distinguish it clearly from all other sensations is known as its modality. The modality of any sense organ is a fixed affair, because no matter how a sense organ is stimulated, the resultant sensation is always the same. For instance: when the eye is turned strongly nasalward and gentle pressure with a finger tip is exerted upon the eyeball, a luminous circle (known as a phosphene) is seen; this is exceedingly brilliant if the experiment be made in complete darkness. Incidentally we may note that visual impressions can be had without any physical light being present. It will be recalled that whether a motor nerve is stimulated chemically, mechanically, or electrically, the result is always the same; namely, a muscle contraction. These facts have been expressed in the *law of specific nerve energies,* according to which the result of the stimulation of a nerve is independent of the nature of the nerve, of the nature of the stimulation, and of the nature of the structure stimulated; it is solely determined by the structure to which the nerve impulse is carried and which is thrown into activity by the impulse.

That the nerve is an indifferent conductor of impulses and takes no part in determining the sensation or action resulting from its stimulation was very decisively demonstrated in nerve crossing experiments. Langley cut the lingual nerve and the cervical sympathetic nerve. The lingual nerve has, it will be recalled, vasodilator fibers (chorda tympani) for some of the salivary glands, while the cervical sympathetic supplies the vasoconstrictors. The cutting of a nerve causes the peripheral end to degenerate, but regeneration usually takes place, at least if the central and peripheral ends can come into communication with each other. Langley, after cutting the above-mentioned nerves, sutured the central end of the lingual onto the peripheral end of the cut cervical sympathetic nerve so that the regenerating lingual fibers followed the course of the old degenerating sympathetic fibers. When regeneration was complete, it was found that stimulation of the regenerated lingual nerve (which normally is the vasodilator) caused constriction of the blood vessels. Langley also sutured the central end of the cut cervical sympathetic onto the peripheral stump of the degenerated lingual nerve and, after the regeneration, stimulation of the cervical sympathetic caused vasodilation.

The result of the stimulation of a nerve is, therefore, independent of the nature of the nerve, but is determined by the organ or structure in which the nerve ends. Stimulation of the optic nerve always causes a sensation of light because this nerve ends, physiologically, in certain brain cells which, on becoming active, always affect our consciousness in such a manner that we are conscious of light. The auditory nerve ends in a different part of the brain, and, when these cells are aroused to activity, we experience a sensation of sound. Consequently, if these two nerves could be cut and crossed, after their regeneration we should hear the lightning and see the thunder.

If neither the sense organ nor its afferent nerve determines the result of the stimulation, then why do we have such highly differentiated organs as eyes and ears? These organs by their highly evolved structure have become exceedingly sensitive to one particular form of change in the environment and are normally not stimulated by any other environmental change. That is, the sense organs are specific and selective. By contrast, the sensory nerve leading from the sense organ is not specific; all impulses are fundamentally alike. The end organs (muscle, glands, sensory areas in the brain, etc.) are highly specific in their action. The greater the number of highly selective sense organs an animal is endowed with, the greater is its capacity for adjusting itself to its environment.

2. QUALITY.—Sensations of the same modality may differ in quality. Thus, we speak of a sound of high pitch, or low pitch; of a red or of green light. While we never confuse sensations of different modality, many people lack the power of discriminating between certain qualities of a sensation. For example, some individuals can not distinguish between red and green; and we have tone-deafness in the unmusical ear.

3. INTENSITY.—It is common knowledge that two sensations of the same quality may differ in intensity. We speak of a dark, or dull, red and of a bright red; the former sends much, and the latter, little red light into the eye. Sensations cannot be measured, but sensations of the same modality and quality may be compared as to their intensity; even this comparison is but qualitative, for while one visual sensation may be of greater intensity (brightness) than another, we cannot say that the first sensation is twice as great as the second. Although we cannot measure the intensity of a sensation, the strength of the stimulus (light, sound, pressure, etc.) can generally be stated quantitatively. Weber discovered a relationship between our ability to detect an increase or decrease in the intensity of a sensation and the

increase or decrease in the strength of the stimulus. This is known as *Weber's law* or the *psychophysical law*, which we may illustrate as follows:

A room illuminated by 100 candles will not appear any brighter to us if the illumination be increased by one-half of one candle; that is, we cannot distinguish between sensation caused by the stimulation by 100 candles and the sensation due to 100½ candles. But increasing the illumination to 101 candles enables most people to notice an increase. Again, if the original light is supplied by 200 candles it is necessary, in order that increase may be noticeable, to add not one but two candles. And to 1,000 candles 10 candles must be added. From this it is evident that *the least perceptible increase in the strength of the stimulus is a constant fraction* (1/100, 2/200, 10/1,000 = 1/100) *of the original stimulus.* This explains why a star emitting less than 1/100th more light than we receive from the bright sky is invisible in the daytime; and why it is dangerous, when the wind shield is covered with dust, to drive against the setting sun. The numerical values vary from one individual to another. For sight it is generally stated at 1/100 to 1/50; for hearing the ratio is 1/10 to 1/20; and for weight (pressure), 1/20 to 1/40. The law, however, does not apply to weak or very strong stimulation.

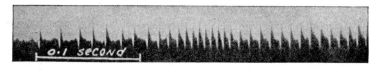

Fig. 226.—Impulses in a single nerve fiber from a frog's muscle spindle stimulated by stretching the muscle. The frequency of the waves increases with the amount of tension applied to the muscle, and then declines as the tension is constant. (Adrian, The Mechanism of Nervous Action, University of Pennsylvania Press.)

Whether a light appears bright or dim also depends upon previous stimulation, as can be readily demonstrated by a simple experiment. With the right eye shielded, look at a very bright light with the left eye; after a few seconds look with the left eye at a medium illuminated wall; the wall appears quite dark. On now closing the left and opening the right eye, the wall takes on a surprising brightness.

The stronger sensation gained from the stronger stimulation is not due to a greater intensity of the impulse, for we have learned that nerve fibers conduct according to the law of all or none. *The frequency of the nerve pulses passing along the fiber determines the intensity of the sensation* (p. 135). This was experimentally demonstrated by Adrian and others in the mechanical stimulation of a single afferent nerve fiber. In Fig. 226 we have the record of the action current evoked by the stretching of a muscle (stimulating the muscle spindle—see Muscle Sense). As the tension upon the muscle was increased (from the left to the middle of Fig. 226), the number of pulses ("spikes" in the tracing) per unit of time increased.

4. ADAPTATION.—In our study of muscles and motor nerves we learned that a constant (galvanic) current applied to a nerve causes a single contraction at the make of the current; during the flow of the current no stimulation occurs; i.e., no impulses are set up. We say that the nerve protoplasm adapts itself to the constant current very quickly. This also holds true, although to a lesser extent, for the stimulation of sense organs. For example: when the degree of stretching the muscle (and therefore the stimulation of the afferent nerve) in Fig. 226 reached a constant quantity (in the middle portion of the tracing), the periodicity of the pulses gradually decreased. The speed with which adaptation sets in differs in the various protoplasms. We are familiar with the fact that a slight bending of a hair causes a distinct sensation, but, if the hair is kept in this new position, the sensation disappears almost immediately. This is true for touch in general, as everyday experience teaches us. On the other hand, it is also a matter of common observation that constant stimulation of the retina is not followed by adaptation for a considerable length of time. Impulses generated by the stretching of a muscle or tendon (muscle sense, or proprioceptive impressions) show far less adaptation. When an individual has been sitting quietly for 10 or 15 minutes, he still knows the position of his feet.

5. EXTENSION.—Some sensations have the characteristic of extensiveness, i.e., we recognize that the source of the stimulation occupies a certain amount of space. This is especially true for the sensations of sight and of touch; muscle and to a certain extent temperature sensations must also be classed with the spatial senses; but the sense of smell is without this characteristic.

6. DURATION.—That a sensation occupies a certain length of time is self-evident. However, the sensation is not necessarily, if ever, coexistent with the stimulus. We have alreay seen that because of adaptation the duration of the sensation may be shorter than that of the stimulation. On the other hand, we shall learn in the following pages that the visual sensations may outlast the period of stimulation and thereby give rise to after-sensations.

7. AFFECTION.—It is doubtful whether a human being ever experiences a pure, simple sensation, for as soon as the presence of the stimulus has been made known to our consciousness, we clothe it with a number of impressions received simultaneously from other sense

organs and with the retained impressions of previous stimulations. It is customary, however, to speak of the agreeableness or disagreeableness of a sensation. The odor of a rose gives one pleasure, that of decaying meat is disagreeable. However, our so-called sensations never being perceived in their pure state, the individual is able to change the unpleasant affective result to an agreeable one, e.g., we learn to enjoy jazz or symphonic music, the bizarre in colors and patterns, and the previously objectionable odor of Limburger cheese. The affection associated with a sensation is therefore not inherent in the sensation.

I. SIGHT

The eye is a mechanism whereby the neuro-epithelium (retina) with which the afferent nerve endings are associated, can be stimulated by light energy. This stimulation gives us three impressions: light, color, and space. In order to obtain space sensations, i.e., the sensations of form, solidity, or perspective, a picture of the object sending the light into the eye must fall upon the retina. To bring this about is the object of nearly the whole structure which we call the eye; before treating of this we must review one or two points concerning the action of light.

Properties of Light.—The word "light" may be used in a subjective or in an objective sense. In the first sense we denote by it the sensation we experience when the retina is stimulated; by the objective sense we mean the ether vibrations which are capable of stimulating the retina. Ether vibrations travel with a velocity of about 186,000 miles per second. The vibrations, or waves, have various lengths; some are too short, others too long to affect the sensory surface; those that have power to do so have wave lengths between 0.00,076 mm. (392,000,000,000,000 waves per second) and 0.00,038 mm. (757,000,000,000,000 waves per second). The longest of these vibrations we call red and the shortest violet; all vibrations shorter than those indicated for the violet and longer than those for the red are invisible to us.

Refraction of Light.—The velocity with which light travels is uniform so long as the medium through which the light travels remains the same, and the waves then travel in straight lines. Let us suppose that a flat piece of glass (*xw*, Fig. 227) is placed in the path of the ray, *bc*. If the velocity of the light in the glass were the same as that in air, the ray would proceed straight onward to *d*. But, because of the physical and chemical differences between air and glass, the speed of the ether vibration is reduced, and, as a result of this reduction in speed, the ray is bent out of its straight course in such a manner that it is bent, or refracted, toward the normal. In Fig. 227, *xy* represents the surface of the glass; the ray, *bc*, strikes that surface at point *c*. At this point we draw a normal to the surface, the line, *ef*. The ray, *bc,* is bent at the point, *c,* so as to approach the normal, *ef,* and describes the course, *ch.* At the point, *h,* the ray strikes the other surface of the glass, *vw,* and enters the air. As the velocity of the light is now increased, the ray is refracted away from the normal

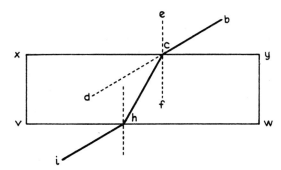

Fig. 227.—Diagram illustrating the refraction of light.

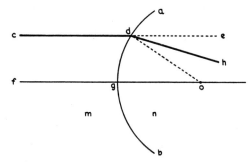

Fig. 228.—Diagram illustrating the refraction of light by a spherical surface.

erected at *h* upon the surface, *vw,* and describes the course, *hi.* The velocity of the light in the glass is less than that in air, consequently we say that the *optical density,* or *index of refraction,* of the glass is greater than that of air. We may generalize: *light in going from a rarer into a denser medium is refracted toward the normal,* and in going from a denser into a rarer medium it is bent from the normal. A ray of light normal to the surface suffers no refraction.

It is immaterial whether the refracting surface is a plane or a spherical surface. Suppose that *ab,* Fig. 228, is a segment of a glass sphere, *n,* to the left of which there is air, *m.* The ray of light, *cd,* strikes the spherical surface of the glass at *d*. As glass has a greater optical density than air, the ray will be refracted toward the normal. The normal to the surface, *ab*, at the point *d* is the radius of the sphere from its center of curvature, *o*, to the point, *d*. The ray would have proceeded to *e* if the glass had not been placed in its path, but now it is bent toward the normal, *do*, and describes the course, *dh*. The ray, *fg*, being normal to the surface, undergoes no refraction and continues through to *o*.

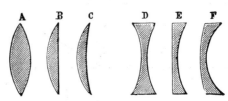

Fig. 229.—Lenses. *A*, biconvex; *B*, plano-convex; *C*, concavo-convex; *D*, biconcave; *E*, plano-concave; *F*, convexo-concave. (Ganot.)

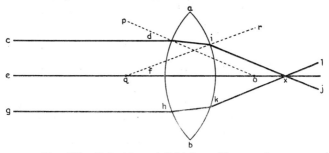

Fig. 230.—Refraction of light by a biconvex lens.

Lenses.—We can readily apply the above to lenses. We speak of spherical and cylindrical lenses. Spherical lenses are lenses whose surfaces are segments of spheres. We have two classes of spherical lenses: convex, or plus, lenses and concave, or minus, lenses, Fig. 229. The passage of light through the convex lens may be briefly described as follows: Let *ab*, Fig. 230, be a convex lens, and let *cd*, *ef*, and *gh* be three parallel rays of light. In reality all rays of light are divergent, but if the light comes from a great distance, the divergence is so small that it may be ignored and the rays may, therefore, be considered parallel. The ray, *cd*, striking the surface of the glass at *d* is refracted toward the normal, *op* (*o* being the center of curvature of the anterior surface of the lens); hence, it will describe the course, *di*. At *i* the ray strikes the posterior surface of the lens and on issuing from the glass into the air is bent away from the normal, *qr*, and describes the course, *ij*. Applying the same process of reasoning to the ray, *gh*, we see that its refracted ray is *kl*. The ray, *ef*, is normal to both the anterior and posterior surfaces (on it are located the centers of the two curvatures) and hence this ray will pass through without undergoing any refraction. From the diagram it will be noticed that these three rays after refraction cross at a common point, *x;* this point is called the *principal focus.*

If the light is situated closer to the lens, the rays are divergent and their point of crossing, on the other side of the lens, lies farther from the lens than *x*, the principal focus. Let *x*, Fig. 231, be the principal focus of the lens and let *a* be a point of light from which issue three rays of light; after refraction they cross at *b* which is called the *conjugate focus* of *a*. If the luminous point lies still closer to the lens, the rays are more divergent and the conjugate focus is situated still farther from the lens. It will be noticed that a convex lens is a gathering, or a converging, system; it brings, or tends to bring, the rays of light to a focus.

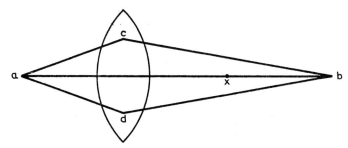

Fig. 231.—Illustrating conjugate foci.

The Diopter.—There are two factors that determine the refractive power of a lens: (*a*) the index of refraction of the lens and (*b*) the radius of curvature of the surfaces. As we have already stated refraction occurs when the light passes from one medium into another having a different optical density. The greater the difference is between the two media, the greater will be the bending of the light. Suppose that the optical density of lens *A* in Fig. 232 is 1.33, as compared with the density of air (1.00), and that its principal focus lies at *x*, say, two inches back of the lens. Lens *B* is similar to lens *A* in shape and size but its optical density is 1.43. The parallel rays falling upon it will be bent more and consequently the principal focus will lie closer to the lens, say, at *y*, one inch back of the lens. Hence, lens *B* is ''stronger'' that is, has a greater refractive power (and also magnifying power) than *A*.

Again, let us suppose we have two lenses made of the same kind of glass and therefore having the same optical density, but one of them,

A in Fig. 233, has surfaces that are segments of larger spheres than the surfaces of the other lens, *B*. More tersely stated, the radii of the curvatures of *B* are shorter than those of *A*. When parallel rays fall upon these lenses, it has been found that the principal focus of *B* lies nearer to the lens than that of *A;* that is, the refractive power of *B* is greater than that of *A*. Evidently, the refractive power of a lens varies inversely as the radius of curvature.

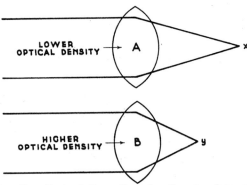

Fig. 232.—Showing the effect of the optical density of a lens on its refracting power.

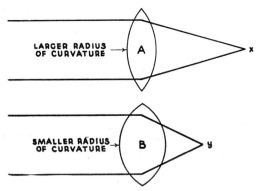

Fig. 233.—Showing the effect of the radius of curvature of a lens on its refracting power.

The strength of a lens is measured in terms of the focal distance. If a lens has the power to focus parallel rays at a point 100 cm. back of the lens, its focal length (distance between the principal focus and the lens) is 100 cm.; such a lens is said to have one *diopter* refractive power. A lens with a focal distance of 25 cm. has 100/25, or 4, diopters refractive power; the power in diopters may, therefore, be found by dividing 100 by the focal length in centimeters.

Images.—When the light from an object falls upon a convex lens and a screen is placed at the proper distance on the other side of the lens, a picture of the object will be thrown upon the screen; this image, as illustrated in Fig. 234, is real and inverted. It will be noticed that we have drawn rays of light from the two extremities of the object (*a* and *b*), and passed them straight through the center of the lens, *n;* the point *n* is called the *nodal point,* which may be defined as a point in an optical system of such a nature that a ray of light passes through it without refraction.* The eye behaves like a simple convex lens, and the images of the objects we look at are therefore inverted.

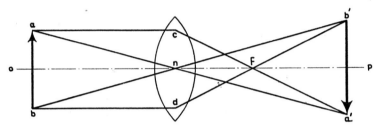

Fig. 234.—Illustrating the formation of an image by a convex lens.

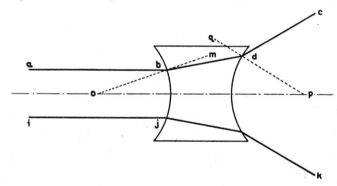

Fig. 235.—Refraction by a concave lens.

Concave lenses are frequently used in spectacles. The ray, *ab,* Fig. 235, striking the surface of the glass at *b,* is bent toward the normal, *om,* and therefore describes the course, *bd.* On entering the air at *d,* the ray is bent away from the normal, *pq,* and describes the course, *de.* In a similar manner, the ray, *ij,* is refracted so that it travels the course, *jk.* From this it is evident that a concave lens is a dispersing system; it scatters the light, and no real images can be formed.

Anatomy of the Eye.—The eyeball is composed of three coats surrounding the transparent media through which the light travels to

*In reality there are two nodal points, but they are situated so close together that, for practical purposes, they may be regarded as one.

reach the endings of the optic nerve. The outer coat, Fig. 236, *sc,* is the sclera, or sclerotic coat; it forms the white of the eye, and is composed of a tough and resistant material called keratin; hence this coat serves well to protect and give shape to the eye. The choroid forms the middle coat, *ch;* it is a vascular coat and its function is to supply nourishment. The innermost coat of the eye, called the retina, *r,* is a nervous coat in which the fibers of the optic nerve, *op. n.,* have their endings. It is the functional coat of the eye upon which the images of the objects must be thrown in order that we shall see them.

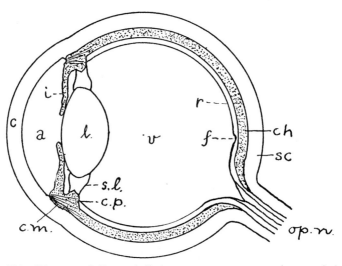

Fig. 236.—Diagram of the eyeball: *c,* cornea; *a,* aqueous humor; *l,* lens; *v,* vitreous humor; *sc,* sclerotic coat; *ch,* choroid coat; *r,* retina; *f,* fovea centralis; *i,* iris; *s.l.,* suspensory ligaments; *c.p.,* ciliary process; *c.m.,* ciliary muscles; *op.n.,* optic nerve.

The anterior portion of the sclera is modified so as to be transparent, forming the glassy part of the eye, the cornea, *c.* Back of this is found a transparent fluidlike medium, the aqueous humor, *a,* posterior to which lies the crystalline lens, *l.* Between the lens and the retina there lies a transparent, jellylike substance, known as the vitreous humor, *v.* These four media are transparent, and, as their optical densities are greater than that of air, the light, on passing into the eye and from one medium of the eye to another, is bent to a greater or lesser extent. When these media lose their transparency, as in cataract of the lens, vision is damaged or altogether destroyed.

In order that an individual may see an object, the image of the object must fall upon the retina. If the focus is situated in front of or behind the retina, the image is blurred and vision indistinct.

Now, we have learned that objects situated at different distances from a lens have their foci also at different points back of the lens; the nearer the object is situated toward the lens, the farther back of the lens the focus lies. The question is, what objects are focused upon the retina? The answer will depend on the condition of the eye, for not all eyes are the same in this respect. Let us first treat of the eye in what we may, for the present, call the normal condition.

The Emmetropic Eye.—Suppose an individual having so-called normal eyes stands near a window, and has his eyes closed; the eyes are then at rest. On opening them he immediately and without any effort sees the buildings across the street clearly and distinctly, but not the specks on the window pane. From this we must conclude that distant objects (twenty or more feet removed) are focused upon the retina of the normal eye, when this eye is in the resting condition. Such an eye is called an *emmetropic eye* and may be defined as *the eye in which the posterior principal focus* (Fig. 237, *c*) *lies upon the retina when the eye is at rest.* When the far object, sending parallel rays, is focused upon the retina, an object, *a*, nearer than 20 feet sends divergent rays and is focused back of the retina, *b*, and cannot be seen distinctly.

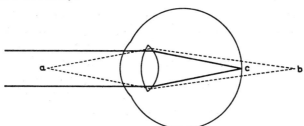

Fig. 237.—The emmetropic eye at rest.

Accommodation.—But we know that the individual with emmetropic eyes can see near objects, if he makes an effort; that is, by some sort of a process he can bring the focus, Fig. 237, *b*, of the near object, *a*, upon his retina. The process by which this is accomplished is called accommodation. To understand how this is brought about we must refer to another point in the anatomy of the eye. From Fig. 236 it will be noticed that anteriorly the choroid coat, *ch*, is enlarged so as to form two important structures, one, the iris, *i*, and the other, the ciliary processes, *cp*. The lens is encircled by about 70 of these thumblike processes. From these processes proceed little cords, suspensory ligaments, *sl*, which are attached to the periphery of the lens, *l*. In this manner the lens is held in position in the more or less fluid contents of the eye. The humors are normally under a certain amount of pressure (intraocular pressure) which, being exerted upon the retina and choroid, forces the ciliary processes apart. This causes tension to be exerted upon the suspensory ligaments which, in turn, pull upon the periphery of the lens. The lens being plastic, the traction exerted by the ligaments flattens it so that its radius of curvature is increased and its refractive power decreased; this is the condition of the lens when the eye is at rest, and, if the eye is emmetropic, the vision is as indicated in Fig. 237.

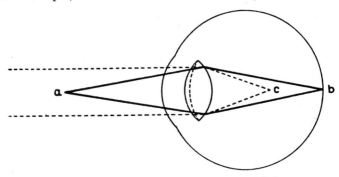

Fig. 238.—The emmetropic eye in accommodation.

From the sclerotic coat near its junction with the cornea there proceed delicate muscle fibers, *cm*, Fig. 236; the other end of these fibers is imbedded in the choroid coat. When these ciliary muscles contract, the choroid coat is drawn forward. This allows the ciliary processes to approach each other and thereby relaxes the suspensory ligaments; then the lens, by virtue of its elasticity, assumes a more spherical form, that is, its radius of curvature is decreased. The eye is then said to be in the accommodated condition. Now, it will be recalled that as the radius of curvature is decreased, the refractive power of the lens is increased. This change in the focusing power we can readily understand by comparing Figs. 237 and 238. In Fig. 237 the eye is at rest and the parallel rays from the distant object focus upon the retina, *c*, while divergent rays from a near object, *a*, focus back of the retina, *b*. When the eye is accommodated, Fig. 238, the anterior surface of the lens has a shorter radius of curvature and a greater refractive power; hence the near object, *a*, has its focus upon the retina, *b*, and is seen distinctly; but the far object, sending parallel rays, is focused in front of the retina, at *c*, and is therefore not seen distinctly.

FAR AND NEAR POINT.—The accommodative power of the eye has a limit; when this limit is reached, the nearest object which is focused upon the retina is called the near point of vision. The far point is the point which the eye sees without accommodation. For the emmetropic eye the far point is infinity (anything beyond twenty feet); the near point is, let us say, six inches.

The ciliary muscles are therefore constantly at work during near vision. In people engaged in near work there are few muscles of the body so constantly used as the ciliary muscles; to preserve their full activity, frequent periods of rest should be allowed. These muscles receive their impulses over the oculomotor, or third cranial, nerve. This nerve is paralyzed by atropin which is sometimes instilled into the eye in order to put it in the resting condition.

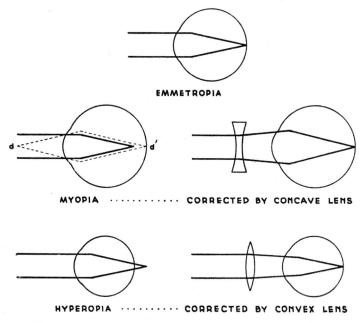

Fig. 239.—Illustrating the optical defect in myopia and in hyperopia and the correction by concave and convex lenses, respectively.

PRESBYOPIA.—The power to accommodate depends, as can be gathered from the above description, upon the elasticity of the lens; the greater the elasticity is, the greater will be the power of accommodation and the closer the near point of vision is situated to the eye. With increasing years the elasticity of the lens gradually decreases, and hence in old age the power of accommodation may be very limited; the near point gradually recedes and the individual has to hold the book or paper farther from his eyes; to this condition the term *presbyopia* (sight of old age) is applied. The loss of the elasticity of the lens (lenticular sclerosis) begins early in life, for it can already be detected at the age of twelve or fourteen, but in the emmetropic eye it gives little or no trouble until the age of forty to forty-five. The waning accommodative power can be supplemented by properly fitted convex glasses.

MYOPIA.—Not all eyes are emmetropic; many are either myopic or hyperopic. Myopia, short-sight, or near-sight, is that condition of the eye in which the posterior principal focus falls in front of the retina, Fig. 239. In myopia, when the eye is at rest, not the far but the relatively near object, d, is focused at d', upon the retina. The far point of vision is therefore nearer than infinity (20 feet) and the near point is nearer than six inches. The cause of myopia is generally an elongation of the eyeball. Weakness of the coats of the eyeball (malnutrition), together with excessive accommodative effort, due to the reading of fine print or to bad illumination, must be regarded as frequent causes of myopia.

From Fig. 239 it can readily be seen that the refractive power of the eye is too great with respect to the position occupied by the retina. Hence, to correct this defect the refractive power must be decreased; or, we may say, the focusing of the light must be delayed. This can be brought about by causing the light entering the eye to be more divergent; as we have learned, a concave lens has this effect.

HYPEROPIA (hypermetropia, long-sight, or far-sight) is generally due to a shortening of the eyeball; in this case the posterior principal focus lies back of the retina, Fig. 239, when the eye is at rest. In this condition no rays of light are focused on the retina and the individual sees nothing distinctly. By accommodation the parallel rays can be brought to a focus upon the retina; in fact, to see anything at all, far or near, the hyperope must always accommodate. The far point of vision for the hyperopic eye does not exist and the near point lies farther than six inches. To correct this defect, the refractive power of the eye must be increased by a convex lens, which causes the parallel rays to be more or less converged before they enter the eye, and therefore to come to a focus sooner.

ASTIGMATISM.—A defect more common and more trying than myopia or hyperopia is astigmatism. So far we have regarded the refracting surfaces of the eye as segments of spheres, but this condition seldom exists. In very many eyes one of the surfaces, let us say the anterior surface of the cornea, has a shape like the back of the bowl of a spoon, that is, the various meridians do not have the same radii of curvature. Suppose the cornea having this shape is placed so as to correspond in position to the spoon with the handle held horizontally. In this position the vertical meridian has a shorter radius of curvature, and hence a greater refractive power, than the horizontal meridian. A vertical beam of light (that is, a beam of light coming

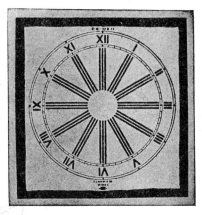

Fig. 240.—Illustration of chart for detecting astigmatism.

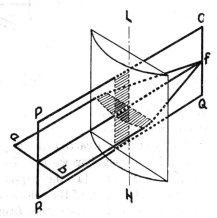

Fig. 241.—Refraction of light by a convex cylindrical lens.

through a vertical slit of extreme narrowness) falling upon such a cornea is focused sooner than a horizontal ray. If the individual looks at radiating lines, Fig. 240, one set is sharply focused and is seen clearly; another set is focused either in front or back of the retina and is seen very indistinctly. In other words, the individual is emmetropic in one plane and myopic or hyperopic in the plane at right angles to this.

In case the difference between the radii of curvature of the meridians is very slight, it does not trouble the individual; this is called physiologic astigmatism. But if the error is great, it seriously interferes with good vision and the defect ought to be corrected, especially if the person is engaged in near work. This is done by cylindrical lenses. Suppose from a cylinder of glass we cut a section parallel with the axis of the cylinder; we obtain a convex cylindrical lens *LH* in Fig. 241. A ray of light, *PR*, parallel with the axis, *LH*, passes straight through without any refraction, *OQ*; but a ray, *ab*, at right angles to the axis is focused at, say, *f*.

The Iris.—The iris, Fig. 236, *i*, is a very thin membrane suspended in front of the lens. It contains pigment granules by which it is rendered opaque. Generally blue at birth, the iris may gradually acquire a darker color—gray, green, or brown—according to the amount of pigment deposited in it. The central aperture, known as the pupil, allows the light to pass through the lens; the iris functions as the diaphragm, or stop, in optical instruments.

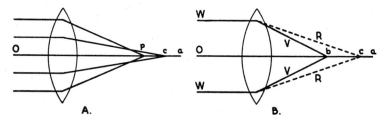

Fig. 242.—*A*, illustrates spherical aberration; *B*, chromatic aberration. (Pearce and Macleod: Physiology, The C. V. Mosby Co.)

There are two sets of muscles in the iris, the circular, or sphincter, muscles, and the radial fibers. The circular fibers run parallel with the rim of the iris, and by their contraction the pupil is constricted. By observing the eyes of our neighbor we can detect two changes taking place during accommodation: (1) the pupils decrease in size, and (2) the eyes converge. The object of the constriction of the pupil lies in the lessening of spherical aberration (*ab*, from; *erro*, to wander). All the rays entering the eye from the object looked at do not focus properly upon the retina. In Fig. 242, *A*, parallel rays fall upon the lens; it will be noticed that the peripheral rays (those nearest the edge of the lens) focus before the more central rays. This defect, known as *spherical aberration*, causes a blurring of the image upon the retina and thereby leads to indistinct vision. By its opacity the iris cuts off some of the peripheral rays and thus lessens the aberration. It can be readily demonstrated that the more divergent are the rays of light entering the eye, the greater is the spherical aber-ration; hence, it is very necessary that during near vision the pupil be reduced in size. The neuromuscular machinery of the eye is so constituted that whenever an impulse is sent to the ciliary muscles for accommodation, an impulse is also brought to the sphincter muscles of the iris for pupil constriction.

Pupil Reflex.—Another condition affecting the size of the pupil is the amount of light entering the eye. This can readily be seen by observing the pupil of an individual passing from a dark to a light room. The constriction brought about in this manner is called the photo-pupil reflex. The object of this reflex is to shield the eye from too great and sudden illumination, and the retina from over-stimulation. The center for the light reflex is located in the mid-brain and the motor nerve fibers for the sphincter muscle leave the midbrain with the third cranial nerve.

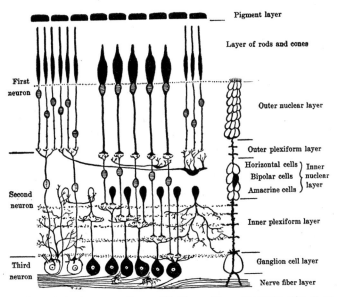

Fig. 243.—Plan of the human retina. (Mettler: Neuroanatomy, The C. V. Mosby Co.)

Atropine (belladonna) paralyzes the endings of the third cranial nerve in the iris and hence it causes pupil dilation. A drug of this sort is called a mydriatic. Another class of drugs, the myotics, cause great pupil constriction; among these are opium and morphine which stimulate the sphincter iridis (pinhole pupil). In the upper region of the spinal cord is a pupil-dilating center—the ciliospinal center; from this center nerve fibers pass by way of the cervical sympathetic to the radial muscle fibers. The ciliospinal center is stimulated by certain con-ditions, among which we may mention great pain, fear, muscular exertion, and great venosity of blood (as in dyspnea and asphyxiation). This last is taken advantage of in gauging the depth of chloroform anesthesia, for when a patient is not getting a sufficient amount of air, or circulatory failure threatens, the excessive carbon dioxide in the blood stimulates the ciliospinal center and the pupils dilate.

The retina, the sensitive coat of the eye, is composed of a layer of neuro-epithelium. Some authors designate this as the first layer of neurons, as in Fig. 243. This is followed successively by the second and by the third layer of neurons.

The neuro-epithelial cells lying next to the choroid have their outer ends highly modified to form the rods and cones. The axons of the third layer of neurons have their cell bodies in the ganglionic layer and proceed to form the nerve fiber layer of the retina. These fibers border on the vitreous humor and leave the eyeball at the blind spot as the optic nerve, Fig. 236, *op.n.*, and proceed to the brain. The bipolar cells (Fig. 243), which constitute the second layer of neurons, are intercalated between the neuro-epithelium and the ganglionic

Fig. 244.—To demonstrate the blind spot.

neurons. The rods and cones are the retinal structures stimulated by light; the impulse thereby generated passes through the bipolar neurons to the neurons of the ganglionic layer. By the axons of these iast cells the impulses are carried to the tween- and midbrain. That the rods and cones are the ultimate elements of sight upon which the light plays may be gathered from the following:

1. THE BLIND SPOT.—Where the optic nerve leaves the eyeball, Fig. 236, there are no rods and cones, and here sight is absent; this forms the *blind spot* of the eye, and can be demonstrated by means of Fig. 244. Hold the page about twelve inches from the right eye, having the left eye closed. Look at the cross; the circle will be seen by indirect vision. On bringing the book a little closer to or a little farther from the face, at a certain distance the circle disappears from view because its image now falls upon the blind spot. Incidentally we may call attention to the great difference between nerve fibers and the receptors. There are more nerve fibers in the blind spot than anywhere else in the retina, but the light falling upon them is incapable of stimulating them; it is only when the light falls upon the specially constructed neuro-epithelium, the rods and concs, that a nerve impulse is generated.

2. THE FOVEA.—There is one small area of the retina in which the rods and cones, especially the latter, are more numerous than in any other part of the retina. This is called the *yellow spot* (macula lutea); its central depression, known as the fovea centralis, *f,* Fig. 236, is formed by slender and very closely packed cones, the rods being absent. This part of the retina has the keenest vision (see next paragraph).

Resolving Power.—By this is meant the ability to discern two discrete luminous bodies as two. On a black surface two white dots, two millimeters apart, are readily recognized as two points when the observer stands three or four feet away. But when this distance is increased to, let us say, ten or twelve feet the two points fuse into one. The basis for this resolving power is generally found in the dimensions of the visual elements (the rods and cones); to explain this we may use Fig. 245. It will be recalled that a ray of light going

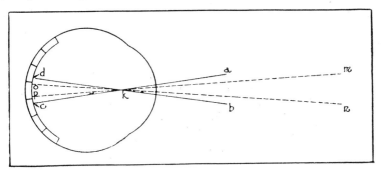

Fig. 245.—Diagram to illustrate visual acuity (see text).

through the nodal point, *k,* of the eye undergoes no refraction. Let *a* and *b* be the two luminous points which have their foci at *c* and *d,* respectively. It is held that, if these two foci, or images, fall upon two discrete cones separated by a third and unstimulated cone, the two retinal images call forth in the brain two discrete sensations, i.e., the individual sees *a* and *b* as two separate objects. If now the points are placed farther from the eye, at *m* and *n,* the foci, *o* and *p,* fall either upon two neighboring cones or upon a single cone; in this case the two points are seen as one object. As the cones are more slender and more densely packed in the fovea than anywhere else, to see the details of an object we always turn our eyes in such a manner that the images of the object fall upon the foveas.

Visual Acuity.—The ability to distinguish the details of an object, for instance, printed letters placed at 20 feet (infinity) from the observer, measures the visual acuity. At a distance of 20 feet an emmetrope can read letters of a certain size; if they are smaller, he is not able to recognize them. Instead of having clear cut images of the letters upon his retina, a person with hyperopia, myopia, or astigmatism has blurred images; this reduces his resolving power, and, therefore, the smallest letters which an emmetrope can read at a distance of 20 feet are too small for the defective eye to decipher. Let us suppose that the smallest letters he can read are those which a normal eye reads at 40 feet; his visual acuity is then said to be 20/40.

Field of Vision.—A considerable part of the periphery of the retina is not utilized because, due to the configuration of the face (nose, eyebrows, etc.), the images of external objects cannot be cast upon it. The total area of the retina upon which images can be thrown is known as the visual field; within this the visual acuity, or resolving power, progressively decreases as we pass from the fovea to the periphery. Objects having their foci outside of the fovea are seen indirectly and indistinctly.

Fig. 246.—An optogram, or retinal picture, of a window, caused by the bleaching of the rhodopsin.

Stimulation of the Retina.—When light falls upon the retina some change must be produced in the sensitive rods and cones in order that a nerve impulse shall be generated and carried to the brain. Many changes are known. In the outer portions of the rods there is present a reddish pigment, *rhodopsin,* or visual purple, which is bleached when exposed to light and has its color restored in the absence of light. It will be noticed that the eye takes on the nature of a photographic camera, not only in its physical properties of transmitting and focusing the light, but also in that it responds to the light like the photographic film by changes in its chemical composition —see Fig. 246.

When a beam of light is thrown upon the retina of a freshly excised eye and a galvanometer is properly affixed, an action current is set up showing that a nerve impulse has been formed. The reader will recall that according to the present view, the nerve impulse is a depolarization of the nerve fiber. How the light causes this depolarization is still a debated matter. It seems most likely that on stimulation of the retina a photochemical change takes place; the chemical compound thereby produced brings about the depolarization. Some hold that the bleaching of the rhodopsin (a chemical change) may play this part; but it is generally believed that this compound is not necessary for ordinary vision. The reasons for this will be discussed in the next paragraph.

Daylight and Twilight Visions.—On stepping from the bright sunlight of the street into a dimly illuminated room we are unable at first to see objects even as large as human beings. Upon remaining in the dim light for a few minutes, we gradually begin to discern the objects about us. On now re-entering the brightly lighted street we are dazzled and for a few seconds vision is very poor; but recovery sets in quite speedily. Our eye is a double organ; one for seeing in bright light and the other, in dim light. The vision in bright light is called *photopia,* or daylight vision; the other is known as *scotopia* (*scotos,* darkness), or twilight vision. These two visions differ in the following respects:

1. In photopic vision the greatest sensitivity of the retina is found in the fovea centralis; in scotopic vision the fovea is blind for all practical purposes, and the retinal area of greatest irritability lies some distance from the fovea. The reader can readily verify this by looking at a very faint star. On looking directly at it (foveal vision) the star is invisible but on shifting the gaze a little to one side of the star, so that its image falls upon an extrafoveal portion of the retina, it is readily perceived.

2. In photopia all colors are readily discernible; in scotopia the eye is totally color-blind. This may be proved by observing the colored wall paper, rug, or flower garden, at early dawn. The objects and patterns are recognized, but only as grays of various intensities; no colors are seen.

3. In the above observation, red objects are not seen at all, not even as gray; the scotopic eye is completely blind to this light.

The Duplicity Theory.—These notable differences between photopic and scotopic vision are explicable only on the assumption that in the retina there are two distinct neural machineries, one of which operates in bright light and the other, in dim light. According to the *duplicity theory of vision,* the apparatus for photopia is found in the cones and that for scotopia, in the rods of the retina. It is usually held that visual purple is found only in the rods, and not in the cones. It will also be recalled that the fovea contains only cones, and that the farther we proceed from the fovea, the greater the number of rods in proportion to the cones. According to the above theory, the bleaching of the rhodopsin is indispensable for the stimulation of the rods. Let us see how the behavior of rhodopsin can explain the differences between daylight and twilight vision.

1. As the fovea contains no rods and therefore no rhodopsin, scotopic vision at the fovea is an impossibility. At a certain distance from the fovea the retina has the greatest concentration of rods and therefore the greatest sensitivity in dim light.

2. It is commonly held that color vision is mediated by the cones, not by the rods. This idea is based upon the observation that our ability to distinguish between the different colors is most acute in the fovea where the cones are most abundant. When lights of various colors are thrown upon the outlying portions of the retina they are seen as colorless; i.e., we are color-blind with the peripheral retina; here the cones are very scarce or entirely absent, although rods are present. According to the duplicity theory scotopia is rod vision and therefore colorless.

3. Rhodopsin, we have learned, is bleached by light. But, like the photographic film, it is not affected by red light and hence, according to the theory, the longest wave lengths of light cannot be seen by the scotopic eye.

Dark Adaptation.—Rhodopsin is altogether bleached by bright light, and it takes time to restore it; hence it can readily be understood why we are temporarily blind on going from a brightly to a very dimly illuminated room. Dark adaptation means a regeneration of the visual purple by which the irritability of the retina is tremendously increased so that a feeble light, which previously made no impression, is now able to set up retinal impulses. V. Kries estimated the increase of retinal sensitivity in dark adaptation to be 270,000 times that present at bright noonday.

While man has both photopic and scotopic vision, some animals have only one or the other. It is for this reason that chickens go to roost at sundown and that owls fly at night. In certain pathologic conditions a person loses the power of dark adaptation; he is then more or less unable to find his way in fairly dim light. This condition is known as night blindness, or nyctalopia. It occurs frequently in people subsisting on an insufficient and monotonous diet. On page 461 we discussed how the administration of foods rich in vitamin A restores the power of dark adaptation. It is held that rhodopsin, upon which night vision depends, is formed by the union of vitamin A with a protein.

Range of Operation.—The eye excels all man-made instruments not only in its sensitiveness to minute disturbances (stimuli), but also in the range over which it is able to function. Every recording or measuring apparatus has its range of operation; we do not weigh diamonds on hay-scales, nor do we register the heat of an electric furnace with a household thermometer. The human eye can function over a range of light intensities varying from the light received from a star of the sixth magnitude to that of full sunlight reflected from a white surface. If the intensity of the former is one, that of the latter is represented by ten billion. While the iris by its constriction is able to reduce somewhat the intensity of the light striking the retina, we owe this enormous range of the eye largely to the two-fold mechanism of the retina above discussed.

The Positive After-Image.—The length of time a stimulus must act in order to call forth a sensation is exceedingly short. An electric spark, of sufficient intensity, lasting only 1/8,000,000 second is visible. But the sensation experienced lasts a great deal longer than this, as the following experiment shows. The eyes having been rested in a dark room for several minutes, let the individual turn on the electric light for a fraction of a second, while his gaze is directed toward the frosted lamp shade. In the succeeding darkness he experiences a reproduction of the visual impression in which many of the details can be recognized. This is known as the positive after-image and demonstrates that our sensations continue to exist after the cessation of the stimulation.

Upon the existence of the after-image is based the fact that we may experience a uniform (steady) sensation although the photic stimulation of the retina is intermittent. When in the dark a live coal is twirled through the air, we see a series of glowing lines. If no positive after-image existed, the live coal would be seen only in the place it actually occupied at any given moment and the light would not appear as a line but as a moving point. The positive after-image ordinarily lasts only a fraction of a second, and, therefore, in order to produce the above-described results, the spark has to be moved with a certain velocity. Upon this principle are based many other phenomena we are acquainted with, such as the motion pictures. The positive after-image is always seen in the same color as the original.

Colors.—Colors are subjective phenomena, that is, they are changes in our consciousness and have no objective existence. What corresponds in the outer world to the color sensations, and by which the sensations are generally produced, are the ether vibrations of various wave lengths. When ether vibrations having a wave length of about 0.00,076 mm. strike the retina, they set up definite changes which create nerve impulses; these impulses arouse the activity of certain brain cells which in some way we interpret as "red." And so for the other wave lengths; each one produces its own specific result in our consciousness. By the mixing of two or more colors (wave lengths of light) other color sensations may be produced. For example, on a color wheel a disk composed of a red and of a green sector is rapidly rotated. Because of the positive after-image there is a physiologic fusion of the red and green and as a result we experience an entirely new sensation, that of yellow.

COMPLEMENTARY COLORS.—It is also possible to mix two colors so as to produce a sensation of white. Such colors are called complementary, e.g., red and greenish blue; yellow and indigo (blue); and violet and greenish yellow.

NEGATIVE AFTER-IMAGE.—If a person looks intently for several seconds at a small yellow card and then at a white sheet of paper, he sees a reproduction of the card in the color complementary to yellow, that is, blue; this is the negative after-image. If in this experiment a sheet of yellow paper be substituted for the white, the individual will discover that the area of the retina previously stimulated by the small yellow square is now yellow-blind. By similar experiments it can readily be shown that black is the negative after-image of white, and white, of black. This phenomenon is also known as successive contrast.

SIMULTANEOUS CONTRAST.—If a narrow strip of gray paper be laid on a sheet of yellow paper and the whole covered by a piece of tissue paper, the gray strip appears in the complementary color, that is, blue.

COLOR BLINDNESS.—It was stated that by mixing two or more colors we were able to produce new sensations. Now, it can readily be demonstrated that all the color sensations that a normal individual can experience may be produced by the proper mixing of the three primary colors, namely, red, green, and blue. For this reason the normal color vision is called trichromatic color vision. For color-blind individuals all the color sensations can be produced by the proper mixing of but two colors and, hence, they have dichromatic color vision. From 2 to 4 per cent of men, and about 0.2 per cent of women are color-blind. The most common form of color blindness is the red-green blindness. The red-blind or green-blind person has more or less difficulty in distinguishing between red and green. As these are the colors used for danger and safety signals, respectively, in traffic on land and sea, it is of great importance that pilots and drivers be examined for color blindness. The methods generally employed for this consist in the matching of two or three standard colors, green, purple, and red; this method was devised by the Swedish physiologist, Holmgren. From a box of skeins of wool of many colors the examinee selects those that match a standard test-skein.

THEORIES OF COLOR VISION.—Scores of theories have been formulated to explain the various phenomena of color vision, such as negative after-images, color mixing, complementary colors, color blindness, etc. As they are all highly involved and as none of them is entirely satisfactory, we shall limit our discussion to a very brief statement of Hering's theory.

Hering's theory postulates the existence in the visual apparatus of three chemical compounds: the red-green, the yellow-blue, and the white-black substance. The reader will please note that while the name is, in each case, compound, the element must be regarded as a single substance. The first and the second of these compounds can be catabolized by ether vibrations of a certain limited range of wave lengths (color) and anabolized by another; the third element is catabolized by all wave lengths of light and anabolized in the absence of light. Let us call these three compounds, R-G, Y-B, and W-B. The results of the catabolism and anabolism can be learned from the following scheme:

COMPOUND	CATABOLIZED BY VIBRATIONS	ANABOLIZED BY VIBRATIONS	SENSATION PRODUCED
R-G	0.00076 mm.	0.00050	Red Green
Y-B	0.00059 mm.	0.00044	Yellow Blue
W-B	By all vibrations	In darkness	White Black

Let us see how Hering's theory attempts to explain color fatigue and negative after-images. The individual has been looking at a square of yellow paper. The Y-B compound in that part of the retina upon which the image of the square fell is greatly decomposed and finally can undergo no further catabolism; this is why the individual, now looking at a large sheet of yellow paper, sees a white or exceedingly pale yellow square on the very intense yellow background. If instead of a sheet of yellow paper, a white sheet is looked at, the yellow light (0.00,059 mm.) cannot cause any decomposition of the Y-B compound, but the blue light (0.00,044 mm.) causes an intense anabolism; the result is a blue after-image.

Projection.—We have become acquainted with the fact that our visual sensations are projected out of the body. This projection takes

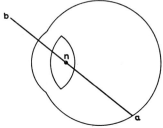

Fig. 247.—Diagram illustrating the law of projection. *a*, point of retina stimulated; *n*, nodal point; *ab*, line of projection.

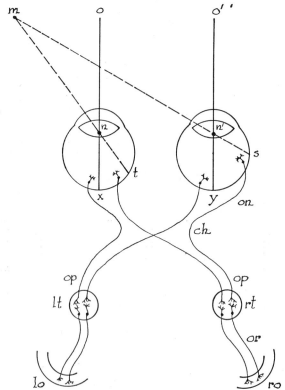

Fig. 248.—Diagram to illustrate the semidecussation of the optic nerve fibers, *on*, at the chiasma, *ch*. Note that the fibers from the nasal half of the left retina and those from the temporal half of the right retina pass by the optic tract, *op*, to the right thalamus, *rt*, of the tween-brain and are thence relayed by the fibers of the optic radiation, *or*, to the occipital lobe, *ro*, of the right cerebral hemisphere. The object of regard, *m*, has its images, *t*, and *s*, on corresponding halves of the two retinas; *x* and *y*, the foveas; *n* and *n'*, the nodal points; *xno* and *yn' o'*, the visual axes.

place in a definite manner, as the following simple experiment indicates. When the tip of the finger is pressed upon the sclerotic coat on the nasal side of the pupil, a circular luminous field, called a phosphene, is seen; this phosphene seems to be situated on the temporal side. When the pressure is applied to the temporal side of the eyeball, the phosphene is situated on the nasal side. The pressure of the finger mechanically stimulates the retina at, say, a in Fig. 247, and the sensation produced is projected in the direction of the line joining a with n, the nodal point; hence the object causing the stimulation appears to be situated at b. By this projection the inverted images on the retina are reinverted, and we see things right side up.

In viewing an object with both eyes, we project the sensation from the bridge of the nose, as the following experiment demonstrates. In a card prick two pinholes as far apart as the distance between the pupils of the eyes. On placing the card close to the face and looking at the bright sky, or lamp shade, only one luminous circle is seen and this appears to be situated in the median plane of the body.

How we acquired this power of projecting our visual impressions is a debated matter. Some hold that it is an inborn faculty (the intuitive, or nativistic, theory); each point on the retina has a definite space value, up or down, to the right or to the left. On the other hand, the empiricists maintain that each individual must learn for himself to associate the stimulation of a certain point of the retina with the definite position in space of the stimulating object. In this learning the proprioceptive impulses from the muscles by which the eyes are moved are of major importance. In Fig. 248, let x and y represent the two foveas; the images of the object m fall upon the retinas at s and t; m is seen indirectly and more or less indistinctly. To see it clearly the eyes must be turned to the left so that the foveas will correspond with the t and s in the respective eyes. By means of the tension of the muscles used for this, the individual learns to associate the retinal points, t and s, with the point in space, m.

Single Vision With Two Eyes.—As we have two eyes, each with its own image, and consequently both optic nerves carrying impulses, we rightfully ask why, under ordinary circumstances, we see the object looked at as a single and not as a double object. We said "under ordinary circumstances" for that we can see double (diplopia) is easily demonstrated. While looking at a certain object with both eyes and seeing it single, with the finger press one eyeball out of its natural position; double vision results. But even without thus influencing the eyes, in the ordinary manner of looking we constantly see certain things double. Hold a finger about 8 inches, and a pencil, say, 20 inches, from the face. Look at the pencil; the finger is seen double. If you have any difficulty in seeing the finger double, close the left eye (while looking at the pencil); the finger lies to the left of the pencil. On now opening the left and closing the right eye, the finger has shifted its position. The experiment may be extended by looking at the near object and seeing the far object double.

Evidently there are many objects that we normally see double, and there are some that we see single. The explanation generally offered is the theory of *identical*, or *corresponding, points*. In Fig. 249 point *a* of one retina and *b* of the other may be regarded as corresponding points, for they lie in the same direction and at the same distance from the two foveas, *y* and *x*, respectively. If the image of an object falls, in the left eye, upon *a*, and in the right eye upon *b*, then that object is seen as a single object; but if the images fall upon *c* and *b*, the object is seen double; *b* and *c* are said to be unidentical or noncorresponding points. The two foveas are identical, and hence their simultaneous stimulation by the two images of an object leads to single vision. Now, the images of the object of regard fall upon the two foveas; consequently the object looked at with attention is normally seen single.

Fig. 249.—To illustrate identical points. *a* and *b*, identical, or corresponding, points; *c* and *b*, unidentical points.

An anatomic basis for this theory has been sought in the semidecussation (crossing over) of the optic nerves. The fibers from the nasal half of each retina cross over, at the chiasma, *m*, Fig. 250, to the other side of the brain (see Fig. 248); hence two images on the corresponding halves of the two retinas produce two impulses that are sent to the same part of the brain. The individual always strives to obtain single and to avoid double vision. To obtain this single vision when the eyes move from one object to another, the movements must be so co-ordinated that the images of the object of regard shall fall on the two foveas.

Ocular Movements; The Eye Muscles.—The motility of the eyes is a matter of common observation. Eye movements are brought about by the six extrinsic muscles. The position of these muscles may be gathered from Fig. 250. The direction in which the individual muscles turn the eyeball, and their innervation are tabulated below:

MUSCLE	DIRECTION	INNERVATION
Rectus Internus	inward	3rd cranial nerve
Rectus Externus	outward	6th cranial (abducens)
Rectus Superior	up and in	3rd cranial (oculomotor)
Rectus Inferior	down and in	3rd cranial
Obliquus Superior	down and out	4th cranial (patheticus)
Obliquus Inferior	up and out	3rd cranial

The turning of the eyeball outward (toward the temporal side) is called abduction; turning it inward (toward the nose), adduction; to bring about these two movements, the external rectus and the internal rectus, respectively, are sufficient. But to raise the gaze straight upward the rectus superior and the obliquus inferior are necessary (so as to neutralize the inward movement caused by

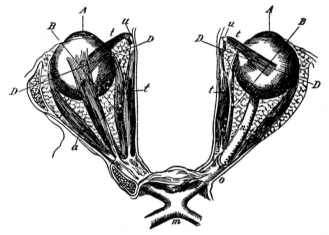

Fig. 250.—Illustrating the extrinsic eye muscles. *n*, optic nerve; *m*, the optic chiasma; *A*, cornea; *a*, the external rectus; *i*, the internal rectus; *s*, the superior rectus; *t*, the superior oblique and, *u*, its pulley; the inferior rectus and oblique are not shown. (Gariel.)

the rectus superior by the outward movement produced by the obliquus inferior). For the same reason, the downward motion requires the rectus inferior and the obliquus superior. For the oblique movements three muscles are necessary. For example; if our eyes are fixed upon a point at the horizon (primary position of the eyes), and we wish to look at an object two feet distant and situated in the median plane of the body and about on a level with the top of the head, both eyes must be moved upward and inward, for which the rectus superior, obliquus inferior, and rectus internus of each eye are used.

To bring this about requires a very careful co-ordination of impulses from the central nervous system, and it is not surprising that, for some reason or other, the mechanism sometimes fails. Most of us are acquainted with the fact that a person in alcoholic intoxication sees double. The co-ordinating mechanism, by which the two eyes are made to work in harmony, is upset by alcohol. The same happens when we become drowsy.

HETEROPHORIA.—When the eyes are in the primary position (looking at an object on the horizon), under normal conditions the visual axes of the eyes are parallel. Thus in Fig. 251, the visual axes yo' and xo are parallel and must be understood to meet at the point of regard, o, situated at infinity. The twelve extrinsic muscles may be said to be at rest in so far that without extra innervation to any one muscle in particular they hold the eyes properly in the primary position. In this condition, without any effort on the part of the individual, the object is seen single. But let us suppose that the external

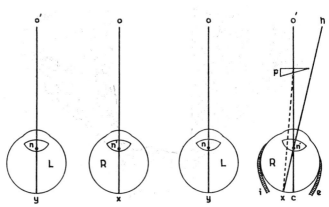

Fig. 251.—To illustrate the parallelism of the visual axes $xn'o$ and yno' in distant vision, the object of regard, o, being situated at infinity; x and y, the foveas, n and n', the nodal points.

Fig. 252.—To illustrate strabismus and its correction.

rectus muscle, e, in Fig. 252, of the right eye is a little stronger than, or has a mechanical advantage over, its antagonist, the rectus internus, i. Suppose such a person is looking at a point on the horizon and that all the extrinsic muscles of the eye receive equal impulses from the central nervous system; because of the greater effect produced by the external rectus muscle, e, the visual axis will be turned outward (temporalward) to a greater or lesser extent. This causes the fovea, x, to be moved toward the nose, and the object, o', will have its focus at c and not on the fovea. Unidentical points (y and c) are stimulated and the individual sees double. But, as we have stated before, there is always a striving for single vision. In the case under consideration, the central nervous system sends impulses to the weaker internal rectus muscle, *i,* of the right eye so as to offset the greater tension of the external rectus, and thereby insure single vision. The individual now has single vision, but his nervous system is taxed by the extra work; this results in "eyestrain."

The above-discussed condition, in which the extrinsic muscles of the eyes are not properly balanced, but in which the individual can, by extra innervation of a certain muscle or group of muscles, remedy the defect, is called heterophoria. In many cases this can be corrected by prismatic lenses whereby the light entering the eye is so deflected from its previous course as to focus upon the fovea. Let us place in front of the right eye, in Fig. 252, a prism, *p,* with its base toward the nose; the ray from *o'* will be bent so as to focus upon the fovea, *x.* By the prism we have accomplished what the patient formerly did by extra innervation and the eyestrain has been relieved.

STRABISMUS.—When the imbalance between the eye muscles is so great that the individual cannot by extra innervation remedy the defect it leads to a deviation of the visual axes, and the person is then said to have strabismus (cross-eye, or squint). This results in double vision; but, fortunately, the person so afflicted learns to neglect one of the images. Strabismus and heterophoria are frequently not due to any muscle trouble but to refractive errors (myopia and hyperopia), therefore properly fitted glasses may correct the fault.

EYESTRAIN can be caused by almost any error of refraction; especially do we find it in hyperopia and astigmatism. It is possible for one eye to be normal while the other is either myopic or hyperopic, or one eye is myopic and the other hyperopic; in all these cases eyestrain results. For hyperopic children the near work at school, especially when small print is used or the light is poor, is almost an impossibility; any attempt to read or write is at the expense of all the accommodation power of which they are capable.

All conditions in which a constant excessive innervation of the muscles for accommodation and convergence, and a constant close observation of indistinct retinal images are necessary, not only cause fatigue, but may be followed by serious mental and physical disturbances. In addition to the disturbances in the eyes themselves, such as pain, constant watering of the eyes, chronic inflammation, compression of the eyeballs, increasing nearsightedness, and distention of the ocular vein, digestive and nervous derangements (insomnia, vertigo, etc.), and serious general debility may follow. It is therefore of prime importance that the eyes be used correctly and not abused, and that, because of the large amount of near work demanded, the eyes of school children be carefully examined. The necessity for such examination is seen from the reports of medical examiners of schools; in one of the northern counties of Indiana 54 per cent of the children were found to have defective vision.

Ocular Hygiene.—Because of the importance of the subject we may suggest a few rules concerning the conditions under which near work should or should not be done.

1. As little near work as possible should be engaged in during the first two or three years of the child's school life. This matter has been investigated by a committee of the British Association for the Advancement of Science, from whose report we may quote the following: "At the age when school life begins the visual apparatus is still immature. The orbits, the eyes themselves, and the muscles and nerves which move them, have still to increase considerably in size. . . . The intricate coordinating mechanism which later will enable the eyes, brain, and the hand to work together with minute precision is awaiting development by training. The acuteness of vision is still below the standard proper to the finished eye. . . . In short, the whole visual apparatus is still unfinished, and is therefore more liable than at a later age to injury by overuse." That school work does to a large extent injure the eyes of the pupils has been proved by statistics showing the increasingly larger percentage of eye defects as the pupils progress from lower to higher grades.

2. The type used in books should be larger than that ordinarily used, the lines should be leaded, and the paper should not be highly glossy.

3. Never hold the book or paper in such a manner that glare is experienced.

4. Reading by dim or flickering light should be avoided.

5. The position of the individual, especially children, is of great importance. A low desk, which necessitates a constant bending forward, not only causes strain upon the eyes but also favors the development of round shoulders and by compressing the superficial veins at the neck causes congestion of the head and eyes. A desk too high may, by raising the right shoulder, be responsible for lateral spinal curvature (scoliosis).

6. When there is the least suspicion of defect or strain, proper examination of the eyes should be made. The notion that the use of spectacles weakens the eyes is ridiculous.

Protective Mechanisms.—The eye is protected in two ways:

1. By the eyelids and the eyelashes which prevent many foreign bodies from entering the eyes.

2. By the tears secreted by the lacrimal glands situated above the eyeball. This fluid prevents the drying of the cornea and the conjunctiva, and washes away foreign bodies; in this it is greatly assisted by the winking of the eyelids. The fifth cranial nerve is the sensory nerve of the cornea, and by its stimulation the reflex secretion of tears and winking are brought about. The tears flow to the inner canthus (angle) of the eye and are collected by the nasal duct and brought to the inferior meatus of the nose (see Fig. 128). On the edge of the lids are found the openings of the ducts of the meibomian glands which secrete a fatty substance; this keeps the tears from flowing over the lids.

II. SENSE OF HEARING

The ear is constructed so that the endings of the auditory, or the eighth cranial, nerve are most effectively stimulated by sound.

Sound.—Sound, in its objective sense, is the vibration of air. When a body, like a violin string, is plucked, it vibrates forward and backward. In so doing it condenses the air in front of it and rarefies the air behind it. These condensations and rarefactions of the air travel at a rate of 1,090 feet per second. As the number of waves per second becomes greater, the pitch of the sound becomes higher; but whether the string be plucked gently or violently does not affect the number of vibrations per second, and consequently the pitch will remain the same. When the string is pulled violently the excursion of the string will be greater and what is called the amplitude of the wave will be larger; this causes the sound to be louder. The *intensity,* or loudness, of a sound therefore depends upon the amplitude of the waves. The human ear can respond to sound waves ranging from 16 to 20,000 or, according to some authors, 40,000 double vibrations per second. Within these limits we can distinguish about 11,000 different pitches. In music the range extends from 32 to 4,800.

A third characteristic of sound is its color. A violin string having 2,000 vibrations per second is set into vibration; a similar string in a piano is also caused to vibrate with the same force as the violin string; the two sounds have the same pitch and the same intensity, but nobody mistakes one for the other. The *color,* or *timbre,* is caused in the following manner: When a string vibrates, it vibrates as a whole forward and backward; the waves thus formed constitute the fundamental sound and determine the pitch of the sound. But the string, at the same time, vibrates in its parts, that is, each half, third, or fourth of the string vibrates independently of the whole string. This causes other waves and other sounds, the overtones, to accompany, and to fuse with, the fundamental wave. These overtones vary for different sorts of strings; each string, in consequence, has its individuality by which we recognize it.

When a sound falls upon an object, like a windowpane, it causes this to vibrate. When a person sings a certain note near a piano, the piano continues for a short time to send out the same note after the singer has stopped because the string which corresponds in number of vibrations to that of the note sung is thrown into sympathetic vibration, or resonance.

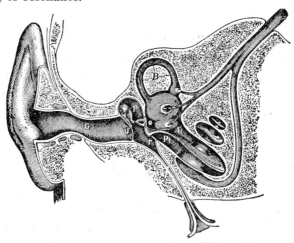

Fig. 253.—Diagram of the right ear. *G*, external auditory meatus; *T*, membrana tympani; *P*, tympanic cavity containing the three auditory ossicles; *o*, oval window; *r*, round window; below *r*, is seen the eustachian tube; *B*, semicircular canal; *S*, cochlea; *Vt*, scala vestibuli; *Pt*, scala tympani. (Czermak.)

The Ear.—The ear is divided into three parts: the external, middle, and internal ear, Fig. 253. The external ear includes: 1. The auricle, or pinna. 2. The external auditory meatus, *G*, a tube leading to 3, the eardrum or tympanic membrane, *T*. On the inner side of the eardrum we have, in the middle ear, a chain of three little bones (auditory ossicles) Fig. 254 called the malleus (hammer), incus (anvil), and stapes (stirrup). The handle of the hammer, Fig. 253, is imbedded in the eardrum, its head forms a joint with the body of the incus. The long process of the incus is articulated with the head of the stapes and the foot of the stapes is fixed by a membrane into the oval window, *o*, Fig. 253.

These little bones are contained in the tympanic cavity, Fig. 253, *P*, of the temporal bone. This cavity is closed to the outside air by the eardrum, *T;* it is shut off from the inner ear by the round and the oval windows, *r* and *o;* from its floor springs the *eustachian tube,* which connects the tympanic cavity with the pharynx. The chain of bones extends from the eardrum across the cavity to the oval window. On the other side of the oval window is found the inner ear. The inner ear consists of a series of winding cavities cut in the temporal bone;

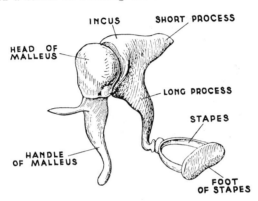

INCUS   SHORT PROCESS

HEAD OF MALLEUS

LONG PROCESS

STAPES

HANDLE OF MALLEUS

FOOT OF STAPES

Fig. 254.—The auditory ossicles.

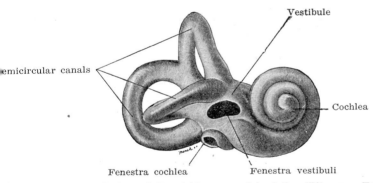

Vestibule

emicircular canals

Cochlea

Fenestra cochlea   Fenestra vestibuli

Fig. 255.—External view of the right osseous labyrinth. (Pitzman: Fundamentals of Human Anatomy, The C. V. Mosby Co.)

this is known as the *osseous,* or *bony, labyrinth,* Fig. 255. Most of these cavities are tubelike, constituting what is known as the *cochlea,* or snail, and the *semicircular canals;* between these two sets of winding tubes there is a dilated connecting part, the *vestibule.*

In these winding canals of the *osseous labyrinth* there is placed a *membranous canal,* or *labyrinth,* Fig. 256, which in general has the shape of the bony canal, except that in the vestibule the membranous canal is composed of two sacs, the *saccule* and *utricle, 5* and *1.* From the utricle spring the three membranous *semicircular canals, 2, 3* and *4;* from the saccule originates the membranous canal, *9,* found in the cochlea of the osseous canal and known as the canal of the cochlea.

The snail, or cochlea, is a spiral-shaped tube making two and a half turns Figs. 255 and 256. In Fig. 257 we have a cross-section of one of the coils. A bony shelf (lamina spiralis ossea, *lso*) reaches out from the wall into the bony canal. From the free edge of this bony shelf extends the basilar membrane, *b,* to the opposite wall; by this

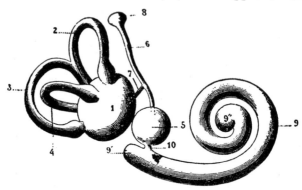

Fig. 256.—Diagram of membranous labyrinth of the right ear. *1,* utricle; *2, 3, 4,* superior, posterior and horizontal semicircular canals; *5,* saccule; *6,* ductus and, *8,* saccus endolymphaticus; *9, 9',* and *9",* canalis cochlearis; *10,* canalis reuniens. (After Testut.)

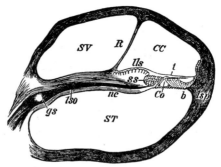

Fig. 257.—Section through one of the coils of the cochlea. *ST,* scala tympani; *SV,* scala vestibuli; *CC,* canalis cochlea; *R,* Reissner's membrane; *lso,* lamina spiralis ossea; *nc,* cochlear nerve; *b,* membrana basilaris; *Co,* rods of Corti; *t,* tectorial membrane. (After Henle.)

the bony canal is divided into two parts, the scala tympani, *ST,* and the scala vestibuli, *SV.* Across this latter canal stretches Reissner's membrane, *R,* thereby forming the canal of the cochlea, *CC,* or the scala media. The scala media, a membranous canal, is filled with endolymph; the other two scalæ contain perilymph. The basilar membrane is constructed of fibers which run transversely and, as its shape is that of a truncated triangle, these fibers are of varying lengths. It is estimated that there are 24,000 fibers in this membrane. On the basilar membrane is found the organ of Corti, the most important parts of which are the hair cells resting on the fibers of the basilar membrane and around which end the fibers of the auditory, or eighth cranial, nerve (see Fig. 258).

The Conduction of Sound to the Nerve Ending.—The air vibrations enter the external auditory meatus. The auricle in man is very rudimentary and it is doubtful whether it plays any great part in collecting and reflecting sound waves. The meatus serves to protect the eardrum from mechanical, and, to a lesser extent, from thermal injuries.

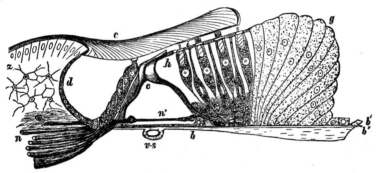

Fig. 258.—Illustration of the organ of Corti. *b*, basilar membrane; *e*, Corti's arch; *g*, supporting cells; *h*, cylindrical cells; *i*, Deiter's hair cells; *c*, membrana tectoria; *n*, and *n′* nerve fibers. (Munk.)

The vibration of the air in the meatus causes the drum to vibrate and this sets the auditory ossicles in motion, Fig. 253. By this the base of the stapes is moved into and out of the oval window. By the vibration of the stapes, the perilymph in the vestibule and in the scala vestibuli is set in motion. As the perilymph bathes the basilar membrane, the waves in the lymph cause this membrane to vibrate, and this in turn disturbs the hair cells resting on the basilar membrane. The hair cells are regarded as the sensory cells, in the same manner as the rods and cones are said to be the visual cells; by their activity the nerve endings are stimulated and nerve impulses generated. How the vibration of the basilar membrane affects the hair cells and how these cells stimulate the nerve endings are still unsettled questions.

The Ear as an Analytic Sense Organ.—The auditory apparatus is, to a large extent, an analytic organ in that very complex sound waves, composed of many air vibrations of various lengths, such as those from an orchestra, can be resolved into many of their components; this enables the hearer to recognize the individual sounds from many of the musical instruments. In this respect the visual mechanism is the reverse, being, as our study of color sensations taught us, a synthetic sense organ (p. 562). As to where and how this resolving of the complex sound takes place is a moot point; we may briefly discuss the commonly accepted resonance theory.

According to Helmholtz the transverse fibers of the basilar membrane serve as a series of resonators. The strings vary in length from the longest (about $\frac{1}{60}$ inch) at the apex to the shortest (about $\frac{1}{400}$ inch) at the base of the cochlea. Similar to the strings of a harp or piano, these strings, even though embedded in a common matrix, are held to vibrate individually. Let us suppose that three fundamental sound waves strike the eardrum simultaneously; the complex vibration set up in the conducting mechanism of the external, middle, and inner ear causes three strings of the basilar membrane to be thrown into sympathetic vibration, each string being attuned to one of the three fundamental sounds (air waves). As a result, three nerve fibers carrying impulses to the brain and three sensations are created, although, as our experience shows us, there is considerable commingling. In favor of the resonance theory we may state that in individuals who are able to perceive only the lower pitched tones (as in boiler-makers' disease), the shorter strings of the basilar membrane have been found to be defective; the apical end of the membrane with its longer strings has been shown to be degenerated in those not able to hear the lower tones. This has also been found to be true in animals in which either the one or the other end of the membrane was experimentally destroyed. Further, the fact that an animal may be fatigued to the lower sounds by the long application of these sounds and at the same time is able to hear the sounds of a higher pitch shows that the membrane does not vibrate as a whole. The human ear is able to distinguish about 11,000 tones of different pitch. As there are about 16,000 hair cells, the number of resonators is sufficiently great to account for the perception of all sounds.

The experiments by Wever and Bray do not seem to fit in with the resonance theory. The exposed cochlea or the auditory nerve of a cat was connected by means of electrodes with a vacuum tube amplifier and this, in turn, with a telephone placed in another room. When words were spoken into the ear of the cat, the listener at the phone heard a faithful reproduction of the spoken words. The air waves (sound) produced in the ear an electric disturbance of the same frequency as that of the sound, and, as in a radio receiver, these electric pulses were transformed into sound waves. These electric pulses must not be confused with the action potential of a nerve fiber, for this structure, because of the refractory period, cannot conduct more than 1,000 pulses per second. For a more detailed discussion larger texts must be consulted.

The Acuity of Hearing.—The relative acuity can be determined by the distance at which a person can hear a certain sound, say, the ticking of a watch. Recently scientifically constructed audiometers have been devised by which the acuity can be accurately measured for sounds ranging from 16 to 33,000 vibrations per second. Efficient hearing depends upon (a) the proper transmission of the sound waves by the conducting mechanism to the hair cells; (b) the generation and conduction of the nerve impulses to the brain and their reception by the brain. Deafness may therefore be of threefold origin: the trouble lies either with the receptor, the conductor or the perception apparatus.

That the eardrum may vibrate freely and thereby set in motion the other conduction mechanism, the air pressure on the two sides of the drum must be the same. A gas inclosed in a body cavity is speedily absorbed by the blood and surrounding tissues, hence the pressure of the gas is gradually reduced. To prevent this from occurring in the tympanic cavity the eustachian tube permits air to flow from the pharynx into the middle ear; thus an equality of pressure on the two sides of the eardrum is assured. In a head cold the eustachian tubes are likely to be occluded; the air in the middle ear is then absorbed and hearing dulled. Impacted cerumen (ear-wax) also impedes the tympanic vibrations. Contrary to the generally accepted idea, puncture of the eardrum has but little effect on hearing, provided the ossicles are not damaged. Because of the close connection between the oral and nasal cavities and the middle ear, catarrhal condition of the nose or throat may endanger the ear. Many diseases, such as mumps, measles, diphtheria, scarlet fever, influenza, and the common head cold may affect various parts of the ear.

The ankylosis (a growing together and rendering joints immobile) of the auditory ossicles or of the foot of the stapes in the oval window also interferes with the conduction of sound waves. Much of the gradually increasing hardness of hearing in elderly people is thus produced. If a vibrating tuning fork is pressed upon the bones of the head, the ears being stopped, the sound is very noticeable; the bones conduct the sound waves to the inner ear and thereby set the lymph in the cochlea in vibration. Normally air conduction is more effective than bone conduction. Certain hearing aids, employed when the ossicles are locked fast, magnify the bone conduction.

Localization.—Our power to locate the source of a sound is not very great. If the source lies to the right or left of us, we have no difficulty in determining it, but if the sound comes from in front, behind, above, or below us, we have no idea in which direction the source lies; it is only by turning the head so that the sound strikes one ear more than the other that we can inform ourselves of its location.

III. LABYRINTHINE IMPRESSIONS

Of the membranous canal described on page 573 only the canal of the cochlea (*9* in Fig. 256; also *Vt* and *Pt* in Fig. 253) is concerned with hearing. The other parts of this canal include three dis-

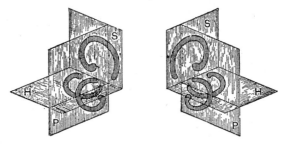

Fig. 259.—Diagram of the semicircular canals; *H*, the horizontal; *S*, the superior vertical; *P*, the posterior vertical. (Ewald.)

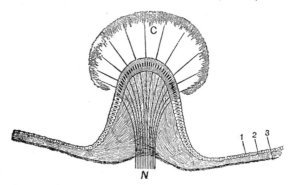

Fig. 260.—Section through the wall of an ampulla, passing through the crista acoustica. *N*, nerve fibers of the vestibular branch of the eighth cranial nerve; *C*, cupula into which the hair cells of the epithelium, *1*, project; *2*, the tunica propria; *3*, fibrous layer of the membranous canal continuous with the periosteum of the bony canal. (Schäfer.)

tinct structures: the utricle, *1*, Fig. 256; the saccule, *5*; and the three semicircular canals *2*, *3*, and *4*. All these parts are filled with endolymph. The three semicircular canals spring from the utricle and are so placed that the three canals in one ear are all at right angles to each other. From Fig. 259, it will also be seen that for each of the three canals in one ear there is a canal parallel to it in the other ear and that each canal has at one end a dilated part, termed the *ampulla*.* In the ampulla is found a structure, the *crista acoustica,* Fig. 260, which may be described as a hillock in which the epithelial cells lining the wall of the canal assume a columnar shape and are provided with cilia. Covering the top of the crista is a gelatinous mass, *C,* into which the cilia project. The vestibular branch of the eighth cranial nerve ends in the neighborhood of these ciliated cells, Fig. 261.

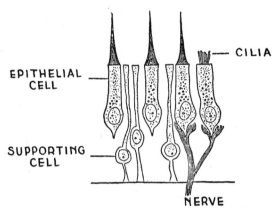

Fig. 261.—Hair cells of the crista acoustica. (Halliburton.)

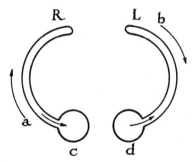

Fig. 262.—Diagram to illustrate the effect of rotation of the head (shown by the arrows *a* and *b*) on the endolymph in the ampullae, *c* and *d,* of the semicircular canals in the right and the left ears.

In each utricle and saccule we find a sensory epithelium known as the macula acoustica. This resembles the above described crista except that lying in among the hairs of the epithelial cells there are found a number of small concretions of calcium carbonate, known as otoliths (*ous, ear; lithos,* stone).

The macula of the utricle and of the saccule give rise to afferent impulses which evoke the "righting reflexes." When the body or

Ampulla, a flask; *crista,* crest.

any member of the body of an animal is placed in an abnormal position, there is an immediate effort to restore it to the normal position; this is called the righting reflex.

The impulses in the macula are generated by the pulling of the otoliths upon the hair cells with which the nerve fibers, *N*, in Figs. 260 and 261, are in close contact. A change in the *position of the head* will, therefore, cause the stimulation of the vestibular branch of the eighth cranial nerve; the impulse is conveyed by way of the brain to the muscles of the neck by which the position of the head, with respect to gravity, is adjusted. In these righting reflexes, the kinesthetic impulses from the neck muscles also play an important part (see p. 586).

The nerve endings in the crista acoustica of the semicircular canals are stimulated by the movements of the endolymph, Fig. 262. When the head is being moved, the endolymph because of its inertia is either forced toward or away from the ampulla and the change in the pressure on the crista thus produced stimulates the nerve fibers. When an individual seated on a piano stool is rotated around a vertical axis, the eyes, head, and trunk are moved in the opposite direction. After cessation of the rotation the eyes move in the direction opposite to their first movements. These *compensatory movements* are generally said to be caused by the stimulation of the semicircular canals.

The destruction of one of the labyrinths in a rabbit causes the eyes to twitch (nystagmus); the head, neck, and trunk are turned toward the side of the lesion and frequently the animal executes what are termed *forced movements*. Instead of sitting quietly in a normal position, the animal assumes abnormal positions and, in some cases, the head of the animal is constantly swung from side to side. When the animal moves, his motions are erratic; he may be continually moving in a circle, or turning somersaults backward or forward. If both the labyrinths are destroyed, the animal is able to maintain the proper position of his head as long as he uses his eyes. The same relationship between the eyes and the labyrinth has been observed in human beings. A normal, blindfolded person placed on a platform readily adjusts the position of his body when the platform is gradually tilted, but deaf-mutes (in whom the inner ear is defective) immediately fall ''as if they were wooden images.''

We may conclude that the impressions from the labyrinth, together with the visual and kinesthetic impressions, are of the greatest value in equilibration, those from the labyrinth being especially concerned with maintaining the normal position of the head. Malfunctioning of this mechanism gives rise to giddiness, nausea, and vomiting.

IV. THE CHEMICAL SENSES—TASTE AND SMELL

The chemical senses—taste and smell—are mediated by the sense organs located in the tongue and nose, respectively. In the mucosa covering the tongue, especially on the tip, edges, and posterior third of the tongue, are found taste buds, which are barrel- or bottle-shaped groups of cells. Some of these cells terminate at their external end in hairs which project into a pore or depression of the bud so that the stimulating agencies may come in direct contact with them. The other end of the taste cells is surrounded by the terminal filaments of the gustatory nerves, Fig. 263. To be tasted, the substance must be in solution, for if the tongue is dried with a towel and a dry lump of sugar is place upon it, there is no sensation until a little saliva has collected between the tongue and the sugar and dissolved the sugar. This explains why insoluble things have no taste.

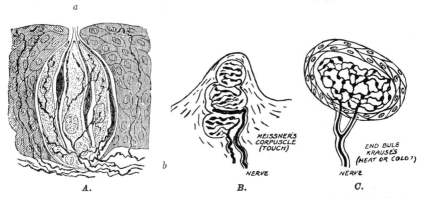

Fig. 263.—A, Taste-bud. a, Taste pore; b, nerve fibers seen entering the taste-bud. (Merkel-Henle.)
B. Meissner's corpuscle. C. End bulb of Krause. (Starling: Human Physiology, J. and A. Churchill Co., Ltd.)

Tastes have been classified as sweet, sour, salt, and bitter; some add an alkaline and a metallic taste. There is no connection between the taste of various compounds and their chemical composition, for chloroform, lead acetate, and sugar all have a sweet taste. But it is also true that the members belonging to the same chemical family generally resemble each other in taste; alkaloids are bitter, alkalies have a soapy taste, all acids are sour, etc. The various tastes are not experienced equally well at all parts of the tongue and mouth. Sweet and salt are best appreciated at the tip of the tongue, sour at the sides, and bitter at the back. This explains the bitter-sweet taste of magnesium sulfate.

Considerable disagreement exists as to the nerves of taste. There is little doubt that the glossopharyngeal, or ninth cranial, nerve is the nerve of taste for the posterior third of the tongue; the facial, or seventh cranial, nerve and, according to some authorities, the trigeminal, or fifth cranial, nerve innervate the anterior two-thirds.

The sense of smell is mediated by the olfactory, or first cranial, nerve which has its endings in the nasal mucosa just above the superior turbinate bone of the nose (Fig. 128). The sense of smell is very closely allied to the sense of taste. In fact many of the so-called tastes (flavors) of certain foods are in reality odors. A piece of raw onion chewed with the nose shut cannot be distinguished from a piece of raw potato. For this reason a cold in the head interferes so largely with appreciating one's food, thus causing loss of appetite.

The value of the sense of smell lies in the following:

1. It creates appetite and thus favors the flow of the digestive juices.

2. It informs us of substances injurious to eat. Decaying food generally has a bad odor, and thus we are warned; however, this is by no means an infallible guide. In these two last-mentioned functions the sense of taste also plays a large part.

3. In many cases the sense of smell tells us of odorous gases which may be harmful when inhaled. Here also, however, the nose is not always to be trusted, as in the case of carbon monoxide.

V. THE CUTANEOUS SENSATIONS

From the skin we obtain impulses that give rise to four sensations, namely, heat, cold, touch, and pain. The first three sensations are limited almost entirely to the skin, and to the ends of the alimentary canal. We have no sense of touch, heat, or cold in the internal organs, as is indicated by the fact that we do not feel the gliding of the various organs, such as the lungs, diaphragm, and heart, along the adjacent structures; nor do we feel the motion of stomach, intestines, etc. We must, however, grant that the structures immediately below the skin may give rise to a sensation of pressure if the stimulation is sufficiently powerful. Pain, on the other hand, can be elicited from many organs.

The four cutaneous sensations are distributed irregularly in a punctiform manner over the skin. By means of a stiff bristle or hair, it is possible to find points on the skin which are insensible to touch; such areas pricked with a needle may give rise to pain. By the use of thin, warm, or cold metal rods, it is possible to find spots or areas that are sensitive to heat or cold and others that are insensitive to these forms of stimulation, Fig. 264. A square centimeter of the palmar surface of the finger tip contains 60 pain and 100 touch spots; the back of the finger has about 100 pain and 9 touch spots.

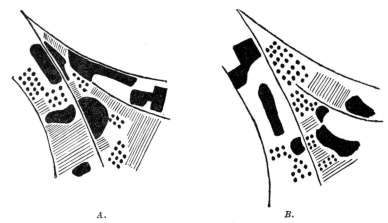

A.   B.

Fig. 264.—Cold spots (A) and heat spots (B) of an area of skin of the right hand. In each case the most intense sensations were experienced in the black areas, less intense in the lined, and least in the dotted. The blank areas represent parts where no special sensation of either kind was experienced. (Goldscheider.)

According to the theory of specific nerve energies, it is generally held that in the skin and adjacent tissues there are several distinct sense organs, each capable of being most efficiently stimulated by one form of stimulus and always giving rise to one definite sensation. These peripheral organs are of many kinds (Fig. 263)—Meissner's, Krause's, and Pacinian corpuscles, and also free nerve endings—but which of these are stimulated by heat, cold, pressure, etc., is an unsettled question. Many hold that Krause's end bulbs are stimulated only by low temperatures, and that even the most intense stimulation of Meissner's corpuscles gives rise to no other sensation than touch or pressure. That distinct nerves mediate the various cutaneous sensations is rendered likely from the following observations:

1. The punctiform manner in which the sense organs are distributed in the skin. This has already been dwelt upon.

2. In certain pathologic disturbances of the central nervous system there results what is called the "dissociation" of the cutaneous sensations. For example, the fingers of a physician who suffered from a spinal disease were perfectly analgesic (incapable of being painfully stimulated), but he was still able to feel the pulse of a patient. Some-

times it happens that the mucosa of the mouth loses its sense of temperature, while that of touch is normal.

3. Pressure upon a nerve trunk may also bring this about. We have all experienced the peculiar effect of a limb going "asleep"; in this state the sensation of cold is lost nearly altogether, but that of heat remains.

4. The application of cocaine to a cutaneous nerve causes, according to Gasser and Erlanger, the disappearance of the sensations in the following order: pain, cold, heat, and touch. From these and other observations it has been concluded that the nerve fibers having the smallest diameter are the first to be affected by cocaine and mediate the sense of pain; the largest fibers are the last to be influenced and convey impulses which arouse the sensation of touch.

5. Certain parts of the body, e.g., the cornea, are devoid of touch sensation but from them painful sensations can readily be obtained. Of other parts the reverse is true.

Fig. 265.—Aristotle's experiment.

Tactile Sensitivity.—The stimulus for touch sensation is the deforming of the skin by unequal pressure. The degree of this sensitivity may be found by means of v. Frey's esthesiometer. From a number of horse hairs of various thicknesses the thinnest one is found which, on being pressed on to the skin until it bends, is able to elicit a touch sensation; the amount of pressure, in grams, equivalent to this stimulation can be determined by means of a pair of scales. This pressure expressed in grams divided by the radius of the hair expressed in mm. gives the tension value of the stimulus. The finger tips and the lips possess the highest degree of tactile sensitivity.

Localization. —By the sense of locality we can tell more or less accurately which part of the skin is touched. In our brain there is, we may say, a field corresponding to the field of the periphery of our body exposed to the environment. Normally two widely separated areas of the skin are simultaneously stimulated by two discrete objects, and two sensations are experienced. When these two areas are brought into close proximity so that they can be simultaneously stimulated by one object, two distinct objects are felt. This is done in Aristotle's experiment, Fig. 265, in which the middle finger is crossed over the index finger and the point of a blunt pencil is moved along the crotch thus formed (compare with corresponding points and diplopia in vision, p. 565).

Tactile Discrimination.—By this is meant the power to discern two discrete sensations when the skin is stimulated at two points. If the stimulated points are very close together, only one sensation is experienced (compare with resolving power of the eye, p. 557). To determine the degree of tactile discrimination for the various regions of the skin, we find the least distance by which the two blunted points of a pair of compasses must be separated in order to be felt as two (the compass test). Tested in this manner the sensitivity of the tip of the tongue and that of the index finger is about 1.1 mm., that of the palm, 8 mm., and that of the middle of the neck, 67 mm.

Pain is, without doubt, one of the most important of all the sensations. Pain receptors are more generally distributed over the skin and in the internal organs of our bodies than any other sensory organ. How necessary the sense of pain is for the preservation of life and health is self-evident.

There are two theories as to the origin of pain. According to one theory, the overstimulation of any sensory end organ (touch, cold, etc.) causes pain; the other theory, conforming to the theory of the specificity of nerves, holds that there are special pain receptors, and only when they are stimulated is pain felt. In favor of the latter theory is the fact that certain parts of our bodies are devoid of the sense of touch while there is a lively sense of pain; this is true of the cornea. On the other hand, for the mucosa of the central portion of the cheek the opposite holds true. Again, in certain diseases of, or injuries to, the central nervous system the sensation of touch may be absent (anesthesia) while the sense of pain remains, or the reverse may be true. In this connection we may recall what was said above concerning the action of local anesthetics, such as cocaine.

It is generally held that the free nerve endings, which do not end in specialized structures such as rods and cones, the taste buds, etc., constitute the receptors for pain. They are the most widely distributed receptors in the body, being found in the skin, cornea, blood vessels, and most visceral organs. In contrast with the specialized receptors, the pain receptors can be stimulated by any form of stimulation if sufficiently intense.

Referred Pain.—Pain can be elicited by stimulating a nerve fiber at any point along its course, but the sensation is always referred, or projected, to the endings of the nerve; this is made evident in the hitting of one's crazy bone, by which the ulnar nerve is stimulated in its course. Pain cannot always be definitely localized, especially when it is severe, and of long duration; the sensation then seems to spread to neighboring parts, as is seen in toothache.

On a previous page we spoke of the pain experienced in internal organs as being "referred" to another and, generally, external part of the body. It seems that when an internal organ receives its nerve supply from a certain segment of the cord which also supplies an external organ, the painful stimulation of the internal organ (which is generally less sensitive than the external organ) is referred to the external organ. But how this anatomical arrangement furnishes a basis for referred pain is not very clear. However, it can be readily understood that a knowledge of referred pain may be of great diagnostic value.

In diseases of some internal organs, certain cutaneous areas may become hyperalgesic (excessively sensitive to pain) so that the least stimulation, such as a gentle touch, or even a breath of air, applied to this part of the skin gives rise to pain. Many internal organs are insensitive to what are generally regarded as painful stimuli. Tumors have been removed from the brains of patients who remained conscious during the entire operation, without causing any pain. Handling, cutting, or cauterizing the intestine never gave rise to expressions of pain. However, pain can be elicited from most hollow organs by an increase in the tension of their walls; this is brought about (1) by great distention (e.g., accumulation of gas in the intestine, or the passage of a gallstone) or (2) by excessive contraction of their musculature (e.g., colic). Pain can be relieved by reducing the conductivity of the nerve, as by compression, cold, drugs (novocain, etc.), or by reducing the sensitiveness of the cerebral cells, as in general anesthesia.

VI. KINESTHETIC, PROPRIOCEPTIVE, OR MOTOR SENSE

It is a well-known fact that we are able to judge the position of our limbs, without the aid of our eyes. We "feel" the degree to which the fingers are bent or the arm is extended. This is well illustrated in our ability to lay our hand, in the dark, upon a certain object whose position in space is known to us.

The muscles and their tendons and the ligaments of the joints are supplied with afferent nerves which end in special sense organs known as muscle or tendon spindles. The muscle spindles, embedded between the muscle fibers, are stimulated by tension whenever the muscle is passively stretched (stretch afferents); the contraction of the muscle reduces or abolishes the tension upon these spindles. The impulses generated in the spindles are sometimes spoken of as motorial, or kinesthetic, impulses; more frequently they are known as proprioceptive (*proprius,* one's own) impulses, in that the stimulations generating these impulses arise from the changes taking place in the body itself and not in the external world. According to Sherrington, from one-third to one-half of the fibers found in a nerve supplying a muscle spring from the cells in the dorsal root ganglia and are therefore afferent. The sensory end organs in tendon and in the junction between muscles and tendons are stimulated in the same manner as the muscle spindles.

While we are but dimly conscious of the kinesthetic impressions (muscle sense), yet their importance can hardly be overestimated. They acquaint us with the position of our limbs in respect to the whole body; as we shall learn in Chap. XXVIII, they are indispensable in establishing muscle tonus and thereby in maintaining the proper posture of the body in standing. In tabes dorsalis certain fibers of the dorsal (sensory) roots of the spinal cord are destroyed, the muscle sense is largely lost; especially is this true for the kinesthetic impressions from the legs. Without looking at them the patient is unable to tell the position of his legs; in consequence there is marked disturbance in walking—locomotor ataxia. With closed eyes, a person with tabes dorsalis is unable to maintain an erect standing position (Romberg's sign). For the righting reflexes (p. 579) the motor impressions are exceedingly important.

VII. HUNGER AND THIRST

Hunger is a sensation projected to the region in the immediate neighborhood of the stomach and is due, as shown by Cannon, to the contraction of the musculature of the stomach; this subject was discussed on p. 384.

Thirst is a sensation associated with a dryness and stickiness of the mouth, tongue, and pharynx. The cause of this dryness may be local, as in the thirst caused by breathing hot, dry air (smoking, e.g.), the inhalation of dust, prolonged speaking, or the eating of dry food. Again, the cause may be general; for example, the thirst experienced after a severe hemorrhage, profuse sweating, or greatly increased renal secretion (as in diabetes); in these instances the loss of water from the blood leads to a deficient secretion of saliva and a consequent dryness of mouth and pharynx. From its influence on the salivary center, we can readily understand that great fear may cause intense thirst. Because of its paralyzing action upon the salivary glands, thirst can also be caused by the administration of atropine; this is relieved by the application of cocaine to the oral mucosa.

CHAPTER XXVIII

REFLEX ACTIONS: THE SPINAL CORD

The stimulation of the receptors studied in the preceding chapter is of no avail unless the impulse generated in the receptor finds expression in the activity of an effector. To transmit the impulse from the former to the latter organs is the primary and fundamental function of the nervous system. We shall learn as we proceed with our subject that in this transmission the impulse may be modified by the ever changing conditions of the nervous system.

The nervous system may be conveniently divided into (1) the central nervous system, comprising the brain and spinal cord, and (2) the peripheral nervous system which includes the cranial and spinal nerves and the autonomic nervous system.

I. ANATOMY

Protective Mechanism.—The central nervous system is composed of approximately 14,000 million neurons, or nerve cells. As in all other organs, these cells are held together in proper arrangement by connective tissue. In addition to the usual forms, we find in the central nervous system a special kind of connective tissue known as *neuroglia* (glia, glue). A neuroglia cell is composed of a cell body from which a large number of delicate fibers radiate in an irregular fashion.

The brain and spinal cord are extremely delicate and very vital organs and must, therefore, be well protected. First of all, they are enveloped in three membranes, or *meninges* (*meninx*, a membrane): the dura mater (a strong fibrous membrane), the arachnoid, and the pia mater. The pia mater (*pia*, tender; *mater*, mother), closely applied to the brain and cord, is a vascular coat and is therefore the nutritive membrane for these organs. Meningitis is an inflammation of these coverings. In addition to these membranes the brain is protected by the rigid cranium, and the spinal cord, by the flexibly joined spinal column composed of 33 vertebrae. In the bones forming the skull and in between the vertebrae we find orifices (foramina) for the exit of the cranial and spinal nerves.

Cerebrospinal Fluid.—Through the entire length of the cord extends a narrow central canal which is continued anteriorly into the brain where in four locations it widens out to form the ventricles of the brain. This central canal and the ventricles, as well as the space between the arachnoid and the pia mater, are filled with a fluid known as the cerebrospinal fluid. It serves as a support and a cushion for the soft structures of the central nervous system.

THE CEREBROSPINAL FLUID is produced by the capillaries of the much folded and highly vascular portions of the pia mater, known as the choroid plexus, lying in the ventricles. From the ventricles it escapes through small openings in the roof of the fourth ventricle into the subarachnoidal space and is then absorbed into the blood stream. If the passage of the fluid into the subarachnoidal space is blocked, it accumulates in the ventricles, giving rise to a form of edema known as hydrocephalus (*hydros,* water; *cephale,* head). In a young child the resultant increased intracranial pressure causes a great increase in the size of the head, and this, needless to state, seriously impedes the development, growth, and function of the brain.

LUMBAR PUNCTURE.—In certain diseases it is desirable to learn the condition of the cerebrospinal fluid. Also, spinal anesthesia can be induced by the injection of the drug into this fluid. The spinal cord extends from the base of the skull to the second lumbar vertebra; here it ends in a large number of nerves which comprise the lower 10 pairs of spinal nerves and are collectively known as the cauda equina. These nerves are enclosed in a sac formed by the meninges and extending to the third sacral vertebra. It is therefore possible to insert a hypodermic needle between the fourth and the fifth lumbar vertebrae and to introduce it into the sac. In this manner some of the cerebrospinal fluid can be sucked into the syringe either for diagnostic purposes or to relieve a too great pressure of the fluid (as in encephalitis, or inflammation of the brain); or drugs can be injected into the fluid.

Spinal Cord.—The spinal cord, situated in the vertebral canal of the vertebral column, is cylindrical in form (Fig. 266), about 18 inches long and 3/4 inch in diameter. As seen in the cross-section shown in Figs. 267 and 275, the cord is almost completely divided into two lateral halves by the ventral, or anterior, and the dorsal, or posterior, median fissures. From the ventral aspect of the cord spring 31 pairs of ventral roots, Fig. 26; we find the same number of dorsal roots. The nerve fibers of the dorsal and ventral roots of one lateral half of a segment of the cord commingle to form the spinal nerve; very soon this divides into many branches to supply

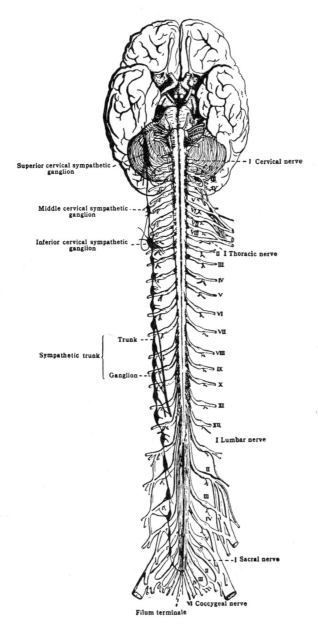

Superior cervical sympathetic ganglion

Middle cervical sympathetic ganglion

Inferior cervical sympathetic ganglion

Sympathetic trunk { Trunk

Ganglion

I Cervical nerve

I Thoracic nerve

I Lumbar nerve

I Sacral nerve

VI Coccygeal nerve

Filum terminale

Fig. 266.—Ventral view of the brain and spinal cord with the spinal nerves and on the left-hand side, the sympathetic nervous chain. (Morris: Anatomy, P. Blakiston's Son and Co.)

various regions of the body. The 31 pairs of spinal nerves are grouped as follows (Fig. 266) :

Cervical	8 pairs
Dorsal	12 pairs
Lumbar	5 pairs
Sacral	5 pairs
Coccygeal	1 pair

Gray Matter and White Matter.—From Chapter V it will be recalled that a typical neuron is composed of a cell body, an axon, and generally two or more dendrons (Fig. 25). In the cell body and its dendrons are found many angular bodies or granules which color deeply with certain stains and are for this reason known as *chromatophile granules* (also called Nissl bodies). These granules, which are not present in the axon, are generally looked upon as reserve food materials.

In the central nervous system the cell bodies are massed to form the gray matter; the axons, surrounded by myelin sheaths, constitute the columns, or tracts, of white matter. In the spinal cord the centrally placed gray matter has, in cross-section, somewhat the shape of the letter H and is surrounded by columns of white matter (Fig. 26). The cell bodies play no special part in the propagation of nerve impulses except, as has earlier been indicated, that upon them depends the nutrition of the entire neuron.

II. THE REFLEX ARC

Afferent and Efferent Nerves.—The connection between the receptors and the effectors is formed in all the more highly evolved animals by not less than two neurons; one of these in Fig. 26, connects the sensory surface with the spinal cord, having passed into the cord by the dorsal root. The second neuron connects the spinal cord with the effector (muscle), having issued from the cord by way of the ventral root. The cell bodies of the dorsal fibers are situated on the fibers a short distance from the cord. The collection of the cell bodies of all the fibers entering the spinal cord by a dorsal root forms a little swelling of the nerve trunk and is known as the spinal ganglion. The cell bodies of the ventral root fibers lie in the ventral horn of the central gray matter.

Degeneration and Regeneration of Nerve Fibers.—From our discussion of Wallerian degeneration (p. 137), it will be seen that cutting the ventral root at *g*, Fig. 267, results in the degeneration of that part of the efferent fibers lying peripherally to the section (i.e., from *h* on) and leads to motor paralysis. On the other hand, section of the dorsal root at *j* causes degeneration of that part of the afferent fibers lying between the cut and the cord and extending into the cord to the synapse; this is associated with the abolishing of the sensory impressions from that part of the body to which the fibers of the cut root are normally supplied. In the regeneration of the nerve fiber which may follow this degeneration, the formation of the myelin sheath does not take place until the completion of the axis cylinder. This also holds true in the growth and development of the central nervous system in the fetus or child. As the nerve fibers in the central nervous system are devoid of neurilemma, it is evident from our discussion on page 137 that no regeneration can take place in the spinal cord or brain.

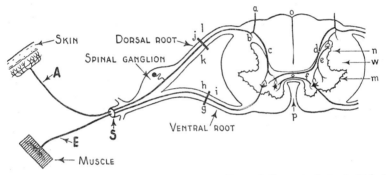

Fig. 267.—Diagram illustrating a cross-section of the spinal cord and the reflex arc. *a*, *b*, and *c*, branches of a dorsal root fiber which has its cell body in the spinal ganglion; *d*, a dorsal root fiber crossing over to the other side of the cord and making contact with the motor neuron; *e*, an internuncial, or association, neuron; *f*, a commissural neuron; *m*, the ventral horn of the central gray matter; *n*, the dorsal horn; *o*, dorsal fissure; *p*, ventral fissure; *A*, an afferent nerve fiber; *E*, an efferent nerve fiber; *S*, a spinal (mixed) nerve. Other letters are explained in the text. (After Ransom.)

Reflex Arc.—In the gray matter of the cord the afferent and the efferent nerve fibers come into contact with each other as shown in Figs. 26 and 275. The point of contact between neurons is known as the *synapse* (*syn*, together; *aptein*, to clasp). Generally we find a third neuron, *e*, in Fig. 267, intercalated between the afferent and the efferent neurons; this is frequently spoken of as an *internuncial neuron*. The neural pathway between the receiving and responding organ is called the reflex arc and forms the *physiologic unit* of the central nervous system.

When a ventral root of the spinal cord is cut, at *g*, Fig. 267, and the peripheral end, *h*, is stimulated, the muscle connected with this nerve is thrown into activity; the nerve conducts the impulse from h, i.e., from the cord, to the responding organs: for this reason the ventral nerves are called efferent nerves. As most efferent nerves convey impulses to the muscles, they are frequently spoken of as motor nerves. Stimulation of the central end, i, has no effect. On the other hand, when the peripheral end, k, of the cut dorsal root is stimulated, there is no effect, while stimulation of the central end, l, causes pain. Hence the dorsal roots contain sensory, or afferent, fibers which carry the impulses toward the central nervous system.

Neural Contiguity.—In regard to the connection between two neurons, it is now generally conceded that at the synapse the branches of the two neurons do not continue the one into the other but only make close contact with each other; that is, there is neural contiguity but not continuity. As evidence of this we may mention the fact that degeneration of an afferent neuron does not extend into the efferent neuron but stops at the synapse. The synapse may be pictured as a gap between two neurons.

The Synapse.—The point of contact formed between two neurons is characterized in several important respects; in some of these it differs quantitatively, if not qualitatively, from the nerve fiber. And it is these peculiarities of the synapse that determine to a large extent the coordinated responses by the animal to environmental changes. In this chapter, as we study the nature of reflex actions, we shall discover the following characteristics of the synapse:

1. The synapse can transmit impulses only in one direction.

2. The synapse offers more resistance to the passage of an impulse than the nerve fiber does.

3. It is highly susceptible to fatigue.

4. It is very vulnerable to the action of many chemical compounds which either increase or decrease its conductivity.

5. There is considerable power of summating and of inhibiting impulses.

6. The synapse is very susceptible to the lack of oxygen.

7. It is highly probable that the transmission of impulses across the synapse differs radically from that along the nerve fiber; the former is of a humoral (chemical), and the latter of an electrical, nature.

The function of the synapse is not merely to serve as a point of communication between two neurons, but as *a structure of greater and highly variable resistance,* i.e., possessing less and variable neural conductivity.

Unidirectional Transmission.—By experimentation it has been shown that in the central nervous system an impulse can pass along a certain route in only one direction. If, in Fig. 267, the afferent nerve, *A*, is stimulated, the impulse passes up to and across the synapse and thence down the efferent nerve, *E*, to the muscle. On the other hand, when *E* is stimulated, the impulse passes up this nerve to the synapse but does not reach the nerve, *A*, as shown by the absence of the action current in *A*. As it has been demonstrated that this blocking of the impulse is due neither to the nerve fiber nor to the cell body, it must be a function of the synapse which allows an impulse to pass over it in one direction but never in the opposite direction; this has been variously called the *irreciprocity of synaptic conduction,* the *law of Forward Direction,* or the *valve action of the synapse.*

Humoral Synaptic Conduction.—It is generally held that the transmission of an impulse from a peripheral nerve to the next protoplasmic structure (a muscle, gland, or another neuron) is brought about by a chemical mediator, either in the form of acetylcholine or an adrenalin-like compound (see pp. 219, 221, 382). It would, therefore, not seem improbable that this method of conduction may also occur across the synapse in the central nervous system. Many features of neural activity (e.g., summation, after-discharge, fatigue) are most explicable on the neurohumoral basis.

Short and Long Reflex Arcs.—While the reflex arc traversed by the nerve impulse is frequently pictured, for the sake of simplicity, as consisting of an afferent fiber making connection with a single efferent neuron (with perhaps an internuncial neuron), in reality the structure of the central nervous system is far more complex. After an afferent fiber has entered the cord by way of the dorsal root, several possibilities are open. It may, as shown at *1* in Fig. 275, make connection with an internuncial neuron, *2*, which takes the impulses to the motor neuron, *3*, on the same side, or with *4* on the opposite side of the cord. In this example the impulse leaves by the same segment of the cord as it entered; this forms a short reflex arc. The majority of the afferent fibers, *a*, soon after entering the cord, split into an ascending, *ab*, and a descending branch, *db*, which respectively travel up or down the cord for a certain distance to make connections with efferent neurons, *e*, at various levels of the cord; these form the long reflex pathways and serve to connect the sense organs of, say, the feet with the muscles of the hands, or the reverse. In their ramifications in the spinal cord (Fig. 275), both the ascending and the descending branches of a single afferent fiber may divide into many branches so as to make synaptic connections with a large number of efferent neurons. This enables an impulse over a single afferent fiber to throw many effectors into action. On the other hand, a given motor fiber may receive impulses from two or more afferent fibers; a simple case of this is illustrated in Fig. 275 where motor fiber, *4*, may receive impulses from the afferent neuron, *1*, and, by intervention of internuncial neurons, from neuron, *a*. In consequence of this arrangement the activity of a given effector may be due to the stimulation of one of several sensory surfaces.

III. REFLEX ACTIONS

When the stimulation of a sensory surface causes activity of a muscle or gland, this action is spoken of as a reflex action. For this a reflex arc is necessary. When a reflex action is a well-defined action and results from the proper stimulation of a definite sensory nerve, the connection between the afferent and the efferent nerves is called a reflex center. Such a center, e.g., the respiratory center, is made up of a large number of synapses formed by the arborizations of the axon and dendron of the afferent and efferent fibers and their internuncial neurons. A reflex action evoked by the stimulation of an afferent nerve is never a single contraction of an individual muscle, such as we elicit by the stimulation of a motor nerve fiber; it is nearly always a complex, coordinated action involving two or more parts, and similar to that executed by the animal in normal life. As our physical and mental life is so largely a stimulus-response phenomenon, the importance of reflex actions cannot be overestimated.

1. **Involuntary.**—Reflexes differ from certain other activities in not being volitionally performed; indeed, reflexes may take place without the individual being conscious of them, as, for example, the constriction of the pupil.

2. **Specificity and Predictability.**—To study reflex actions it is necessary that the brain, which so largely influences the results of sensory stimulation, be removed. When this is done, as in a frog by pithing the brain with a needle thrust through the foramen magnum, the animal is known as a "spinal animal." Immediately after this operation the frog is perfectly flaccid, appears lifeless, and responds to no form of stimulation. This condition of spinal or neural shock passes off after a variable length of time and proper stimulation now evokes reflexes. These reflexes are very precise: that is, when once we have learned that under stated conditions a given stimulus produces a certain reflex action, we can predict with

much certainty that the next application of this stimulus will call forth the same response. In a normal animal, especially in a more highly organized animal such as the dog, the result of a given stimulus may vary largely and cannot always be foretold, as common observation teaches us. This is due to the difference in the organization of the cerebrum and that of the spinal cord. In the cord the neural structure is relatively simple; a given afferent nerve fiber makes a very limited number of functional connections with efferent neurons and therefore the number of possible reflex actions following the stimulation of this afferent fiber is not great. But in the brain any given afferent impulse finds a multitude of outlets, and the number of possible responses is large. In the next place, the spinal cord is a fixed neural machine, it is not susceptible to modification by present stimuli. The spinal animal is a reflex machine, like a penny-in-the-slot machine. The cerebrum, on the other hand, is plastic, i.e., it is, especially in man, highly modifiable by present experiences; it is capable of "learning."

3. **Reflex Time.**—Not only does the synapse effectively block the impulse seeking to go in the abnormal direction, but it also offers more or less resistance to the passage of the impulse going in what we may call the normal direction. When the toes of a spinal frog are dipped in acid or are pinched, it takes a measurable length of time for the frog to remove them; this time, called the reflex time, is composed of the length of time it requires for the impulse to travel over the afferent and efferent nerves, the latent period of the muscle itself, and the time consumed in the passages of the impulse over the synapses. This last factor is called the central reflex time. In frogs this is about 0.01 second; in cats it varies between 0.003 and 0.005 second.

The length of the central reflex time is variable, depending upon the condition of the central nervous system, as is seen in fatigue and the influence of various chemical substances. The greater the number of synapses the impulse travels over, the greater will be the delay.

The effect of alcohol on the simplest neural activity, namely, the reflexes, has been investigated by Dodge and Benedict. They found that 30 c.c. of alcohol increased the latent period of the knee-jerk 10 per cent and decreased the thickening of the quadriceps, the contraction of which throws the leg forward, by 46 per cent. The latent period for the eyelid reflex was increased by 7 per cent and the extent of the movement of the lid was decreased by 19 per cent. Hence the reflex actions are slowed and lessened (see Chap. XXIX).

4. Purposefulness.—Reflex actions are generally characterized by being useful; they seem to be executed with a purpose. For example, when a spinal frog is suspended so that the lower legs hang free, and a small piece of filter paper moistened with dilute acetic acid is placed upon the thigh, the frog raises its foot and with it locates and removes the offending body. If the toes on the side operated upon are held so that the frog cannot use the leg on this side, the other leg will be employed. To a layman it may seem as if the spinal cord knows what it is about, as if it possesses consciousness.

We may give another example of this purposefulness. The muscles by which the limbs are bent are called the flexors and those which cause the straightening of the various parts of the limb are known as extensors; for example, the biceps is one of the flexors of the forearm, and the triceps is the extensor; these muscles are, therefore, antagonistic muscles. When the paw of a spinal dog is pricked with a pin, the flexors of the leg are thrown into action and the leg is drawn up; on the other hand, if pressure is applied to the ball of the foot, the leg is straightened and pressed down by the action of the extensors. It will be noticed that these actions taking place in the spinal animal, and, therefore, in the absence of consciousness, are of the same nature as those occurring daily in the life of the conscious dog. When a dog steps upon a sharp object which causes pain, the leg is hastily withdrawn; but when the paw comes in contact with the firm ground, the animal extends the leg and rests his weight upon it. In summary: *a reflex action is purposive and adaptive in that it is conducive to the well-being of the organism.*

The mechanism for the purposiveness of the above-described actions may lie in two factors: in the specificity of the sense organs and in neural connections. The touch or pressure corpuscles in the skin have a very low threshold for pressure stimulation but are not at all affected by that form of stimulation which normally results in pain. The reverse is true for the sense organs for noxious stimuli. If now we assume that the nerve fibers of the first-mentioned sense organs find their connection in the spinal cord with the motor neurons for the extensor muscles, and those of the nociceptors, with the flexor, the above-described purposive actions must inevitably occur.

5. Muscle Tonus: Proprioceptive Impulses.—When a muscle, or a group of muscles, is not displaying any outward sign of contraction, as, e.g., when the arms hang idly by the sides of the body, we might conclude that these muscles are in the state of complete relaxation. This, however, is generally not the true state of affairs, for these muscles, even though apparently at rest, are constantly in a state of mild contraction. This can be effectively demonstrated in the following experiment: A frog, with its brain destroyed, is suspended by means of a hook passed through the lower jaw; this frog will hang motionless for a long time and the muscles of the hind legs appear, at first sight, to be fully relaxed. It will be noticed that the hind legs have certain characteristic bends at hip, knee, ankle, and toes. Let us now open the abdomen and cut the roots of the left sciatic nerve, which innervates the musculature of the leg. This causes the left leg to hang a little more nearly straight, the toes to reach a little lower than those of the right leg, and the characteristic bends are not as marked as on the right side. These changes are due to the complete relaxing of the musculature which is now no longer receiving impulses from the spinal cord and is flaccid to the touch.

The constant mild contraction which muscles exhibit under normal conditions and which is present in the spinal frog is known as muscle tonus. Instead of cutting the sciatic trunk which contains both afferent and efferent fibers, the severing of only the dorsal (afferent) roots produces the same results, showing that the afferent impulses are necessary for the generation of tonus. As removal of the skin does not abolish the tonus in the frog, the afferent impulses must originate in the muscles and tendons.

It will be recalled that there flow from the skeletal muscles and tendons afferent impulses known as the proprioceptive, or kinesthetic, impulses. These impulses are formed in the afferent nerve endings (muscle spindles) and tendon organs as a result of stretching; on reaching the spinal cord, they are transferred by the efferent fibers to the muscle in which the impulses originated. The muscle is thereby reflexly thrown into a state of contraction; this is sometimes spoken of as the *stretch reflex*. In the frog of the above experiment, the action of gravity upon the legs causes a continual stretching of the muscles and tendons, and as a result the proprioceptive impulses are reflexly producing a continuous but subdued contraction of the muscles (tonus) by which they resist further stretching. The same phenomenon is well illustrated by the muscles which elevate the inferior maxilla. Due to gravity, the lower jaw has a constant tendency to drop; but the proprioceptive impulses created by the stretching of the muscles keep them in constant tonus, and as a result the mouth is kept closed. These and similarly acting muscles are very appropriately called *antigravity muscles*. When gravity is no longer allowed to stretch the muscles, as during the recumbent position of the body, the tonus of these muscles is lessened. It is also lessened during sleep.

Muscle tonus is sometimes spoken of as a residual contraction or an incomplete relaxation of the muscle fibers. This interpretation, however, is not in accordance with the all-or-none theory of muscle fiber activity. It is highly likely that in a muscle with a certain amount of tonus a few fibers are contracted maximally; as these fibers undergo fatigue, others are thrown into activity. This may explain why a muscle can remain in tone for an almost unlimited time without experiencing fatigue. As the pull upon the muscle is gradually increased and the muscle is thereby increasingly stretched, more and more fibers are thrown into contraction so that the degree of tonicity increases with the demand. See Posture, p. 655.

The degree of tonus varies; it is less at the close of the day, especially if the individual is fatigued; it is diminished by sleep and anesthesia, depending upon the depth of these states. Tonus is influenced by mental excitement; joy and hope find expression in augmented facial tonus, erect shoulders and firm step; grief and worry lead to depression, hence the phrase, "his face fell," or "down in the mouth." While tonus can also be diminished voluntarily, its origin does not depend upon volitional impulses.

At this point we may call attention to the difference between the tonus of smooth and of skeletal muscles. While the former (as well shown by the action of sphincters) have an intrinsic tone and are therefore not dependent upon external nervous impulses, the tonus of a skeletal muscle is always a reflex action.

6. **Tendon, or Myotatic, Reflexes.**—When one lets the lower legs hang free, as by sitting on the edge of a table, striking the patellar ligament just below the knee-cap causes the lower leg to be extended and the foot to be kicked forward. This, known as the knee-jerk, or patellar reflex, is an example of the class of reflexes called tendon, myotatic, or stretch reflexes. The origin of these reflexes may be gathered from the accompanying diagram, Fig. 268. The patellar ligament, or tendon, attached to the tibia may be regarded as a continuation of the tendon of the quadriceps extensor by which the lower leg is extended. When this ligament is tapped, a slight and sudden stretching of the extensor muscle stimulates the proprioceptive sense organs in the muscle and its tendon; the impulse is conveyed by the afferent fiber from the extensor (the anterior femoral nerve) to the third and fourth lumbar segments of the cord and the efferent impulse thus created is sent back by the motor fiber to the muscle causing it to contract. The great sensitivity of the sensory end organs in the muscle may be learned from the fact that the stretching of a muscle by as little as $\frac{1}{20}$ mm. and for as short a length of time as

$\frac{1}{20}$ of a second is sufficient to evoke the jerk. Another example of tendon reflexes is the extension of the foot by the contraction of the gastrocnemius muscle when the tendon of Achilles is struck.

A tendon reflex is now regarded as a sudden increase in the muscle tonus normally present, and the magnitude of the reflex varies directly as the degree of the tonus; the first is, therefore, an index of the second. Conditions which increase muscle tonus, such as mental excitement or hyperexcitability of the nervous system, as in hysteria

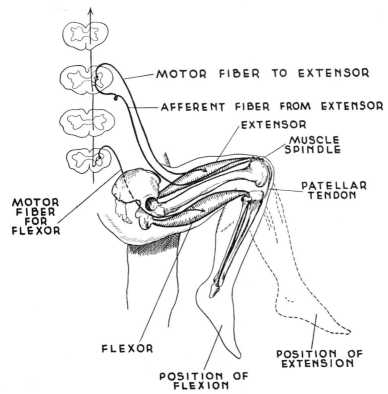

MOTOR FIBER TO EXTENSOR

AFFERENT FIBER FROM EXTENSOR

EXTENSOR

MUSCLE SPINDLE

PATELLAR TENDON

MOTOR FIBER FOR FLEXOR

FLEXOR

POSITION OF FLEXION

POSITION OF EXTENSION

Fig. 268.—Diagram to illustrate the knee-jerk. (Mettler: Neuroanatomy, The C. V. Mosby Co.)

and strychnine poisoning, also increase the extent of the knee-jerk; on the other hand, any decrease in the irritability of the nervous system (as by sleep, alcohol, a restful state of mind, etc.) is associated with a decrease in this reflex. From the above description it is evident that destruction of the dorsal fibers in the spinal cord as in tabes dorsalis (locomotor ataxia, the result of syphilis), or of the ventral horn cells as in infantile paralysis (anterior poliomyelitis—*polio,* gray; *muelos,* marrow) abolishes the knee-jerk. See also page 639.

7. Inhibition of Reflexes.—Most of us are familiar with the fact that an oncoming sneeze can be stopped by pressure applied to the upper lip. Sneezing is caused by a discharge of impulses from the respiratory center in the medulla, and the repression of the sneeze we may picture to ourselves somewhat in the following manner. The sneeze was initiated by, let us say, a cold draught striking the skin at *a* in Fig. 269. The impulse is sent from *a* to the center *H* where it is transferred from neuron *1* to *2* and from *2* to *3* across the two synapses *b* and *c,* and thence to the muscles, *d.* Now the synapses in the reflex arc always offer more or less resistance to the passage

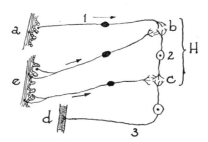

Fig. 269.—To illustrate inhibition of reflexes.

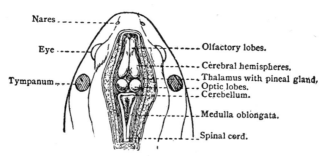

Fig. 270.—Diagram showing the brain of a frog.

of the nerve impulse from one neuron to another, and the resistance thus offered is variable, being influenced by many conditions. One of these conditions is the previous or simultaneous transmission of another impulse affecting the synapse. In Fig. 269 let us suppose that *e* is the sensory nerve of the skin of the lip which we stimulate by pressure; the impulse generated by its stimulation travels either to the synapse *b* or to *c,* causing the synaptic resistance to be increased, so that the impulse from *a* cannot pass to the muscles, *d.* Such an action is spoken of as the blocking of an impulse or inhibition of the reflex.

The inhibition of reflexes is a common phenomenon in the central nervous system. It is of the greatest importance for the proper execution of useful and necessary actions as is illustrated by the following laboratory experiment. Just back of the cerebral hemispheres in the frog's brain are located the optic lobes, Fig. 270. Let us remove the hemispheres only by making a transverse cut just back of the eyes. Now dip the long toe of the frog in 0.2 per cent sulfuric acid; the reflex time is found to be, say, one second. If a few crystals of sodium chloride are now placed upon the optic lobes, the reflex time, as determined in the manner just described, may be lengthened to ten or twenty seconds; and frequently the reflex action does not take place at all. The stimulation of the upper part of the central nervous system (optic lobes, in this instance) causes an inhibition of the reflexes from the lower part of the central nervous system.

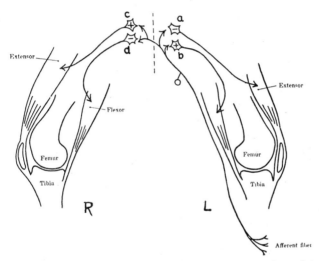

Fig. 271.—Diagram (after Sherrington) to illustrate the reciprocal innervation of antagonistic muscles. Excitation indicated by plus signs; inhibition indicated by minus signs. (From Mettler: Neuroanatomy, The C. V. Mosby Co.)

8. Reciprocal Innervation of Antagonistic Muscles.—If the paw of a spinal dog be pricked with a pin, as described in the above experiment, the flexors are not only thrown into greater contraction, but the tonus of the extensors is, pari passu, inhibited; that is, the subdued contraction of those muscles by which the extension of the leg is produced is lessened. This phenomenon is called the reciprocal innervation of antagonistic muscles. The advantage of this is apparent. But this matter of co-ordination of reflexes is still more complicated. There are not only an excitation of the flexors and an inhibition of the extensors of the leg that is painfully stimulated, but in the other leg there are excitation of the extensors and inhibition of the flexors.

This result is similar to that which occurs during normal life when the dog steps with one paw upon a sharp object (see Temporal Summation, p. 606).

From these experiments it is evident that very complex and highly co-ordinated reflexes are exhibited by the spinal animal. How can these be explained? The answer lies in the nerve connections, excitation, and inhibition as illustrated in Fig. 271. The afferent neuron which has peripheral endings in the skin, is in communication (not necessarily so directly as indicated in the diagram, but by the intervention of other neurons) with the nerves innervating the extensors and flexors of both legs. Nerves b and d are motor nerves for the left flexor and the right flexor, respectively; a and c are the motor nerves for the left extensor and the right extensor, respectively. When the afferent cutaneous nerve is painfully stimulated, all four of the above-named motor neurons receive impulses; but while the impulses received by b and c excite these neurons and thus cause contraction of the left flexor and the right extensor, the impulses received by a and d lead to inhibition of these neurons and thereby lessen the activity of the left extensor and of the right flexor. The inhibition of the antagonistic muscle, when the agonist is excited, is a gradual process, keeping pace with the contraction of the agonist. The co-ordination of this complicated reflex, which, as we said, is identical with the action of the neuromuscular mechanism during the normal life of the animal, is a question, therefore, largely of proper nerve connections, excitation and inhibition.

The dire results of the lack of the reciprocal innervation of antagonistic muscles by their proper excitation and inhibition are well illustrated in the effects of strychnine and tetanus toxin. Strychnine reduces synaptic resistance throughout the entire central nervous system so that the slightest stimulation of a sensory surface causes widespread muscular activity; and the inhibitory effects which normally accompany a reflex action seem to be converted into excitation. As the extensors in the frog's limbs are more powerful than the flexors, a frog under the influence of strychnine will become rigid in a fully extended position; as a result the frog may be held horizontally by holding it by the toes of the hind legs. See also section 13 of this chapter. When a patient with lockjaw wishes to open his mouth, instead of inhibiting the masseter and temporal muscles (by which the jaw is raised), these muscles, as well as the digastric and mylohyoid (the lowerers of the jaw) are excited; as a result the stronger closers overbalance the openers. It has been suggested that this may also explain the inability to swallow in case of hydrophobia.

We may at this point call attention to a marked difference between the inhibitory mechanism of the skeletal muscles and that of the cardiac and smooth muscles. While the cardiac muscle, and, for example, the intestinal muscles, are supplied directly with efferent inhibitory nerves (the vagus and splanchnic nerves, respectively), no inhibitory nerves to skeletal muscles of vertebrates are known. The inhibition of the last-named muscles is brought about by inhibition of the tonic discharges by their motor nerve.

In speaking of the innervation of antagonistic muscles, we must not fail to mention that antagonistic muscles are frequently called upon to contract simultaneously. For example, the forearm may be rigidly extended so that a considerable amount of external force is needed either to raise or to lower it; this is the result of the simultaneous contraction of both the flexors and the extensors. Whenever any part of the body or the whole body must be held in a rigid state, as in standing, antagonistic muscles are thrown into action at the same time.

9. **Spatial Summation of Impulses.**—The stimulation of two distinct sense organs may lead to the same reflex. Sudden chilling of the skin, under proper conditions, causes a sneeze; a bright light thrown into the eyes may have the same result. Such sensory stimulations are therefore able to reinforce each other. For example, the stimulation of the skin is not sufficiently strong to induce a sneeze; on now looking into a bright light (which by itself may also be subliminal) the sneeze takes place promptly. In Fig. 269, the skin, *e*, and the eyes, *a*, send their impulses to the sneeze center, *H*. From here the impulse reaches the responding organ, *d*, by the neuron, *3*. The impulse coming from *e*, although it was incapable of passing through the synapse at *b*, leaves its imprint upon the synapse. This imprint may be the local excitatory state (p. 129) which, although by itself too feeble, on being reinforced by the impulse arriving from *a* is able to generate an impulse in the neuron, *2*. According to the neurohumoral theory, the insufficient amount of the intermediate substance formed by the ineffective impulse from *e* is augmented by that formed by the impulse arriving at the center from *a*.

In the above experiment and diagram, the efferent neuron, *3*, leading to the muscle, *d*, is used by the impulses from two (*a* and *e*), or frequently from more than two, sense organs; for this reason the efferent nerve is called the *final common pathway*. In contrast with this, the afferent neuron leading from the sense organ *a*, or that from *e*, is used only by the impulses generated in its particular receptor; the sensory nerve fiber is, therefore, a *private pathway*. This explains why we find, according to Ingbert, fully three times as many afferent as efferent spinal nerve fibers. It must be evident that only those afferent impulses which lead to the same final common pathway can reinforce each other.

10. **Temporal Summation.**—It will be recalled from p. 129 that two subliminal stimuli may reinforce each other, so that a nerve impulse is generated. This also applies to the reflexes. A single induction shock applied to a sensory nerve, *a*, in Fig. 269, even though sufficiently strong to create an impulse, is generally ineffective in causing the contraction of muscle *d*, but a series of from 10 to 40 shocks is followed by a response. The mechanism of temporal summation* is similar to that of spatial reinforcement, if we accept the humoral theory of synaptic conduction. The principles underlying spatial and temporal summation or facilitation form, no doubt, the basis of habit formation (see subject, Conditioned Reflexes, in the next chapter).

Two sensory stimulations can cause summation only if the results of the stimulations are individually of the same nature and therefore reinforce each other; the impulses thus generated will then use the same final common pathway. But if the results of the two stimulations are antagonistic to each other, no reinforcement, but inhibition, takes place; in other words, the execution of every reflex action is associated with the inhibition of all reflexes antagonistic to the one taking place. This is especially true for the protective reflexes which are generally induced by noxious stimuli, accompanied with pain, and designed to maintain the welfare of the body. Common observation teaches us that these reflexes always have the right of way over less urgent reflexes; the limping of a dog with a sore foot is an illustration to the point.

11. **Graded Synaptic Resistance.**—All the various sensory neurons in the central nervous system may communicate with all the motor neurons in it; theoretically the impulse over any given sensory nerve may be transmitted to any efferent nerve—see Section 13. Normally this does not happen because, while all synapses offer resistance to the transmission of impulses, the amount is not the same for all. To illustrate by means of Fig. 272: The sensory surface *a* is connected, by means of the afferent nerve *k*, with neuron *l*, which in turn is connected with the two efferent neurons, *m* and *n*, innervating the two muscles, *e* and *f*. Between these two efferent neurons (*m* and *n*) and the neuron *l* are the two synapses *c* and *d;* of these two, *d*, let us say,

---

*To these phenomena various terms have been applied, such as augmentation, induction, facilitation, canalization, reinforcement, etc.

offers more resistance than *c*. If under these conditions a medium strength stimulus is applied to *a*, the impulse will be able to pass *c* and cause muscle *e* to contract, but muscle *f* will remain quiet because the greater resistance at *d* blocks the impulse. In other words, the impulse follows the pathway of least neural resistance, which is the pathway most frequently used. When the stimulation of *a* is severe, the impulse may break through the high resistance at *d* and both muscles will contract.

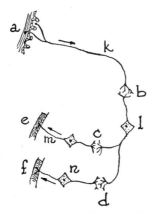

Fig. 272.—To illustrate graded synaptic resistance.

We may illustrate the above by a simple experiment. Placing a finger of the right hand upon an uncomfortably warm object causes the reflex contraction of the flexors of the right arm, and the hand is withdrawn; but, if the object is very hot so that a severe stimulation occurs, both arms are thrown into action. Indeed, with a very strong stimulation, the impulses may spread to the muscles of the legs; to those of the chest and the larynx, the individual crying out with pain; the impulses may cause the pupils of the eyes to dilate; the heart will no doubt be affected; constriction of certain blood vessels takes place; the adrenals may be caused to secrete more abundantly; the impulses reach the cerebrum and a sensation of pain is created. If all the various synapses offered the same amount of resistance, the impulses from the slightest stimulation would flow into so many efferent channels and produce such a multitude of actions that the result would be highly inco-ordinated and of no value to the organism. Following the humoral theory, graded synaptic resistance is a matter of the concentration of the hormones formed at the various synapses.

12. **Irradiation.**—The spreading of impulses throughout the central nervous system is known as irradiation. The extent of this

spreading is determined by the strength and duration of the stimulus applied to the afferent nerve and by the amount of resistance offered by the synapses of the various reflex arcs. The impulse from a feeble sensory stimulation leaves the spinal cord on the same side and at the same segment by which it entered—a unilateral reflex. A somewhat stronger impulse may cross over to the other side of the cord but leaves at the same segment. When the afferent impulse is still stronger, it may pass up or down the cord and issue at two or more segments, but the resulting activities are of a cooperative nature so as to give rise to orderly and useful reflexes.

13. Convulsive Reflexes.—Under certain conditions a mild stimulation of a single sensory nerve fiber may irradiate throughout the whole extent of the central nervous system and may send efferent impulses to practically every muscle of the body; the result is known as a convulsive reflex, or a convulsion. A convulsive reflex, distinguished from the other reflexes, not only is more general, but the

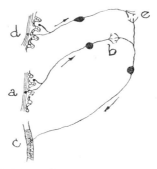

Fig. 273.—To illustrate synaptic fatigue.

resultant action is usually not properly co-ordinated and not purposeful. Convulsive reflexes may be caused by an abnormal condition of the central nervous system, as in strychnine poisoning, tetanus (lockjaw), and hydrophobia, by which the resistance offered by the synapses is greatly reduced; they may also be caused by a powerful sensory stimulation as in severe cases of neuralgia. The cessation of the convulsive reflexes on the severing of the dorsal (afferent) root fibers demonstrates that the functions of the cord do not occur spontaneously. Under the most favorable circumstances (strychnine poisoning) the spinal cord fails to discharge impulses unless it previously received impulses from the receptors.

14. Fatigue of Reflexes.—The response of a muscle, c in Fig. 273, to long-continued stimulation of a given sensory surface, a, soon shows fatigue. If now another receptor, d, which discharges impulses by the same final common pathway to the muscle be stimulated, responses of renewed vigor ensue. Clearly, the muscle was not fatigued and, as we have learned, the nerve fiber cannot undergo fatigue; hence, the synapse at *b* must have been the seat of the fatigue. As in a muscle-nerve preparation, the part of the central nervous system most susceptible to fatigue is the junction between two histologic structures; i.e., the synapse.

The greater susceptibility of the synapse to chemical changes is also illustrated by the more pronounced influence of anesthetics (ether) upon this structure as compared with that upon nerve fibers and muscles. Again, while in a frog the reflexes are abolished in about thirty minutes because of lack of oxygen, the nerve trunks retain their power of conductivity for three or more hours under the same condition.

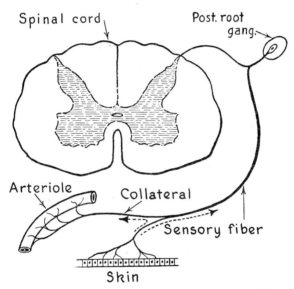

Fig. 274.—Diagram of an axon reflex in a sensory nerve fiber of the skin. (Macleod; Physiology in Modern Medicine, The C. V. Mosby Co.)

15. **After-Discharge.**—The strong stimulation of an afferent nerve may cause impulses to flow into the efferent nerve after the cessation of the afferent stimulation. This after-discharge originates in the reflex center and may continue from 0.1 second to several seconds. It may find an explanation in the humoral theory.

16. **The Axon Reflex.**—A peculiar reflex action which does not involve the central nervous system was discovered by Bruce. The application of mustard oil to the skin, Fig. 274, causes a dilation of the cutaneous blood vessels. As this result was obtained after cutting of the sensory nerve root the impulse cannot

have traveled through the spinal cord. That the peripheral cutaneous nerve fibers were involved, however, was demonstrated by the absence of the vascular reaction after the fibers were locally anesthetized.

The explanation of this phenomenon generally accepted is as follows: The cutaneous fiber gives off a collateral which innervates the blood vessels. An impulse generated by the stimulation of the sensory cutaneous fiber passes up this fiber, and, at the junction with the collateral, spreads into the collateral and thus reaches the blood vessel.

While other instances of axon reflexes have been discovered experimentally, the above is the only known axon reflex to operate normally in the animal body.

IV. THE CORD AS A CONDUCTOR

We have stated on various occasions that the primary function of the nervous system is to connect physiologically the receptors with the effectors. Since it is frequently desirable that a single given

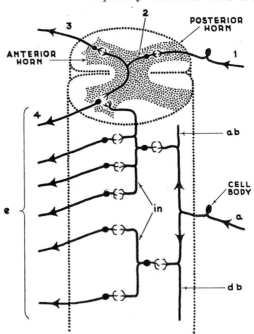

Fig. 275.—Diagram illustrating the neural connections in the cord. *1* and *a*, afferent neurons; *ab*, ascending branch; *db*, descending branch; *3*, *4*, and *e*, efferent neurons; *2* and *in*, internuncial neurons.

afferent neuron be in communication with 2 or even 20 efferent neurons distributed to as many responding organs, a place for these manifold neural connections must be supplied. This is the fundamental function of the brain and spinal cord, the gray matter of which may be compared with the central exchange of a telephone system where the wire carrying the incoming message is plugged in with the one carrying the message to the desired party. How the manner of the "plugging in" may be modified by delay (as in fatigue), inhibition, spatial and temporal facilitation, etc., we have considered in the foregoing pages.

If the stimulation of a sensory fiber causes a crossed reflex, an internuncial neuron always constitutes part of the reflex arc, *2,* Fig. 275. Again, some of the sensory fibers, *1,* Fig. 284, after entering the cord and other fibers, *2′,* originating in the cord, run up the entire length of the cord to end around neurons lying in higher parts of the nervous system. Other fibers, the projection fibers in Fig. 285, originating from cell bodies lying in the upper portions of the brain pursue their way down the cord for various distances. In the spinal cord the above-mentioned fibers are grouped around the gray matter in columns and tracts which we shall now briefly describe.

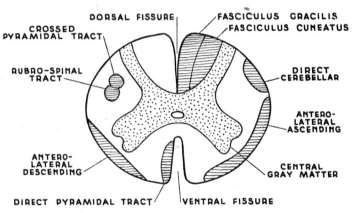

Fig. 276.—Diagram of a cross-section of the spinal cord. The gray matter is stippled. On the right, the shaded areas are columns containing ascending fibers; on the left, descending fibers.

Ascending and Descending Fibers.—As stated in the preceding paragraph, some of the fibers constituting the white matter of the cord carry impulses from the lower to the higher levels of the cord and even to the brain; these are called ascending, or afferent, fibers. Other fibers conduct impulses from the brain or upper parts of the cord to various lower levels of the cord; these are descending, or efferent, fibers. If at a certain level the cord be cut across, the ascending fibers, which have their cell bodies below the section, will degenerate above the cut; the descending fibers degenerate below the section. By making sections at various levels of the cord or brain and noting the position of the ascending and descending degenerating fibers (by histologic staining processes), the various fibers have been traced from their points of origin to the next relaying neuron. In this manner, and by observing pathologic conditions in man, it has been determined that the fibers conveying impulses up or down the cord are arranged in an orderly manner. We have space to mention only a few outstanding facts, and these can be better understood after we have become somewhat acquainted with the physiology of the brain; we shall therefore refer to these matters again in the following chapter.

In the cross-section of the cord shown in Fig. 276, the shaded areas in the right-hand half indicate the position of the ascending, and those in the left half, the descending fibers. It will be noticed that there are four main columns of fibers carrying ascending impulses: the two dorsal columns, namely, the fasciculus gracilis (column of Goll), and the fasciculus cuneatus (column of Burdach), carrying the impulses from muscles, tendons, and ligaments (proprioceptive) to the cerebrum and cerebellum. Some of these impulses are also conducted to the cerebellum by the direct cerebellar and by the indirect cerebellar (in the antero-lateral ascending) tracts. The posterior root fibers which conduct the impulses of heat, cold, touch, and pain end in the cord and make connections with fibers in the antero-lateral ascending tract.

Impulses from the cortex of the cerebral hemispheres (p. 622) descend in the cord by the crossed and the direct cortico-spinal, or pyramidal tracts. The cerebellum and other brain stations below the hemispheres send impulses down the cord in the rubro-spinal and the antero-lateral descending tracts. It will be noticed that there is quite a large amount of the white matter of the cord that is classed with neither the ascending nor the descending tracts; these areas, called the ground bundles, contain both short ascending and descending fibers which run up or down the cord for short distances and serve to connect neighboring segments of the cord. The fibers in the ground bundle, or fasciculus proprius, are sometimes referred to as association fibers.

CHAPTER XXIX

THE BRAIN

I. ANATOMY

The brain may conveniently be divided into three major divisions: the brain stem, the cerebrum, and the cerebellum (Fig. 277). The brain stem may be regarded as a much modified prolongation of the spinal cord; the cerebrum and the cerebellum are developed as two large expansions of the stem. In the lower vertebrates, the fishes, the brain stem and the cerebellum are fairly well developed, but the cerebrum is altogether lacking or but poorly represented. With advances in the scale of animal life, through the amphibians, reptiles, birds, and mammals, the cerebrum gradually not only becomes larger in size as compared with the rest of the brain but acquires, especially in the highest mammals and more particularly in man, a dominant place. We may therefore speak of the brain stem and cerebellum as the old brain; the cerebrum is of much later origin.

The brain stem is generally divided (Fig. 282) into:

1. Tween-brain; this includes the thalamus and geniculate bodies.
2. Mid-brain (corpora quadrigemina, cerebral peduncles).
3. Hind-brain (pons varolii from which spring the cerebellum and the cerebellar peduncles).
4. After-brain, or the medulla oblongata.

That part of the brain anterior to the tween-brain we shall designate as the fore-brain, using this term as synonymous with cerebrum or cerebral hemispheres.

The primary and fundamental function of the central nervous system, it will be recalled, is to furnish connections of various complexity between the afferent nerve fibers carrying impulses from the receiving organs and the efferent fibers transmitting impulses to the effectors. The brain and spinal cord constitute the great switchboard of our neural telephone system. The arrangement of the gray and white matter in the stem is much the same as that of the cord, inasmuch as the gray matter is centrally located and surrounded by the white nerve fibers. It is in the *central gray matter* that the above-mentioned connections between afferent and efferent fibers are made. In the lower forms of life with relatively few afferent and efferent fibers, this central gray matter of cord and brain stem was quite sufficient for the existing needs. But as the complexity of the receiving and the responding organs increased and as life could be more effectively carried on by a greater discrimination between the various stimuli befalling the animal and by a greater variety of responses to any given stimulus, a more extensive switchboard was required. This demand was met by the evolution of the cerebellum and, to a far greater extent, of the cerebrum. This last-named structure, similar to the old brain and spinal cord, is primarily concerned with receiving impulses from the many sense organs and, having properly evaluated these impulses, to discharge efferent impulses to the muscles and glands. It is exceedingly important to note that in thus receiving

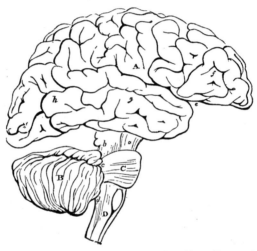

Fig. 277.—The brain as seen from the right side. Some of the parts are separated from each other. A, the cerebral hemisphere with f, the frontal, g, the temporal, and, h, the occipital lobes; e, fissure of Sylvius; B, cerebellum; C, pons varolii; D, medulla oblongata; a, peduncles of the cerebrum; b, c, d, superior, middle, and inferior peduncles of the cerebellum; a and b form the midbrain. (From Quain.)

and discharging impulses, *the cerebrum never makes direct neural connections with any receiving or responding organ;* it can only receive impulses from the sense organs and discharge impulses to the effectors by way of the old connections laid down in the brain stem and spinal cord.

Cortical Gray Matter.—In the human brain the two hemispheres of the cerebrum almost entirely overlap and conceal the rest of the brain, Figs. 266 and 278. Its gray matter is deposited as a mantle, or cortex (Fig. 280), on the exterior and covers the white matter lying in the interior of the hemispheres.

At many places the gray matter of the cortex dips down into the brain so that folds, or convolutions, Fig. 277, are formed which give

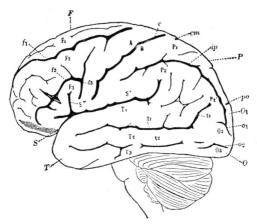

Fig. 278.—The brain, showing the main lobes and convolutions of the cerebrum, viewed from the left. *F*, the frontal lobe with F_1, F_2, and F_3, its superior, middle, and inferior convolutions; *A*, the precentral and, *B*, the postcentral convolutions; P, the parietal lobe with P_1 and P_2 the superior and inferior parietal convolutions; O_1, O_2 and O_3, the first, second, and third occipital convolutions; T_1, T_2 and T_3, the superior (first), middle, and inferior convolutions of the temporal lobe; *c*, central, or rolandiac, fissure; *S*, fissure of Sylvius.

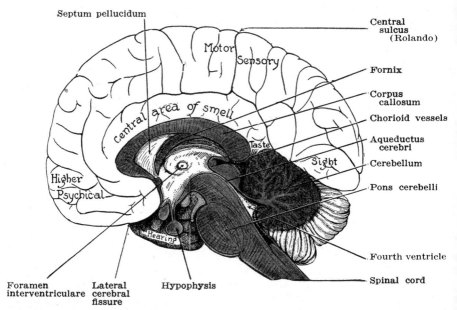

Fig. 279.—Medial surface of the brain.—(Pitzman: Fundamentals of Human Anatomy, The C. V. Mosby Co.)

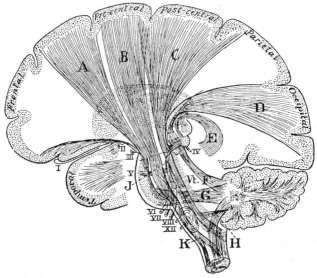

Fig. 280.—Diagram showing the projection fibers of the cerebral cortex and the fibers of the cerebellar peduncles. *A*, tract connecting the frontal convolutions with the cells lying in the pons; these cells are connected with the cerebellum by means of the middle cerebellar peduncle, *G*, *B*, the motor fibers of the pyramidal tracts which after crossing over to the opposite side in the medulla, *K*, descend the cord. *C*, the sensory fibers carrying the impulses for the tactile and motorial sensations to the postcentral gyrus. *D*, the visual tract; *E*, the auditory tract; *F*, the superior and *H*, the inferior cerebellar peduncles. The Roman numerals indicate the cranial nerves. The stippled areas indicate gray matter. (Starr.)

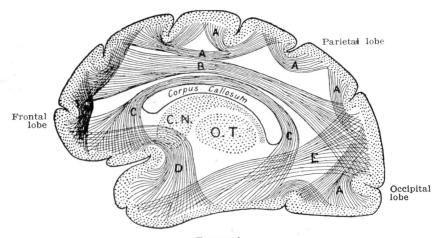

Fig. 281.—Diagram illustrating the association fibers of the cerebral hemispheres. *A*, between adjacent convolutions; *B*, between frontal and occipital areas; *C*, and *D*, between frontal and temporal areas; *E*, between occipital and temporal areas; *C. N.*, caudate nucleus; *O. T.*, optic thalamus. Gray matter is stippled. (Starr.)

the hemispheres, viewed from above, much the appearance of the kernel of an English walnut. By this means the amount of cortical gray matter is much increased; in general, the higher animals have a more convoluted cortex than the lower animals. The major divisions of the brain and the convolutions (gyri) of the convex surface included in each division are as follows (Figs. 277 and 278):

Frontal Lobe:
> Superior, middle, and inferior frontal and the precentral convolutions.

Parietal Lobe:
> Superior and inferior parietal and the postcentral convolutions.

Occipital Lobe:
> Superior and lateral occipital convolutions.

Temporal Lobe:
> Superior, middle, and inferior temporal convolutions.

The White Matter.—The nerve fibers, composing the white matter of the interior of the hemispheres, are processes either of the cortical cells or of the cells located in the central gray matter of the brain stem or spinal cord, Fig. 280. They are:

1. PROJECTION FIBERS which carry impulses
> *a.* Afferently from the cell bodies lying in the brain stem or cord to the cortex, and
> *b.* Efferently from the cortex to the lower parts of the central nervous system.

2. ASSOCIATION FIBERS which originate in cortical cells and carry impulses to other areas of the cortex on the same side, Fig. 281.

3. COMMISSURAL FIBERS which link the two cerebral hemispheres. The corpus callosum, shown in cross-section in Fig. 281, is composed of such fibers. By this and other commissures the parts of one hemisphere are connected with the various parts in the other.

II. THE BRAIN STEM

The various parts of the brain stem serve three purposes:

(*a*) Similar to the white columns of the cord, they afford passageway for nerve fibers in passing to lower or to higher levels in the nervous system.

(*b*) In the masses of gray matter located in these parts, impulses from above or below may be relayed to distant areas of the brain or cord. This will be specially considered in the next section.

(*c*) All the twelve pairs of cranial nerves (with the exception of the first pair, the olfactory nerve) are directly connected with the brain stem, either afferently or efferently or both. The efferent cranial nerves have their cells of origin in the central gray matter of the brain stem, and, therefore, the various parts of the brain stem can

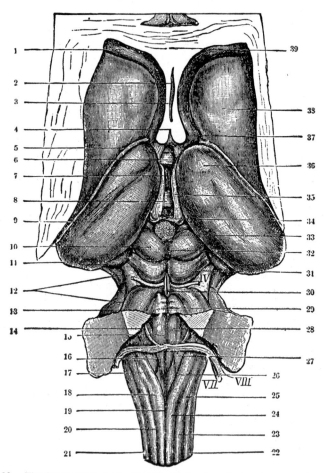

Fig. 282.—The brain stem and adjacent parts, dorsal view. *1*, anterior horn of lateral ventricle; *2*, fifth ventricle; *6*, anterior commissure; *7*, third ventricle; *8*, middle commissure; *10* and *31*, the corpora quadrigemina; *11*, the internal geniculate bodies; *13*, pons; *17*, restiforme body of the medulla; *19*, posterior fissure; *22*, lateral columns of the cord; *23*, funiculus cuneatus; *24*, funiculus gracilis; *33*, pineal body; *36*, thalamus; *38*, caudate nucleus; *39*, corpus callosum; *IV, VII,* and *VIII,* cranial nerves. (Gordinier.)

act as reflex centers. For example, some of the fibers of the third cranial nerve (the oculomotor) have their origin in the pupil-constricting center in the mid-brain. On the dorsal aspect of the mid-brain are seen four prominences, the corpora quadrigemina—Fig. 282,

10 and *31*—in which end some of the fibers of the optic nerve. The impulses created in the retina by strong photic stimulation are carried to these corpora; from there they are relayed to the constricting center and thence by the third cranial nerve to the sphincter muscle of the iris (p. 555) which on contraction causes constriction of the pupil. In our previous studies we have become acquainted with a number of important neural centers located in the last portion of the brain stem (the medulla oblongata), such as the respiratory and the cardio-inhibitory center.

III. THE THALAMUS AND THE CORTEX

Of special interest is a large mass of gray matter lying in the tween-brain, namely, the thalamus (Figs. 281, 282, *36*, and 283), and certain smaller masses lying in the immediate neighborhood, the geniculate bodies (Fig. 282, *11*), which in our discussion we shall include with the thalamus. The reason for their importance is twofold: (*a*) the thalamus is the seat of certain sensations (p. 627) and (*b*) it forms the chief relay station for impulses to the cortex.

The great anatomical distinction between the central gray matter of the cord and brain stem and the cortical gray matter lies in the fact that while many cells in the central gray matter send their fibers to the skeletal muscles and this gray matter is in direct neural connection with the receptors, this is never true for the cells in the cortical gray matter;* in other words, no single neuron connects the cortex with either the receiving or the responding organs. The influence which the impulses originating in the receptor have upon the cortex and the control exercised by the cortex over the skeletal muscle are always mediated by the intervention of neurons whose cell bodies lie in the central gray matter. The following will explain this readily.

Three Orders of Sensory Neurons.—The fibers carrying the impulses generated by the tactile, thermal, or painful stimulation of the skin, *e* in Fig. 284, enter the spinal cord by the dorsal root, *1'*, proceed upward for some distance and make synaptic connections with the neurons, *2'*. These neurons, called the second order of sensory neurons, *2'*, cross over to the other side of the cord and pass upward through the cord, medulla oblongata, pons, and midbrain to end around cells lying in the thalamus of the tween-brain. Here synaptic connections are made with the third order of sensory neurons, *3'*, which carry the impulses to the cortex of the postcentral convolution.

---

*The only exception to this is the olfactory nerve.

The kinesthetic impulses from the muscle spindles are carried in a similar manner, excepting that the neurons of the first order (Fig. 284, *1*) ascend in the columns of Goll and Burdach to end in arborizations around cells lying in the nucleus gracilis in the medulla. The cells of these nuclei send their axons, *2*, forward and after crossing to the other side of the medulla (and now known as the fillet, or lemniscus) pass through the brain stem and end in the thalamus. By the third order of neurons, *3*, the impulses are carried to the postcentral convolution. A neural arrangement similar to the above also exists for the eyes. The sensory epithelium of the retina is formed by the rods and cones, Fig. 243. The bipolar neurons convey the impulses to the ganglionic cells whose fibers constitute the optic nerve,

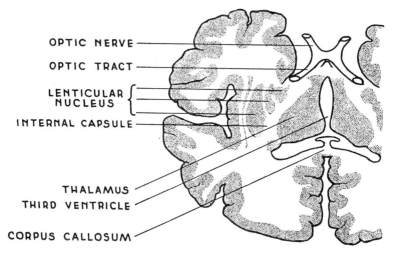

OPTIC NERVE

OPTIC TRACT

LENTICULAR NUCLEUS

INTERNAL CAPSULE

THALAMUS

THIRD VENTRICLE

CORPUS CALLOSUM

Fig. 283.—A transverse vertical section through the brain, showing the basal ganglia and the internal capsule. (Hewer and Sandes: The Nervous System, The C. V. Mosby Co.)

Fig. 284. By the optic nerve fibers the impulses are propagated to the external geniculate body which may be regarded as belonging to the thalamus. From here the projection fibers, *3″* in Fig. 284, convey the impulses to the occipital lobe of the cortex. The thalamus (*thalomos*, chamber) *may, therefore, be regarded as the port of entry for all incoming impulses on their way to the cortex.*

We may summarize: (*a*) All sensory impulses proceeding to the cortex traverse a chain of three neurons (primary, secondary and tertiary sensory neurons); (*b*) all impulses pass through the thalamus; (*c*) the impulses originating from stimuli to the left of the body are received by the right cerebral cortex and vice versa.

The Internal Capsule and the Projection Fibers.—The afferent fibers of the third order, which originate in the thalamus on their way to the cortex, pass through a very narrow passage between three masses of gray matter: the lenticular and the caudate neuclei and the thalamus, Figs. 281, 282, and 283. This passage is known as

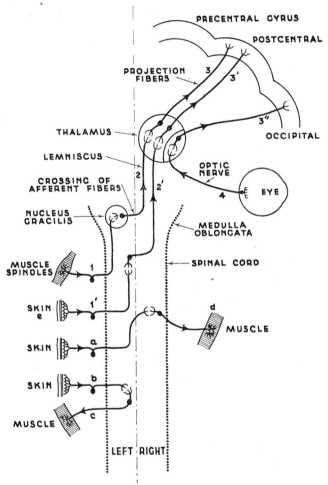

Fig. 284.—Diagram illustrating the most important ascending neural pathways between the spinal cord and the cerebral cortex. The internuncial neurons in *a* and *b* have been omitted. For explanation, see text.

the internal capsule, Fig. 283. On their way from the capsule to the cortex they spread out, like a funnel, and form the afferent projection fibers shown in Fig. 280. Collectively this mass of fibers is sometimes called the *corona radiata*. The fibers, Fig. 280, *C*, of the corona carrying the impressions for tactile and kinesthetic sensations

end in the postcentral convolution; those for vision, *D*, are known as
the optic radiation and end in the occipital lobe; those for hearing, *E*,
end in the temporal lobe.

Pathway Out of the Cortex.—As we shall learn shortly, the so-
called volitional impulses for the skeletal muscles are sometimes said
to "originate" in the precentral convolution, *A*, Fig. 278. The
cells, Fig. 285, lying in this area send out their fibers, called the di-

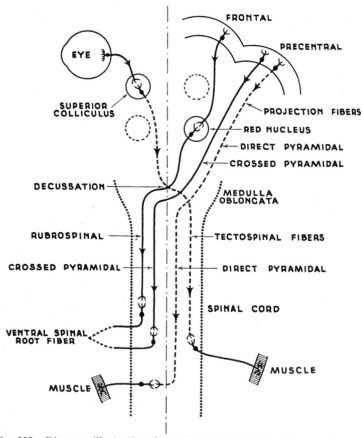

Fig. 285.—Diagram illustrating the main motor pathways between the cerebral
cortex and the nuclei of the brain stem and the efferent neurons of the spinal
cord.

rect or crossed pyramidal, or cortico-spinal, fibers through the interior
of the hemispheres. The pyramidal fibers form an important part
of the efferent projection fibers, *B* in Fig. 280, and with the afferent
fibers discussed above pass through the internal capsule. From here
they continue their way through the mid-brain and pons into the
medulla. In the medulla most of them cross over (decussation) to

the opposite side and enter the spinal cord; descending in the crossed pyramidal, or cortico-spinal, tract in Figs. 276 and 285, of the cord they end around neurons in the gray matter of the anterior horn. The spinal cells send out their fibers to the skeletal muscles. The pyramidal fibers from the cortex that do not cross over in the medulla pass down in the direct pyramidal, or cortico-spinal, tract (Figs. 276 and 285) and cross in the cord before making synaptic connections with the cells of the anterior horn. From this we may conclude that a *two-neuron pathway is concerned in conveying volitional impulses to the muscles and that each hemisphere governs the contralateral side of the body.*

IV. LOCALIZATION OF FUNCTION OF THE CEREBRAL CORTEX

By direct stimulation and by the removal of various parts of the cerebral cortex it was found that all areas do not perform the same function. Some areas were found to be more intimately associated with the activity of skeletal muscles; other regions appears to be more concerned with the reception of impulses from the body; an extensive amount of cortex seemed to function neither in the first nor in the second capacity. In accordance with these facts we may divide the cortex into: (1) motor areas, (2) sensory areas, (3) association areas (Fig. 286).

A. The Motor Areas

The stimulation of the precentral convolution (Figs. 278, *A;* 279, and 286) throws certain skeletal muscles into action and as a result the animal executes definite movements, such as extending or flexing the hind leg, closing the jaw, etc. It is therefore a motor area. This area is divided into many smaller areas, each of which is associated with a definite and restricted group of muscles so that the contractions resulting from the stimulation of any one of these smaller areas are limited to a few muscles. In the precentral convolution the various parts of the body are represented in a definite order; the leg area lies near the top, that is, next to the longitudinal fissure, the shoulder and arm area next, and at the lowest part of the convolution is the area for the muscles of the head. The experimental stimulation of any one of the motor areas in the precentral gyrus in a conscious patient did not elicit any sensation, except such as is normally associated with the contraction of a muscle or the movement of a limb.

Certain abnormal conditions, for example, a tumor, a splinter of bone, or the depression of the skull by fracture may stimulate one of the motor areas and thereby cause a certain muscle or group of related muscles to contract. As the impulse gradually spreads from this area to neighboring areas, there is an orderly ''march'' of the convulsions; for example, when the seat of irritation is in the hand area, the muscles of the hand will be the first to contract; this is followed by those of the forearm, upper arm, shoulder, face, trunk, etc. These convulsions, sometimes designated as Jacksonian epilepsy (''fits''), are generally abolished by the removal of the irritating body.

Upper and Lower Motor Neurons.—It will be recalled that the connection between the precentral motor area of the cortex and the skeletal muscle is formed by two neurons: the upper neuron whose pyramidal fiber extends from the cortex to the gray matter of the cord, and the lower neuron extending from the cord, by way of the efferent spinal root, to the muscle. As extirpation of a certain part of the precentral convolution is followed by the loss of the voluntary contraction of the muscle or muscles normally thrown into action by the stimulation of this area, the precentral area* is frequently spoken of as the seat of volitional motor impulses (see infra).

From the above description it is evident that the paralysis of a muscle may be due: (a) to the destruction of the pyramidal fibers of the upper neuron in the internal capsule, brain stem, or spinal cord or (b) to injury to the lower neuron. The former occurs not seldom as the result of a thrombus or embolus in a blood vessel, or the rupturing of the vessel, in or near the internal capsule, as, for example, in apoplexy (*plesso,* to strike), or a ''stroke.'' Generally this takes place only on one side of the brain and therefore leads to paralysis on the opposite side of the body (hemiplegia). As an example of a lesion of the lower neurons we may mention infantile paralysis, or anterior poliomyelitis. The results of lesions in these two locations differ in that:

a. Destruction of the pyramidal fibers abolishes the so-called volitional contractions but reflex contractions mediated by the brain stem or spinal cord and their efferent nerves are still possible, for proper stimulation of an afferent nerve or a sensory surface may result in a visible contraction. A person unable voluntarily to contract a certain muscle or group of muscles of the face (as in smiling) will, under the influence of a strong emotion, use these muscles. As the afferent impulses for muscle tonus still have access to the second neuron of the efferent chain, the muscles are not entirely relaxed. Lesions of the upper motor neurons are not associated with any

---

*The old term, Rolandic area, is frequently used.

wasting of the muscles except such as is due to loss of voluntary contractions—*atrophy of disuse.*

b. When the lower motor neurons are involved, the paralysis is complete, both voluntary and reflex; and, as the tonicity is entirely abolished, the muscles are flaccid and they undergo great wasting—*atrophy of denervation.*

B. The Sensory Areas

In our discussion of the anatomy we have seen that the nerve fibers from the sensory surfaces find their second relay station in the thalamus (Fig. 284) or neighboring structures. From here fibers

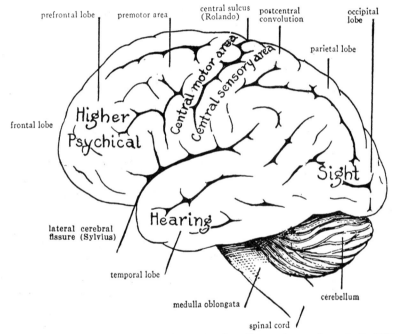

Fig. 286.—Lateral view of the brain showing the motor and sensory areas. (Pitzman: Fundamentals of Human Anatomy, The C. V. Mosby Co.)

of the third order proceed in the corona radiata (afferent projection fibers) to the various sensory areas of the cortex. Extirpation of these areas causes no motor paralysis, but is associated with a disturbance in the sensations. The stimulation of these areas also causes movements of the skeletal muscles; these movements, however, are comparable to those obtained by the stimulation of posterior spinal roots, and may therefore be looked upon as higher reflex actions. According to the sense organ concerned, the sensory areas are divided into:

1. **Body-Sense Area.**—The kinesthetic impulses from the muscles and the tendons and the impulses from the skin and the underlying tissues are brought by the above-described route to the contralateral postcentral convolution (Figs. 280, 284, and 286). This area is therefore known as the somesthetic (*soma,* body; *aisthesis,* sensation) or body-sense area. However, certain neighboring structures, such as the superior parietal lobe (Fig. 278, P_1), are also concerned in this function. The somesthetic area receives impulses by which we become aware (*a*) of the position of our limbs in space, (*b*) of the particular area of the skin stimulated (localization, p. 584), (*c*) of the number of discrete points of the skin stimulated (tactile discrimination), and (*d*) of the relative weight of an object placed upon the supported hand. By the proper evaluation of these various items of information and by the proper synthesis of the necessary factors we arrive at a conclusion as to the weight, texture, size, and shape of an object; i.e., we have three-dimensional knowledge, or stereognosis (*stereo,* solid; *gnosis,* knowledge). It is also in this area that we appreciate slight differences in the intensity of stimuli leading to pain and temperature sensations.

2. **The visual area** (Figs. 279 and 286) occupies that part of the occipital lobe known as the cuneus, and receives the impulses by means of the tween-brain and optic radiation (*D,* in Fig. 280) from the retina. When the upper part of this area is stimulated, the eyes are turned downward; stimulation of the lower part causes the eyes to be turned upward. Destruction of one occipital lobe results in blindness of the corresponding halves of both retinas, and therefore of the opposite sides of the field of vision. The reason for this lies in the semidecussation of the optic nerves, as illustrated in Fig. 249. From this figure it will be seen that destruction of the left occipital lobe must cause blindness of the left half of both the right and the left eyes, and blot out the right field of vision.

Surrounding the visuosensory center where the fibers of the optic radiation terminate is a field the destruction of which brings about a condition in which the individual retains the power to see but fails to recognize what he sees. This is sometimes called mind, or psychic, blindness.

3. **The Auditory Area.**—The temporal lobe, Fig. 281, receives the auditory radiation (*E,* Fig. 280) whose fibers receive impulses, by way of the internal geniculate bodies, from the auditory nerve. Hence it is generally stated that the center for hearing is located in the temporal lobe, especially in its superior convolution. Stimulation

of the inferior gyrus on one side causes the animal to prick up his ears and turn his eyes and head in the opposite direction.

4. **The center for the sense of smell** is said to be located in the uncus of the hippocampal convolution (Fig. 279).

5. **The center for taste** is held by some to be situated near the center for smell.

The Thalamus and Sensations.—It is generally agreed that the cerebral cortex is the great organ of consciousness; in it the incoming impulses arouse those changes which we call sensations. But it is now held that the activities of some portions of the thalamus, which are better developed in man than in the lower animals, are also associated with the production of certain sensations; however, these differ materially from the sensations aroused in the cortex. In certain diseases of the cerebrum the individual undergoes a remarkable change in his interpretation of the stimulations befalling him. On clasping a glass of hot water, he has an exaggerated feeling of heat and his response to this impression is excessive. The normal person has the power to discriminate between relatively small variations in temperature or pressure; he is able to localize the source of the stimulation with respect to his own body; by his sensations he recognizes the shape and weight of the object; and the texture (hardness, smoothness, etc.) of the object is known to him. This refined and composite mental impression of the stimulating object (the epicritic sensations) gives the individual a better and more thorough interpretation of the outside world.

In contrast, the thalamic sensations are crude (protopathic) and are evoked only by extreme stimulations (heat by temperatures above 38° C. and cold, below 24° C.); they call forth little more than the feeling of comfort or discomfort, or of pleasure or pain; that is, the thalamic activity influences largely the affective aspect of our sensations. The responses associated with these gross sensations partake of the all-or-none phenomenon; hence the exaggerated movements. Because of its greater power to appreciate small variations in the strength of the stimuli and to correlate the various impulses brought to it over different fibers (heat, pressure, contact, etc.), the cortex is able to respond in a graded manner to the stimuli. Moreover, the influence of former similar stimulations modifies the response to a present stimulus.

C. Association Areas: Integration

When the motor and the sensory areas have been properly located, there still remains a large amount of cortex unaccounted for. These areas do not receive either sensory or motor projection fibers from the corona radiata; and, therefore, unlike the sensory and motor areas they are not directly connected with the central gray matter. Their stimulation causes no activity of skeletal muscles, and their removal leads to no sensory or motor paralysis. For this reason they were formerly spoken of as latent, or silent areas; at present they are known as the association areas. As these areas are not only the most extensive but also have the greatest complexity of structure in the human brain, they must serve in a manner that distinguishes man, at least quantitatively, from the lower animals.

That man does not excel in the multiplicity of muscles; that he is by no manner of means the fleetest, nimblest, or strongest animal; that in some respects his sense organs are inferior are well known. What characterizes man is the larger number of ways in which he is able to meet a given environmental situation.

INTEGRATION

In very lowly organized forms of life the afferent impulse from a certain sense organ may call forth activity without much, if any, regard to the impulses from other sources; many environmental changes inimical to life pass unnoticed; and frequently the various responding organs do not cooperate with each other in the necessary adjustment. It is somewhat comparable to a horde of very primitive savages fighting another horde; each man largely fights for and by himself as best he can. With ever greater development there comes more and more of that integration (*integer,* whole) which insures the coordinated activity of many individuals for a mutually beneficial end. The horde thereby becomes a well-organized, highly-disciplined, and well-officered army.

The mechanism by which this integration is brought about is one of the most important as well as one of the most mysterious phases of our life. No doubt the various factors, such as spatial and temporal summation, rhythmicity of the nerve impulse, inhibition, and graded synaptic resistance, which so largely modify conduction in the spinal cord, play an increasingly important part. But whether in this manner it is possible to explain integration in its entirety and thus transform the cerebral hemispheres into a glorified spinal cord and all its activities into magnified reflexes is doubted by some investigators. "Mental experience still eludes analysis in terms of reflex action." But whatever factors are able to render understandable any cortical operation should be welcomed in our endeavor to unravel the intricacies of cerebration.

Three factors are apparently of prime importance: (1) each sense organ is associated with a great number of discrete groups of muscles in various parts of the body; (2) the result of the stimulation of certain sense organs may be modified by the simultaneous impulses from practically all the other sense organs; (3) the result may also be modified more or less by the effects of previous stimulation not only of this particular but of other sense organs (memory). That the above factors may be operative necessitates: (*a*) a large number of neural connections between the sense organs and the responding organs, (*b*) a plastic or modifiable neural machinery. These factors we may now discuss somewhat in detail.

a. Neural Connections.—It will be recalled that neurons may be classed as afferent, efferent, and internuncial neurons. In the spinal cord and brain stem a very large number of neurons belong to the first and second of these classes. In the cortical gray matter, none of the millions of neurons (excepting a few forming the olfactory nerves) belong to these two classes; they all serve exclusively as internuncial neurons. Compared with those found in the cortex, the number of internuncial neurons in the central gray matter is very limited.

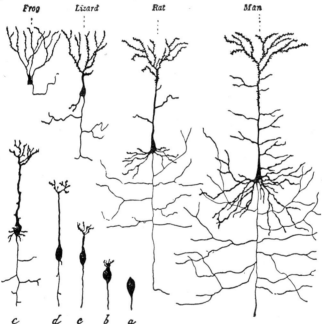

Fig. 287.—Cells from the cerebral cortex of frog, lizard, rat, and man, showing the progressive increase in size and complexity. The cells *a, b, c, d,* and *e,* show the development of the pyramidal cells in the embryo. (Ramon y Cajal.)

The neurons in the cortical gray matter differ from those in the central gray matter in their complexity of structure. Furthermore the cells in the highly developed cortex of man are more complex than those found in the cortex of the lower animals. In Fig. 287 is shown the simplicity of the cortical neurons of the frog and lizard as compared with those of rat or man. Because of this difference in structural complexity the number of synaptic connections possible between the afferent and efferent fibers and their internuncial neurons is tremendously greater in man than in any of the lower animals.* For the large number of internuncial neurons between the incoming and outgoing cortical impulses room must be found. We find the cells of origin of the internuncial, or, as they are known in brain anatomy, the association fibers in the association areas. Attention has already been drawn to the fact that these fibers are connected in every conceivable manner with the various sensory and motor areas; Fig. 281.

As an illustration of the widespread ramifications of the neurons and their countless connections with each other and therefore demonstrating the necessity for integration, let us take the stimulation of the eyes. Impulses from the retina are brought to the external geniculate bodies, which we may regard as subsidiary of the thalamus; thence the impulses, by the afferent projection fibers, reach the occipital lobes of the cortex. Each optic nerve contains not less than 400,000 nerve fibers, each one capable of conveying impulses to the brain. Such a large number of afferent fibers is able to make an almost countless number of junctions, by way of association fibers, with the cortically efferent neurons. And it is a familiar fact that photic impulses may affect the salivary glands, the heart, muscles of the blood vessels and alimentary canal, the skeletal muscles of the eyes, neck, arms, trunk (respiration), and legs. If all these incoming impulses were allowed to descend to all these organs, orderliness of activity would be out of the question. But to make matters worse, the 1,200,000 (according to Ingbert) sensory fibers of the dorsal roots and the added thousands of the nerves of taste, smell, and hearing, are all potentially connected with the cortex. Many of these fibers are stimulated constantly, and were no unification to take place, bedlam would ensue. But the information gathered by the various receiving organs (the intelligence department of our body) is sent to the association areas (the headquarters) by which each item of information is properly evaluated and from which the proper orders can be sent by way of the central gray matter (the subordinate officers) to the various effectors (the soldiers in the ranks).

IMPORTANCE OF AFFERENT IMPULSES.—As the general officers cannot intelligently dispatch orders without ample information gathered by the intelligence department, so it seems impossible for the cortical cells to innervate the skeletal muscles of the body without

*Someone has estimated that on a basis of 10,000 million cortical neurons, the possible number of connections between them reaches the inconceivable magnitude of 1 followed by 15,000,000 ciphers. To print this number would require about 10 books of the type and size of this volume.

having received the proper sensory impulses. The reader may verify this, at least in one instance, by the following simple experiment: Swallowing is by many looked upon as an act which can be initiated by the will at any moment and volitionally executed. However, if we swallow the saliva present in the mouth and then immediately try to swallow again, we find it impossible to do so; "swallowing nothing" is an impossibility. For the muscular action of swallowing to take place, the muscles must be innervated, and, to obtain this innervation, certain sensory nerves must be stimulated; in this instance the sensory stimulation is the contact of the saliva or food with the walls of the mouth and pharynx.

Standing is also generally regarded as a volitional act; yet the indispensability of the afferent stimulations is well shown by the following:

A normal person, standing erect and with feet close together, finds no difficulty in maintaining this position when he closes his eyes, because the remaining afferent impulses (tactile, kinesthetic, and labyrinthine) are sufficient to cause the central nervous system to discharge the proper impulses to the muscles of equilibration. But in locomotor ataxia, or tabes dorsalis, the patient has lost his kinesthetic sensations and when the eyes are closed there remain only two sources of afferent impulses (labyrinthine and tactile); these are not sufficient to enable the nervous system properly to coordinate the muscles of equilibration; no matter how desirous the patient may be of standing, he is unable to do so.

In view of the above-mentioned facts, it is hardly correct to speak of the cortical motor areas as the seat of volitional impulses. The desire to perform a certain muscular act, let us say the closing of one's hand, is not formulated in that small cortical area the artificial stimulation of which results in this action. A motor area in the precentral convolution merely represents a point in the efferent nerve pathway of a reflex arc, and must not be regarded as endowed with any mysterious function not possessed by other parts of the arc.

A little introspection shows us that most of our so-called volitional choices are determined by present stimulations as modified by past experiences; *an experience is a stimulus-response phenomenon*. But even if we should grant the absolute freedom of choice, the execution of that choice is impossible without sensory impulses, as the above-discussed facts demonstrated. To emphasize this, we may add the following: When all the dorsal (sensory) spinal roots supplied to the fore limb in a monkey or man are severed, that limb is never again used for grasping; the complete absence of both the cutaneous and kinesthetic sensations has permanently paralyzed it for volitional activities. However, this paralysis is not associated with the cortical motor cells or their projection fibers, for the artificial stimulation of these areas in the precentral convolution elicits the normal contractions of the muscles and thereby the movement of the various parts of the limb.

b. Fixity and Plasticity of the Nervous System.—We have seen that, because of the relative paucity of the internuncial neurons in the gray matter of the cord and their simplicity of structure, the number of possible synaptic junctions is quite limited. Various neural connections in this gray matter are operative at birth, for the newborn child exhibits many reflex actions, such as sucking, swallowing, grasping, crying, urination, etc.; we frequently, but incorrectly, speak of them as being performed "instinctively." Although the activities of the spinal reflexes may be modified by augmentation, inhibition, after discharge and fatigue, the stimulation of a given afferent nerve always induces a certain type of response. In other words, the construction and therefore the operation of the cord gray matter are "fixed"; hence the responses are mechanical and predictable.

In this respect the cortical gray matter and its fibers are radically different. In the newborn, for all practical purposes, none of the millions of neural pathways in the cerebral cortex is active or operative; so far as we have knowledge, the infant is a pure reflex organism. Although in all probability the cortical cells do not increase in number after birth (except, according to some observers, during the first year of life), they continue to grow and develop so that an increasingly large number of synaptic connections is gradually made between the various parts of the cortex and between the cortex and the already functioning central gray matter. This formation of new neural pathways begins soon, if not immediately, after birth, and in a human being, in all probability, never needs to stop. It is by the formation of new neural patterns that an individual acquires new ways of responding to the stimulation of the receptors, i.e., he learns. *Its high degree of teachableness is the great outstanding attribute of the cerebral cortex.* To study this modifiability was, until Pavlov commenced his work on conditioned reflexes about 30 years ago, almost entirely a subjective matter and scarcely capable of objective demonstration and scientific interpretation.

CONDITIONED REFLEXES

In contrast with innate activities, there are other reactions which must be learned. A hungry dog, on being shown a piece of meat, has an increased flow of saliva; the hearing of a musical sound has no such effect. But Pavlov caused a certain tone to be produced while a hungry dog was shown and subsequently given a piece of meat. This experiment was repeated for a number of days; finally the dog's nervous system was so altered that the hearing of the particular sound was always followed, when the dog was hungry, by a flow of saliva, even though the meat was not shown or given. In ordinary speech we would say that the dog had learned to associate the hearing of this sound with the obtaining of a piece of meat; the flow of saliva was in anticipation, one might say, of a future stimulus.

The stimulus of eating the meat (taste) which is immediately followed by a flow of saliva is known as the *unconditioned stimulus* and the reflex evoked by it is the *unconditioned reflex;* the sound stimulus to which the animal finally learns to respond by salivation Pavlov called the *conditioned stimulus,* and the reflex called forth by this stimulus is the *conditioned reflex.* As we shall use these four terms a large number of times in the next few pages, we may abbreviate them as the US, UR, CS, and the CR, respectively. All learning, physical and mental, and all education depend upon the formation of CR; we may therefore profitably look into them a little more closely. As the reader proceeds from one paragraph to another, he might well stop to compare the results obtained by experiments on the dog's salivary glands with his own mental development.

1. **Relation Between Conditioned and Unconditioned Reflexes.**— The fundamental distinction between these two reflexes lies in the fact that UR are inborn; the CR are never acquired spontaneously; a CS is always associated with an US in the formation of a CR. The CS may either occur simultaneously with, or it may precede, the US, but no CR is ever formed by a CS following an US.

In the forming of CR various sense organs, such as the skin, nose, ears, and eyes, have been used. Conditioned reflexes have been obtained from the salivary glands, the skeletal muscles, the alimentary canal, vasomotor system, etc.

2. **Proper Sequence.**—The shorter the lapse of time between the CS and the US the more quickly the CR is established. A strong CS leads more rapidly to the formation of a new reflex; but if excessively strong it hinders. Again, a discontinuous conditioned stimulus has greater effect than a continuous stimulus.

3. **Weakening of Conditioned Reflexes.**—When the CS which created the new reflex is not applied for some time, the CR becomes weakened, but not entirely lost; it can be revived by a few applica-

tions of the conditioned and unconditioned stimuli. The less well the CR is established, the sooner it is lost.

4. The Extinction of Conditioned Reflexes.—If a CR has been established and the CS is then applied several times without the application of the US, the CR decreases and finally becomes entirely extinct. To illustrate: Salivation took place on the sounding of a certain musical note; if now this note is sounded a number of times without any meat being given to the dog, the amount of saliva secreted after the application of the CS becomes less and less and finally none is formed. However, when the CR has undergone only a partial decay, it can be speedily revived by the application of the US. The less firmly the CR has been formed (by but a few trials with both the CS and US), the sooner it becomes extinct.

5. Specificity and Discrimination.—When a musical sound of a certain pitch, say that of a tuning fork having 800 vibrations per second, is the CS, the animal will respond not only to sounds of this pitch but also to those considerably higher or lower. But if, while the animal is being conditioned to the sound of 800 vibrations, another sound of either slightly higher or lower pitch is also used but is never accompanied with, or followed by, the giving of any meat, the animal is finally able to discriminate between a sound of 800 and one of 812 vibrations per second. We may fittingly compare the poorly trained cortex to the poorly constructed radio receiver of a few years ago; the well-trained and thoroughly ''conditioned'' cortex is comparable to the modern set of great selectivity.

6. Summation.—It is possible also to cause summation of conditioned reflexes. A dog secreted 60 drops of saliva to the CS of smelling camphor; to the stimulation of the skin it responded with 30 drops; when the two stimulations were applied simultaneously the yield was 90 drops in the same length of time.

7. Inhibition.—Conditioned reflexes are very susceptible to inhibition. When the CS, for example, the stimulation of the skin, has been given and an unexpected sound occurs before the US is applied, the CR does not take place, or only feebly (distraction). Let us suppose that the CR to a sound has been thoroughly established. If the same sound is used but is immediately followed by a light stimulus and no meat is given, the animal does not acquire a CR to this combination of stimuli. The sound stimulus by itself causes salivation; but when the light stimulus is also used, it acts as an inhibitor to the sound stimulus.

8. Association.—To establish an altogether new CR, the CS must always be associated with the US; without this the CR cannot be

formed. *Learning always proceeds from the known to the unknown.*
Let us suppose that the animal is conditioned to a flash of light. If
now simultaneously with this a second stimulus, say, a musical note,
is applied, the animal associates the second stimulus with the first
CS so that, after a time, when only the note is heard (without the
light stimulus), the reaction takes place. In this manner one CR
may be built upon a previously acquired reflex; but in animals CR
beyond the third order have never been observed.

9. **Relation of Conditioned Reflexes to the Cortex.**—The formation of conditioned reflexes is dependent upon the cerebral cortex.
When the entire cortex is removed all CR are lost and cannot be regained; the UR, on the other hand, remain, for the inborn reflexes are
mediated by the central gray matter. The result of the ablation
of a limited area of the cortex depends upon the particular area and
the amount of cortex removed. To illustrate: A dog has been conditioned to a sound stimulus. Both temporal lobes (generally regarded as the site of hearing) are now removed with the following
results: (*a*) The unconditioned sound reflexes, such as pricking up
the ears, remain. (*b*) The conditioned reflexes based upon sound
stimulation of a simple nature, e.g., the striking of a gong, are temporarily lost but may be recovered to a limited extent. (*c*) The conditioned reflexes based upon more complex sound stimulation, e.g., the
calling of the dog's name, which require a greater power of analysis
and discrimination, spoken of in paragraph 5, are completely and
permanently lost.

The study of CR has thrown much light upon the intricate problems of animal psychology. For example: It has been shown by
conditioning the salivary secretion to sound stimulation that a dog
can hear sound waves of a rapidity of 120,000 vibrations per second,
a pitch far beyond the power of the human ear to recognize. On
the other hand, a dog is unable to distinguish between the various
colors if the intensities of the light coming from the colored objects
are equal; that is, while the animal can detect small differences in
light intensities, he is color-blind.

10. **Conditioned Reflexes Are Not Inherited.**—We stated a little
while ago that the salivation on seeing or smelling a piece of meat
is an UR. This, however, is not quite the truth. Newborn puppies
were reared without ever tasting meat but acquired reflex salivation
to various other forms of stimuli; when they were a year old, the
seeing or smelling of meat caused no flow of saliva. Although thousands of generations of dogs had successively acquired this CR, yet
each new generation has to learn it for itself. *Acquired reflexes are*

not transmitted from parents to their offspring. The acquired knowledge, skill, and education of a thousand generations of ancestors has never given the newborn offspring a better start. Education must start "from scratch" with each generation.

11. **Mass Action Versus Localization.**—Recent experiments by Lashley have shown that, at least in the lower animals, the physiologic and psychologic cerebral activity in response to a given stimulus and in the retention of a CR may be a more or less diffused process in which a large part of the cortex, rather than a sharply localized area, is concerned. This investigator found that, after a rat had learned how to run a maze or open a trapdoor in order to get at its food, a certain amount of its cortex could be removed without abolishing the newly organized habit, and this irrespective of the location of the lesion. Removal of more than a certain percentage of the cortex interferes with the retention of the habit or the formation of the habit in an untrained animal, and the extent of this loss in function is dependent on the amount of cortex destroyed and not on its location (excepting as noted below). The more complicated the problem learned, the greater the loss of function following the extirpation of a given amount of cortex. The results of his experiments on rats point "to the equivalence of function of all parts of the cerebral cortex for learning" and he therefore concludes that "the capacity to learn is dependent upon the amount of functional cortical tissue and not upon its anatomical specialization." To the above Lashley found one exception: If a rat had been taught to distinguish between an illuminated and a darkened compartment, the removal of the so-called visual cortex in the occipital lobe completely abolished the brightness discrimination habit, but destruction of no other part of the cortex had a comparable effect.

D. Dominance of the Cerebral Cortex

In the evolution of animal life, the central gray matter developed long before the cortical gray matter; hence in the lower animals the former is of far greater importance. As animals rose higher in the phylogenetic scale,* the cortical gray matter became greater in quantity and its connections with the cells of the primitive gray stem became more extensive; that is, the cortical gray matter was added to the nervous mechanisms already existing. And as the amount of cortical matter and its number of connections with the cells of the gray stem increased, its importance in the responses of the animal increased.

---

*Phylogeny (*phylon*, tribe; *gen,* to become), the history of the evolution of the race.

The various stages in the development of the individual (ontogeny) are, to a certain extent, a recapitulation of phylogeny. In the embryo the gray matter of cord and brain stem is formed considerably before the cortex. The newborn child, it will be recalled, has many true reflexes, but cortical activity lags far behind. As an illustration of this we may take the act of urination. In the newborn child the distention of the bladder is a stimulus for the urination center in the sacral cord (p. 528), in consequence of which proper impulses are discharged to the musculature of the bladder. The process is a true, unconscious reflex. But as the child grows older neural connections are made between the sacral cord and the cortex so that the latter on receiving sensory impulses from the bladder may either excite or inhibit the lower center. Urination is now said to be a voluntary process. So completely has the lower center surrendered its control to the higher center that only in abnormal conditions does it regain its former independence.

Removal of the Cerebral Hemispheres.—The great difference between the development and domination of the cortex in the higher as compared with that in the lower animals is well brought out in the results of the removal of the cortex. In the frog this operation produces very little change, for a decerebrate frog is able to hop and swim; it avoids obstacles in its way, hence it is able to see; placed on its back, it turns over; it has the power of maintaining its equilibrium when the board upon which it is placed is tilted. Indeed, after the ablation of the cerebrum, if the thalamus, Fig. 270, is uninjured, it may be difficult for an inexperienced person to detect any change.

The ablation of the entire cortex in a higher animal is followed by graver results; but as there is much discrepancy in the results obtained by various workers, we shall not enter into the details. Goltz kept a decorticated dog alive for one and one-half years. The immediate result was a complete paralysis, but this gradually disappeared and the animal became very active in moving about. He was able to maintain his normal posture and the "righting reflexes" (p. 579) were not interfered with; the taste reflexes were present as shown by the fact that the dog rejected bitter food. He also reacted violently to cutaneous stimulation. Pupillary constriction and closure of the lids followed stimulation by light, but whether any sight remained was very doubtful. As the cortex contains the chief association areas, its removal abolishes all reactions dependent upon the neural modifications brought by past experiences. Goltz reports that while at first the decorticated dog was not able to take up food and had to be fed, he finally learned to eat when his nose was held in contact with food. All psychic functions were lost, for the dog never showed any signs of dreaming; he exhibited no pleasure when petted nor fear when threatened; the sexual responses were absent; he knew neither friend nor foe.

Rothmann's decerebrate dog finally learned to avoid obstacles and to hunt for food, but Dresel reports that a decerebrate dog never walks without stimulation (e.g., by hunger) and never learns anything. These discrepancies are perhaps due to a difference in the removal of subcortical structures.

In regard to human beings, it would seem almost impossible for a man ever to survive an accident that destroyed the major portion of his cerebrum. The case of a four-year-old child has been recorded in which the postmortem examination showed the complete absence of cerebral hemispheres. From the time it was born until it died, it never acquired any new reactions, that is, it never "learned" anything; it slept nearly all the time (if one can speak of sleeping in such a case); it showed no signs of recognizing its mother or any other signs of consciousness. Even the cutaneous and general sensibility could not be determined.

In the lower animals, therefore, the reflex arcs of the lower levels (utilizing the central gray matter) can operate to an exceedingly large extent independently of the cortex. For example, a frog, after ablation of the cerebral hemispheres, can utilize its visual impulses for all its actions; the same is true of the impulses from the ears. But in the higher animals this independence on the part of the lower reflex arcs has been surrendered to the cortex, and when this part is removed many of the reactions to environmental changes cease. In a decerebrate dog the impulses which the optic nerves bring to the subcortical stations find no outlet whatever to the muscles; hence these impulses cannot be utilized in the avoidance of obstacles. It is the penalty the lower centers pay for the greater specialization of the higher centers.

The great control exercised over the lower centers by the cortex is, on its efferent side, largely mediated by means of the pyramidal tract fibers which link the motor (precentral) areas of the cortex with the motor nuclei of the cord and brain stem. The higher the animal is in the scale of life, the more abundant are the fibers of this corticospinal system. In the frog these fibers are entirely absent; in the mouse a little more than 1 per cent of all the cord fibers are pyramidal fibers; in the rabbit, 5 per cent; in the cat, 7.7 per cent; in man, almost 12 per cent. It must, therefore, be apparent why extensive voluntary motor paralysis attends the interruption of the pyramidal tract fibers by hemorrhage or embolism in the brain.

E. Association Areas and Intelligence

In the earlier part of the last century the so-called science of phrenology claimed to have discovered a cortical center for every imaginable intellectual, emotional, and esthetic faculty. When it was shown that large portions of the cortex can be lost without any serious changes in the intellectual and moral faculties, this "science" died a natural death. Intelligence is no longer looked upon as a single psychic faculty which can be located in a definite and circumscribed area of the brain. *All mental activity begins with the reception of afferent impulses* from the various sense organs, and, to be of any benefit to the individual, must lead to the discharge of impulses to the responding organs. The former of these processes is the function of the various cortical sensory areas and the latter, of the motor areas, and, as we have seen, between these two lie the association areas; mental activity must therefore be regarded as a function of the entire cortex. But intelligence as something distinct, if possible, from the receiving and sending of impulses, is frequently attributed to the activity of the association areas, especially of the prefrontal lobes. Two facts favor this view: These areas are larger in extent and their association fibers are more numerous and more ramifying in man than in any of the lower animals; in the next place, the fibers of these areas acquire their myelin sheaths later than do those of any other part of the cortex. But as to the results of the removal or degeneration of one or both of the prefrontal lobes there is much inconsistency in the reports of different observers. It is perhaps best to assume that while there is no doubt that superiority of intellect is associated with a more highly organized cortical structure, the psychic functions of associated memory, judgment, volition, etc., are not localized but depend upon the integrity of the cortex as a whole.

Cortical Inhibition.—We have had more than one occasion to speak of the restraining influence exerted by the cortex upon neuromuscular activity. And when we consider the continual stream of afferent impulses entering the central nervous system (p. 630), the urgent need for this inhibition is self-evident. The strength and the extent of cortical inhibition vary with the ever changing conditions of both the body and the cortex itself as the following shows.

1. THE PATELLAR REFLEX.—It will be recalled that striking the patellar ligament causes contraction of the rectus femoris muscle and extension of the leg. If just previously to, or simultaneously with,

the tapping of the ligament, the individual clenches his fist or makes any other strong voluntary action, or if a loud noise is made in his immediate neighborhood, the extent of the knee-jerk is markedly increased. Under the ordinary conditions the cortex exercises a restraint over the activity of the cord and thus limits the extent of the knee-jerk; but when the cortex is engaged in the execution of a forcible voluntary effort, the usual inhibition is somewhat abated and a more powerful neural discharge flows to the quadriceps muscles. This is frequently spoken of as *the release from restraint, or from inhibition.*

2. THALAMIC ACTIVITY.—We have in a previous section seen that the thalamus may be the seat of certain exaggerated sensations. In fact, some hold that the thalamus and neighboring parts constitute the machinery for the emotional expressions (facial, e.g.) of rage, fear, joy, etc. A person in whom the volitional (cortical) control of the facial muscles was lost so that he was unable to open or close his eyes or mouth assumed the correct facial expression when overcome by grief or joy. In the absence of cortical control the individual gives way violently and excessively to his feelings. The deadening effect of alcohol upon cortical inhibition reveals itself by the unrestrained joy or anger an intoxicated individual exhibits upon the slightest occasion, long before the exceedingly complex and highly coordinated activities, such as speech, are affected.

3. ATTENTION.—The power of the cortex to inhibit the flow of certain impulses while others are allowed free play is the basis of the common phenomenon of attention. In concentration all afferent impulses that threaten to interfere with the prosecution of the thing we are after must be repressed and the passage of all helpful impulses must be facilitated. Again, to exercise a strong will is to inhibit all impulses that would lead us astray and to give the "right of way" to those that are conducive to attaining the goal set before us. It has therefore been well said that inhibition plays a rôle in bodily economy that can scarcely be overestimated. But while inhibition of certain neural activities is necessary for the accomplishing of anything worth while, too great a general inhibition works disastrously. Fear exercises a potent inhibition on the activity of some cortical cells, thereby restraining the individual from doing well, or at all, that for which he may be naturally fitted (inferiority complex). Ridding oneself of these inhibitory psychic influences renders possible normal mental activity.

The inhibitory power of the cortex has its limits; certain organic reflexes are beyond its sphere of influence. The uncontrollable responses to stimuli are the basis of the modern "lie-detector" which registers the irrepressible respiratory, cardiac, or vasomotor reactions to certain questions put to the suspect.

4. The Prefrontal Lobes.—That the prefrontal lobes are especially concerned in this important function of inhibition is rendered very probable by the results of surgical removal of these lobes in man. The person exhibited a lack of restraint (as shown by his extreme boasting, aggressiveness and hostility), a great difficulty in fixing his attention upon any subject, a flightiness of ideas, and emotional instability. In common speech, individuals lacking this prefrontal inhibitory power let their emotions outrun their wits. Jacobsen, working on the removal of these lobes in monkeys, reports the loss of memory for recent, but not for long past, events (much as we frequently see in senile loss of memory), and great distractibility, as shown by the inability to keep in mind more than one aspect of a problem under consideration.

Aphasia.—Lesions in certain parts of what have been called the association areas may cause disturbances known as aphasia. Aphasia, in its broadest meaning, is the partial or total loss of the power to understand written or spoken language, or of the power to express thought in speech or writing. The injuries causing aphasia in right-handed people are situated in the left cerebral hemisphere. There are four main types of aphasia:

1. Aphemia, or Motor Aphasia.—A lesion in the left third, or inferior, frontal convolution, also known as Broca's convolution (F_3, Fig. 278), causes a loss of the power to communicate one's thoughts by speech. The lesion is held to lie close to the cortical center for the muscles of phonation, but aphemia (*pheme*, voice) is not due to any motor paralysis of the muscles of phonation, for the person is able to make sounds, but the sounds produced constitute a mere jargon.

2. Agraphia.—In this disorder the power to express one's thoughts in writing is lost, although the power to do so by speech is retained. The cortical defect is said to be located in the second (middle) frontal convolution near the motor center for the hand and arm. In agraphia there is no loss of the power to use the fingers and hand; merely the ability to express thought by means of these organs is lost.

3. Alexia.—A person previously able to read loses the power to recognize and understand printed or written words—word-blindness or alexia (*a*, not; *lexis*, word). The strokes of the letter can be seen and the letters can be distinguished from each other, but their meaning is gone. The cortical disturbance for this disorder is said to lie

in the inferior parietal lobe near the border of the temporal and occipital lobes, an area, it will be noted, situated in close proximity to the sensory and psychic visual centers.

4. SENSORY APHASIA.—In this disturbance the power to understand spoken words is lost (word-deafness). The cortical lesion is said to be in the first (superior) temporal convolution, near the auditory center.

Until a few years ago these four disturbances were held to be fairly sharply marked off from each other and to be associated with four quite distinct cerebral lesions. But Marie and others have thrown much doubt upon the existence of these centers. It is now generally held that the whole of the temporal and part of the parietal lobe and the lower frontal convolution are concerned with the appreciation of language. By means of association fibers these lobes are very closely

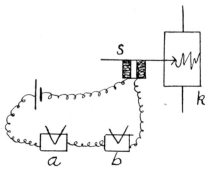

Fig. 288.—Apparatus for determining the reaction time. *a*, and *b*, electric keys; *s*, a magnetic signal; *k*, kymograph.

connected with the areas generally described as sensory (visual and auditory) and motor in function. We must not regard the four above-mentioned centers as circumscribed cortical areas where four language faculties reside; they are points in the tracts of association fibers that connect the various sensory and motor areas.

Reaction Time.—We have seen that a certain length of time is required for the execution of a reflex action—the reflex time. This concerns itself chiefly with the activities mediated by the central gray matter of the spinal cord and brain stem. But when the cerebral cortex participates in a neural process, many more neurons and synapses are involved, and the time is greatly lengthened.

Perhaps the simplest possible mental process of which the rapidity can be determined with great accuracy is the responding to a signal. The time elapsing between the stimulation of the receptor and the voluntary response to it is known as the reaction time. This may be determined in the following manner: In an electric circuit there are inserted two simple contact keys, *a* and *b*, Fig. 288, and a signal magnet, the lever of which is drawn down when both the keys are closed and is raised when one or both keys are open. The depressing and the raising of the lever of the signal magnet and the vibration of a tuning fork which vibrates, let us say, 100 times per second are recorded on a fast-moving kymograph. The person whose reaction to stimulation is to be tested (call him *A*) operates key *a;* the investigator, *B*, operates key *b*. At the outset, key *a* is closed; this has no effect on the signal magnet because key *b* is open and the circuit is not complete. Now *B* closes his key, *b;* this completes the circuit and the lever of the signal magnet is drawn down, *a* in Fig. 289. As soon as *A* sees this movement, he releases his key, *a*, thereby breaking the circuit and causing the lever to rise at *b*. In a similar

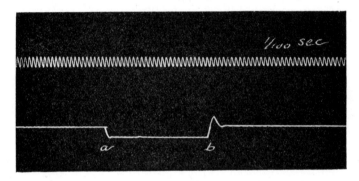

Fig. 289.—Tracing showing the reaction time for sight.

way we may determine the reaction time for hearing, touch, pain, etc. The average reaction time for sight is 0.20 second; for hearing, 0.17; for touch, 0.15 second. It is increased by fatigue, mental excitement and worry. It may be somewhat decreased by an increase in the intensity of the stimulus and to a very slight extent by practice.

Let us suppose that the mental process is made a little more complex by introducing what is called in psychology, dilemma, or choice. We may arrange the experiment so that the subject is to respond with his right hand to a green, and with the left hand to a red, signal. The reaction time is now increased by about 0.15 second.

We may increase the complexity of the psychic process still more by asking the subject to respond to a given test word with an appropriate word. Thus: the test word is "book"; the rapidity with which the subject replies with a word such as "look," "took," "library," "author," etc., indicates the speed of a somewhat complicated mental action. And when the subject responds with one of the last two words instead of the rhyming, irrelevant word "look" or "took," a higher order of association is called into play; this association was acquired by the individual later in life and demands a greater number of synaptic connections.

Alcohol.—Many drugs affect the functioning of the cerebral cortex unfavorably and thereby increase the reaction time. Among these is alcohol, which, excepting for the first few minutes and then only in the simpler, uncomplicatied stimulations, always delays mental activity and lengthens the reaction time. Not only is the response to test words delayed but also words of a lower, instead of the higher, association are used. This is in accord with the general law that *the associations later formed in life are the first to disappear in retrogressive changes.* The effects of alcohol on the human body and on physical and mental efficiency as shown by an exceedingly large number of experiments conducted at the Boston Nutrition Laboratory were summarized as: "decreased reflex irritability, slower reaction, less keen, i.e., higher sensory thresholds, slower muscular movements, less adequate and accurate muscular control, and less agile mental operations. The whole . . . picture . . . is one of decreased human efficiency."*

V. GROWTH AND METABOLISM

Growth of the Brain.—In the human body there is, except to a limited extent in the cerebellum, no formation of nerve cells after birth, and normally the neurons remain throughout life. In case of injury, no regeneration of neurons takes place in the central nervous system. At birth many of the fibers to and from the brain are not myelinated. Now, it seems that the appearance of the function of a nerve fiber goes hand in hand with the formation of the myelin sheath. In a newborn guinea pig the fibers are fully myelinated, while in a rat most fibers are devoid of this sheath; this may account for the helpless condition of the newborn rat as contrasted with that of the guinea pig. Stimulation of the motor areas in an infant yielded no responses. The pyramidal fibers in a child do not complete their myelination until well along the second year, i.e., at about the time the child learns to walk. The association fibers (the machinery of memory) are the last to become myelinated.

After birth the growth of the brain (which determines, no doubt, the mental age) is due to an increase in the size of the cells and,

---

*This interpretation agrees with the conclusion reached by Benedict that "whenever an apparent excitation occurs as a result of alcohol it is either demonstrably (as in the case of the pulse rate, the reflexes, memory and the threshold) or probably (as in the eye reaction) due to a relatively overbalancing depression of the controlling and inhibitory processes."

more particularly, to the increase in the number, the length, and extent of distribution of the neural processes; by this each neuron is able to establish an increasingly larger number of connections with other cerebral cells (see Fig. 287). How long this proliferation of neural fibers and the formation of more and firmer connections continues is a question; some hold that it never ceases. According to this view, the power to learn should not rapidly wane with increasing years, as is commonly supposed. Experiments have shown that rats during middle age or even senescence learn to run the maze as rapidly as during puberty. Stone found that persons at 35 or 40 years acquire knowledge more readily than school children, and Hunter concludes that we are "left without a factual basis for the hypothesis that the plasticity of the nervous system varies with age." In mental old age the psychic functions (especially memory) lose their power because of the decreased blood supply to certain cortical regions, or, perhaps, of lessened endocrine secretions.

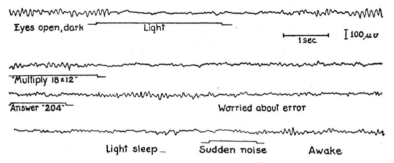

Fig. 290.—Electro-encephalograms. (Davis and Davis: Arch. Neurol. and Psychiat. 36: 214, 1936.)

Metabolism.—Although the total metabolism of the brain, as measured by the consumption of glucose and oxygen, is of no mean order as compared with that of other organs, yet mental work has an almost negligible influence on metabolism. According to Benedict, all the energy required to perform one hour's intensive mental work can be obtained from one-half of a peanut (about 2.5 Cal.). Notwithstanding this, few tissues are more susceptible to the lack of oxygen than the cortical gray matter. It is a well-known fact that a few moments' interruption in the oxygen supply brings about unconsciousness, and complete deprivation of oxygen causes irremediable damage to most cerebral cells in about four minutes. During cerebral activity there is a consumption of glucose and a production of lactic acid.

Electro-encephalograms, or Brain Waves.—In 1929 Berger discovered that cortical activity is associated, similar to that of muscles and peripheral nerves, with changes in electrical potential. By means of electrodes placed upon the skull, these waves can be recorded, as shown in Fig. 290. Two types of waves have been detected; the alpha waves which have a frequency of about 10 per second and the smaller beta waves occurring at a rate from 17 to 50 per second. These two types of waves may be superposed upon each other. The general nature of the electro-encephalogram varies from one person to another, but those taken at intervals of several weeks from the same individual are quite constant. In identical twins they are exceedingly similar. The alpha waves are best seen when the individual sits quietly with eyes closed and mind at ease; stimulation by light, as shown in Fig. 290, *A*, decreases them. In deep sleep, *D*, they are generally absent. Mental efforts and emotions depress them, *B* and *C*.

Mental Fatigue.

—It is a question whether mental fatigue exists. Considering the exceedingly small amount of energy consumed and the abundant blood supply to the brain, the available energy seems inexhaustible. Many tests have been made, especially with children, which seem to indicate that even one hour's study materially reduces mental power. However, the results obtained in Thorndike's laboratory and elsewhere do not substantiate this conclusion. A student, for four days of twelve hours each, mentally (without help of paper and pencil) multiplied such numbers as 4937×5862; the results were such that "if anybody were prepared to maintain that . . . it has not been possible to discover any diminution of capacity for work, no matter how prolonged or difficult the task, no convincing experimental evidence could be brought to confute him." Concerning the feeling of fatigue, which most of us have experienced, Thorndike says, "Fatigue in the vague popular sense means that we are less willing rather than that we are less able, . . ." Fulton, on the other hand, maintains that "there is ample evidence for believing that the process by which nerve impulses are controlled at the higher levels of integration is one eminently susceptible of fatigue."

Granting that mental fatigue is a possibility, little can be said about the structures undergoing this change. Even the seat of the fatigue due to voluntary muscular work is a debated question. Some hold that when we voluntarily fatigue a muscle, the fatigue is central, that is, the neurons of the motor area or their connections have lost their irritability. Others deny this, claiming that the fatigue is peripheral, affecting the nerve endings in the muscle and the muscle itself. Some have laid stress upon the chemical and physical changes taking place in the nerve cell body as a result of prolonged activity. Hodge, examining the nerve cells of the brain and the cord of birds and comparing the appearance of these cells on the morning after a night's rest with that in the evening after a day's flight, found that after the day's activity the amount of protoplasm in the cells is less and that it contains many vacuoles (small spaces in the protoplasm filled with gas or liquid, and perhaps with waste products). Also there is a shrinkage in the size of the nuclei of the nerve cells and in extreme fatigue the Nissl bodies undergo disintegration. All these changes are recovered from by proper rest.

Sleep.—Closely linked with fatigue, in most people's mind, is that almost universal phenomenon known as sleep. The most significant feature of sleep is the loss, to a greater or lesser extent, of consciousness, a function generally associated with cortical activity. But as decorticated dogs are said by some investigators also to sleep, a broader meaning of this almost indefinable term must be sought. Again, sleep, a state from which the individual can be aroused by ordinary and harmless stimuli, must be differentiated from those conditions that simulate sleep, e.g., coma, hypnosis, and syncope (p. 650).

LESSENED ACTIVITIES.—During sleep there is a depression of the various psychic and physical functions, the extent of which varies for the different functions and from one individual to another.

The Nervous System.—That the threshold of irritability is increased and that the individual reacts less readily and less critically to changes in his environment are matters of everyday observation. Certain reflexes, such as the knee-jerk, may be lost almost entirely, if not entirely; other reflex centers, e.g., the photo-pupil constricting center in the mid-brain and the vital centers in the medulla, are but little influenced. The suspension of the activity of the skeletal muscles is never complete and varies largely in different individuals. From our study of brain waves it is evident that, at least during deep sleep, there is a marked reduction in cerebral activity, but as to the particular change or changes in the cortex responsible for or accompanying sleep little is known. All parts of the cortex may not be under the influence of sleep to the same extent at all times, for while a comparatively loud noise of no importance to the sleeper, such as the rumbling of street cars, may pass unnoticed, the slight noise of guarded footsteps may awaken him instantly.

Circulatory Changes.—The heart rate may be decreased to about 50 per minute. The peripheral blood vessels generally dilate so that the volume of the arm, for example, increases; but the relatively small drop in blood pressure (from 10 to 25 mm. Hg) indicates that this vascular dilation is limited. Dreaming may increase the pressure 40 or 50 mm. above that during waking hours. The vasomotor center may react to auditory stimulation, even though the sleeper is not aroused by it. Toward the time of awakening the pressure gradually rises.

The secretions of saliva, tears, urine, mucus of the nose, etc., are diminished.

The respiration is slower and generally deeper and more audible.

The metabolism is markedly decreased, the body temperature falls somewhat and the urine contains more acids and phosphates. It should, however, be stated that the vascular and metabolic changes are no greater than those experienced during perfect relaxation of the body in its waking state.

THEORIES OF THE CAUSE OF SLEEP.—As to the cause of sleep many theories have been formulated, none of which explains the phenomenon in its entirety. For want of space the details of these theories cannot be gone into; we shall merely state the salient features.

1. *The Anemia Theory.*—Mosso, among others, held a lessened flow of blood through the brain to be the inducing factor. Howell accounted for this decreased cerebral circulation by a reduction in the irritability of the vasomotor center. Although it cannot be gainsaid that curtailing the amount of blood to the brain may induce sleep (as seen in the somnolence after a hemorrhage), this theory is not supported by certain recent observations which show that, instead of cerebral anemia, the brain receives a larger blood supply during sleep than at other times. We have already seen that a fall in blood pressure is not always experienced in sleep. It is also difficult to understand why sleep, as a restorative measure, should be caused by a decrease in the blood supply upon which the recuperation of any organ absolutely depends.

2. *The Neuron Theory.*—We have in an earlier chapter spoken of fatigue in the neuromuscular system and found that the junctions between anatomically distinct structures, as between nerve fiber and muscle fiber, or between one neuron and another, are very susceptible to fatigue. There is great temptation to associate sleep with fatigue; and for this reason it seems highly probable that the synapses, especially those of the cerebral cortex, are involved. By a reduction in their conductivity the flow of impulses throughout the central nervous system is blocked and thereby causes the lessened activities. Some observers stress the withdrawal of the neural arborizations in the synapse; others assume a more profound biochemical change. However, fatigue as a necessary factor in sleep is not always apparent, as shown by the regularity of sleep in some persons who do very little physical or mental work. And how can we explain that an individual may accustom himself to falling asleep at any stated time of the day?

3. *The Chemical Theory* holds that toxic compounds formed during activity gradually inhibit the functions of the cerebral cells. This theory is supported by the fact that the injection of cerebrospinal fluid obtained from an animal deprived of sleep for some time into a fully awake animal induces sleep. But again the question, why the regular sleep habits of people who have little cause to generate hypnotoxins?

4. *Theory of Decreased Afferent Impulses.*—In one of the more recent theories, the cessation of afferent impulses streaming into the central nervous system is emphasized as an important cause of sleep. It is, of course, common knowledge that darkness, the absence of sound, and a comfortable bed (by which no part of the body is excessively stimulated by pressure) are external conditions which are highly favorable to sleep, and that to fight off sleep the muscles must be kept in action. Expanding these well-known facts, Kleitman concludes that the lessening of the proprioceptive impressions from the muscles, either by fatigue or voluntarily, is a large factor in precipitating sleep.

The more thoroughly one believes that the cerebral cortex, like the spinal cord, possesses no spontaneity and only reacts upon receiving impulses from the stimulations by the outside world or the body itself, the more attractive this theory becomes. As someone has said, sleep is the natural, resting state of the cortex, similar to the fully relaxed condition of a muscle. Only as a stimulus is applied does activity manifest itself; and, as a consequence, the withdrawal of all stimulation must bring the organ to its resting state. Synaptic fatigue may help to do this by lessening the opportunity for the impulses to ascend to the cortex.

5. *The Inhibition Theory; The Sleep Center.*—In the pathologic condition of epidemic encephalitis (inflammation of the brain) the patient is in a state of deep and and prolonged sleep—sleeping sickness. In this disease the hypothalamus (a structure near the thalamus in the tween-brain) is involved. Experimental injury to this portion of the brain by the insertion of a needle causes prolonged sleep. Recently Hess succeeded in producing sleep by electrical stimulation of the hypothalamus. It is therefore held by some that the activity of a sleep center in this part of the brain decreases the function of the cerebral cortex; its action is comparable to that of the cardioinhibitory center in governing the activity of the heart.

THE INTENSITY OF SLEEP is measured by the strength of a stimulus, a sound, for example, necessary to arouse the sleeper. In many people the deepest sleep is experienced during the first or second hour, but in others it may occur later.

THE VALUE OF SLEEP is so apparent that little needs to be said concerning it. In experiments quoted by Kleitman rabbits lived from 8 to 31 days and dogs from 14 to 77 days without sleep. After death, marked changes were observed in the cortical cells of the frontal lobes. Loss of sleep in man causes a decrease in the rapidity and power of mental operations.

How much sleep is needed by an individual varies with conditions. We all know that children need a great deal more than adults. For some time after birth a child spends the whole day, excepting feeding periods, in what may be called sleep. Children from five to eight years need eleven or twelve hours; from nine to ten years, ten or eleven hours; from eleven to fifteen years, nine or ten hours. Some adults can get along with six, or even less than six, hours of sleep; others may need more than eight; each individual must determine this for himself. Elderly people get along with a smaller allowance. While an insufficiency of sleep is detrimental, overindulgence may also be harmful, for it decreases the mental powers and encourages the habit of laziness. It is stated that the length of the sleep period is of more importance than the intensity of the sleep; the last five hours of light sleep are more beneficial than the first three of deeper sleep.

Syncope.—In syncope (*syn*, together; *koptein*, to strike) there is a complete and sudden loss of consciousness. The causes of fainting are varied and the condition is not fully understood. Most frequently it is due to cerebral anemia; this generally results from the depressor effects upon the heart or vasomotor system because of excessive stimulation of the carotid sinus. Heart block, the retarding influence of gravity upon venous circulation, and hemorrhage may also bring on a faint. It is stated that a ventricular stoppage of from 3 to 5 beats may cause a momentary loss of consciousness; a cessation of heartbeat from $1\frac{1}{2}$ to 2 minutes is regarded as fatal.

VI. THE CEREBELLUM

Like the cerebral hemispheres, the cerebellum has an external, cortical, layer of gray matter covering the inner white fibers. Here also, the cortex is folded so as to produce convolutions and thus increase the amount of gray matter (Figs. 278, 279, and 291). The microscopic structure of the cortex is very complex.

The cerebellum is divided into a central lobe, or vermis, and two hemispheres, Figs. 277 and 291. It is connected with the rest of the central nervous system by means of three tracts, called the inferior, middle, and superior cerebellar peduncles. The fibers passing through the peduncles connect the cortex, directly or indirectly, with the various parts of the body and with the other divisions of the brain. We may state the most important connections as follows:

1. By the fibers of the inferior peduncle (restiform body, Fig. 277, *d*, and Fig. 292, *3*) the cerebellum receives afferent impulses from three sources:

(*a*) The fibers of the direct cerebellar tract, Fig. 293, carry the kinesthetic impulses from muscles, tendons, and ligaments to the cerebellum on the same side.

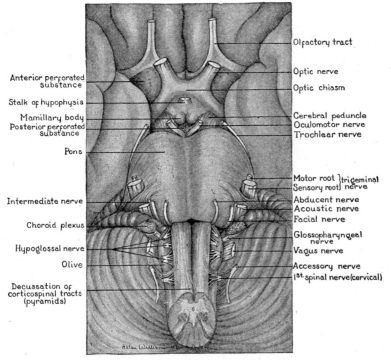

Olfactory tract

Optic nerve

Optic chiasm

Anterior perforated substance

Stalk of hypophysis

Mamillary body
Posterior perforated substance

Pons

Cerebral peduncle
Oculomotor nerve
Trochlear nerve

Motor root } trigeminal
Sensory root } nerve

Abducent nerve
Acoustic nerve
Facial nerve

Intermediate nerve

Choroid plexus

Hypoglossal nerve

Olive

Decussation of corticospinal tracts (pyramids)

Glossopharyngeal nerve
Vagus nerve

Accessory nerve
1st spinal nerve (cervical)

Fig. 291.—Brain stem from below, showing attachment of cranial nerves. (Francis: Fundamentals of Anatomy, The C. V. Mosby Co.)

(*b*) The fibers of the columns of Goll and Burdach end in the nucleus gracilis and cuneatus in the medulla. From here a new relay takes the kinesthetic impulses to the cerebellum.

(*c*) Some of the fibers originating in the vestibular nuclei (end stations of the vestibular nerve), also make connections with the cerebellum on the same side.

(d) Efferent fibers leave the cerebellum to end in the vestibular nuclei; thence by the fibers of the vestibulo-spinal tract the impulses are brought to the gray matter of the cord.

2. The middle peduncle. The pons, as can be gathered from Fig. 277, lies just below the cerebellum; in fact the pons forms the ventral part and the cerebellum, the dorsal part of the hind-brain. In the pons are located gray masses, composed of nerve cell bodies (nucleus pontis). Some of the cells of the nucleus pontis, Fig. 293, and also of the dentate nucleus, lying in the cerebellum itself, send their fibers through the middle peduncle (Fig. 292, 9) to the opposite cerebellar hemisphere. The cells in the nucleus pontis receive fibers (the cortico-pontine, Fig. 293) which carry impulses from the cerebral cortex to this nucleus and thence to the opposite cerebellar hemisphere.

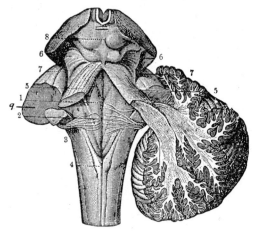

Fig. 292.—Dorsal view of the brain stem with part of the right cerebellar hemisphere. 1, the fourth ventricle; 3, inferior restiform body; 5, the superior, and 9, the middle peduncles which have all been cut across on the left side; 4, funiculus gracilis; 6, the fillet; 8, corpora quadrigemina. (After Gordinier.)

3. The superior peduncle, Fig. 292, 5, contains:

(a) Fibers passing from the cerebellum to the opposite thalamus, and thence by a new relay to the cerebral cortex.

(b) Fibers which carry impulses from the cerebellum to the opposite red nucleus; a new relay, after crossing the median plane, carries the impulses down the rubro-spinal tract, Figs. 276 and 293, to the gray matter of the cord.

(c) The indirect cerebellar tract fibers originating in the gray matter of the cord, carry impulses to the cerebellum on the same side.

The important point to be gotten from this anatomic description is that the cerebellum is connected by both afferent and efferent nerves with the same side of the spinal cord and thus with the skeletal muscles on the same side of the body; it is connected afferently and efferently with the opposite cerebral hemisphere.

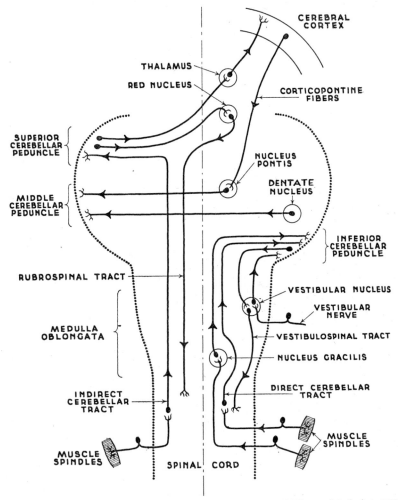

Fig. 293.—To illustrate the pathway in the superior, middle, and inferior cerebellar peduncles and the neural connection of the cerebellum with the spinal cord and cerebrum.

Loss of Cerebellar Function.—Extirpation in animals of a part of the cerebellum causes great incoordination of the muscles of the body, especially of those used in locomotion (Fig. 294); in standing the legs are set wide apart (in order to preserve the equilibrium of the body) and the body sways backward and forward; in turning a corner or otherwise changing the direction or the rate of locomotion, the animal is very likely to fall because of the lack of coordination between the fore and hind legs. When the cerebellar cortex is stimulated, the animal turns its eyes and head toward the stimulated side. The limbs on the side stimulated may be moved also.

In man, disturbances of this organ cause lack of coordination in the action of the muscles concerned in walking; the patient has a reeling walk, like that of an intoxicated person (cerebellar ataxia). The willed actions begin very abruptly, are continued beyond the necessary time, and are associated with tremors. In consequence, voluntary movements are very jerky, and the stronger the voluntary attempt, the more pronounced are these disorders. This is especially seen in the patient's speech and eye movements (nystagmus). In case of tumors growing in this region, the patient may have great giddiness, vertigo, and nausea. In contrast with the cerebrum, destruction of the cerebellum does not cause any disturbance in the sensations or psychic life.

Fig. 294.—Position of the legs in locomotion after destruction of the vermis of the cerebellum. (Morat and Doyon.)

Functions of the Cerebellum.—From the manifold afferent connections which the muscles, tendons, and ligaments make with this organ, it must be regarded as the head ganglion of the proprioceptive system. On the efferent side its extensive influence upon the activity of the skeletal muscles is apparent. From the large number of theories as to its function, we may perhaps gather (a) that the cerebellum has no special function of its own and (b) that it is very closely associated with the cerebrum in governing activities begun by that organ. Normally the starting of a voluntary action, such as that of walking, is a function of the cerebral hemispheres; but when once the action has begun, the coordination of the various incoming and outgoing impulses (especially with reference to the antagonistic muscles) is delegated to the cerebellum. Its activity secures the harmonious cooperation of separate muscle groups. In its absence there is a loss of muscle tonus and of strength and steadiness of the contractions.

Posture.—Having briefly considered the great disturbances in equilibrium brought about by malfunctioning of the cerebellum, we may at this time summarize what we have on various occasions learned about maintaining the proper position of the body. In its erect posture the body is physically very unstable, inasmuch as the center of gravity lies fairly high over a narrow base of support. To maintain this position, notwithstanding the force of gravity, a large number of muscles must be thrown into coordinated activity. These muscles are sometimes spoken of as the *antigravity muscles;* by them the head is held erect, the lower jaw is raised against the upper, the spine is maintained in a nearly vertical position, and the whole body is supported by the legs.

For adequate innervation of the muscles concerned in standing, the central nervous system receives impulses from four sources: The eyes (visual impulses), the labyrinth of the inner ear (impulses of equilibrium), muscles and tendons (kinesthetic impulses).

The impulses from the labyrinth and the eyes are chiefly concerned with maintaining the erect position of the head. We touched upon labyrinthine impressions in a previous chapter. The importance of the visual impression may be gathered from the fact that animals deprived of the labyrinthine organs are able, after a few days, properly to orientate the head, but on bandaging the eyes this power is lost.

By means of the kinesthetic impulses from the muscles of the neck (as in tilting the head), we are informed not only of the position of the head in space (for this the two previously mentioned impulses suffice) but also of the position of the trunk with respect to the head. Tilting the body from the perpendicular to one side stretches the muscles, tendons, and ligaments on the opposite side of the trunk and legs; this creates kinesthetic impulses which set up myotatic reflexes in these same muscles and thereby readjust the body. The indispensableness of the kinesthetic impulses is well illustrated in tabes dorsalis in which the degeneration of certain dorsal root fibers (which travel up the columns of Goll and Burdach) prevents the kinesthetic sensation. In this state the patient, with eyes closed, is unable to stand (Romberg's sign).

VII. THE CRANIAL NERVES

The brain gives rise to 12 pairs of cranial nerves, Figs. 266 and 291. Some of them are afferent, some are efferent, and a few contain both afferent and efferent fibers.

1. The FIRST CRANIAL, OR OLFACTORY, NERVE carries the impulses for the sensation of smell, and is chemically stimulated by gases. The cell bodies lie in the upper part of the nasal mucosa, and the fibers from these cell bodies pass to the olfactory bulb. From there a new relay takes the impulses to the sensory area of smell in the hippocampus (Fig. 279).

2. The SECOND CRANIAL, OR OPTIC, NERVE. See Figs. 250 and 266. Its origin was described on page 556. From the retina, the optic nerve fibers take the impulse to the external geniculate bodies (Fig. 284) of the tween-brain. From there the projection fibers pass through the internal capsule (Fig. 283) and in the optic radiation of the corona (projection fibers—Fig. 280, *D*) reach the occipital lobes of the hemispheres. It will be recalled (Fig. 249) that the fibers from the nasal half of each retina cross over in the chiasma, *ch,* to the opposite optic tract, *op;* due to this arrangement the right occipital lobe, *ro,* receives the impulses from the objects, *m,* lying to the left of the body. A few of the fibers of the optic nerve end in the midbrain and there make synaptic connections with the third, fourth, and sixth cranial nerves.

3. The THIRD CRANIAL, OR OCULOMOTOR, NERVE (Fig. 291) is the motor nerve for four of the six extrinsic eye muscles and for the raiser of the upper eyelid.

4. The FOURTH CRANIAL, OR TROCHLEAR, NERVE innervates the superior oblique muscle of the eyeball.

5. The FIFTH CRANIAL, OR TRIGEMINAL, NERVE issues from the pons of the brain stem. It resembles the spinal nerves in being composed of a sensory and a very much smaller motor root. The cell bodies of the sensory fibers lie in the Gasserian ganglion outside of the brain; their fibers are distributed by three branches to the skin of the face, to the eyeball, the mucosa of mouth and nose and the teeth. The motor fibers innervate the muscles of mastication.

6. The SIXTH CRANIAL, OR ABDUCENS, NERVE is the motor nerve for the external rectus muscle of the eyeball.

7. The SEVENTH CRANIAL, OR FACIAL, NERVE is the motor nerve for the muscles of the face, ears, and scalp. Some claim that this nerve also contains gustatory fibers (see p. 581).

8. The EIGHTH CRANIAL, OR AUDITORY, NERVE, Figs. 280 and 291, is a sensory nerve composed of two parts, the cochlear and the vestibular; these have been considered under the heading of the Ear.

9. The NINTH CRANIAL, OR GLOSSOPHARYNGEAL, NERVE is a mixed nerve. Its motor branches supply the muscles of the pharynx and the base of the tongue (glossa). It supplies fibers for the parotid (sali-

vary) gland. Its sensory fibers are supplied to the tongue and pharynx and together with the seventh cranial constitute the nerves of taste.

10. THE TENTH CRANIAL, VAGUS, OR PNEUMOGASTRIC, NERVE is a mixed nerve of which we have spoken on several occasions. The motor fibers are supplied to the muscles of the larynx and of the alimentary canal (from the esophagus to the large intestines), and its inhibitory fibers control the heart. The glands of the stomach and the pancreas are innervated by this nerve. Its sensory fibers end in the mucous membranes of larynx, trachea, lungs, esophagus, stomach, gallbladder, and intestines.

11. THE ELEVENTH CRANIAL, OR SPINAL ACCESSORY, NERVE is a motor nerve for the sternomastoid and trapezius muscles, and sends many other motor fibers directly into the vagus nerve.

12. THE TWELFTH CRANIAL, OR HYPOGLOSSUS, NERVE is the motor nerve for the muscles of the tongue and larynx.

VIII. THE MEDULLA OBLONGATA

The medulla oblongata is the connection between the spinal cord and all the brain anterior to the medulla, Figs. 266 and 291. Its functions may be briefly stated as follows:

1. Through the medulla pass the fibers from the lower to the higher parts of the central nervous system (e.g., the cerebellar tracts), and from the higher to the lower (e.g., the pyramidal tracts).

2. In it are relayed many of the fibers connecting the higher with its lower parts. This is seen in the nucleus gracilis and nucleus cuneatus where the fibers from the posterior columns of the spinal cord find their cells of reception; these cells are the cells of origin of the fillet fibers which carry the impulses to the thalamus. From the thalamus tertiary fibers carry the impulses to the cerebral cortex.

3. Its gray matter is directly connected with certain of the cranial nerves (see Figs. 284 and 285); some of these have their cells of origin in the medulla (motor nerves); others find their cells of reception here (sensory nerves).

4. In the medulla are located some of the most important nerve centers of the body, most of which we have studied somewhat in detail. To recapitulate, in it are located the centers for respiration, phonation, vasoconstriction, vasodilation, cardiac inhibition and acceleration, mastication, deglutition, vomiting, salivary and gastric secretions, and perspiration.

Judged by its functions, the medulla is easily seen to be very necessary for governing the vegetative functions of the body.

CHAPTER XXX

THE AUTONOMIC NERVOUS SYSTEM*

In a previous chapter we have seen that somatic nerves make direct connection between the central nervous system and the peripheral organs. This is true for the motor fibers which originate from cell bodies lying in the central gray matter, and for the sensory fibers springing from cell bodies located in the dorsal root ganglia. These medullated nerve fibers are not interrupted, or relayed, in their passage from the central nervous system to the peripheral organs. It is by means of the somatic nerves that the central nervous system regulates the activity of the skeletal muscles and body posture, and thus makes possible the proper adjustment between the body and its environment. While generally reflex in nature, these muscular activities are sometimes spoken of as being under voluntary control.

In contrast with this, we have cells lying in the gray matter of the cord which send medullated fibers out by the ventral root. These fibers leave the root by what is known as the white ramus and end in a ganglion (lateral or collateral). This is shown on the right-hand side of Fig. 295. In the ganglion the fibers make synaptic connection with neurons which send their nonmedullated (gray) fibers out by the gray ramus to rejoin the ventral root, and with the somatic fibers of the spinal nerve, they proceed to the various parts of the body. The organs innervated by these nonmedullated fibers are the smooth muscles, the heart, the glands, and the contractile element of the capillaries.

The system here briefly described is known as the autonomic nervous system. It is by means of this efferent system that the central nervous system is connected with the four above-named classes of peripheral organs, and this connection, it will be noticed, is by means of a two-neurons chain. The first neuron, the *preganglionic fiber,* extends from the cord to the autonomic ganglion (broken line in Fig. 295); the second, or postganglionic fiber, extends from the ganglion to the peripheral organs. We may say that, to a large extent, it is the function of the autonomic nervous system to regulate the activities of the various organs (exclusive of the skeletal muscles) so as to maintain a uniform condition of the internal environment, or medium— *homeostasis.*

---

*This system is also known as the visceral, involuntary, or vegetative nervous system.

Sympathetic and Parasympathetic Nervous System.—The cell bodies which give rise to preganglionic fibers lie in four divisions of the central gray matter: 1, in the mid-brain; 2, in the medulla oblongata; 3, in the thoracolumbar region of the cord; 4, in the first three segments of the sacral cord. It is customary to designate that part of the autonomic nervous system springing from the thoracolumbar cord as the sympathetic nervous system, and that part originating from the other three divisions, as the parasympathetic nervous system.

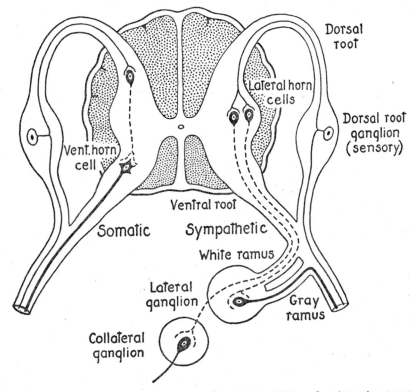

Fig. 295.—Diagram to illustrate somatic (at the left) and autonomic nerves (at the right). The preganglionic fibers are represented by broken lines; the postganglionic by heavy black lines. (Pearce and Macleod: Physiology, The C. V. Mosby Co.)

Lateral and Collateral Ganglia.—The ganglia of the autonomic nervous system may be grouped, according to their location, into three classes. Many of the preganglionic fibers of the sympathetic system end in a chain of ganglia lying along the vertebral column. These are called the lateral, or vertebral, ganglia of the sympathetic chain, Fig. 266. Other fibers from the thoracolumbar cord send their preganglionic fibers to the collateral ganglia which lie a short distance from the spinal column; among these are the semilunar and superior mesenteric ganglia (lying in the solar plexus) and the inferior mesenteric. In Plate III these are shown as situated to the right of the sympathetic chain. The great splanchnic nerve, of which we have spoken on more than one occasion, is composed of the preganglionic fibers to these collateral ganglia. From the lateral and collateral ganglia, the postganglionic fibers supply many organs as can be gathered from Plate III: dilators for the pupil; vasoconstrictors for the blood vessels of skin, stomach, intestines, kidneys, etc.; secretory nerves for the sweat glands; cardiac accelerator fibers; motor fibers for the ileocolic and the internal anal sphincter; inhibitory fibers for the muscles of the stomach, intestine, and bladder; pilomotor nerves for erectors of the hairs.

TERMINAL GANGLIA.—The ganglia of the parasympathetic nervous system differ from the above in that they lie (as shown in Plate III) in, or very near to, the organ they are innervating and, in consequence, the postganglionic fibers are very short. The sacral portion of this system supplies the lower part of the colon, the rectum, internal anal sphincter, the bladder and its sphincter, and the blood vessels of the genital organs. The preganglionic fibers from the second, third, and fourth sacral nerves unite to form a single nerve trunk known as the pelvic nerve, or the nervus erigens. On arriving at the terminal ganglia, the impulses are carried by the postganglionic fibers to the organs.

The only preganglionic fibers from the mid-brain leave by the third cranial nerve, and end in the ciliary ganglion just back of the eyeball; the postganglionic fibers innervate the muscles of accommodation and the sphincter of the iris. By the seventh and ninth cranial nerves from the medulla preganglionic fibers proceed to the salivary glands where are located their terminal ganglia; the postganglionic fibers innervate the secretory cells and the blood vessels of these glands. From the medulla also spring the preganglionic fibers distributed with the large vagus nerve to the heart (cardiac inhibitory), stomach, small intestines, upper part of the colon, liver, pancreas, and kidneys.

After this brief description of the anatomy of the autonomic nervous system we may consider its most important functions:

1. AUTONOMY.—The many and varied organs listed above as receiving autonomic nerves differ from those innervated by the somatic nerves in having a large measure of autonomy, of which the skeletal muscles are entirely devoid. We have had occasion to speak of this in

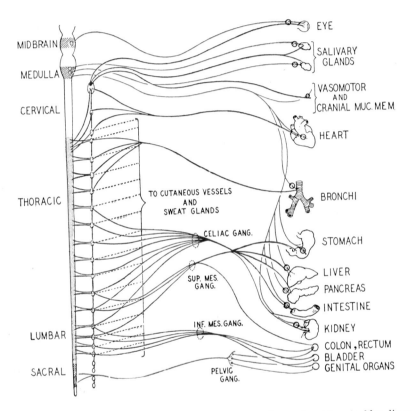

Plate III.—The autonomic nervous system. Craniosacral outflow in blue lines. Thoracicolumbar outflow to cutaneous vessels and sweat glands in dotted red lines and to other structures in solid red lines. (After Meyer and Gottlieb.) (Francis, Knowlton, Tuttle: Textbook of Anatomy and Physiology, The C. V. Mosby Co.)

connection with the automatic action of the heart and stomach, and the recovery of vascular tonus after the nerve supply to the arteries had been severed.

2. No Sharp Localization.—Inasmuch as there are in the autonomic system many more postganglionic than preganglionic fibers, a preganglionic fiber generally makes connections with a number of postganglionic fibers. This allows an impulse over a single preganglionic fiber to be very widely distributed to many organs, or to many parts of a single organ, simultaneously; hence, no sharp localization, such as we meet with in the skeletal musculature, is possible.

3. No Reflexes.—The autonomic nervous system does not act as an independent reflex machine. If any afferent fibers are found in the autonomic nerves (as in the vagus from the heart, or in the splanchnics from the intestines) these have, like all other afferent nerves, their cells of origin in the dorsal ganglia and therefore do not belong to the autonomic system proper. Any impulse carried by them in order to reach the visceral organ must pass through the central nervous system.

4. Double and Antagonistic Nerve Supply.—As can be gathered from Plate III, nearly all organs supplied with autonomic nerves receive two innervations: one from the sympathetic and one from the parasympathetic. We have seen this to be true for the heart which receives a branch from the vagus (parasympathetic) and from the cervical sympathetic. In many instances this double nerve supply is mutually antagonistic. For the heart the vagus is the inhibitory, and the sympathetic, the accelerator, nerve. Stimulation of the preganglionic fibers in the third cranial nerve (from the midbrain) causes the pupil to constrict, while stimulation of the cervical sympathetic brings about dilation.

In general, it is perhaps correct to say that the musculature of the stomach and the small and large intestines is innervated for excitation by the parasympathetic system (vagal and sacral) and for inhibition by the sympathetic (see Figs. 182 and 183). The sphincters receive excitatory impulses from the sympathetic and inhibitory impulses from the parasympathetic nerves, Fig. 174.

5. Sympathetic System Not Indispensable.—Cannon succeeded in keeping a cat from which the entire sympathetic nervous system had been removed alive for three and one-half years. Although there was no change in muscle tonus, the capacity for muscular work was reduced by 35 per cent. This great curtailment naturally follows the extirpation of the neural machinery necessary for the acceleration of the heart, proper distribution of the blood by the constriction of the

abdominal blood vessels, dilation of the bronchioles, the cooling of the body by sweating, the increase in red blood cells by the contraction of the spleen, the increase in the glucose of the blood, and the secretion of adrenalin. The animal for the same reason was unable to defend itself against cold by the erection of its hairs and the vasoconstriction of the cutaneous blood vessels; and unless kept in a warm room it was constantly shivering and in danger of experiencing a fall in body temperature. Neither was it able to withstand hemorrhages or anoxemia.

6. THE EMERGENCY FUNCTION OF THE SYMPATHETIC NERVOUS SYSTEM.—It will be noticed from the above discussion that we are here dealing with the factors concerned in Cannon's emergency theory of adrenal activity (p. 487). By means of the skeletal muscles innervated by the cranio-spinal (somatic) nerves the body as a whole adjusts itself to changes in the environment. To do this, the cells constituting this neuro-muscular machinery must be properly supplied with food, the removal of the waste products must be attended to; in short, a suitable environment (the internal medium) must be provided for them. To maintain the constancy of this internal medium when extra demands are made upon it, as in great muscular exertion and emotional excitement, in asphyxia, hypoglycemia, exposure to cold, and hemorrhage, is the business of a large number of organs which are extensively governed by the sympathico-adrenal system (see next section).

Humoral Theory of Synaptic Conduction.—On various occasions we have spoken of the transmission of the impulse from one protoplasmic structure to another by means of chemical compounds created by the impulse at the termination of the first structure (pp. 219 and 486). Two such compounds are known: acetylcholine* and adrenalin, or an adrenalin-like compound called sympathin. In the main, we may say that acetylcholine is formed at the terminals of all postganglionic fibers of the parasympathetic nerves; and, with a couple of exceptions to be noted presently, adrenalin is manufactured at the endings of the postganglionic fibers of the sympathetic nerves. The former nerves are therefore spoken of as cholinergic;* the latter, as adrenergic.

The evidence for the production of acetylcholine in the heart during stimulation of the vagus was presented on page 219. By similar procedure this substance was detected in the blood flowing from the stomach during vagal stimulation and in that from the salivary gland when the chorda tympani of the seventh cranial nerve was

---

*As-et-il-ko'-lin; ko-lin-er'-jik; ad-ren-er'-jik.

stimulated. This, no doubt, applies to all the organs innervated by either the cranial or the sacral portion of the parasympathetic system, and the injection of acetylcholine affects all these organs to a greater or lesser extent. That the effect of acetylcholine may be confined to the organ whose nerve is being stimulated and may not spread nor outlast the stimulation of this nerve to too great an extent, there is present in the blood and tissues a substance known as choline esterase which rapidly destroys acetylcholine. This destruction is prevented if eserine (also called physostigmine) is added to the blood. Atropine, on the other hand, prevents the action of acetylcholine and thus depresses the parasympathetic system; this explains why a heart inhibited by vagal stimulation is revived by atropine (p. 220).

At the terminals of the postganglionic fibers of the sympathetic system an adrenalin-like compound is formed. The distribution of these nerves was discussed in a previous paragraph. Adrenalin injected into an animal produces the same effects as the stimulation of the sympathetic nerves themselves. Because of this intimate relationship between the hormone and the sympathetic nervous system we speak of the sympathico-adrenal system (see p. 486).

To the general statement that sympathetic nerves are adrenergic, two exceptions must be made: the sweat glands are innervated by the sympathetic nerves, but stimulation of these nerves causes acetylcholine to be formed. The same is true for the vasodilator fibers. Acetylcholine is also produced at the junction of the preganglionic fibers with the ganglionic cell in both the sympathetic and parasympathetic system; and, according to Dale, it also mediates the transfer of the activity of the somatic motor fiber to the cells of the skeletal muscles.

CHAPTER XXXI

REPRODUCTION

Living beings reproduce themselves, in which respect they are sharply differentiated from inanimate bodies. In the very lowest forms of life reproduction is a comparatively simple process; in unicellular plants or animals the cell, during asexual reproduction, divides into two parts, each part growing until it has acquired the usual size of the full-grown organism. In the more highly organized forms particular cells, the reproductive cells, are set aside for this purpose, and in most animals the union of two distinct cells is necessary. These two cells, the male and female germ cells, are produced by special reproductive glands, or gonads (*gonos*, seed), namely, the testis of the male and the ovary of the female. In addition to the primary, there are secondary (accessory) sex organs; in the male these comprise the vas deferens, seminal vesicles, prostate, Cowper's glands, and penis; in the female, fallopian tubes (oviducts), uterus, vagina, clitoris, and mammary glands. We may briefly review the anatomy of these structures.

I. THE MALE GENERATIVE ORGANS

The testes are two oval bodies placed in the scrotum, Fig. 296. Like all glands, the testis, *1*, Fig. 297, may be considered as composed of a large number of small tubes, the *seminiferous tubules,* which on uniting with each other form a long and much convoluted tube. This tube, known as the tube of the epididymis, *2*, is closely applied to the posterior surface of the testis and gives rise to the vas deferens, or the seminal duct, *3*, which constitutes the excretory duct of the testis. The vas deferens, inclosed with the arteries, veins, and nerves in the spermatic cord, passes out of the scrotum into the abdomen, and reaches the posterior portion of the side of the bladder as shown in Figs. 296 and 297. It then curves forward, closely applied to the bladder, *A,* and opens into the urethra, *B,* shortly after this leaves the bladder. In reaching the urethra, the vas deferens passes through the *prostate gland* (Fig. 297, *5*) which lies around the urethra close to the bladder and which discharges its secretion by many small ducts into the urethra. A little lower down is found Cowper's gland, *6,* which also is connected with the urethra.

Many parts of the seminiferous tubules and the vas deferens are supplied with cilia and the walls of the last-named structure are well supplied with muscle tissue. Near its opening into the urethra the vas deferens is slightly dilated, *3'*, and gives off a long, narrow pouch, the *seminal vesicle, 4*. (See also Fig. 296.)

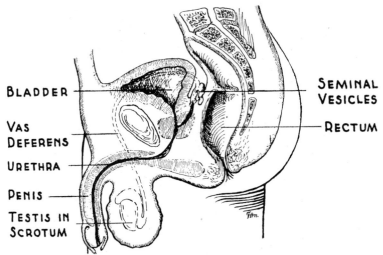

Fig. 296.—Diagram of the male genital organs. (Krogh and Drinker: Human Physiology, Courtesy of Lea and Febiger.)

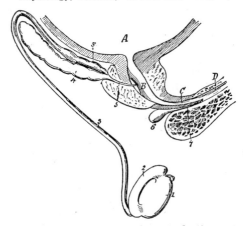

Fig. 297.—Diagram illustrating the male reproductive organs. *1*, right testicle; *2*, epididymis; *3*, vas deferens; *3'*, the dilated portion of the vas deferens known as the ampulla; *4*, seminal vesicle; *5*, prostate; *6*, Cowper's gland; *7*, its duct; *A*, bladder; *B* and *C*, the urethra; *D*, the urethra passing through the penis. (Testut.)

Spermatozoa.—Certain of the epithelial cells which line the seminiferous tubules give rise, by a complex process of cell division, to the male germ cell, the spermatozoon. The human spermatozoon,

Fig. 298, consists of a head, middle piece, tail, and end piece, and measures about 0.05 mm. in length. The head is formed almost altogether from the nucleus of the epithelial cell which gave rise to the spermatozoon.

Due to the pressure caused by their continual formation, the spermatozoa are constantly moved forward through the ducts; this motion is aided by the cilia of the tubes. The number of spermatozoa produced is enormous; during a single ejaculation as many as 300,000,000 may be discharged. The ducts, seminal vesicles, the prostate, and Cowper's glands form a more or less fluid secretion in which the ejaculated spermatozoa are found; this complete fluid formed by these various parts is known as the seminal fluid, or semen.

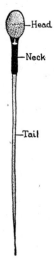

Fig. 298.—Human spermatozoon. (Francis: Fundamentals of Anatomy, The C. V. Mosby Co.)

The seminal fluid passes through the various ducts spoken of above and the urethra which courses through the penis. This latter organ is composed of cavernous, or erectile, tissue which consists chiefly of connective tissue inclosing numerous spaces, or venous sinuses. Some of the arteries of this erectile tissue empty into these spaces; in other instances the spaces are in communication with the veins which carry the blood from the penis. When the arteries dilate, a large volume of blood is sent to the organ; as the veins are small, and are perhaps partly compressed by the contraction of certain muscles (the erector penis and the bulbocavernosus muscles), this large supply of blood fills the venous spaces and erection of the penis takes place. The arterial dilation may be brought about reflexly by the stimulation of the sensory nerves of the genitals; the center for this reflex lies in the lumbar part of the spinal cord and the efferent nerves (vasodilator) are found in the first and second sacral nerves (pelvic nerves, or nervi erigentes). The center may also be influenced by mental conditions.

Puberty is the period at which the gonads become mature and commence to function. In the male this is shown by an increase in the size of the testes due to the growth of the interstitial cells and the beginning of spermatogenesis. At this time the secondary sexual characteristics, such as the growth of beard and pubic hair, the deepening of the voice, etc., also appear. This generally occurs about the age of fifteen. Subsequent to this, involuntary emissions of semen during sleep occur at certain intervals. The influence of the pituitary and the testicular hormones will be considered on page 672.

II. THE FEMALE GENERATIVE ORGANS

The various phases of the activity of the female reproductive organs, both primary and secondary, may conveniently be considered under the headings of ovulation, menstruation, gestation or pregnancy, parturition, and lactation.

A. Ovulation

The relation of the female reproductive organs to the other organs of the pelvic cavity can be gathered from Figs. 299 and 300. The body of the *ovary,* Fig. 301, may be considered as made up of connective tissue, *2,* surrounded by a layer of cuboidal cells, *1.* This outer layer is called the *germinal epithelium* and some of its cells by successive divisions give rise to the ova so abundantly found in the ovaries of a child. In forming the ova, the germinal epithelium at a certain spot dips down into the body of the ovary and by the growth of connective tissue of the stroma a mass of epithelial cells becomes separated from the main layer. One cell of this mass gives rise to the immature ovum, or ovocyte, while the remaining cells form a layer around the ovum. These ovocytes can be seen, in Fig. 301 and 302, situated near the border of the ovary. The cells surrounding the ovum continue to grow in number and, by the formation of a liquid, *follicular fluid,* the cells immediately surrounding the ovum become separated from the outside cells, giving rise to what is known as the *graafian follicle,* Figs. 301 and 302, *7, 8* and *9.* As the follicle continues to grow in size, it moves nearer to the surface of the ovary.

In the extreme right of Fig. 302 is represented part of a well-developed graafian follicle, showing the layer of cells, *a,* lining the follicle, and the cells, *b,* surrounding the ovum, *c.* The immature ovum is a large cell containing a nucleus, or germinal vesicle, *d,* with

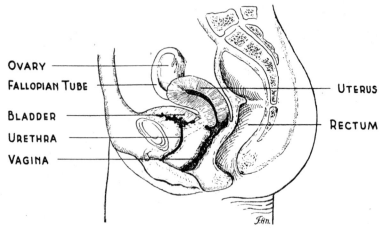

Fig. 299.—Diagram of the female genital organs. (Krogh and Drinker: Human Physiology, Courtesy of Lea and Febiger.)

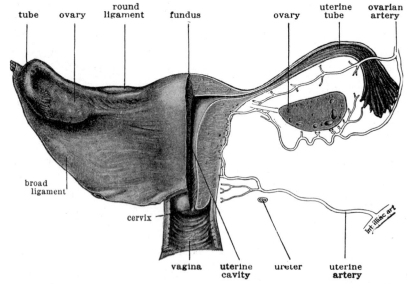

Fig. 300.—Diagram of the female reproductive organs, posterior view, with right side laid open. (From Pitzman: Fundamentals of Human Anatomy, The C. V. Mosby Co.)

the enclosed nucleolus, or germinal spot, *e.* After reaching a certain size the graafian follicle ruptures, and the egg is liberated, a process known as *ovulation.*

The Corpus Luteum.—The cells, *a*, of the ruptured graafian follicle give rise to a mass of yellow cells which inclose the blood clot formed from the blood escaping from the vessels of the ovary during the liberation of the egg. This yellow mass, the *corpus luteum* (Fig. 301, *10*), plays a very important part to which we shall allude presently. If the ovum is fertilized, the corpus luteum enlarges and re-

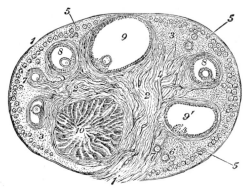

Fig. 301.—Section of an ovary (cat) showing *1*, the free and *1'*, the attached border; *2*, the connective tissue stroma with *4*, blood vessels; *5*, graafian follicles of which *6, 7, 8*, and *9*, are more advanced forms; *10*, a corpus luteum. (Schrön.)

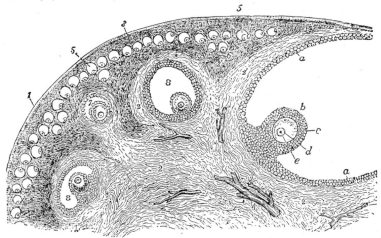

Fig. 302.—Section of an ovary showing graafian follicles, *5, 7, 8; c*, ovum with its germinal vesicle, *d*, and germinal spot, *e; 1*, germinal epithelium; *2*, connective tissue stroma; *4*, blood vessel. (Schrön.)

mains during the first seven months of gestation; if the ovum is not fertilized, the corpus luteum degenerates and is absorbed in two or three weeks. It is estimated that the ovaries of a young child may contain as many as 70,000 follicles; most of these are already present at birth. The larger number of the follicles degenerate and are absorbed, only a very limited number of the ova being liberated. It is of interest to note that, in contrast with the very large number of spermatozoa produced by the male, only from 300 to 400 ripe ova are produced during the reproductive life of the female. The human ovum measures about one-fourth of a millimeter in diameter.

The Fallopian Tubes.—The fallopian tubes, or oviducts, Figs. 300 and 308, spring from the angles of the uterus and extend outward toward the ovaries with which, however, they make no connections, the open end of the tube being situated some distance from the ovary. This end is funnel-shaped and fringed, or fimbriated. The mucous lining of the tubes is ciliated, and in the wall are found muscle fibers.

When the ovocyte has been set free it finds its way into the open end of the fallopian tube and is carried to the uterus. How it passes through the space which separates the ovary from the fimbriated end of the tube is not settled, but it is very likely that the currents set up by the cilia convey the egg forward.

Puberty.—In the young female the graafian follicles do not reach maturity; but at about the age of 14 they begin to ripen and are then set free, as described above. With the liberation of the first ovum many changes, physical and psychical, take place in the individual. The peculiar development of the skeleton (especially the enlargement of the pelvis) and the depositing of fat on the hips and breasts cause the body to assume a more feminine type. The secondary sex organs, uterus, vagina, and mammae, undergo a marked increase in growth and the sex characteristics make their appearance. As in the male, pubescence in the female is accompanied by hetero-sexual (*hetero,* other) inclinations.

But not only is there an increased growth and development; sexual activity now begins with the appearance of the first menstruation. These uterine activities continue rhythmically (about every 28 days) during the sexual life which ends at about the age of 45 to 50. The cessation of the menses is known as the menopause, climacteric, or change of life, and is sometimes accompanied by serious physical and mental disturbances.

B. Menstruation

The uterus is a hollow, thick-walled muscular organ (Fig. 300). It is lined with a mucosa *(the endometrium)* which is well supplied with glands and is covered with columnar ciliated epithelium. Previous to the beginning of the flow there is a great dilation of the blood vessels of the uterus so that the mucosa becomes thicker, much congested with blood, and somewhat edematous. If pregnancy does not take place, there is a rupturing of a large number of small blood vessels, and a part of the mucosa is disintegrated and discharged with the escaping blood. The extent of this destruction is a disputed point. After the flow has continued for about five days, a healing of the mucosa takes place; the epithelium is replaced, and the mucosa increases in thickness and its glands, in length. Menstruation is frequently preceded or accompanied by more or less discomfort, and pain in the head and back; when the flow comes with great difficulty (dysmenorrhea), these pains may be very severe. The amount of blood lost varies from 30 to 200 c.c.

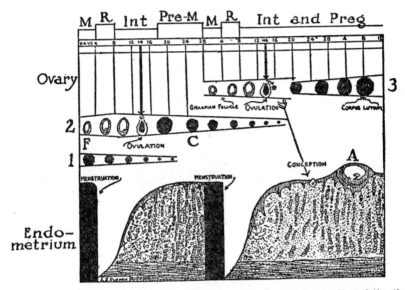

Fig. 303.—Diagram illustrating the changes in the uterine wall and in the ovary during the menstrual cycle. *M*, menstrual period; *R*, resting stage; *Int*, the interval; *Pre-M*, premenstrual stage; *Preg*, pregnancy. The number of days occupied by each period is indicated below the letters. *F*, follicle; *C*, corpus luteum; *1*, *2* and *3*, the history of three follicles. (Modified from Parvey: Endocrinology 16: 225, 1932.)

Relation of Menstruation and Ovulation.—To understand the relation between these two events, four factors must be kept in mind: (*a*) The uterine mucosa, (*b*) the graafian follicle, (*c*) the liberated ovum, and (*d*) the corpus luteum. The time from one menstrual period to the next may be divided into four parts: The menstrual period, the resting stage, the interval, and the premenstrual stage. In describing these, Fig. 303, which sketches about two and one-half lunar months, will be of great value. The diagram depicts the events occurring simultaneously in the ovary and the endometrium (mucosa) of the uterus. The first of these are shown in the upper and the second, in the lower part of the picture. Of the ovarian changes three cycles, *1*, *2*, and *3*, are shown; these cycles overlap each other more or less. The ovarian changes, *2*, when pregnancy does not occur, consist in the growth of the graafian follicle, *F*, in the liberation of the ovum (ovulation), and the subsequent formation and then gradual disappearance of the corpus luteum, *C*.

1. THE MENSTRUAL PERIOD.—During this period, lasting from the first to about the fourth day (in Fig. 303, *M;* the dark rectangular area), an ovarian follicle is developing, *2;* and the corpus luteum, *1,* of the previous menstrual period is gradually dwindling in size. During this time the endometrium is greatly disintegrated, as shown by its thickness at the end of the menstrual period.

2. THE RESTING STAGE.—At the beginning of the resting stage, *R,* in Fig. 303 which occupies the next four days following the end of menstruation, *M,* the endometrium remains very thin, there being but little regeneration.

3. THE INTERVAL.—During the succeeding eight days, the interval period, there is a great change in that, by the growth of its cells, the endometrium rapidly increases in thickness and the uterine glands become much enlarged. As shown in Fig. 303, *2,* about halfway through this period occurs the ovulation from the follicle which has meanwhile been developing.

4. THE PREMENSTRUAL STAGE.—The regeneration of the endometrium has been almost completed at the beginning of the premenstrual period, *Pre-M,* which lasts from the eighteenth to the twenty-eighth day. During this period the corpus luteum *C,* Fig. 303 gradually decreases in size, *2,* and a new follicle is maturing. At the end of this period the cycle begins once more with the next menstruation.

If the ovum is fertilized by a spermatozoon (see a subsequent paragraph), it becomes embedded in the uterine wall (conception; *A,* Fig. 303) and the corpus luteum, *3,* does not degenerate but continues to grow and persists till about the seventh month of pregnancy; during this time there is no menstruation.

According to this view, "menstruation itself marks a frustration of nature—the acknowledgment of failure of fertilization." However, the above-outlined association between ovulation and menstruation is not to be regarded as an ironclad relationship; for either event may happen without the other. From the foregoing description and the fact that neither the spermatozoon nor the unfertilized ovum lives longer than two to four days, it is evident that the period of greatest fertility extends from about the thirteenth to the seventeenth day after the beginning of menstruation.

C. Hormones and Sex Life

No other field of physiology so beautifully demonstrates the absolute dependence of the development and function of a large system of organs upon the stimulating and controlling influence of a large number of hormones as that of the reproductive organs. These hormones are of two distinct sources: 1. pituitary body; 2. the gonads (ovaries and testes). The pituitary hormones control the growth, development, and function of the gonads only; they do not influence the accessory sex organs. The gonadal hormones control the development and functions of the accessory sex organs; they have no effect upon the gonads themselves (see Fig. 304).

a. Pituitary Gonadotropic Hormones.—The removal of the pituitary body in the immature animal, or its failure to develop, arrests the growth and development of the gonads and indirectly of the accessory organs. In the adult it results in the atrophy of the gonads both in the male and in the female, the production of ova or spermatozoa ceases, and sex instincts vanish. That these results are due to the lack of gonadotropic hormones normally secreted by the pituitary body is evident from the fact that the injection of an extract from the pituitary gland restores these organs to their normal state.

1. THE FOLLICLE-STIMULATING HORMONE.—In the female the anterior lobe of the pituitary body forms two distinct gonadotropic hormones. One, the follicle-stimulating hormone, is responsible for the growth of the ovary and makes possible the maturation of the ovarian follicle and its germinal cell. In the male a corresponding hormone stimulates the multiplication and maturation of the cells of the seminiferous tubules of the testis. This hormone, therefore, acts upon the reproductive epithelium of both male and female; in the former it controls the production of spermatozoa, in the latter, of ova.

We may here emphasize that pituitary hormones have no direct influence on the accessory sex organs.

2. THE LUTEINIZING HORMONE.—This second pituitary hormone controls, in the female, the growth, development, and continued existence of the corpus luteum. Because of this stimulating action, the luteinizing hormone is indirectly responsible for several other factors in sex life; these will be considered in a subsequent section.

b. Ovarian Hormones.—The growth of the follicle, under the influence of the pituitary hormone, is associated, as we have seen, with the formation of a follicular fluid, which is liberated by the rupturing of the follicle during ovulation. This fluid contains a hormone generally known as estrone.

1. ESTRONE.—This hormone, recently obtained in a crystalline form, on injection produces a number of important changes. In the immature animal it accelerates the growth of secondary sex organs, such as enlargement of the mammary gland, especially of the duct system; increases the musculature of the uterus, and causes changes in the vagina. All these changes arouse the mating instinct of the animal and finally culminate in what is known as the estrus ("heat," or rut), during which mating is possible; for this reason it is called the *estrogenic hormone*, or estrone.* Estrone also prepares the uterine wall for the reception of the fertilized ovum. In the mature female

---

*Various names are given to this and other closely related estrogenic hormones: theelin, folliculin, estradiol, estrin.

animal in which the genital tract and mammae have undergone atrophy because of removal of the ovaries, the administration of estrone stimulates these organs to renewed growth and activity.

In human beings similar results have been obtained and we may therefore conclude that it is the appearance of the estrogens at the time of puberty which, in the female, stimulates the growth of the accessory sex organs and the secondary sex characteristics and brings on the uterine changes during menstruation. Castration in the young stops the growth of these organs; the sex characteristics (such as the sexual difference in the skeleton and in the depositing of fat) also fail to develop. In a woman the distressing physical and mental symptoms of the menopause are somewhat relieved by estrogens. But the administration of pituitary hormone to a castrated animal causes none of the above-mentioned changes, because it finds no ovarian follicle to stimulate. On the other hand, estrone has no influence upon the growth or function of the ovary itself.

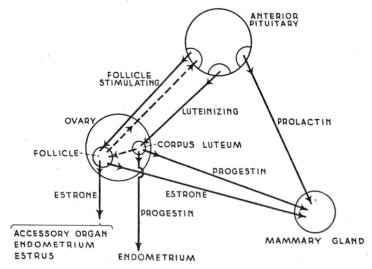

Fig. 304.—Diagram to illustrate the pituitary and ovarian hormones. Full lines indicate stimulating influence; broken lines, inhibition.

During pregnancy the amount of estrone formed is increased not only by the ovary, but also by the placenta (see p. 681). The hormone is then present in larger amounts in the blood and is excreted in the urine. The latter (from pregnant mares) furnishes the source of the commercial estrogens.

2. PROGESTERONE.—In the development of the corpus luteum there is produced a second ovarian hormone, variously known as proges-

terone, progestin, or lutin. We may note the following activities of progesterone: (1) By continuing the work of estrone upon the uterus, it sensitizes the mucosa of this organ for the reception of the fertilized ovum and the maintenance of the embryo; for in all mammals (except man and the guinea pig) the removal of the corpus luteum makes the retention of the ovum and, therefore, pregnancy, impossible. (2) Progesterone inhibits the maturation of graafian follicles, ovulation, and the secretion of estrone and thereby prevents the estrus cycle in lower animals, and menstruation in women. (3) It also stimulates further growth of the mammary glands, provided these have previously been acted upon by estrone. We therefore see that in some respects these two ovarian hormones are synergic and in other respects, antagonistic.

An *anterior pituitary-like hormone* is found abundantly in the urine during pregnancy; this has been used as an almost unfailing test for pregnancy. The injection of a small quantity of urine of a pregnant woman into an immature female mouse, rat, or rabbit stimulates the reproductive organs and results in estrus (''heat'') and the characteristic changes in the genital tract spoken of above. It is generally held that this hormone is formed in the placenta.

The Male Sex Hormone.—The growth of the testes and the production of spermatozoa are controlled by an anterior pituitary hormone. Extirpation of the pituitary in the young male animal leads to arrested development of the gonads; injection of the pituitary hormone accelerates their growth. It is now believed that this hormone is identical with the follicle-stimulating hormone of the female.

Testosterone.—The activity of the testis produces spermatozoa and a male hormone, testosterone. This hormone stimulates the development of the accessory sex organs (vas deferens, prostate, vesicles); it also induces secondary sexual characteristics. Castration in the immature animal prevents further development of these organs; the injection of the testicular hormone restores their growth and activity. Testosterone is found in the urine of all males, but less in that of adolescents than in that of adults. Sollenberger finds ''a definite relationship between the amount of male sex hormone in the urine of adolescent boys and their maturity of interests and attitudes and their social relations.'' The removal of the gonads (castration, spaying) in domestic animals clearly demonstrates a considerable effect on metabolism. Physical activity and metabolism are decreased, and there is a marked tendency to adiposity. It has, however, not been demonstrated that in man it hastens senility or shortens the span of life.

The implanting of a testis from another animal into a castrated animal may cause great changes in the accessory sex organs and in the male characteristics as long as the graft lives; but "there is no acceptable evidence that it has any rejuvenating effect." Ligation of the vas deferens or vasectomy does not modify the production of testicular hormone. It should also be remembered that the testicular hormones have no effect upon the testes themselves. Whether the sexual and mating instincts in man or animals depend upon testicular hormones is doubtful.

Reciprocal Relation.—The relation between the pituitary and the gonads is, to a certain extent, reciprocal. Castration, in either sex, leads to increased activity on the part of the prepituitary. On the other hand, the injection of the estrogens lessens the production of gonadotropic hormone by the pituitary and in this manner may inhibit the growth of either the ovaries or the testes.

D. Gestation

Maturation of the Ovum.—Soon after the immature egg-cell has been liberated and before fertilization can take place, it undergoes certain characteristic changes. It will be recalled from the introductory chapter, that in indirect cell division the chromosomes (the number of which is constant for the cells of any given species) divide longitudinally into two equal parts, each daughter cell receiving half of the number of chromosomes thus formed; by this the number of chromosomes in all the cells of the body remains the same. During the process of maturation, by which the ovum acquires the power of being fertilized by the spermatozoon, the egg undergoes two cell divisions, which differ considerably from the ordinary cell division, in that by these divisions the number of chromosomes is reduced to one-half of the number present in the ovocyte and in the general cells of the body. The formation of the spermatozoon from the spermatocyte of the seminiferous tubule is also associated with a reduction in the number of the chromosomes. Hence, both the matured egg and the spermatozoon contain only one-half of the number of chromosomes peculiar to the cells of that species. It is also held that during maturation the egg loses its centrosome and thus becomes incapable of any further division, if not fertilized.

Fertilization of the Ovum.—As stated above, if the matured egg is not fertilized, it ceases to undergo any further division and perishes. But if spermatozoa are present, one of these may enter the egg, and further division and growth of the egg sets in. This union of the male and the female germ cells, known as fertilization, takes place in the fallopian tubes. Notwithstanding the currents set up by the cilia of the uterus and the fallopian tubes, the spermatozoa by their own motility penetrate from the vagina into the uterus and tubes. How the spermatozoa find the egg and how one of them finds its way into the egg are not well understood. It is possible that the phenomenon of chemotaxis (p. 155) may play an important part.

When a spermatozoon has entered the egg, the tail disappears, and the head, which is composed of the original nucleus of the spermatocyte with only half its chromosomes, becomes spherical in shape. This is known as the male pronucleus, while the nucleus of the mature ovum is the female pronucleus. These two nuclei unite to form one single nucleus, the segmentation nucleus, which now possesses the number of chromosomes characteristic of the species, half of these being of maternal and half of paternal origin. In the subsequent divisions of the fertilized ovum, by the usual manner of karyokinesis (Chap. I), the chromosomes divide longitudinally, and each daughter cell thereby receives one-half of the paternal and one-half of the maternal chromosomes.

Genes and Heredity.—The number of chromosomes in the cell varies from one animal to another but is constant in any given animal; thus, in man each cell contains 48 chromosomes. According to the current theory each chromosome is composed of a large number of discrete bodies, known as *genes*, arranged in a definite order like a string of beads. These invisible chromosomal elements are regarded as the bearers of the hereditary characteristics of plants and animals. They must be looked upon as colloidal material; in fact, some regard them as giant protein molecules. These life-units possess the power of growth, of multiplying themselves, and of directing the chemical changes in the living body.

Mutations.—Because of the lengthwise splitting of the chromosomes, the number and the order of the several genes in a given chromosome are preserved during the division of the cell from one generation to the next. Sometimes the genes undergo, for unknown reasons, a change in composition or arrangement in the chromosomes of the ovum or spermatozoon; this causes changes in the characteristics of the offspring in which it differs materially from its parents. These changes in transmitted characteristics, known as mutations, can also be produced artificially. Muller accomplished it by exposing fruit flies (*Drosophila*) to x-rays. "The genes have been knocked out of place and more or less violently rearranged, resulting in forms of life wholly new to the universe."

How the genes by their individual chemical composition or by their number and spatial arrangement in the chromosomes determine, as some hold, the physical and mental characteristics of the offspring is unknown to us, but it seems that, "each individual . . . is the product of the activity of all these genes and heredity is the result of the shuffling of these genes in each generation." For a discussion of these interesting and, from a eugenic point of view, important questions, the reader is referred to the copious literature on this subject.

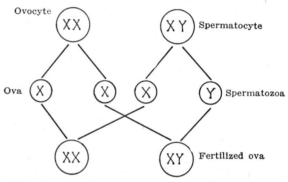

Fig. 305.—Diagram to illustrate the inheritance of sex.

Determination of Sex.—In the human ovocyte and spermatocyte are two chromosomes which determine the sex of the offspring. In the ovocyte these two sex chromosomes are similar and are known as the X chromosomes. By the cell division occurring during maturation, there is, as we have seen, a reduction of the chromosomes; in consequence each egg contains but one X chromosome. One of the two sex chromosomes of the spermatocyte is similar to that present in the ovum and is, therefore, also called the X chromosome; the second sex chromosome is considerably shorter and is designated as the Y chromosome. As the result of the next cell division and reduction in chromosomes, one spermatozoon contains the X, and the other, the Y chromosome, Fig. 305.

By the subsequent union of the ovum with a spermatozoon containing the X chromosome, a cell with two X chromosomes or female cells, results; on the other hand, the union of the ovum with a spermatozoon possessing the Y chromosome, gives rise to a cell containing one X and one Y chromosome, or a male cell. This is illustrated in Fig. 304. Since the genes in the sex chromosome determine the sex, the sex of the offspring is, according to this theory, determined at the time of fertilization. Certain characteristics of the offspring are determined by genes located in the sex chromosomes; these are said to be *sex-linked characteristics*, e.g., color blindness and hemophilia.

Reversal of Sex.—However, evidence has been presented that at least in some animals, the sex of the offspring may be determined by other than the chromosomal factor, and that sex reversal is possible. Riddle stresses the rate of metabolism; a sustained increase in the rate of metabolism favors the production of males and may transform immature females into males, and, conversely, a decrease in the metabolic rate is conducive to the development of females. It is therefore possible for the thyroid and other endocrine organs to influence the sex of the offspring. Witschi discovered that female tadpoles kept in warm water (90° F.) acquired the male reproductive organs, and, conversely, keeping male tadpoles in cold water caused a reversal in the female direction. In another experiment, a high protein diet fed to male rats and a low protein diet fed to females led to a sex ratio of 145 males to 100 females; reversing the diet resulted in 92 males to 100 females. This is also in agreement with the fact that in young children and animals the basal metabolism is 3 to 14 per cent higher in males than in females, and that, when subjected to a lower external temperature, the increased rate of oxidation and heat production is greater in males. This may also explain why the number of red blood cells and the amount of hemoglobin differ in the two sexes.

In mature animals sex reversal is also possible. Steinach transplanted an ovary into a castrated male rat, and the animal acquired many of the sex instincts of the female. Riddle relates the case of a hen, mother of chickens, that in later years became a cock in appearance and the father of two chicks. Autopsy revealed destruction of the left ovary, which is the only functioning ovary in a hen.

Germ Plasm.—As development of the ovum proceeds (by growth and cell division and differentiation) certain cells, destined to form the germinal epithelium of the ovary or the seminiferous tubule of the testis, are set apart very early. They remain unspecialized and at maturity produce new germ cells. As these cells contain the usual number of chromosomes, one-half of which are derived from the father and the other half from the mother, it will be seen that here we have a physical continuity from parent to child not only through one but through countless generations.

Fetal Membranes.—The fertilization of the ovum is associated, as already discussed, with a continued growth of the uterine mucosa, under the influence of estrone and progesterone. About ten days after fertilization, the ovum arrives in the uterus; and on coming in contact with the mucosa, it begins, we may say, to digest a limited area of this membrane. This allows it to sink into the mucosa, Fig. 306, which by continued growth soon covers the ovum, Fig. 307. In this manner, the details of which we cannot go into, the embryo soon becomes surrounded by two membranes, the amnion and the chorion, Fig. 308. Between the amnion and the embryo exists a relatively large space; this cavity is filled with the amniotic fluid in which the embryo rests. The outermost membrane, the chorion, develops papillae, or villi, Fig. 307, which penetrate into the mucosa of the uterus, as is shown in Fig. 308. That part of the uterine mucosa by which the ovum is directly attached to the wall of the uterus grows much in thickness

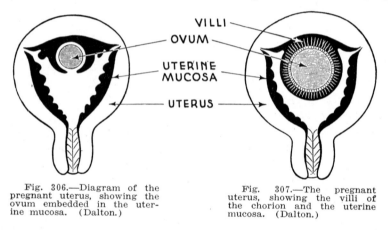

Fig. 306.—Diagram of the pregnant uterus, showing the ovum embedded in the uterine mucosa. (Dalton.)

Fig. 307.—The pregnant uterus, showing the villi of the chorion and the uterine mucosa. (Dalton.)

and in it are developed blood sinuses, or blood spaces, which connect the maternal arteries with the veins. This area is known as the decidua basalis, or serotina. From the blood vessels of the embryo there arise two arteries, the umbilical arteries, which leave the body at the umbilicus, or navel, and through the umbilical cord, Fig. 308, proceed to the chorion; in the villi of this membrane they form a large network of capillaries. As already stated, the chorion fuses intimately with the decidua serotina of the uterus (Fig. 308); the villi of the chorion eat their way into this part of the uterine mucosa so that the very terminations of the villi lie in the blood sinuses spoken of above. As the capillaries of the umbilical arteries lie in these villi, it can be readily seen that there is a close connection between the blood of the embryo and that of the mother, although they are always separated from each other by the capillary wall and by the cells of the villus intervening between the capillaries and the blood spaces. The blood is carried by the single umbilical vein, which also passes through the umbilical cord, back to the heart of the embryo.

The Placenta.—That part of the uterine mucosa by which the embryo is attached to the wall of the uterus (spoken of as the decidua basalis, or serotina) together with the fetal membrane, the chorion, which forms such an intimate union with this mucosa, constitutes the placenta. Part of this structure is therefore maternal and contains large blood spaces; part of it is fetal and in it the circulation is through regular capillaries. The placenta is the nutritive and excre-

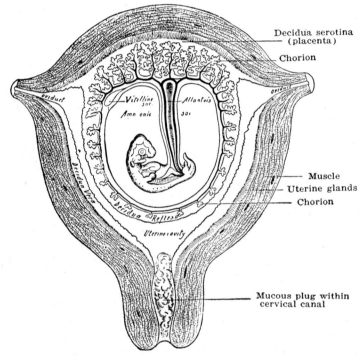

Fig. 308.—Diagram illustrating the uterus at the seventh week of pregnancy. (From Turner and McHose: Effective Living, The C. V. Mosby Co.)

tory organ for the embryo, for through this membrane an exchange of material takes place between the maternal and the fetal blood; in this manner the embryo acquires its food and oxygen and loses its waste products. Hence, the blood passing from the placenta through the umbilical vein back to the child is arterial (comparable to the pulmonary vein) and contains the food required for growth; the umbilical arteries carry the venous blood with the waste products. The fetal liver stores up the fat-soluble vitamins, A and D; the water-soluble vitamins are not stored, although the fetal blood may be richer in vitamin C than the maternal blood. The production of hormones by the placenta was spoken of previously.

As the only connection between the mother and the fetus is furnished by the placenta through which all substances exchanged must pass, it is inconceivable that any mental state of the mother can influence the growth and development of any part of the fetus (prenatal influences).

The placenta also bars nearly all bacteria that may be found in the maternal blood, the outstanding exception being the germ of syphilis *(Spirochaeta pallida)*; and congenital syphilis (not hereditary, but by intra-uterine infection) is therefore possible.

E. Parturition

After the full term of gestation—in the human being about 280 days after the last menstruation—the fetus is expelled from the uterus. During pregnancy there is a great development of the walls of this organ. The virgin uterus has a capacity of about 2 to 5 c.c.; at full term its volume has increased to 5,000 or 7,000 c.c., and its weight is about 30 times as great. The increase in size is chiefly due to an extremely great increase in the size of the plain muscle fibers and perhaps also to the formation of new fibers.

By the contractions of the uterine musculature, pressure is exerted upon the fetus, thereby causing the fetus to move toward the mouth of the uterus. This is aided, to a greater or lesser extent, by the contraction of the muscles of the abdominal wall, with diaphragm fixed and glottis closed. In consequence of this pressure and because of the relaxation of its circular muscle fibers the mouth of the uterus dilates. When a sufficient amount of pressure has been generated, the membranes surrounding the fetus rupture and part of the amniotic fluid escapes. By the continued contraction of the muscles and by a further relaxing of the soft parts, the child is delivered through the mouth of the uterus and vagina.

After this the contractions cease for ten to twenty minutes, when they are resumed and the fetal membranes and the placenta, being torn away from the wall of the uterus, are expelled as the "afterbirth." This results in the escape of a certain amount of blood from the blood spaces of the placenta; but by the strong contractions of the wall of the uterus, the ruptured vessels are mechanically occluded, and thus prevent any further hemorrhage.

As to the cause of the contractions of the uterine musculature, there is no very definite knowledge. It is more than likely that it is not of neural origin, for Goltz demonstrated that in a dog complete destruction of all the nerves supplied to the uterus does not interfere with pregnancy or parturition. Nevertheless, there is located in the lumbo-sacral cord a center capable of influencing this activity, for it is well known that certain mental conditions and also the stimulation of sensory nerves may hasten parturition in the human being (miscarriage by fright). Much evidence has been brought forth to show that it is due to the generation of hormones, either in the body of the mother or in the fetus.

F. Lactation

Mammary Glands.—Due to the stimulating action of the ovarian hormone, estrone, the mammary glands increase in size at the onset of puberty. This growth, however, concerns the connective tissue and duct system mostly and to a lesser extent that of the secreting cells. During pregnancy the ovarian hormone, progestin, causes a very marked enlargement and development of the secreting cells. It is now quite generally held that the secretion of milk at childbirth is initiated by the pituitary hormone known as *prolactin* (p. 501).

Lactation.—Two or three days after the birth of the child the glands begin to secrete milk. Before this they have formed a scanty amount of an opalescent fluid known as colostrum. While the existence of secretory nerves for the mammary glands seems very probable, at least in man, no experimental evidence is known proving any nerves to exercise such control. When the secretion of milk has once begun, it is kept up by the regular emptying of the ducts as occurs during the nursing of the infant. Somehow or other the emptying of these ducts stimulates the gland cells; if nursing is discontinued, the secretion stops and the gland cells degenerate. It has been shown in lower animals, however, that the continued flow of milk is also dependent upon the pituitary hormone, for ablation of this gland in a lactating animal stops the secretion.

The amount of milk secreted per day varies largely in different individuals and increases during the first six or seven months and then decreases. On the third day, about 200 c.c. are secreted; during the twenty-eighth week the amount may be a little over 900 c.c. Lactation generally continues from six to nine months. The milk of each mammal is peculiarly adapted to the needs of its young. Table XXXV gives a comparison of human and cow's milk:

TABLE XXXV

| | WATER | PROTEINS | | FAT | LACTOSE | SALTS |
		CASEIN	ALBUMIN			
Human milk	88.5	1.20	0.50	5.5	7.0	0.2
Cow's milk	87.1	3.02	0.53	3.7	4.8	0.7

The heat value of milk varies, but may be placed at about 20 Calories per ounce. During the first few months the daily requirement is from 100 to 120 Calories per kilogram for the normal infant. The energy requirement gradually then diminishes, so that by the end of the first year it is approximately 90 Calories per kilogram.

The importance of breast feeding, as compared with artificial feeding, is well illustrated in Table XXXVI. This is the record of 20,000 infants in Chicago during the years 1929 to 1934; among them occurred 218 deaths. The percentage of infants entirely breast fed, partially breast fed, and entirely artificially fed, and the percentage of deaths in each class leaves little doubt (although other factors, poverty, ignorance, e.g., may have been contributing factors) of the desirability of breast feeding.

TABLE XXXVI

	PER CENT OF TOTAL	PER CENT OF DEATHS
Entirely breast fed	48.5	6.7
Partially breast fed	43.0	27.2
Artificially fed	8.5	66.1

Growth.—The average weight of a newborn infant is about 7 pounds; the average height is 20 inches, but it must be remembered that the height-weight characteristics depend on the race and family type. Table XXXVII shows the average height and weight of white males from ages 1 to 6 years. Both the height and the weight of female white children are slightly less than that of males.

TABLE XXXVII

AGE YEARS	HEIGHT IN.	WEIGHT LB.
1	30	21.5
2	34	27.0
3	37	31.5
4	40	35.5
5	43	39.5

GLOSSARY

Prefixes and Suffixes

a-, not, without (apnea)
ab-, from, away (absorption)
ad-, to, toward (adrenals)
ag-, af-, as-, see *ad-*
-algia, pain, complaint (neuralgia)
amylo-, starch (amylopsin)
an-, not, without (anemia)
ana-, up (anabolism)
-ase, termination denoting a ferment (amylase)
anti-, opposite, opposed to (antitoxin)
auto-, self (automatism)
bi-, two, twice (biceps)
bili-, pertaining to bile (bilirubin)
calci-, calcium, lime (calcification)
calor-, heat (calorimeter)
cata-, down (catalysis)
cerebro-, pertaining to the large brain
chole-, bile
chrom-, color (chromosome)
-cidal, killing (bactericidal)
-cle, small (ventricle)
co-, com-, con-, cor-, with, together
coll-, glue (colloids)
contra-, opposite (contralateral)
corpus-, body (corpuscle)
-cyt-, cell (leucocyte)
-dermic, -dermis, skin (hypodermic)
di-, two, twice (dichromatic)
dia-, through, apart (diaphragm)
dis-, negative (disinfect)
dys-, bad (dyspepsia)
em-, en-, endo-, in, into (embolus)
-emia, blood (anemia)
entero-, intestine (enterokinase)
epi-, upon (epidermis)
erythro-, red (erythrocyte)
ex-, out (expiration)
-fer-, to carry (afferent)
-fract-, break (refraction)
-gastric, stomach (pneumogastric)
-gen, or gen-, producing (glycogen)
-glosso-, tongue (hypoglossal)
glyc-, glucose, sugar (glycosuria)
-gnosis, knowledge (diagnosis)
-gog or -gogue, leading (secretogog)
-graph, to write (kymograph)
hemo-, blood (hemorrhage)
hetero-, other, different (heterogeneous)

hydro-, water (hydrolytic)
hyper-, over, above measure (hypertrophy)
hypo-, under, less than (hypodermic)
in-, in, into (insertion)
in-, not, without (insufficiency)
inter-, between, together (intercostal)
intra-, within (intrathoracic)
ir-, not (irreciprocity; irregular)
-itis, inflammation (tonsillitis)
-ject-, to throw (injection)
kata-, down (katabolism)
kin-, to move (kinesthetic, kinetic)
-lac-, milk (lactose)
leuco- or leuko-, white (leucocyte)
lympho-, pertaining to lymph (lymphocyte)
-lysin, -lysis, -lytic, dissolving, destruction (hemolysis)
macro-, large (macrophages)
mal-, bad (malnutrition)
-meter-, measure (manometer)
micro-, small (micro-organism)
mole-, mass, body (molecule)
mono-, one (monosaccharides)
myo-, muscle (myoglobin)
neur-, pertaining to nerves (neurasthenia)
nephr-, kidneys (nephritis)
-oid, like (ameboid)
-ole, small (bronchiole)
-opia, sight (myopia)
-osis, a condition (cyanosis); a process (phagocytosis)
oste- or osteo-, bone (osteology)
ovi-, ovo-, egg (oviduct)
para-, near, by, beside (parathyroid)
patho-, suffering, disease (pathology)
peri-, around, near (pericardium)
phago-, to eat (phagocyte)
-phil-, loving (hemophilia)
-plasm-, form (cytoplasm)
-plegia, or -plexy, stroke (apoplexy)
-pnea, breathing (dyspnea)
pneumo-, air, lungs (pneumonia)
poly-, many (polysaccharides)
post-, behind, after (postganglionic)
pre-, before, in front of (precentral)
pro-, before, giving rise to (proferment)
proto-, first (protoplasm)

proprio-, one's own (proprioceptive)
pseudo-, false (pseudopod)
psycho-, mind (psychology)
pulmo-, lung (pulmotor)
re-, back, again (regurgitation)
-renal, kidney (adrenal)
sarco-, flesh, muscle (sarcostyle)
-sclero-, hard (sclera, sclerosis)
semi-, half (semicircular)
-some-, body (chromosome)
-sthenia, strength (asthenia)
sub-, under, below (subnormal)

-tax, -taxis, order, arrangement (thermotaxis)
thermo-, heat (thermogenesis)
-thromb-, clot, coagulation (thrombin)
-tome, -tomy, to cut (tonsillectomy)
trans-, beyond, through (transudation)
-ule, small (saccule)
-uria, pertaining to urine (glycosuria)
vaso-, pertaining to blood vessels (vasodilation)

Glossary

A

Absorption, the transfer of materials from a free surface into the blood.

Acapnia, a marked decrease of CO_2 in the blood.

Acid-base balance, the proper ratio of H and OH ions in the blood.

Acidemia, a relative increase in the H ions in the blood.

Acidosis, a condition in which the concentration of the bicarbonates in the blood is below normal.

Action current, the electric current generated when the active and inactive parts of a protoplasmic structure are connected by an outside circuit.

Adequate stimulus, that form of stimulus which is most efficient for a given structure.

Adipose tissue, a form of connective tissue in which fat is extensively deposited.

Adrenalin, one of the hormones of the medullary adrenals.

Adrenals, two glands of internal secretion lying just above the kidneys.

Afferent nerve, a nerve which carries impulses to the central nervous system.

Albuminoids, a division of the simple proteins; the scleroproteins.

Alkali reserve, the amount of bicarbonate in the blood (or body) available for neutralizing acids.

Alveolar air, the air found in the end pockets of the lungs.

Alveolus, one of the terminal air pockets of the lung.

Amino acid, an organic acid containing an NH_2 and COOH group and having both basic and acidic properties. The building-stones of proteins.

Anabolism, the building up of protoplasm from the simpler food molecules.

Anaerobic, living best or only without air.

Anemia, a lack of the proper number of red blood cells per cubic millimeter of blood or of the proper percentage of hemoglobin.

Anesthesia, the condition of total or partial loss of sensibility, especially to touch.

Anoxemia, the lack of the proper amount of oxygen in the blood.

Antagonistic muscles, muscles that oppose each other in their action.

Antiferment, a compound which counteracts or neutralizes the action of a ferment or enzyme.

Antiketogenic foods, foods that tend to reduce the formation of ketones in the body.

Antiseptic, having the power to prevent growth of bacteria; a drug having this power.

Antrum, a cavity or hollow space (as in a bone); the lower part of the stomach.

Aorta, the large artery springing from the left ventricle.

Apnea, the temporary cessation of breathing.

Arachnoid, one of the meninges of brain and spinal cord.

Areolar tissue, a form of connective tissue in which the bundles of inelastic fibers and the elastic fibers form an open meshwork in the ground substance.

Arteriosclerosis, a loss of elasticity or a hardening of an artery.

Artery, a vessel carrying blood from the heart.

Assimilation, the building of material into protoplasm; anabolism.

Astigmatism, a refractive error of the eye in which the various meridians of the cornea (or lens) do not have the same radius of curvature.

Astringent, a drug causing contraction of tissues and arresting hemorrhage, diarrhea, etc.

Atrium, one of the cavities of the heart which receives the blood; auricle.

Atrophy, a wasting away of a tissue or organ due to a decrease in protoplasm.

Atropine, a poisonous alkaloid derived from the deadly nightshade (atropa) and the seeds of the thorn apple.

Auricle, see *atrium.*

Auriculo-ventricular bundle, a bundle of a peculiar tissue that conducts the impulse from the auricle to the ventricle; the bundle of His.

Autolysis, the disintegration of a cell or tissue by its own enzymes.

Avitaminosis, a disease due to lack of vitamins.

Axis cylinder, the axon of a nerve fiber.

Axon, one of the protoplasmic processes of a neuron; it carries the impulse away from the cell body.

B

Basal metabolism, the minimum expenditure of energy compatible with life.

Bilirubin, a red pigment found in the bile.

Biliverdin, a greenish pigment derived from bilirubin.

Biuret test, a test for native proteins and peptones.

Bleeder, an individual afflicted with hemophilia.

Blind spot, an area of the retina where the optic nerve leaves the eyeball; it is insensitive to light.

Blood pressure, the force which the blood exerts against the walls of the vessels or heart.

Bowman's capsule, a saclike structure formed by the invaginated end of a uriniferous tubule of the kidneys.

Bronchus, one of the air tubes formed by the division of the trachea.

Buffer substance, a compound which has the power to combine with either acid or base, thus helping to maintain the acid-base balance.

Bundle of His, see *auriculo-ventricular bundle.*

C

Calorie, the unit of heat energy.

Calorimeter, apparatus for measuring the amount of heat produced by a chemical action or by an animal body.

Carbhemoglobin, the compound formed by the union of hemoglobin and CO_2.

Carbohydrates, a group of chemical compounds which includes the various sugars and starches; particularly the aldehydes or ketoses of hexatomic alcohol; the molecule, composed of C, H and O, contains 6, or a multiple of 6, carbon atoms and twice as many H as O atoms.

Carbon monoxide, a gas formed by the union of one atom of C and one of O; CO.

Carboxyhemoglobin, a compound formed by the union of hemoglobin and carbon monoxide.

Cardia, the sphincter between the esophagus and stomach.

Caries, the chemical destruction of the mineral ingredients of the teeth.

Casein, a protein found in milk.

Catabolism, the destructive phase of metabolism; the disintegration of protoplasm.

Catalase, a ferment having the power to decompose hydrogen peroxide.

Catalysis, the chemical action aided or retarded by a catalyzer.

Catalyst, see *catalyzer.*

Catalyzer, a chemical agent that accelerates a chemical action without itself undergoing any permanent change.

Cataract, an opacity of the crystalline lens and destructive to vision.

Cellulose, a polysaccharide; the woody part of vegetable foods and largely indigestible.

Centrosome, one of the constituents of a cell playing a part in cell division.

Cerebellum, one of the divisions of the brain; the hind-brain.

Cerebrospinal fluid, a lymphlike fluid found in the cavities and canals of the brain and spinal cord and between the meninges.

Cerebrum, one of the divisions of the brain, the large fore-brain.

Cerumen, ear wax.

Chemotaxis, the property of a motile cell or organism to move towards or away from a chemical reagent.

Cholesterol, a fatlike compound found in animal tissues and fluids (bile).

Chromatin, a deeply staining material of the nucleus; it gives rise to the chromosomes.

Chromoprotein, a simple protein chemically united with a pigment compound; e.g., hemoglobin.

Chromosomes, the cellular elements regarded as the carriers of hereditary characteristics; see *chromatin.*

Chronaxie, the length of time which a stimulus having twice the intensity of the rheobase (liminal stimulus) must act upon a protoplasmic structure in order to produce a response.

Chyle, the contents of the intestinal lymph vessels.

Chyme, the partially digested food, leaving the stomach.

Cilium, a threadlike strand of protoplasm projecting beyond the body of a cell.

Coagulation, the transformation of a soluble into an insoluble protein.

Cochlea, the portion of the inner ear concerned with the reception of sound waves and the generation of auditory impulses.

Collagen, a protein found in bones, cartilage, and white fibrous tissue.

Colloid, substance that diffuses and dialyzes slowly or not at all and gives rise to but a small amount of osmotic pressure; opposed to crystalloids.

Colon, the large intestine excepting the cecum and rectum.

Commissural fibers, nerve fibers connecting one lateral half of the brain or cord with the other.

Complemental air, the amount of air which can be inspired in addition to the tidal air by forcible inspiration.

Complementary colors, a pair of colors that on mixing, physically or physiologically, produce white.

Conduction, the passage of an impulse along a protoplasmic structure.

Cones, the cones, together with the rods, constitute the sensitive elements of the retina where, by photic stimulation, the visual impulses are generated.

Congestion, a large amount of blood in a certain part of the body.

Conjugated protein, a simple protein united with some other compound, such as pigment (chromoprotein), carbohydrate (glycoprotein), etc.

Contractility, the power of a protoplasmic structure to change its form or shape.

Convoluted tubule, a portion of the uriniferous tubule.

Coordination, the harmonious operation of two or more parts of a protoplasmic structure.

Cornea, the transparent glassy part of the outer coat of the eye.

Coronary arteries, the vessels supplying the heart muscle.

Corpora quadrigemina, four little rounded elevations on the dorsal surface of the mid-brain.

Corresponding points, or areas, of the two retinas so located that their simultaneous stimulation by one external object causes binocular single vision.

Cortical gray matter, the gray matter, composed of nerve cell bodies, found in the outer layer of the cerebrum and cerebellum.

Cortin, a hormone formed in the cortical adrenals.

Cranial nerves, twelve pairs of nerves springing from the brain.

Creatinine, a nitrogenous waste product.

Crenation, the shriveling of a red blood cell due to withdrawal of water.

Cretinism, a dwarfed and malformed condition of the body caused by hypofunction of the thyroid in infancy.

Critical temperature, that degree of the external temperature at which the heat production in a warm-blooded animal is increased.

Crypts of Lieberkuehn, tubular glands in the intestinal wall.

Crystalloid, a chemical compound which, in solution, gives rise to osmotic pressure and dialyzes through a semipermeable membrane.

Curare, a drug which paralyzes the motor nerve endings in the skeletal muscles.

Cuticle, the outer skin; the epidermis.

Cyanosis, a bluish discoloration of the skin caused by the presence of excessive venous blood.

Cytoplasm, the protoplasm to the exclusion of the nucleus.

Cytotoxins, chemical compounds injurious to cells.

D

Day vision, the vision present in bright light, in distinction to night or twilight vision; photopia.

Dead space, the amount of space of the respiratory tract in which no, or very little, respiration takes place (the nasal passage, trachea, bronchi, bronchioles).

Deamination, the chemical process by which the amid group, NH_2, is split from amino acid.

Defecation, the emptying of the bowels.

Deficiency disease, a disease caused by the lack of necessary ingredients in the diet (especially vitamins).

Deglutition, swallowing.

Delirium cordis, the incoordinate contraction of the heart muscle fibers.

Dendrite, see dendron.

Dendron, one of the short, branched processes of a neuron; the receiving process; dendrite.

Dermis, the true (lower) skin.

Detoxifying, destroying the poisonous action.

Dextrose, glucose, a monosaccharide.

Diabetes mellitus, a pathologic condition in which the carbohydrates are not used by the body and are excreted in the urine.

Dialysis, the passing of a substance in solution through a membrane.

Diaphragm, the muscular sheath which separates the thorax from the abdomen; a muscle of inspiration.

Diastole, the relaxation of the heart muscle and the dilation of the heart cavities.

Diastolic pressure, the blood pressure in an artery during the diastole of the heart.

Dick's test, a test for the susceptibility of an individual to scarlet fever.

Diffusion, the spreading of the molecules of a gas or of a substance in solution.

Digestion, a process of hydrolytic cleavage of the large food-molecules into smaller and more dialyzable molecules; a chemical process by which the food is rendered absorbable by the cells.

Diopter, the unit of refractive power of a lens, or of the eye.

Diplopia, double vision; seeing one object as two.

Disaccharides, a class of carbohydrates having the general formula, $C_{12}H_{22}O_{11}$; e.g., cane sugar.

Diuretic, a compound which increases the activity of the kidneys.

Dropsy, an unusually large amount of lymph in a certain part of the body; edema.

Duodenum, the first portion of the small intestine.

Dura mater, the outermost of the three meninges covering the brain and spinal cord.

Dyspnea, labored breathing.

E

Edema, dropsy.

Effectors, the responding organs, i.e., the muscles and glands.

Efferent nerve, a nerve which carries impulses out of the central nervous system.

Effort syndrome, an excessive increase in heart action and respiration accompanying muscle work; ''irritable heart.''

Elastic tissue, connective tissue in which the yellow elastic fibers predominate.

Electrolyte, a substance which ionizes in solution and aids in the conduction of an electric current.

Electrometer, an instrument for detecting and measuring electric currents.

Electron, unit of negative electricity.

Elimination, excretion; the emptying of the bowels.

Embolism, a condition in which a floating aggregate of matter (e.g., a blood clot) blocks a blood vessel.

Emesis, vomiting.

Emetic, a drug causing vomiting.

Emmetropia, the condition of the unaccommodated eye in which the posterior principal focus lies on the retina.

Endocrine organ, an organ having an internal secretion.

Endothelium, the epithelial lining found in the heart, blood vessels, and lymphatics.

Energy, the power to do work, or to produce a change.

Enterokinase, the ferment which transforms trypsinogen into trypsin.

Enzyme, an unorganized ferment; an organic catalyst.

Epidermis, the outer skin; cuticle.

Epiglottis, a fibrous, cartilaginous lid at the base of the tongue and above the larynx.

Epinephrin, adrenalin.

Epiphysis, a part of a bone which ossifies separately before uniting with the main part of the bone.

Epithelium, a form of tissue which covers the outer and inner surfaces of the body.

Equilibration, the process whereby an animal gains or maintains its physical equilibrium.

Erepsin, an intestinal enzyme which splits peptones into amino acids.

Ergograph, an instrument for recording mechanical work done by a muscle or group of muscles.

Ergosterol, a sterol which on irradiation with ultraviolet light acquires the properties of vitamin D.

Erythroblast, a red bone-marrow cell which gives rise to a red blood cell.

Erythrocyte, a red blood cell.

Ester, the product formed by the interaction of an acid with an alcohol; ethereal salt.

Estrus, the heat, or rut, of animals during the mating season; sexual desire.

Eupnea, normal, quiet breathing.

Eustachian tube, a tube connecting the middle ear with the pharynx.

Excitation, a stimulation which is followed by increased protoplasmic activity.

Excretion, the transfer of waste products from the blood onto a free surface.

Exudate, the material transferred from the blood stream into the tissue spaces.

F

Facilitation of reflexes, summation of reflexes.

Fallopian tube, the duct by which the egg is transferred from the immediate neighborhood of the ovary to the uterus; oviduct.

Fasciculus cuneatus, one of the afferent tracts of white matter in the dorsal columns of the spinal cord.

Fasciculus gracilis, one of the afferent tracts of the spinal cord.

Fat, a compound formed by the action of one molecule of glycerol and three of a fatty acid.

Fatigue, loss of irritability or of the normal function of a structure due to previous work.

Fermentation, a chemical change produced, or accelerated, by the presence of a ferment.

Fetus, the unborn offspring of a mammal during its later stages of development.

Fibrillation, the incoordinate contraction of muscle fibers.

Fibrin, the insoluble protein formed from fibrinogen during coagulation of the blood.

Fibrinogen, a soluble protein in the plasma which is transformed into fibrin when the blood is shed.

Filtration, the passing of a fluid under pressure through a membrane or filter.

Flatulence, the presence of a large amount of gas in the alimentary canal.

Focal distance, the distance between the refracting surface and the posterior principal focus.

Foodstuffs, the alimentary principles: water, salts, fat, carbohydrates, proteins, and vitamins.

Fovea centralis, a small area of the retina where, in daylight vision, the power of discriminating details is the greatest.

G

Ganglion, a collection of nerve cell bodies outside of the central nervous system.

Gastrin, a hormone secreted by the pyloric mucosa of the stomach.

Gelatin, an incomplete protein derived from collagen of white fibrous tissue.

Gene, the unit of which the chromosomes are composed; a carrier of hereditary characteristics.

Geniculate bodies, masses of gray matter located in the tween-brain.

Glomerulus, a tuft of small blood vessels in Bowman's capsule of the uriniferous tubule.

Glottis, the opening between the vocal cords.

Glucose, a monosaccharide; dextrose, or grape sugar.

Glycerin, see glycerol.

Glycerol, a tri-atomic alcohol, $C_3H_5(OH)_3$, found in combination with three molecules of a fatty acid in fats.

Glycine, see glycocoll.

Glycocoll, a simple amino acid; amino-acetic acid; glycin.

Glycogen, a polysaccharide derived in the body from glucose; especially found in the liver and muscles.

Glycogenesis, the manufacture of glycogen from glucose.

Glycosuria, the presence of glucose in the urine.

Gonads, the reproductive glands: the testes and ovaries.

Graafian follicle, a vesicular body in the ovary which contains the ovum.

Gustatory, pertaining to taste.

Gyrus, a convolution of the brain.

H

Hemopoiesis, the formation of red blood corpuscles.

Hemocytometer, an instrument for counting the number of blood cells.

Hemoglobin, a chromoprotein found in the red blood cells and having a great affinity for oxygen.

Hemoglobinometer, an instrument for determining the percentage of hemoglobin in the blood; hemometer.

Hemolysins, agencies which destroy the red blood cells.

Hemolysis, the destruction of the red blood cells.

Hemometer, a hemoglobinometer.

Hemophilia, the condition in which the coagulation time of the blood is prolonged.

Hemorrhage, the escape of blood from the blood vessels.

Hemorrhoid, the varicose condition of the rectal or anal veins; a pile.

Heparin, a compound obtained from the liver which delays blood coagulation.

Heterophoria, cross-eyedness; strabismus.

Histamine, a capillary poison obtained from histidin.

Histidin, an amino acid.

Histiocytes, the fixed macrophages.

Homoiothermic, having a constant body temperature.

Hormone, a chemical compound formed by certain structures (generally ductless glands) which is absorbed into the blood stream and influences the growth, development, or function of some other part of the body.

Humoral, pertaining to the humors (fluids or semifluids) of the body.

Hydrocarbon, a compound composed of carbon and hydrogen; e.g., methane, CH_4.

Hydrolysis, the splitting of a larger into a number of smaller molecules, through the addition of one or more molecules of water.

Hydroxyl ion, an ion composed of one atom of O and H each and carrying one negative electrical charge.

Hyperglycemia, an excessive amount of glucose in the blood.

Hyperopia, farsightedness.

Hyperpnea, increased rate and depth of respiration.

Hypertension, an abnormally high tension; especially that of blood pressure.

Hypertrophy, an increase in the size of an organ due to an increased amount of protoplasm.

Hypoglycemia, an abnormally low percentage of glucose in the blood.

Hypophysis cerebri, the pituitary body.

Hypotension, an abnormally low tension, especially that of blood pressure.

Hyperemia, a greater amount of blood than usual in a given part; congestion.

I

Impulse, nerve, a change in a nerve fiber induced by stimulation and traveling throughout the fiber.

Inhibition, the lessening or temporary cessation of function following stimulation.

Insulin, the hormone of the islets of Langerhans of the pancreas necessary for carbohydrate metabolism.

Intrathoracic, within the thorax.

Intravascular, within the blood vessels.

Invertase, an enzyme capable of splitting cane sugar into glucose and fructose.

Ions, the products formed by the electrolytic dissociation of a molecule and carrying one or more positive or negative electrical charges.

Iris, the pigmented diaphragm directly in front of the lens of the eye.

Irradiated, having been affected by ultraviolet light, generally spoken of in connection with the production of vitamin D.

Irritability, the power of protoplasm to respond to stimulation.

Islands of Langerhans, isolated groups of particular cells in the pancreas concerned with the production of insulin.

Isosmotic, having equal osmotic pressure.

J

Jaundice, the presence of bile in the blood.

K

Karyokinesis, cell division by mitosis.

Keratin, a highly insoluble, indigestible scleroprotein found in skin, nails, etc.

Ketone, a chemical compound formed by the oxidation of a secondary alcohol and characterized by the $C = O$ group.

Kilogrammeter, the unit of mechanical work; equivalent to raising one kilogram to the height of one meter.

Kinase, a ferment of ferments; it activates a proenzyme.

Kinesthetic sensation, the proprioceptive sensation by which we judge of the position and movement of our limbs.

L

Lacrimal, pertaining to tears.

Lactase, an enzyme splitting lactose into glucose and galactose.

Lactation, secretion of milk; suckling.

Lacteals, the lymphatic vessels of the intestine.

Lactic acid, an acid formed from carbohydrates, as in the souring of milk, having the formula $C_3H_6O_3$.

Lactose, milk sugar.

Latent period, the length of time elapsing between the stimulus and the response.

Lecithan, a compound protein composed of a simple protein and lecithin.

Lecithin, a complex fat containing phosphoric acid and a nitrogenous base known as cholin.

Leucemia, a pathologic condition in which the number of white blood cells is greatly increased.

Leucocyte, a white blood corpuscle.

Ligament, a white fibrous structure which binds, e.g., one bone to another.

Lipase, a fat-splitting enzyme.

Lipid, fat and fatlike substances.

Lymph, the fluid found in the lymph vessels and spaces.

Lymphocyte, a certain type of leucocyte.

M

Macrophage, a cell of the loose connective tissue having the power of phagocytosis; a resting wandering cell; histiocyte.

Malpighian body, the beginning of the uriniferous tubule and composed of the Bowman's capsule and the glomerulus.

Maltase, an enzyme splitting maltose into glucose.

Maltose, a disaccharide.

Manometer, an instrument for measuring pressure.

Mastication, chewing.

Maturation, ripening.

Meibomian glands, sebaceous glands of the eyelids.

Meissner's plexus, a network of nerves in the submucosa of the small intestine.

Meninges, the three membranes covering the central nervous system.

Meningitis, inflammation of the meninges.

Menopause, the cessation of the periodic menstruations; climacteric.

Menstruation, the periodic changes in the uterus during the sexual life.

Mesentery, a fold of the peritoneum which connects the intestine to the posterior wall of the abdomen.

Metabolism, the sum total of the chemical changes occurring in the body; the combined anabolism and catabolism.

Micturition, urination.

Mitral, pertaining to the bicuspid valve.

Molar solution, a solution which contains in 1,000 c.c. as many grams of the solute as molecular weight of the solute.

Molecular solution, a molar solution.

Monosaccharides, a class of carbohydrates of which the hexoses have the formula, $C_6H_{12}O_6$.

Motor areas, the areas of the cerebral cortex which on stimulation give rise to muscular action.

Mucin, a glycoprotein found in saliva, etc.

Mucosa, a membrane lining the cavities and tubes communicating with the surface of the body and secreting a mucous fluid.

Mydriatic, a drug which dilates the pupil.

Myelin sheath, the inner covering of a medullated nerve fiber.

Myocardium, the muscle tissue of the heart.

Myogen, a protein found in muscles.

Myoneural junction, the motor end-plates of a muscle; the structure between the muscle and its nerve.

Myopia, nearsightedness.

Myosin, a protein found in muscles.

Myotic, a drug which causes constriction of the pupil.

Myxedema, a pathologic condition of the adult, associated with malfunction of the thyroid, in which the subcutaneous tissue becomes filled with a mucinlike material.

N

Narcotic, a drug that relieves pain and induces sleep; in large doses it causes stupor, coma, death.

Nerve, a bundle of nerve fibers.

Nerve cell, a neuron.

Nerve fiber, a prolongation of the cell body of a neuron covered with one or more sheaths.

Neurilemma, the outermost covering of a nerve fiber.

Neuron, a nerve cell.

Niacin, a vitamin chemically known as nicotinic acid.

Nitrogenous equilibrium, that condition of the body in which the amount of nitrogen ingested equals that egested.

Nuclein, a compound protein found in the nucleus.

Nucleus, a highly differentiated body lying in the cytoplasm of a cell; the organ of cellular nutrition and reproduction.

Nystagmus, involuntary and abnormal oscillatory movements of the eyes.

O

Obesity, the state of being excessively fat.

Occipital lobe, the hindermost lobe of the cerebral cortex.

Olein, one of the chemical fats found in the body fat and having a low melting point.

Omentum, a fold of the peritoneum connecting the stomach with the other abdominal viscera.

Opsonin, a chemical compound by which bacteria are prepared for phagocytosis by the white blood cells.

Organ, a structure composed of two or more tissues and performing a special function.

Osmosis, the diffusion through a membrane of the solvent (water, e.g.) from a lower to a more concentrated solution.

Osmotic pressure, the pressure generated by osmosis.

Ossification, the hardening of bone; calcification.

Otoliths, concretions found in the utricles and saccules of the inner ear.

Ovary, the female sex gland which forms the ovum.

Ovulation, the setting free of the ovum from the ovary.

Oxalated blood, blood to which a soluble oxalate (e.g., potassium oxalate) has been added to prevent its coagulation.

Oxygen, one of the constituents of the air.

Oxyhemoglobin, hemoglobin united with oxygen.

Oxyntic cells, the acid-secreting cells of the stomach; the parietal cells.

P

Palmitin, one of the chemical fats found in the body fat.

Pancreas, an abdominal organ secreting the pancreatic juice and containing the islands of Langerhans.

Parasympathetic nervous system, that part of the autonomic nervous system in which the preganglionic fibers spring from the mid-brain, medulla, or the sacral region of the cord.

Parathyroids, four glands of internal secretion lying upon or embedded in the thyroid gland.

Parturition, childbirth.

Patellar reflex, the knee-jerk; the throwing forward of the leg due to the tapping of the patellar ligament.

Pathogenic, disease producing.

Pellagra, a deficiency disease, claimed to be due to the lack of nicotinic acid.

Pepsin, the proteolytic enzyme of the gastric juice.

Peptid, a compound composed of two or more amino acids and formed by the splitting of peptones.

Peptone, a derived protein formed by digestion from native proteins.

Pericardium, the closed membranous sac surrounding the heart.

Periosteum, the fibrous membrane surrounding a bone.

Peristalsis, the wavelike muscular movement of a tube (e.g., intestine) by which the contents are moved forward.

Peritoneum, a serous membrane lining the abdominal cavity and enveloping the viscera.

Peroxidase, an enzyme which liberates active oxygen from a peroxide (e.g., H_2O_2).

Phagocyte, a cell able to engulf solid particles.

Phagocytosis, the process by which a cell engulfs solid particles.

Pharynx, a pouchlike structure extending from the base of the skull to the level of the sixth cervical vertebra; into it open the mouth, posterior nares, eustachian tubes, esophagus, and trachea.

Phosphatid, a complex fat, e.g., lecithin.

Phosphoprotein, a phosphorus-containing protein; e.g., casein and vitellin.

Photopia, daylight, or bright-light, vision.

Pia mater, the innermost of the three meninges.

Pineal gland, a small body situated on the dorsal aspect of the brain.

Pituitary body, an endocrine organ situated on the ventral aspect of the brain.

Placenta, a membranous structure which forms, with the umbilical cord, the connection between the uterine wall and the fetus and through which the exchange of material between mother and fetus takes place.

Plasma, the liquid portion of the blood.

Plasma membrane, the outer layer of the cytoplasm which is claimed to possess semipermeability.

Plasmolysis, the shrinkage of the protoplasm due to the withdrawal of liquid from the cell by a hypertonic solution.

Platelets, thrombocytes; one of the three classes of blood corpuscles.

Plethysmograph, an instrument for measuring or recording the changes in the volume of an organ.

Pleura, the serous membrane covering the lungs.

Plexus, a network, especially of veins or nerves.

Pneumogastric nerve, the tenth cranial, or the vagus, nerve.

Pneumograph, an instrument for recording the respiratory movements.

Pneumothorax, the condition of having air in the thoracic cavity and outside of the lungs.

Poikilothermic animals, animals with a variable body temperature; cold-blooded animals.

Polysaccharides, a class of carbohydrates having the general formula, $(C_6H_{10}O_5)n$; e.g., starch.

Portal vein, the vein conveying the venous blood from the small and large intestines, spleen, and stomach to the liver.

Presbyopia, loss of accommodation due to hardening of the crystalline lens; the sight of old age.

Pressor nerve, an afferent nerve which on stimulation causes an increase in blood pressure by reflexly constricting the blood vessels.

Proferment, the antecedent of an enzyme.

Proprioceptive impulses, impulses received from the muscles, tendons, and joints by which the position and movements of limbs are made known. Some also include the impulses from the semicircular canals, etc.

Prostate gland, a gland of the reproductive system of the male, situated at the base of the bladder and surrounding the mouth of the urethra.

Proteins, nitrogenous compounds formed by the union of many amino acids.

Proton, the unit of positive electricity.

Prothrombin, the material from which thrombin is formed.

Pseudopod or **pseudopodium,** a temporary projection of a portion of the protoplasm of a naked cell; an organ of locomotion.

Psychic, pertaining to the mind.

Ptyalin, a starch-splitting enzyme of the saliva.

Puberty, that period of life at which the young of either sex becomes capable of reproduction.

Pulse, a rhythmical dilation of the artery caused by the systolic output.

Pulse pressure, the difference between the systolic and diastolic pressures.

Pupil, the central aperture of the iris.

Putrefaction, the bacterial decomposition of protein material, associated with fetid odor.

Pylorus, the part where stomach and small intestine meet.

Pyramidal fibers, the cortico-spinal nerve fibers, springing from cell bodies in the precentral convolution and extending into the spinal cord.

R

Rachitis, a disturbance in bone formation; rickets.

Receptor, an organ for the reception of stimuli; sense organ.

Reflex or **reflex action,** an action induced by the stimulation of a receptor and carried on without the intervention of the will.

Refractory period, the period of reduced irritability during the activity of a protoplasmic structure.

Renal, pertaining to the kidneys.

Rennin, a milk-clotting enzyme.

Respiration, the exchange of gases between an organism and its environment; the muscular movements by which a fresh supply of oxygen is brought to the respiratory organs.

Retina, the innermost coat of the eye which is stimulated by light.

Rheobase, the threshold, or liminal, stimulus.

Rhodopsin, a pigment in the rods of the retina, held to be necessary for scotopic, or twilight, vision.

Rickets, rachitis.

Rigor mortis, the stiffening or hardening of the muscles soon after death.

Rod, one of the visual cells of the retina.

S

Saccule, one of the divisions of the labyrinth of the inner ear; a sense organ of equilibrium.

Saponification, the splitting of fat into fatty acid and glycerol; the formation of soap from fat by the action of an alkali.

Sarcolemma, the delicate sheath surrounding a muscle fiber.

Sarcoplasm, the more liquid portion of a muscle fiber in which the sarcostyles are embedded.

Sarcostyles, the fibrils of a muscle fiber; myofibrils.

Sclera, the outer, white, coat of the eyeball.

Scorbutus, scurvy.

Scotopia, the vision in very dim light; twilight vision.

Scurvy, a pathologic condition due to lack of vitamin C.

Sebaceous glands, the oil glands of the skin.

Sebum, the oil secreted by the oil gland.

Secretin, a hormone formed in the wall of the small intestine which induces the secretion of pancreatic juice.

Secretion, the transfer of a substance from the blood onto a free surface by means of a gland.

Secretogog, a substance that stimulates glandular activity.

Semidecussation, half-crossing; e.g., the crossing of the nerve fibers from the nasal half of each retina to the opposite side of the brain.

Sensation, a change in consciousness caused by the stimulation of a sensory surface.

Serum, the liquid part of coagulated blood.

Sino-auricular node, a mass of tissue lying in the wall of the right auricle and in which the impulse for the heartbeat originates.

Sinus, a cavity or recess; e.g., the cavities in the bones of the face.

Sinus venosus, the contractile structure of a frog's heart into which the systemic veins empty and which discharges its blood into the right auricle.

Soap, a compound formed by the union of a fatty acid and a base.

Somatic, pertaining to the body.

Somatic nerves, the nerves directly connected with the central nervous system, in distinction to the autonomic nerves.

Sphincter, a circular muscle surrounding and closing an opening; e.g., the pyloric sphincter, the sphincter of the iris.

Sphygmograph, an instrument for recording the pulse.

Sphygmomanometer, an instrument for determining the amount of blood pressure.

Spirometer, an instrument for determining the amount of air respired.

Spontaneity, the property of a protoplasmic structure to initiate its own activity without external excitation.

Steapsin, a fat-splitting enzyme of the pancreas.

Stearin, one of the chemical fats found in the body fat.

Stereognosis, the recognition of the solidity and form of an object by means of the touch, pressure, and muscle senses.

Stimulus, a change in the environment which modifies the activity of protoplasm.

Styptic, a chemical which stops a hemorrhage by constricting the blood vessel.

Sudoriferous, pertaining to sweat.

Suprarenals, the adrenals.

Synapse or synapsis, the junction between two neurons.

Syncope, fainting.

Synovial fluid, a form of lymph which bathes the synovial membrane covering the ends of a bone in a joint.

Systole, the contraction of the heart muscle.

Systolic pressure, the arterial pressure during the systole of the heart.

Systolic sound, the sound formed during the systole of the heart.

T

Tendon, a connective tissue structure which binds a muscle to a bone.

Testis, the male reproductive gland.

Tetanus, a sustained contraction of a muscle produced by the complete fusion of twitches.

Thalamus, a mass of gray matter in the tween-brain.

Thermogenesis, the production of heat in the body.

Threshold stimulus, the liminal, or minimal, stimulus; the rheobase.

Thrombin, the agent which causes the coagulation of the blood.

Thromboplastin, one of the agents necessary in the formation of thrombin.

Thrombus, a clot formed in the vessels and adhering to the walls of the vessels.

Thymus, a gland of internal secretion.

Thyroid gland, a gland of internal secretion.

Thyroxin, a hormone produced by the thyroid gland.

Tidal air, the amount of air inspired or expired during quiet respiration.

Tissue, an aggregate of similar cells.

Tissue fluid, the fluid found in the tissue spaces; lymph.

Tonus, a subdued continuous contraction of a muscle by which it resists stretching.

Toxemia, a condition in which the blood contains poisons formed either by the body itself or by microorganisms; blood poisoning.

Toxin, a poisonous compound of animal or vegetable origin.

Trachea, the windpipe leading from the pharynx to the bronchi.

Transudate, the material passing through the capillary wall from the blood into the surrounding spaces.

Tricuspid valve, the valve between the right auricle and ventricle.

Trigeminal nerve, the fifth cranial nerve supplying sensory fibers to the face, teeth, etc.

Trophic, pertaining to nutrition or nourishment.

Trypsin, a proteolytic enzyme found in the intestine.

Trypsinogen, the material found in the pancreatic juice from which trypsin is formed.

Tryptophan, an amino acid.

Twitch, a single contraction of a muscle.

Tyrosine, an amino acid.

U

Urea, a nitrogenous waste product found in the urine.

Ureometer, an instrument for determining the amount of urea in the urine.

Ureter, the duct which conveys the urine from the kidney to the bladder.

Urethra, the duct by which the urine is voided.

Uric acid, a nitrogenous waste product found in the urine.

Urinometer, an instrument for determining the specific gravity of the urine.

Uterus, one of the secondary sex organs in mammals in which the egg and fetus develop previous to birth; the womb.

V

Vagus, the tenth cranial, or pneumogastric, nerve which innervates the heart, bronchi, lungs, stomach, pancreas, small intestine, etc.

Vas deferens, the duct conveying the spermatozoa to the urethra.

Vasoconstrictor nerve, a nerve which causes constriction of a blood vessel.

Vasodilator nerve, a nerve which causes dilation of a blood vessel.

Vegetative nervous system, the autonomic nervous system.

Vena cava, one of the large veins communicating with the right auricle.

Venous blood, blood returning from the tissues and containing more CO_2 and less oxygen than arterial blood.

Venule, a small vein.

Vertigo, dizziness; giddiness.

Villus, a minute structure of the intestinal mucosa projecting into the lumen of the intestines; an organ of absorption.

Viosterol, a compound having the properties of vitamin D.

Visual acuity, the power of the visual apparatus to distinguish the detail of an object, such as the letters of a printed page.

Vital capacity, the amount of air that can be taken into the lungs by the most forcible inspiration after the deepest expiration; respiratory capacity.

Vitamin, one of the alimentary principles.

Vitellin, a protein of the egg yolk.

X

Xerophthalmia, a pathologic condition of the cornea of the eye due to the lack of vitamin A.

Y

Yellow spot, an area of great sensitivity of the retina; macula lutea.

Z

Zein, an incomplete protein found in corn.

Zymase, the alcoholic enzyme present in yeast.

Zymogen, the material from which an enzyme is formed.

SELECTED REFERENCES

General

Annual Review of Physiology, American Physiological Society, Annual Reviews, Inc., Stanford University P.O., Calif., Vols. 1-5.

Bard, Philip: Macleod's Physiology in Modern Medicine, ed. 9, St. Louis, 1941, The C. V. Mosby Co.

Best, C. H., and Taylor, N. B.: The Physiological Basis of Medical Practice, ed. 3, Baltimore, 1943, Williams and Wilkins.

Biological Symposia, Lancaster, Pa., The Jaques Cattell Press, Vol. 9.

Cold Spring Harbor Symposia on Quantitative Biology, Vol. 5, Cold Spring Harbor Biological Laboratory, 1937.

Kahn, F.: Man in Structure and Function, New York, 1943, Alfred A. Knopf.

Recent Advances in Physiology, Philadelphia, P. Blakiston's Son and Co., Vols. I to VI.

Turner, C. E.: Personal Hygiene, St. Louis, 1937, The C. V. Mosby Co.

Turner, C. E., and McHose, E.: Effective Living, St. Louis, 1941, The C. V. Mosby Co.

Wiggers, C. J.: Physiology in Health and Disease, ed. 3, Philadelphia, 1939, Lea and Febiger.

Protoplasm

Huxley, T. H.: Physical Basis of Life, New York, 1896, D. Appleton and Co.

The Cell and Protoplasm. A Symposium, Lancaster, Pa., 1940, Science Press.

Tissues

Kendall, J. I.: The Microscopic Anatomy of Vertebrates, Philadelphia, 1940, Lea and Febiger.

Lambert, A. E.: Introduction and Guide to the Study of Histology, Philadelphia, 1938, P. Blakiston's Son & Co.

Morris' Human Anatomy, ed. 10, Philadelphia, 1942, The Blakiston Co.

Translocation of Materials

Adolph, E. F.: Physiological Regulation, Lancaster, Pa., 1943, Jaques Cattell Press.

Heilbrunn, L. V.: An Outline of General Physiology, Philadelphia, 1937, W. B. Saunders.

Muscle Physiology

Biological Symposia (Muscle), Lancaster, Pa., 1941, The Jaques Cattell Press, Vol. III.

Gould, H. G., and Dye, J. A.: Exercise and Its Physiology, New York, 1932, A. S. Barnes & Co.

Nervous System

Berry, R. J. A.: Your Brain and Its Story, New York, 1939, Oxford University Press.

Cannon, W. B., and Rosenblueth, A.: Autonomic Neuro-effector Systems, New York, 1937, The Macmillan Co.

Frolov, Y. P.: Pavlov and His School, New York, 1937, Oxford University Press.

Fulton, John F.: Physiology of the Nervous System, New York, 1938, Oxford University Press.

Gellhorn, Ernst: Autonomic Regulation, New York, 1943, Interscience Publishers, Inc.

Haggard, H. W., and Jellinek, E. M.: Alcohol Explored, New York, 1942, Doubleday, Doran & Co.

Kuntz, A.: The Autonomic Nervous System, Philadelphia, 1934, Lea and Febiger.
Ranson, S. W.: Anatomy of the Nervous System, ed. 7, Philadelphia, 1943, W. B. Saunders Co.
Sherington, C. S.: Reflex Activity of the Spinal Cord, 1932, Charendon Press.
Symposium on the Synapse, Springfield, Ill., 1939, Charles C Thomas.

Blood and Circulation

Blood, Heart and Circulation, A Symposium, Lancaster, Pa., 1940, Science Press.
Kilduffe, R. A., and DeBakey, M.: The Blood Bank and the Technique and Therapeutics of Transfusion, St. Louis, 1942, The C. V. Mosby Co.
Vaughan, W. T.: Allergy, ed. 2, St. Louis, 1934, The C. V. Mosby Co.

Tissue Fluid

Drinker, C. K., and Field, M. E.: Lymphatics, Lymph and Tissue Fluid, Baltimore, 1933, Williams and Wilkins Co.
Krogh, A.: Anatomy and Physiology of Capillaries, New Haven, Conn., 1929, Yale University Press.

Respiration

A Symposium on Respiratory Enzymes, Madison, 1942, University of Wisconsin Press.
Armstrong, H. G.: Principles and Practice of Aviation Medicine, Baltimore, 1939, Williams and Wilkins Co.
Haldane, J. S., and Priestly, J. G.: Respiration, New Haven, Conn., 1935, Yale University Press.
Henderson, Y.: Adventures in Respiration, Baltimore, 1938, Williams and Wilkins Co.

Food and Digestion

Alvarez, W. C.: The Mechanism of the Digestive Tract, ed. 2, William Heinemann.
Bodansky, Meyer: Introduction to Physiological Chemistry, ed. 4, New York, 1938, John Wiley and Sons.
Cannon, W. B.: Digestion and Health, New York, 1936, W. W. Norton & Co.
Verzár, F.: Absorption From the Intestine, New York, 1936, Longmans, Green and Co.
Wolf, S., and Wolff, H. G.: Human Gastric Function, New York, 1943, Oxford University Press.

Metabolism

Diseases of Metabolism, edited by G. G. Duncan, Philadelphia, 1942, W. B. Saunders Co.
DuBois, E. F.: Basal Metabolism in Health and Disease, ed. 3, Philadelphia, 1936, Lea and Febiger.
Eddy, W. H., and Dalldorf, G.: The Avitaminoses, Baltimore, 1941, Williams and Wilkins Co.
Holmes, E.: The Metabolism of Living Tissue, 1937, Cambridge University Press.
Lusk, Graham: The Elements of the Science of Nutrition, ed. 4, Philadelphia, 1928, W. B. Saunders Co.
McCollum, E. V., Orent-Keiles, E., and Day, H. G.: The Newer Knowledge of Nutrition, New York, 1939, The Macmillan Co.
Sherman, H. C.: Chemistry of Food and Nutrition, New York, 1941, the Macmillan Co.
The Biological Action of the Vitamins, A Symposium, Chicago, 1942, University of Chicago Press.
Vitamin Content of Foods, 1937, U. S. Department of Agriculture, No. 275.
Vitamins, A Symposium, Chicago, 1939, The American Medical Association.

Hormones

Cannon, W. B.: Bodily Changes in Pain, Hunger, Fear, and Rage, New York, 1929, D. Appleton-Century Co.
Cannon, W. B.: Wisdom of the Body, New York, 1939, W. W. Norton & Co.

Glandular Physiology and Pathology. A Symposium, Chicago, 1942, The American Medical Association.

Grollman, A.: Essentials of Endocrinology, Philadelphia, 1941, J. B. Lippincott Co.

Hoskins, R. G.: Endocrinology, New York, 1941, W. W. Norton & Co.

The Pituitary Gland, Published by Association for Research in Nervous and Mental Diseases, Baltimore, Williams and Wilkins Co., Vol. 7.

Renal Secretion

Peters, J. P.: Body Water, Springfield, Ill., 1935, Charles C Thomas.

Smith, H. W.: The Physiology of the Kidney, New York, 1937, Oxford University Press.

Body Temperature

DuBois, E. F.: The Mechanism of Heat Loss and Temperature Regulation, 1937, Stanford University Press.

Reproduction

Corner, George: The Hormones in Human Reproduction, Princeton, 1942, Princeton University Press.

INDEX

A

Aberration, spherical, 554
Absorption, 32, 369
  carbohydrate, 370
  fats, 156, 371
  gastric, 372
  influenced by digestibility, 479
  intestinal, 372, 373
  mechanism of, 373
  protein, 370, 396
  salts, 369
  seat of, 372
  water, 369, 389
Acapnia, 299
Accommodation, in eye, 549
Acetone, 415, 421
Acetonuria, 415, 421
Acetylcholine, 662
  influence on alimentary canal, 382
    on arteries, 251
    on heart, 219, 220, 486
    on muscles, 663
Acid metaproteins, 326, 349
Acid-base balance, 146, 300, 516
Acidemia (see Acidosis)
Acid-forming foods, 478
Acidity of fluids, 144, 145
Acidosis, 147, 300, 313, 421, 456
Acids, 143, 144
  acetic, 321
  amino (see Amino acids)
  butyric, 321
  fatty, 320, 321, 457
  formation of, in body, 300, 421, 517
  lactic (see Lactic acid)
  linoleic, 457
  organic, 321
Acromegaly, 499
Action current, 124, 558
  potential, 125, 128
Activators of food, 294
  of oxygen, 294
"Acute indigestion," 209
Adaptation, 39, 129, 541
  margin of, in heart, 207
Addison's disease, 485, 489
Adenoids, 270
Adipose tissue (see Tissues)
Adjustment, 39, 42, 139
Adrenalin, 263, 416, 485, 662
  alimentary canal, 382, 388
  blood, 485
  blood vessels, 230, 235, 243, 485, 488
  body temperature, 514
  fatigue, 486
  heart, 220, 485
  hemorrhage, 161
  metabolism, 416, 445, 486

Adrenalin—Cont'd
  reproductive organs, 489
  synapse, 662
Adrenals, 416, 484 ff., 501
Adrenergic nerves, 662
Adrenin (see Adrenalin)
Adsorption, 72, 420
Afferent nerves, 80, 592
After-birth, 682
After-brain (see Medulla oblongata)
After-damp, 310
After-discharge, 609
After-images, negative, 562
  positive, 561
After-sensation, 541
Agar, 391
Age, influence on blood pressure, 194
  blood vessels, 239
  body temperature, 507
  bones, 436
  diet, 452
  heartbeat, 210
  metabolism, 442, 452
  respiration, 280, 281
Agglutinins, 164
Agraphia, 641
Air, composition of, 283
  conditioning of, 509
  humidity of, 509
  hunger, 421
Alanine, 329, 395, 452
Albinism, 532
Albuminates (see Metaproteins)
Albuminoids, 324
Albumins, 141, 324, 395, 452
Albuminuria, 263, 525
Alcohol, composition, 318
  fermentation, 45, 317
  food value, 315
  influence on antibodies, 165
    body temperature, 511
    central nervous system, 597, 640,
      644
    circulation, 207, 232
    conductivity, 133
    heart, 207
    muscle work, 112
    phagocytosis, 156
    vision, 568
Aldehydes, 319
Alexia, 641
Alimentary canal, anatomy of, 332
  movements of, 375 ff.
  principles (see Foodstuffs)
Alkali reserves, 146, 309
Alkalinity of blood, 146, 147
  of fluids, 144, 145
Alkalosis, 147, 301

Gravity, effect of, on circulation, 246
  on lymph flow, 263
Gray matter of nervous system, 79, 592
  ramus, 658
Ground bundles, 612
Growth, 34, 407, 430
  hormone, 498
  influenced by amino-acids, 453
    calcium, 433
    pineal gland, 504
    pituitary, 499
    thymus, 503
    thyroid, 492
    vitamins, 465
  of brain, 644
  of infant, 684
  protein requirement during, 452
Gustatory nerves, 581
Gyri, of brain, 614

H

Habits, 606, 632
Hair, 530
Hallucination, 535
Hay fever, 167
Hearing, 571 ff.
  acuity, 577
  analysis by, 575
  localization of, 578
  range of, 577
Heart, 195, 250
  action of, 195 ff.
  adrenalin, effect of, 485
  anatomy, 169
  block, 198
  efficiency, 308
  energy of, 209
  failure, 206, 239
  impulse, origin of, 195
    conduction of, 197
  muscle, 205
  nutrition of, 208, 209
  reserve power of, 207
  sounds, 203
  stretching of, 206
  valves (see Valves)
  work, influence of, on (see Muscle work)
Heartbeat, 195
  force of, 205, 207, 217
  nervous control of, 211
  origin, 195
  rate of, 210
Heartburn, 380
Heat (see Calorie)
  exhaustion, 511
  of body (see Body temperature)
    loss of, 508 ff.
    production, 104, 507
      seat of, 508
      sources of, 507
    regulation, 512
      center for, 513

Heat—Cont'd
  radiation, 508
  sensation of, 582
  stroke, 511
  value of foods, 437, 450, 456, 508
Heller's test, 329
Helmholtz's double layer, 126
  theory of sound perception, 576
Heme, 148, 150
Hemin crystals, 155
Hemiplegia, 624
Hemocytometer, 148
Hemoglobin, 148 ff.
Hemoglobinometer, 149
Hemoglobinuria, 165
Hemolysins, 166
Hemolysis, 73, 153, 165, 361
Hemometer, 149
Hemophilia, 162
Hemopoiesis, 150
Hemopoietin, 152
Hemorrhage, 150, 158, 160, 161, 222, 468
Hemorrhoid, 392
Hemostatics, 328
Heparin, 161
Hepatic veins, 410
Heredity, 677
Hering's color theory, 563
Hernia, 334
Heterophoria, 568
Hexose-phosphate, 434
Hiccough, 312
Hind brain, 613
Hippuric acid, 400, 518
Hirudin, 160
Histamine, 232, 263, 354
Histidine, 330, 403
Histiocytes, 156
Hives, 170, 262
Homeostasis, 140, 516, 658
Homoiothermic animals, 506
Hormones, 82, 457, 481 (see also Adrenals, Thyroid, Pituitary, etc.)
  influence on metabolism (see Metabolism)
  interrelationship of, 505
  number of, 483
  sex (see Sex)
Humidity of air, 509
Humoral theory of conduction (see Neurohumoral theory)
Hunger, 384, 587
Hydrocarbons, 318
Hydrochloric acid, 348, 349, 363
Hydrogel, 65
Hydrogen ions, 143
Hydrolysis, 47, 317, 335
Hydrolytic cleavage (see Hydrolysis)
Hydrometer, 142
Hydrosol, 65, 335
Hydroxyl ions, 143
Hyperemia, 235, 263